AH

MANUAL OF STRESSED SKIN DIAPHRAGM DESIGN

MANUAL OF STRESSED SKIN DIAPHRAGM DESIGN

J. M. Davies and E. R. Bryan
Professors of Structural Engineering, University of Salford

GRANADA
London Toronto Sydney New York

Granada Publishing Limited – Technical Books Division
Frogmore, St Albans, Herts AL2 2NF
and
36 Golden Square, London W1R 4AH
866 United Nations Plaza, New York, NY 10017, USA
117 York Street, Sydney, NSW 2000, Australia
100 Skyway Avenue, Rexdale, Ontario, Canada M9W 3A6
61 Beach Road, Auckland, New Zealand

ISBN 0 246 11484 3

First published in Great Britain 1982 by Granada Publishing

British Library Cataloguing in Publication Data

Davies, J.M.
Manual of stressed skin diaphragm design.
1. Walls 2. Diaphragms (Structural engineering)
I. Title II. Bryan, E.R.
624.1'821 TH2247

Printed in Great Britain

Contents

Preface

After many years of virtual neglect, engineers are beginning to appreciate that there is enormous structural potential in the steel skin of a building. To neglect its influence on the performance of the structure as a whole is to waste a valuable asset. As steel becomes increasingly expensive, it becomes more important to realise this benefit both in traditional construction and by devising innovative structural forms designed to exploit it to the full.

The potential benefits of stressed skin diaphragm action first became apparent over 25 years ago when tests on actual buildings revealed stresses and deflections considerably smaller than those predicted by the usual design calculations. The nature of these buildings was such that the enhanced performance could only be attributed to the beneficial effect of the cladding. Since that time, continuous and extensive research has allowed the effect to be fully quantified and used in practical applications in many parts of the world.

The first book on the subject, *The Stressed Skin Design of Steel Buildings* by the second author, was published in 1973 and set out the principles of the design method together with design expressions and worked examples. The book is now out of print and has not been reprinted, since many of the design expressions in it have been superseded by more refined formulae obtained through recent research. However, the basic principles have remained unaltered.

The increasing utilisation of the diaphragm effect has been accompanied by the appearance of several National and International Codes of Practice and other Codes are known to be in the course of preparation. Of particular significance was the publication in 1977 by the European Convention for Constructional Steelwork of European Recommendations for the Stressed Skin Design of Steel Structures. The authors played an influential part in the preparation of these Recommendations which can be regarded as the definitive document of the state of the art at that time. The present book is strongly influenced by the European Recommendations and includes design procedures that are fully in accord with them. It also takes advantage of more recent research so that the coverage of the subject is complete and fully up-to-date.

The book has three parts. The first part is a design manual and gives all the information that a designer needs in order to be able to apply stressed skin design to most of the situations commonly found in practice. Chapters 1 to 6 describe the design procedure in detail and include all the relevant design expressions. Chapter 7 is a long chapter which gives a comprehensive set of worked examples. In chapter 8, a number of actual buildings using stressed skin construction are described. Part I is concluded by chapter 9 in which the design expressions are summarised and in which all the relevant design tables are collected together.

Part II of the book describes the derivation of the design expressions and summarises some of the more important pieces of research and testing which have led to the present state of the art. It also describes some of the more novel aspects of stressed skin action such as folded plate roofs in chapter 15 and light gauge steel shells in chapter 16. Stressed skin diaphragms can also be used to brace end gables and eaves, and to stabilise rafters. Consideration of these topics with some further worked examples is given in chapter 17.

The behaviour of fasteners is crucial to diaphragm action and this is discussed in chapter 13. The results of many fastener tests, from which design values for most practical situations can be deduced, are included in chapter 9.

An outline of diaphragm action in multi-storey buildings is given in chapter 18 and Part II is concluded in chapter 19 with a review of some practical considerations. Finally, Part III gives a complete list of all the relevant references known to the authors so that the reader can follow up any particular aspect by referring to the original work.

A particular advantage given by stressed skin calculations is that they describe the real behaviour of a structure much more accurately than calculations that consider frame action alone. This book is therefore written in the hope that it will not only lead to more efficient and enterprising structural design but also that it will help engineers and architects to achieve a fuller understanding of how real buildings behave.

The authors would like to express their gratitude to the many individuals who have helped to make the publication of this book possible. Various Research Fellows and Research Students have worked on the subject and the authors gladly acknowledge their contribution to the state of the knowledge. Particular thanks are due to Mrs J. Blood for typing the manuscript, Mr R. Bennett for preparing the diagrams and Mr C. Tivey for many of the photographs.

PART ONE

DESIGN METHOD AND EXAMPLES

CHAPTER ONE

Introduction

1.1 Historical background

Interest in stressed skin design dates back to the early 1950s when tests on steel portal framed structures revealed measured stresses and deflections that were considerably smaller than those predicted by the usual design calculations. The structures concerned were of the factory or warehouse type without internal floors or partitions so that the only explanation for the reduced stresses was that the profiled steel sheet cladding was helping the frames to carry the load. This reasoning prompted the second author to commence research into the stiffening effect of light steel cladding and this research has continued first at the University of Manchester and later at the University of Salford up to the present time.

A landmark in the development of the principles of stressed skin design was the publication of the first book on the subject[1.57]* and this remained the only comprehensive work on the subject until the publication by the European Convention for Constructional Steelwork of the *European Recommendations for the Stressed Skin Design of Steel Structures.*[1.99] These recommendations are based on the work of the authors and are now widely recognised as the definitive reference on the subject. The design procedures and expressions which are described in the present book are fully in accordance with the European recommendations. An important feature of the authors' work has been the development of simple methods of calculation and design aids and these will be fully described in the following chapters.

1.2 The present situation

At the time of writing, stressed skin design is not incorporated in the provisions of the relevant British Standard specification for 'The use of structural steel in building'

* A comprehensive bibliography containing over 200 references in chronological order is given at the end of the book.

(*B.S. 449*) and this has tended to restrict its application to certain types of building. However, the draft of a new standard[1.113] containing clauses permitting stressed skin design was released for public comment in 1978. The present position is that the new British Standard on 'The structural use of steelwork in building' will be *B.S. 5950* and that stressed skin design will constitute Part 9.

To date, the majority of stressed skin structures built in Britain have been system built and indeed many of the major systems used for low-rise steel framed construction (e.g. CLASP, SEAC, SCOLA) rely on stressed skin action for their stability. In the early 1970s, at the height of the school building programme, stressed skin structures to the value of many millions of pounds per annum were built in the CLASP and SEAC systems alone. Figs. 1.1 and 1.2 show typical stressed skin structures of this type.

Fig. 1.1 SEAC school building.

Another type of structure for which stressed skin design has been used has been the major prestige structure which has justified the trouble of obtaining a Building Regulations waiver to permit this approach to design. A notable example of this type is the New Covent Garden fruit and vegetable market shown in fig. 1.3. The acceptance of stressed skin design for this project by the Greater London Council represented an important step forward in the practical utilisation of the stressed skin principle.

Relevant national Standards either exist or are in draft form in Australia, Canada, Czechoslovakia, Germany and Sweden. In the U.S.A., stressed skin design based on testing has been permitted for many years[1.15] together with associated empirical and semi-empirical methods of design[1.41, 1.48] and numerous structures

Fig. 1.2 CLASP computer building at Nottingham.

Fig. 1.3 New Covent Garden fruit and vegetable market. (*Photograph by Handford Photography*)

have been built on this basis, notably in California where lateral load requirements are high due to the possibility of earthquakes. At present, a committee of the American Iron and Steel Institute is working on a code for design by calculation and drafts are in circulation.[1.114]

1.3 Principles of diaphragm action

Historically, stressed skin or diaphragm action was first appreciated in pitched roof portal frame structures of the type shown in fig. 1.4.

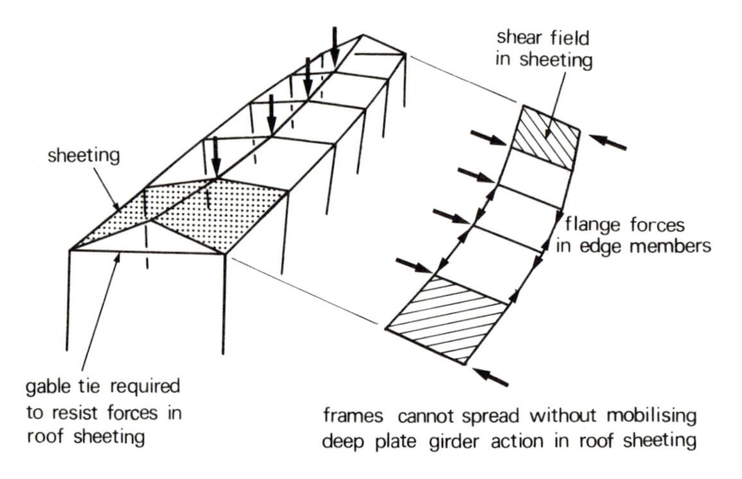

Fig. 1.4 Stressed skin action in a pitched roof portal frame structure carrying vertical load.

As vertical load is applied to the frames there is a tendency for the apexes to move downwards and the eaves to move outwards and this movement cannot take place without causing in-plane deflections of the roof sheeting. The sheeting has considerable in-plane stiffness and tends to resist this displacement by acting, together with the supporting purlins, in the manner of a deep plate girder. The purlins act as flanges carrying the axial forces due to bending and the sheeting acts as the web carrying the shear. Because of the proportions of typical roof planes, shear forces and shear deformations predominate over bending effects so that stressed skin design is primarily concerned with the effect of shear. Axial forces in the purlins caused by bending and their corresponding displacements are also significant and must be considered. Evidently the stressed skin action shown in fig. 1.4 relies on restraint at the gables, usually in the form of an eaves tie, to carry the end reactions from the deep plate girder action described above. As such a restraint is usually present for reasons other than that of promoting stressed skin action, stressed skin action is almost always present, whether or not the designer is aware of it.

Although initial interest in stressed skin design arose from a consideration of the behaviour of pitched roof portal frames, more recently attention has been concentrated on flat-roofed structures of the type shown in fig. 1.5. Here side loads at

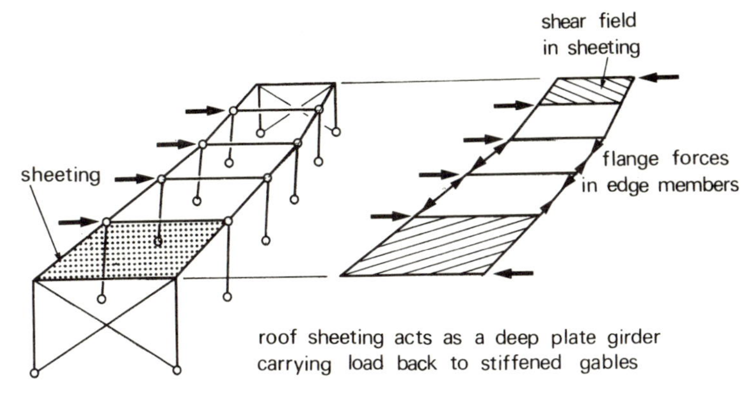

Fig. 1.5 Stressed skin action in a flat-roofed structure with non-rigid frames.

eaves level are applied directly in the plane of the sheeting so that such loads are very efficiently resisted by the stressed skin action of the sheeting which acts as a deep plate girder in the manner described above. This form of stressed skin action is so effective that it is often possible to dispense with both rigid-jointed frame action and wind bracing in this type of structure and to rely entirely on the sheeting for stability. As before, stressed skin action is dependent on there being provision at the gables to carry the end reactions from the roof diaphragm. This may take the form of diagonal bracing as shown in fig. 1.5, or alternatively the sheeted gable may itself act as a diaphragm carrying the forces in the roof to the foundations. It is clear that in fig. 1.5 stressed skin action is of no help in carrying vertical load and this leads to an important general principle, namely that stressed skin action only helps to carry loads that cause displacement of the joints of the structure in the plane of the sheeting. It is of no help in resisting the 'no sway' distribution of load. It follows that for the pitched roof frame of fig. 1.4 stressed skin action is also of considerable benefit in resisting side load on the structure but that, for vertical load, the influence of stressed skin action depends on the angle of pitch of the roof and as this reduces so do the benefits of stressed skin action.

1.4 Types of building suitable for stressed skin design

It is convenient to divide stressed skin structures into two distinct types, as follows:

1.4.1 Type 1. Diaphragms acting alone

This is typically a low-rise, flat-roofed structure in which the connections between the beams and the columns are nominally pinned and the stability of the structure depends entirely on diaphragm action in the roof and intermediate floors (if any). In Britain this has been by far the most frequent use of stressed skin design and is the basis of a number of building systems. As a result, not only is wind bracing omitted in the plane of the roof but it is claimed that even greater savings are possible as a consequence of the simplification of the system and the reduction in the number of components and joint details. The New Covent Garden fruit and vegetable market (fig. 1.3) is also an example of this type.

1.4.2 Type 2. Diaphragms acting in conjunction with rigid-jointed frames

This is more in the nature of conventional construction where it is recognised that load is shared between the cladding and the frames and as a consequence the amount of material in the frames may be reduced. Typical situations where stressed skin construction may advantageously be employed are:

(a) in tied portal frames where the design of the stanchions is governed by side load considerations;
(b) in tall pitched roof frames, particularly those containing cranes, where the lateral deflection at eaves level is critical;
(c) in tall, rectangular-framed buildings where relative lateral movement between the gable frame and the intermediate frames causes considerable forces in the cladding, whether or not this is considered in the design of the frames;
(d) structures subject to a lateral point load. Stressed skin action is particularly effective in distributing such a point load among adjacent frames.

It should be noted that in pitched roof frames with roof pitches of the order of 6° as currently constructed in the U.K., stressed skin action is unlikely to be of significant benefit in resisting uniformly distributed vertical loads. As a general guide, unless the diaphragm is very lightly loaded, deflections are likely to be excessive or the benefit of stressed skin action small if the ratio of span to depth of a diaphragm exceeds about four.

1.5 Suitable cladding for stressed skin action

Some degree of stressed skin action is present with all cladding materials but if the effect is to be quantified and incorporated in the design process it is essential that there is a high degree of reliability as regards both strength and stiffness. This necessity removes from consideration materials which are brittle (e.g. asbestos cement) and fasteners which rely on friction (e.g. hook bolts) and concentrates attention on profiled metal sheet fastened to the supporting structure through the troughs of the corrugations. The material may be steel or aluminium and may be used as a sheeting or decking as shown in fig. 1.6.

1.6 Suitable fasteners for stressed skin design

Stressed skin action makes considerable demands on the fastening system and, indeed, the ultimate strength of most diaphragms is dependent on the strength of the fastenings. With the exception of hook bolts, most fastening systems in current use are suitable for stressed skin design. Some typical and suitable fastenings are shown in fig. 1.7.

1.7 Necessary conditions for stressed skin action

The necessary conditions for satisfactory stressed skin action should now be clear and may be summarised as follows:

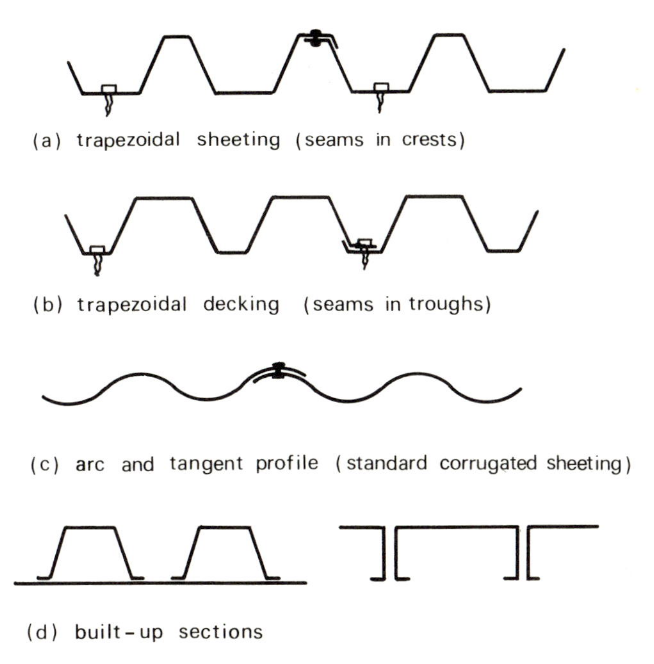

Fig. 1.6 Suitable cladding profiles for diaphragm action: (a) trapezoidal sheeting (seams in crests), (b) trapezoidal decking (seams in troughs), (c) arc and tangent profile (standard corrugated sheeting), (d) built-up sections.

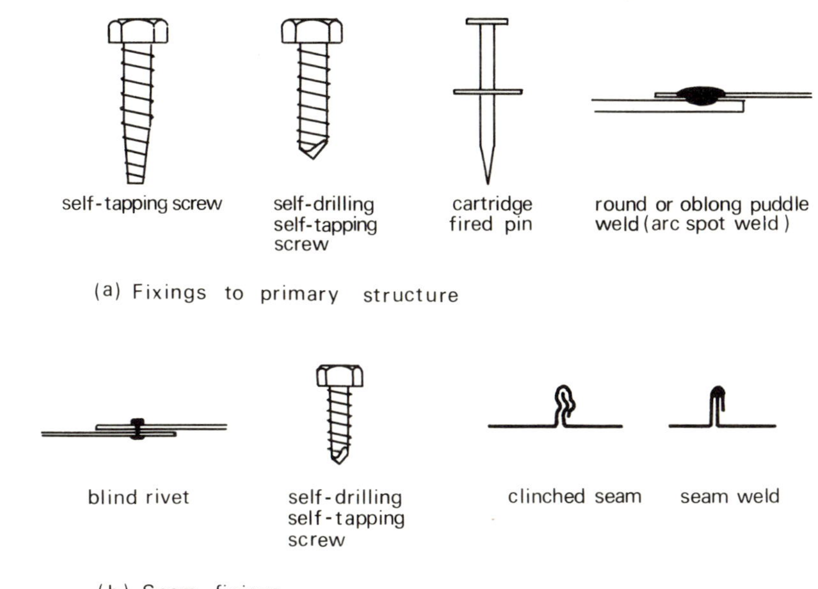

Fig. 1.7 Some suitable fasteners for stressed skin design: (a) fixings to primary structure, (b) seam fixings.

(a) Suitable structural members and connections shall be provided to transmit forces arising from diaphragm action to the main structural framework and thence to the foundations.
(b) The seams between adjacent sheet or decking units shall be welded or fastened by rivets, self-tapping screws or other similar fasteners of a type which will not work loose in service nor pull out or fail in shear before causing tearing of the sheeting or decking material.
(c) Both ends of each individual sheet or decking unit shall be attached directly to the supporting members by welding or by means of self-tapping screws, cartridge-fired pins, bolts or other fasteners of a type which will not work loose in service nor pull out or fail in shear before causing tearing of the cladding material. All such fasteners shall be fixed through the troughs of the corrugations and shall connect the sheeting directly and tightly to the supporting member. Hook bolts or other fasteners which transmit shear forces by friction are not adequate.
(d) All diaphragms shall be provided with edge members in the direction of the span of the diaphragm and these members and their connections shall be of sufficient capacity to carry the flange forces arising from diaphragm action.

Stressed skin diaphragms may incorporate significant openings although there are certain restrictions on these which are considered in chapter 5.

1.8 Loading and load factors

Stressed skin action is considered to be particularly suitable for resisting loads such as wind load and snow load which are themselves applied through the cladding, so that if the cladding is for any reason removed so also is most of the load. It is therefore recommended that stressed skin design should be applied primarily to buildings in which the main consideration is exclusion of the weather. Cladding may also be considered to be suitable in resisting the load from light runways and the surge from overhead cranes and it is particularly effective in such cases. In pitched roof buildings, the cladding may also be very effective in resisting spread of the crane rails. Diaphragm action should not be used to resist large permanent loads.

In general, the load factors used in stressed skin design should be the same as those for normal structural steelwork. However, modern codes of practice tend to be expressed in terms of limit state design in which the safety of the structure is a combination of load and material factors. The design strength of a diaphragm is very strongly influenced by the design strength of the fasteners and, because of the statistical nature of fastener strength, some special provisions are required for the characteristic strength of fasteners and the appropriate material factor. This question is discussed in the next chapter.

1.9 Economic advantages of stressed skin design

It is, of course, extremely difficult to obtain quantitative information regarding the economics of any form of steel construction including a realistic assessment of the costs of fabrication and erection. This is particularly true when assessing the benefits of stressed skin construction where the savings may be not only in the weight of the steel framing but also in simplified detailing and in simplified design office procedures and where these savings may in certain circumstances be partly offset against the cost of a small number of extra fasteners and constraints in the erection programme.

However, a detailed economic study on a stressed skin structure was carried out by Committee 17 (now TC7) of the European Convention for Constructional Steelwork.[1.95] In this study, the two alternative structures shown in fig. 1.8 were fully

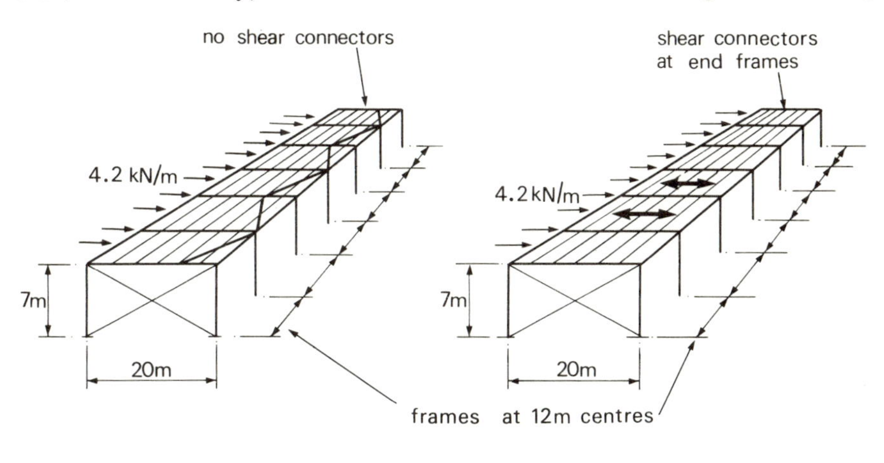

Fig. 1.8 Structures for cost study: (a) wind bracing, (b) diaphragm action.

detailed and costed in various countries in Europe for all aspects of construction except erection. The results of this study were remarkably consistent between the various countries and are summarised in fig. 1.9 which gives the difference in cost

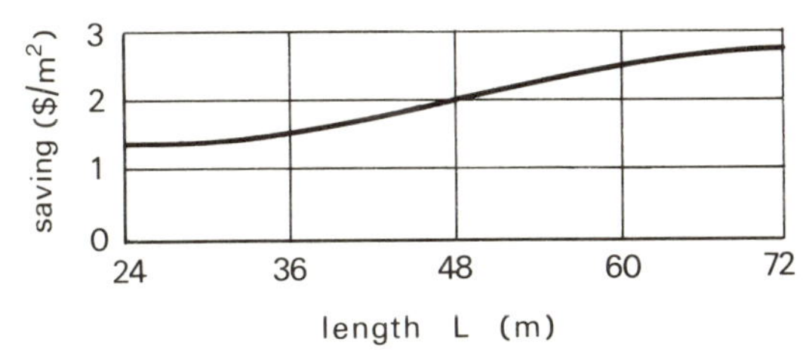

Fig. 1.9 Cost saving per square metre by using stressed skin action.

(June 1976) between the wind bracing for system A and the additional fasteners for system B. The savings represent about 10% of the total cost of the steelwork and sheeting.

The performances of the above structures were also evaluated and are summarised in table 1.1. It is worthy of note that in system A the end fasteners between the

Table 1.1 Performance of structure used for cost study

	System A		System B
	Wind bracing only	Wind bracing and sheeting	Diaphragm action
Deflection due to wind load	46 mm	22 mm	38 mm

sheeting and the supporting members would be overstressed at the working load. This is often the case in rectangular clad structures and although there is no suggestion that such structures might be unsafe there are potential difficulties in keeping them watertight. Proper consideration of the forces in the sheeting and its fasteners using the principles of stressed skin design avoids such difficulties. Indeed, it has been suggested that one of the major contributions of stressed skin design is that it describes the *true* behaviour of the completed building rather than the idealised behaviour of the frame. This aspect of the work is important since interaction between the frame and the sheeting occurs whether or not it is taken into account. However, the potential economy of the method is also regarded as being of major importance.

1.10 Other types of stressed skin structure

The earlier sections of this chapter have discussed the application of diaphragm action in structures of essentially conventional construction whereby benefit may be taken of the considerable in-plane stiffness and strength of metal cladding. It may well be, however, that the full potential benefits of stressed skin design will not be realised until structures are conceived and designed with stressed skin action in mind in a rather more fundamental manner than hitherto. There is the opportunity for many exciting innovations in this field and some of the known possibilities will be briefly reviewed in this section. A number of these will be discussed in more detail in later chapters.

1.10.1 Light gauge steel folded plate

This is a logical development of the pitched roof portal frame in which intermediate framing is eliminated and plate elements, consisting solely of fold-line members and sheeting, span the clear distance between the gables. Fig. 1.10 illustrates a typical situation in which the primary roof structure consists of only two elements together with their associated fasteners, namely: fold-line members which are usually cold formed from flat plate and profiled metal sheeting spanning between fold-line members. Many light gauge steel folded plate roofs have been built in the U.S.A. and fig. 1.11 shows a typical example.

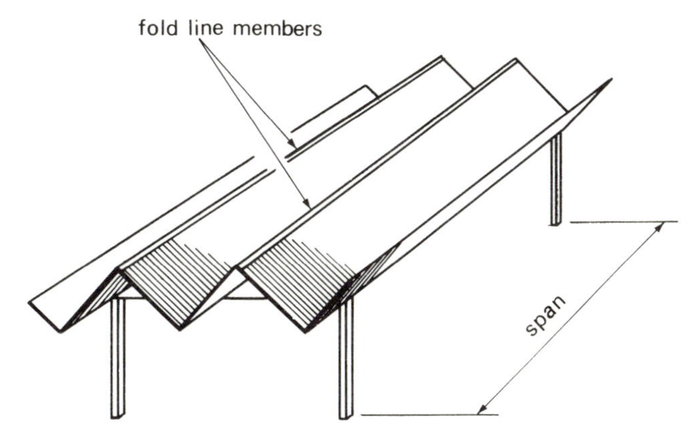

Fig. 1.10 Typical light gauge steel folded plate construction.

Fig. 1.11 Light gauge steel folded plate roof in the U.S.A.

Light gauge steel folded plates may be tapered, giving rise to alternative shapes such as the pleated dome shown in fig. 1.12. Furthermore, there are many alternative cross-sections in addition to the simple saw-tooth shown in figs. 1.10 and 1.11.

1.10.2 Light gauge steel hyperbolic paraboloid

The hyperbolic paraboloid is a particularly advantageous geometric form for light gauge steel construction because profiled steel sheets warp readily into this shape.

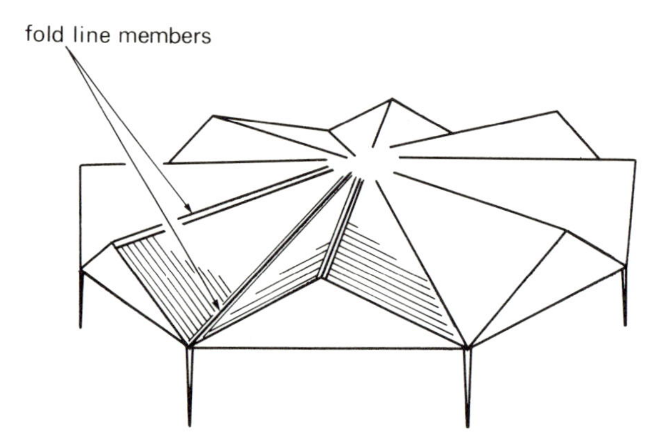

Fig. 1.12 Pleated dome formed from light gauge steel folded plates.

This makes possible a wide range of attractive roof shapes such as those shown in fig. 1.13. At the time of writing, the light gauge steel hyperbolic paraboloid formed the largest light gauge steel structures in the world, namely the large aircraft hangars at Los Angeles and San Francisco.[4.10,4.11,4.12,4.14]

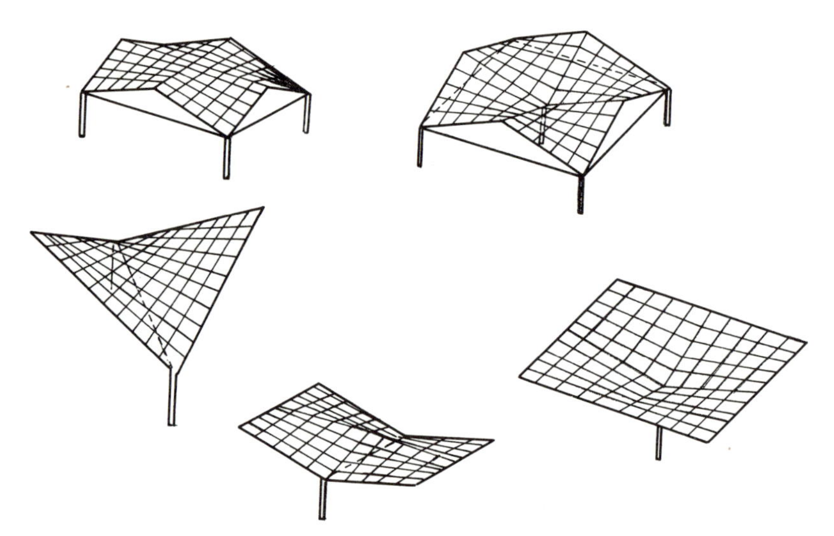

Fig. 1.13 Roof structures comprising light gauge steel hypar elements with linear edge stiffening.

1.10.3 Light gauge steel cylindrical shells

Alternative shell-like configurations may be obtained by permanently curving profiled steel sheet rather than warping it. The usual application involves rolling previously profiled sheet to form a cylindrical surface but other shapes may be possible. Cylindrical steel shell roofs, both with and without internal framing, have been built rather spasmodically over many years. Figure 1.14 shows a particularly early example built at the end of the last century.

Fig. 1.14 Cylindrical shell roof of a chemical factory.

Light gauge steel cylindrical shells are also used for agricultural buildings such as Dutch barns and silos for storing grain.

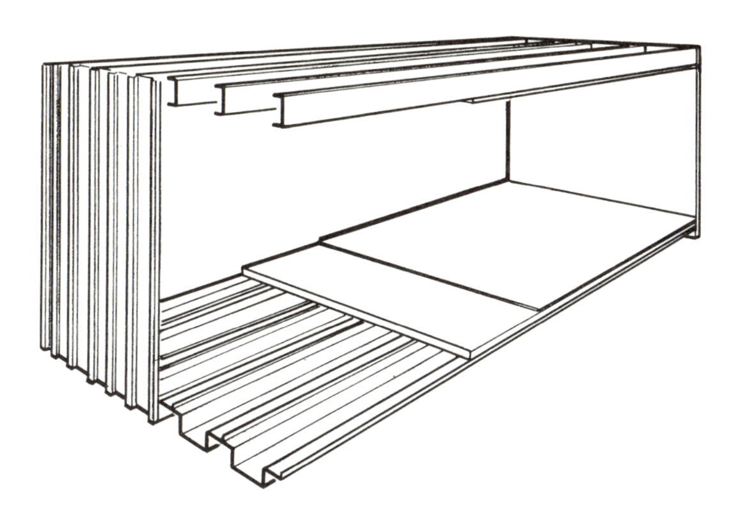

Fig. 1.15 Box unit for modular dwelling construction.

1.10.4 Stressed skin boxes

Diaphragm action can also be utilised in box-unit construction, individual boxes being built up using light gauge profiled members for walls, floor and roof. A typical unit is shown in fig. 1.15. Such box units can be prefabricated and finished internally in the factory before being transported to site. They are frequently used as single-storey portable buildings but can be built to stack to several storeys high. They can also be used in combination to form quite extensive building layouts.

1.10.5 The use of vertical diaphragms to control sway

Common types of vertical stabilising systems in both low-rise and multi-storey buildings (e.g. diagonal bracing or masonry or concrete shear walls) can be replaced by vertical diaphragms whose major shear-carrying component is profiled steel sheeting or other similar cold-formed steel walling. Such diaphragms can serve also as the walls of lift shafts or as the core for partition finishing materials with consequent economic advantage. The behaviour is very similar to that of the more familiar horizontal roof diaphragms.

CHAPTER TWO

The basic shear panel

2.1 Basic arrangements and definitions

A *diaphragm* may be considered to be a very deep beam in which the depth is the dimension parallel to the applied load and the span is the dimension perpendicular to the applied load. The profiled steel sheeting may span either perpendicular or parallel to the span of the diaphragm. The two basic arrangements and some fundamental definitions are shown in fig. 2.1. Diaphragms arise in a wide variety of shapes and sizes and often have a depth that is greater than the span. In such cases it is a good general principle to neglect the additional depth and to satisfy the rule that the depth of a diaphragm should never be considered to be greater than its span.

2.2 Types of diaphragm

Each of the two types of diaphragm shown in fig. 2.1 may be fastened to the supporting structure in two different ways: the diaphragm attached on all four sides (termed direct shear transfer) when the sheeting is fixed to both the perpendicular and to the parallel members; the diaphragm attached on two sides only (termed indirect shear transfer) when the sheeting is fixed only to the perpendicular members. There are thus four basic cases to consider, as shown in fig. 2.2, together with a further sub-division of case (3): case 3(a) with shear connectors (or their equivalent) at the gable rafters only and case 3(b) with no shear connectors at any rafters. It may be noted that the *European Recommendations for the Stressed Skin Design of Steel Structures*[1.99] do not permit case 3(b) but in this book it is assumed that this arrangement may be used for lightly-loaded diaphragms.

2.3 Components of an individual panel

The design unit of a diaphragm is an *individual panel*. It is defined as the area bounded by the edge members and by two adjacent rafters irrespective of whether

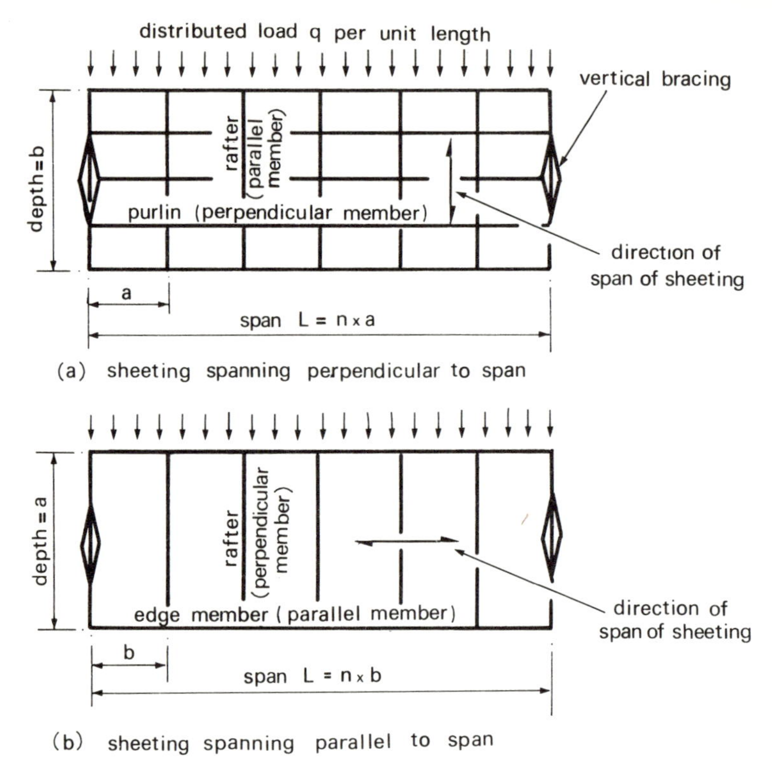

Fig. 2.1 Basic diaphragm arrangements: (a) sheeting spanning perpendicular to span, (b) sheeting spanning parallel to span.

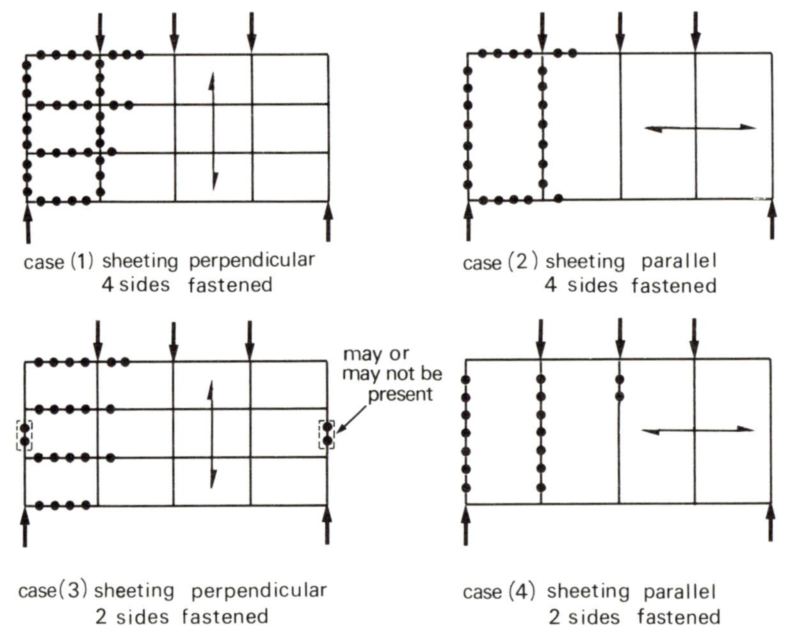

Fig. 2.2 Alternative fastener arrangements: case (1) sheeting perpendicular, 4 sides

(*cont. facing page*)

the rafters are considered as parallel members or perpendicular members (defined in fig. 2.1). Fig. 2.3 shows a typical individual panel (sheeting spanning perpendicular to the span of the diaphragm) which is itself an assembly of a large number of components, all of which contribute to its behaviour under load. The components are defined with reference to this panel and are as follows:

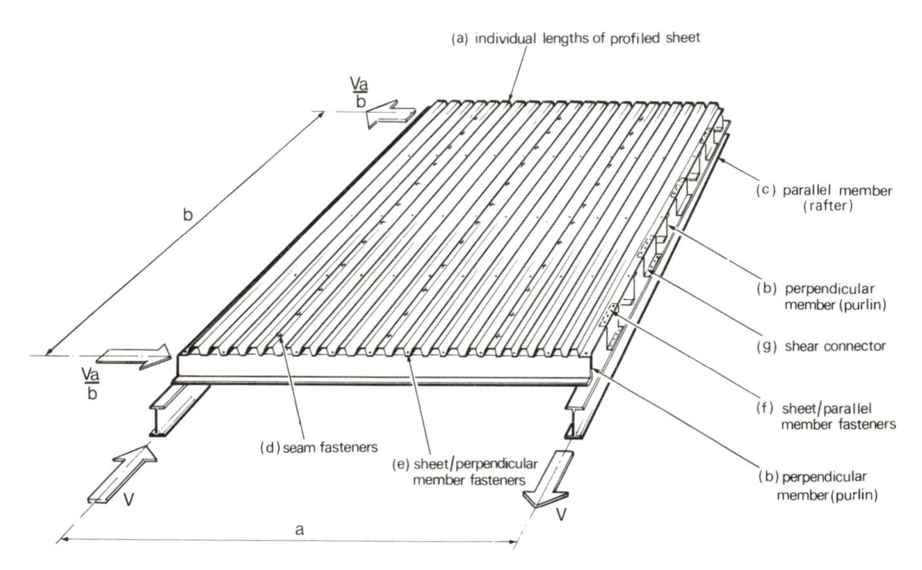

Fig. 2.3 Basic arrangement of an individual panel.

(a) Individual lengths of profiled steel or aluminium sheeting. The profiled steel or aluminium cladding shown in fig. 2.3 may take the form of 'sheeting', in which case it forms the outer skin of the building with any necessary insulation, etc. being positioned below, or it may alternatively take the form of 'decking' in which case a built-up roof consisting of insulation, waterproofing, etc. may be positioned on top of the steel cladding. The two cases are illustrated in fig. 2.4. Throughout this book, unless it is necessary to differentiate between sheeting and decking, the term sheeting may be taken to be a general term embracing the two.

(b) Perpendicular members (purlins in fig. 2.3). It is a fundamental requirement that the sheeting is firmly fastened to these members through the troughs of the profile.

(c) Parallel members (rafters in fig. 2.3).

(d) Seam fasteners (connecting longitudinal edges of adjacent sheet widths). When a well designed diaphragm (or indeed any diaphragm of usual proportions) is loaded up to failure, the usual mode of failure is by tearing of the sheet material at each fastener along a seam or sidelap between two adjacent sheets. Provided that the fasteners do not fail prematurely in a brittle manner, this is a ductile and readily

---

Fig. 2.2 (cont.)
fastened; case (2) sheeting parallel, 4 sides fastened; case (3) sheeting perpendicular, 2 sides fastened; case (4) sheeting parallel, 2 sides fastened.

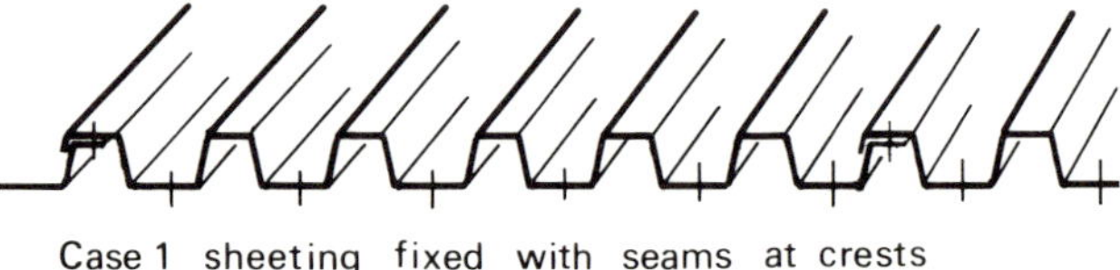

Fig. 2.4 Illustrating profiled metal cladding fixed as sheeting or decking: case (1) sheeting fixed with seams at crests; case (2) sheeting fixed with seams in troughs (decking).

predictable mode of failure so that it is good practice to always design stressed skin diaphragms for a seam failure.

(e) Sheet to perpendicular member fasteners. The main requirement here is a direct connection between the sheeting and the supporting members. The usual fasteners used in practice at the present time such as self-drilling, self-tapping screws and shot-fired pins are perfectly satisfactory in this respect but hook bolts are not because they rely on friction and do not provide a sufficiently reliable connection between the sheeting and the purlins below. Sheet to purlin fasteners at the ends of the sheets are not usually critical as regards strength but the spacing has a profound influence on the flexibility of the diaphragm. A diaphragm in which fasteners pass through every trough is much stiffer than a similar diaphragm in which the fasteners only pass through alternate troughs of the profile.

(f) Sheet to parallel member fasteners. These may be considered to be optional in that effective stressed skin action takes place, though less efficiently, when they are omitted, i.e. when the sheeting is fastened to the perpendicular members only. When the parallel and perpendicular members are at the same level, the provision of these fasteners presents no problem. When, as is more often the case, the perpendicular members (purlins) pass over the parallel members (rafters) the provision of sheet to parallel member fasteners necessitates the use of shear connectors.

(g) Shear connectors. These are devices for enhancing stressed skin action by connecting the sheeting directly to the supporting structure on four sides. They are often conveniently fabricated from purlin offcuts and their cost can be offset because when they are present only the simplest purlin to rafter connections are required.

(h) Connections between perpendicular and parallel members (purlin to rafter connections). If shear connectors are used, the purlin to rafter connections are unimportant from the point of view of stressed skin design. If there are no shear connectors and the sheeting is connected to the supporting structure on two sides only, then the shear forces produced by stressed skin action have to pass from the supporting structure into the sheeting through the purlin to rafter connections and the sheet to purlin fasteners. This makes considerable demands on these fasteners, particularly the sheet to purlin fasteners adjacent to the rafters. Some degree of stiffening in the purlin to rafter connections is clearly necessary though details that are satisfactory in other respects are likely to be satisfactory also for stressed skin action.

2.4 Determination of flexibility and strength

When an individual panel is loaded in shear up to failure, the load-deflection curve has the form shown in fig. 2.5. The flexibility c of a diaphragm (mm/kN) is defined as the reciprocal of the slope of the linear elastic part of the curve and the strength V_{ult}(kN) is defined as the maximum load sustained. In a well designed diaphragm, the failure is ductile and V_{ult} is associated with a clearly defined plateau of plastic deformation with no fall-off in load. The determination of c and V_{ult} for an individual panel is crucial to stressed skin theory. This determination may be undertaken in a number of ways and these will be described in Part II but for the practical design of the vast majority of diaphragms only one method is important, namely the use of simple design expressions. However, before proceeding to discuss the appropriate design expressions it is convenient to first review the determination of the relevant properties of the various fasteners which are crucial to the design process whichever method is used.

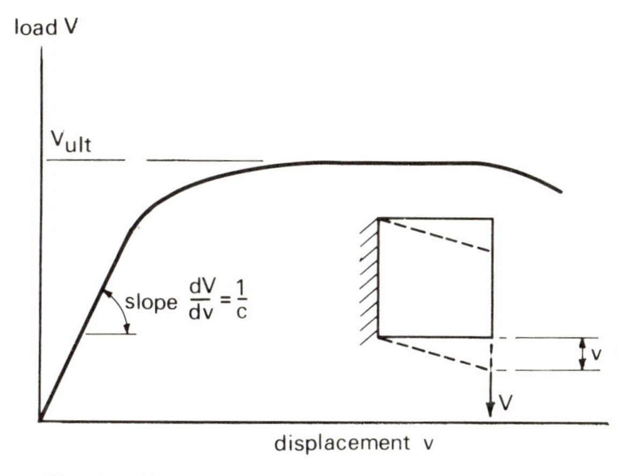

Fig. 2.5 Typical load–deflection curve of panel.

2.5 Fastener characteristics

In order to avoid a brittle ‘progressive’ failure, it is necessary that fastener failure should be ductile. When failure is by tearing of the sheeting in the vicinity of the fastener, this is always the case, whereas failure of the fastener itself is likely to be brittle and should be avoided. Fortunately, most fasteners in current use and in combination with typical sheet thicknesses do give a ductile failure so that the satisfaction of this requirement is not a problem. The failure mode in an individual case, as well as the appropriate value of ultimate load and slip can only be reliably determined by testing. Full details of the necessary procedures are given in reference 6.18. The usual method is to carry out the test on a two fastener lap joint placed in a tensile testing machine as shown in fig. 2.6. This test gives an average

Fig. 2.6 Typical test to determine fastener properties.

load-deflection curve for the two fasteners and from this the ultimate load and the flexibility (or slip) can be determined in the manner described in chapter 13. Because of the somewhat variable nature of the results obtained from tests on fasteners, it is necessary to carry out several tests on a given arrangement and to interpret the results statistically. For fastener strength, this interpretation gives a characteristic strength which is equal to the average ultimate load minus about two standard deviations (depending on the number of tests conducted). Some typical characteristic strengths and flexibilities obtained on this basis are given in tables 9.9 to 9.11.* It should be appreciated that for failure of a complete diaphragm it is necessary for a number of fasteners to fail simultaneously and therefore the statistically based design procedure is quite conservative. The results shown in tables 9.9 to 9.11 can, of course, be used in appropriate cases as the basis for diaphragm design. In the course of time, it is expected that a collection of such results will be built up that is sufficiently comprehensive to render testing unnecessary. For the present, if results are not available from which a reliable estimate of the fastener properties for a particular application can be made, it may be necessary to test before the design can be justified. The necessary testing is both quick and cheap.

When estimating fastener properties for the purpose of design, the following general points should be noted:

(a) Fasteners are essentially of two types, namely: those used for thin-to-thick connections, i.e. sheet to purlin or sheet to shear connector fasteners, and those used for thin-to-thin connections, i.e. seam fasteners.

(b) Results for self drilling, self-tapping screws are influenced by the presence or otherwise of a neoprene washer. They are also influenced by the size of the metal washer. Characteristic strengths are very nearly proportional to the thickness of the thinner sheet and, for small changes of thickness, test results may be extrapolated on this basis. This will usually give safe results for a reduction in thickness and slightly unsafe results for an increase in thickness.

(c) Characteristic strengths are to some extent influenced by both the yield strength and the ultimate strength of the thinner lapped plate. The ultimate strength is usually considered to be the more important of the two. The results in tables 9.9 and 9.10 were obtained for typical British sheet with a nominal yield strength of the order of 250 N/mm^2. Higher fastener strengths are obtained when sheeting with a nominal yield stress of (say) 350 N/mm^2 is used. Fastener strengths for higher grade material may be adjusted on the basis of the ultimate strength.

(d) The development of full fastener strength is dependent on the fastener being positioned a sufficient distance from the edge of the sheet. The following edge distance requirements have been found to be satisfactory and are incorporated in the *European Recommendations for the Stressed Skin Design of Steel Structures.*[1.99]

(i) The edge distance of seam fasteners and shear connector fasteners, if they are to be included in the design calculations, measured from the centre of the hole, should not be less than 1.5 times the diameter of the fastener or less than 8 mm.

(ii) The edge distance of all fasteners other than seam fasteners and shear connector fasteners, if they are to be included in the design calculations, measured from the centre of the hole shall not be less than 1.5 times the diameter of the fastener or less than 10 mm.

* In order to avoid repetition of useful tables, these are collected together in chapter 9 at the end of Part I together with a summary of the basic design expressions and a complete list of symbols.

(iii) The end distance of all fasteners measured in the direction of the span of the sheeting shall not be less than three times the diameter of the fastener or less than 20 mm.

(e) Flexibility values are very variable and are to a large extent independent of material thickness and strength.

Finally, it may be noted that for limit state design, the design strength of a given fastener is given by the characteristic strength divided by a material factor γ_m. In the *European Recommendations for the Stressed Skin Design of Steel Structures*,[1.99] γ_m is taken as 1.11 so that the design strength is taken as 0.9 times the characteristic strength.

2.6 Principles and assumptions in design expressions

The simple design expressions which follow are based on two basic assumptions both of which have been justified by comparison with detailed finite element analysis and test results. Full details of the basis of these expressions are given in Part II. The basic assumptions are: an internal force distribution is assumed which is based on simple equilibrium of individual sheet widths; it is assumed that the flexibility of a complete panel may be obtained by summing the separate flexibilities due to the various possibile movements and deformations within the panel.

On the basis of these assumptions, design expressions have been derived from which may be calculated the design load for failure in each of the possible failure modes and the flexibility of the complete panel. The expressions which follow in sections 2.7 and 2.8 apply to a single cantilever panel of the type shown in figs. 2.3 and 2.5 with the sheeting spanning perpendicular to the span of the panel. In section 2.9 the modifications necessary when the sheeting spans parallel to the span of the panel are considered. In chapter 3, the additional considerations when panels are assembled to form diaphragm beams are considered. Finally the complete design procedure is summarised in chapter 9.

2.7 Expressions for diaphragm strength (cantilever panel, sheeting perpendicular to span)

The design strength of a diaphragm is obtained by considering the strength with respect to each of the possible failure modes in turn and choosing the lowest. However, it is highly desirable that the design process should ensure that failure is ductile and, as the most frequently encountered failure modes are the most ductile, a requirement is incorporated in the *European Recommendations for the Stressed Skin Design of Steel Structures*[1.99] that non-ductile failure modes should have a strength at least 25% greater than the calculated design strength of the diaphragm. The same requirement is incorporated in the design procedures described in this book. The following failure modes must be considered:

(a) failure along a line of seam fasteners;

(b) failure in the sheet to parallel member (shear connector) fasteners (where these are provided, i.e. cases (1) (2) and (3)a in fig. 2.2);

(c) failure in the sheet to perpendicular member fasteners near the gables or rafters for diaphragms fastened on two sides only. This failure occurs in a direction parallel to the span of the sheeting - see fig. 2.7 and cases (3) and (4) in fig. 2.2;
(d) overall shear buckling of the sheeting;
(e) failure in the sheet to perpendicular member (purlin) fasteners in a direction perpendicular to the span of the sheeting (see fig. 2.8);
(f) failure of the edge member in compression or combined compression and bending.

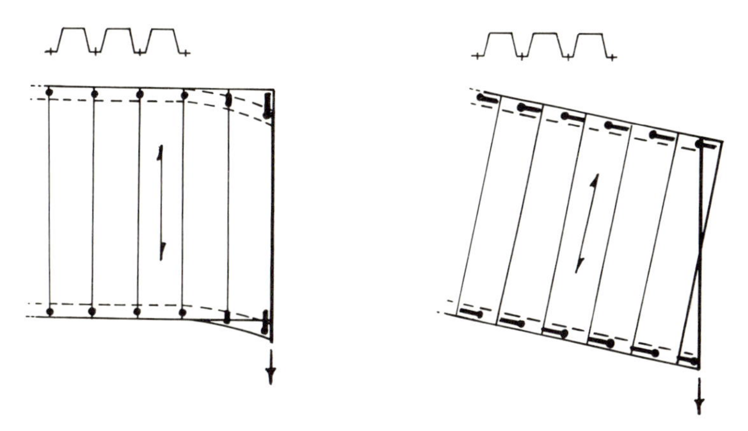

Fig. 2.7 Illustrating failure mode (c). **Fig. 2.8** Illustrating failure mode (e).

The preferable and ductile failure modes are (a), (b) and (c) whereas those requiring a 25% higher failure load are (d), (e) and (f). Each of these failure modes will now be reviewed in turn. In each case the design expressions will be first derived for a cantilever diaphragm with the sheeting spanning perpendicular to the span of the diaphragm. The alternative arrangements with the sheeting spanning parallel to the span or with panels assembled to form diaphragm beams will be considered later.

2.7.1 Expression for seam failure

When failure at a seam takes place it invariably involves simultaneous failure of all the individual fasteners forming the seam. The design expression reflects this and also takes account of the fact that seam failure cannot take place without some movement taking place in the adjacent sheet to perpendicular member fasteners. Fig. 2.9 shows this in a typical seam failure. Seam failure is the most common form of failure and also the most ductile so that a well designed diaphragm will frequently fail in this way. The expression for the design strength for this mode of failure is:

$$V_{ult} = n_s F_s + \frac{\beta_1}{\beta_3} n_p F_p \tag{2.1}$$

where n_s = total number of seam fasteners per side lap (excluding those which pass through both sheets and the supporting purlins),

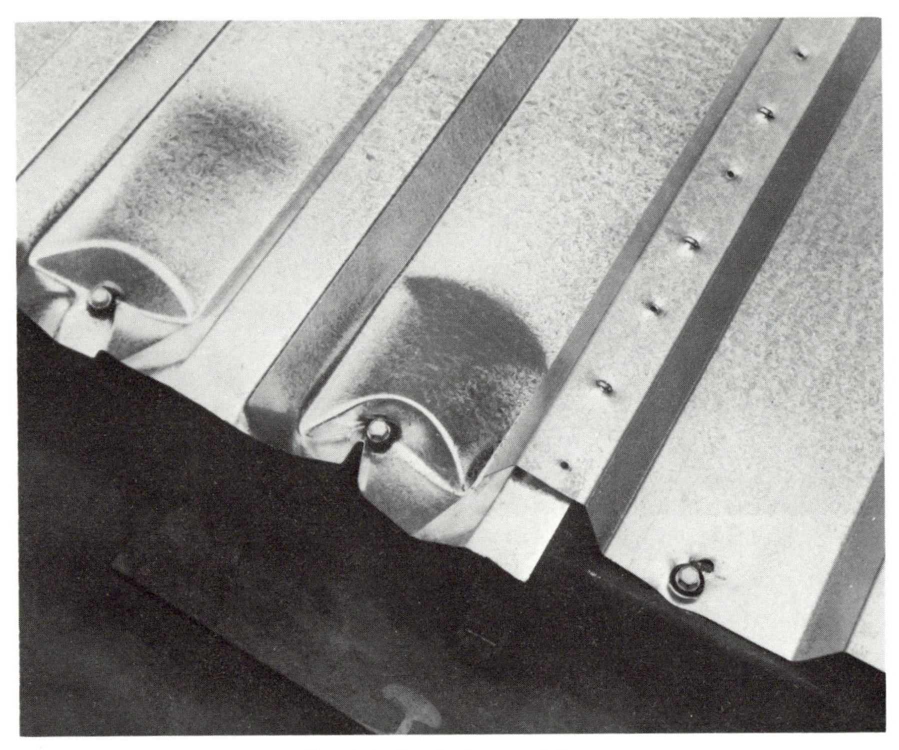

Fig. 2.9 Typical seam failure.

n_p = total number of perpendicular members (purlins) within the depth of the panel,

F_s = design strength of an individual seam fastener,

F_p = design strength of an individual sheet to perpendicular member fastener,

β_1 = factor given in table 9.5* which depends on n_f and also on whether the profiled metal cladding is fixed as sheeting or decking as shown in fig. 2.10,

n_f = number of sheet to perpendicular member fasteners per member per sheet width,

β_3 = (distance between outermost fasteners across sheet width) ÷ (sheet cover width),
= $(n_f - 1)/n_f$ for sheeting (case (a) fig. 2.10),
= 1.0 for decking (case (b) in fig. 2.10).

Typical arrangements of seams in sheeting and decking, showing how n_s, n_f, etc. are calculated, are shown in fig. 2.10. The above expression (2.1) makes the reasonable

* In order to avoid repetition of tables of factors and to improve the usefulness of this book as a practical design aid the tables are collected together at the end of Part I together with a summary of the basic design expressions and a complete list of symbols.

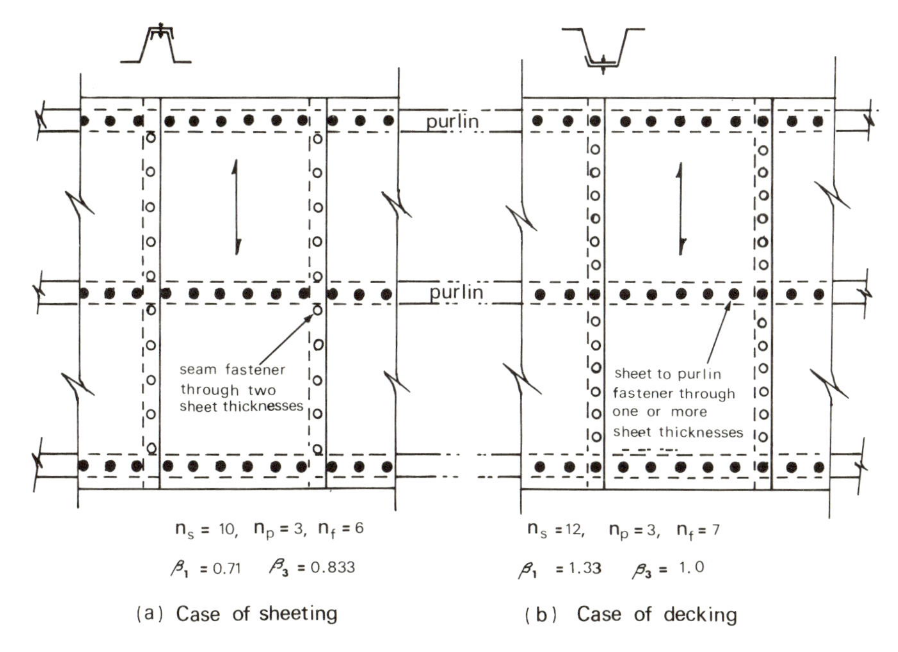

Fig. 2.10 Alternative seam arrangements: (a) case of sheeting, (b) case of decking.

assumption that the fasteners which pass through both sheet thicknesses into the supporting member below contribute to the seam strength. Tests have shown that this is the case. However, with a small number of decking profiles in current usage, the lap detail is such that the full strength of these fasteners may not be attained. Figure 2.11 illustrates the problem. Furthermore, some profiles have an odd number

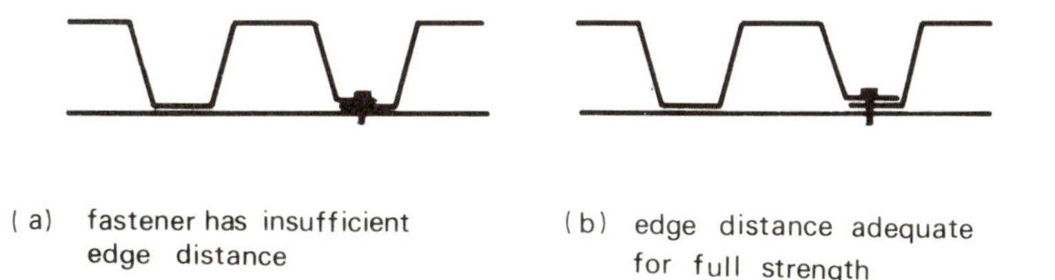

Fig. 2.11 Alternative lap details for decking influencing strength of sheet to perpendicular member fasteners: (a) fastener has insufficient edge distance, (b) edge distance adequate for full strength.

of corrugations per cover width. When these are fastened to the supporting structure through alternate troughs some of the sheet to supporting member fasteners on the line of a given seam will be missing. In such cases it is conservative to neglect these fasteners completely and to express the seam strength simply as

$$V_{ult} = n_s F_s \tag{2.2}$$

Fig. 2.12 Typical failure in shear connector fasteners.

2.7.2 Failure in fasteners to shear connectors

For simplicity, it is conservative to assume that all of the shear force on a line of shear connectors is taken by the fasteners to these shear connectors and to neglect any contribution made by the sheet to perpendicular member fasteners. This leads to the simple expression

$$V_{\text{ult}} = n_{sc} F_{sc} \tag{2.3}$$

where n_{sc} = total number of shear connector fasteners in line,
F_{sc} = design strength of an individual shear connector fastener.
Figure 2.12 shows a typical failure in the fasteners to a shear connector in which the material below the fasteners has torn into a slot giving an extremely ductile failure with a long plastic plateau before any significant loss of load.

2.7.3 Failure in the sheet to perpendicular member fasteners in a direction parallel to the span of the sheeting (two sides fastened only)

When shear connectors or their equivalent are omitted and the diaphragm is fastened on two sides only, the load applied to the panel must be transferred to the sheeting through the parallel to perpendicular member (purlin to rafter) connections and the sheet to perpendicular member (purlin) fasteners. This makes considerable demands on these fasteners and in particular on the fasteners near to the line of application of the load. Fig. 2.13 shows a typical distribution of forces in the sheet to perpendicular member fasteners along the length of the member. It is evident that there is a high force in the fastener on the line of the load and that other adjacent fasteners are also affected though to a lesser extent. Thus the critical design condition is the

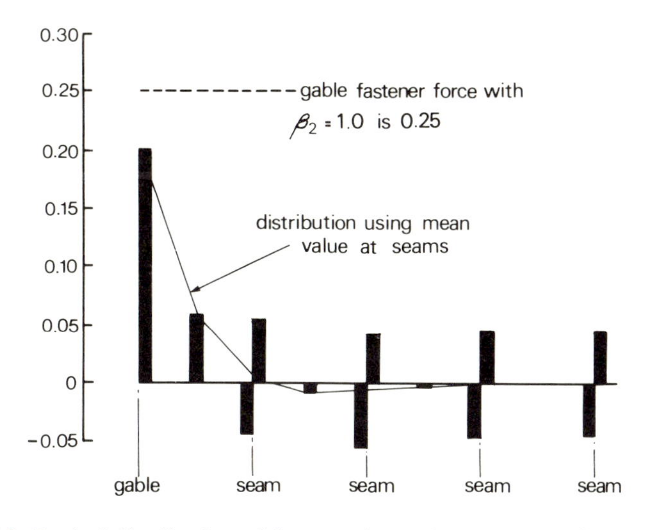

Fig. 2.13 Typical distribution of fastener force along a perpendicular member.

capacity of the fasteners on the line of the load and this is given by:

$$V_{ult} = \beta_2 n_p F_p \tag{2.4}$$

where n_p = total number of perpendicular members (purlins) within the depth of the panel,

F_p = design strength of an individual sheet to perpendicular member fastener (kN),

β_2 = factor given in table 9.5 which depends on n_f and takes account of the influence of adjacent fasteners,

n_f = number of sheet to perpendicular member fasteners per member per sheet width.

Many tests on individual purlin to rafter connections have been carried out covering a wide range of practical situations and these are summarised in table 9.12. Figure 2.14 shows such a test in progress. There is a very wide range of strengths tabulated

Fig. 2.14 Test to determine the strength and flexibility of a typical purlin to rafter connection.

in table 9.12 and only in the very weakest cases will the connection fail before the adjacent sheet to purlin fasteners. Nevertheless it is advisable to check this mode of failure using the expression

$$V_{ult} = n_p F_{pr} \tag{2.5}$$

where F_{pr} = design strength of an individual purlin to rafter connection (kN).

2.7.4 Failure due to shear buckling

Fig. 2.15 shows a typical example of this form of failure in which the entire profiled sheet buckles into one or more waves inclined at an angle to the direction of span

Fig. 2.15 Typical example of shear buckling of profiled sheeting.

of the sheeting. The theoretical treatment of this problem was initially given by Easley[1.71] and later modified by Lawson[1.90] resulting in the following expression which is remarkably simple bearing in mind the complex nature of the problem:

$$V_{crit} = \frac{18}{b} D_x^{\frac{1}{4}} D_y^{\frac{3}{4}} (n_p - 1)^2 \tag{2.6}$$

where V_{crit} = the critical buckling load,

D_x,D_y = bending stiffness of profiled sheets per unit length perpendicular and parallel to the corrugations respectively (usually in units of $kNmm^2/mm$),

n_p = total number of perpendicular members (purlins) within the depth of the panel,

b = depth of panel.

Thus: $D_x = (Et^3d)/[12(1-\nu^2)u]$ and $D_y = (EI_y)/d$

where E = Young's modulus,

I_y = second moment of area about the neutral axis for a single corrugation,

u = perimeter length of a single corrugation.

It follows that, in order to ensure a ductile design with an additional 25% reserve of safety against buckling, it is required for design purposes that

$$\frac{14.4}{b} D_x^{\frac{1}{4}} D_y^{\frac{3}{4}} (n_p - 1)^2 \geqslant V^* \tag{2.7}$$

where V^* = design strength of panel, i.e. lowest strength obtained in other failure modes.

This will be found to be amply conservative in all practical situations. It should be noted that the above theory makes the assumption that the sheet to supporting member fasteners are sufficiently close together to confine the buckling wave to a region between adjacent members. In the vast majority of practical diaphragms this will be the case. However, when diaphragms are constructed in arc and tangent profile with a 75 mm pitch it is common practice to fasten through every third corrugation. In view of the relatively low height of the profile (19 mm) this is a sheeting which is particularly sensitive to shear buckling and this fastener arrangement may not be sufficient to satisfy the above assumption. It is therefore strongly recommended that, if shear buckling is at all critical, standard 75 mm arc and tangent profile sheeting should be fastened to the supporting structure at not more than 150 mm centres.

2.7.5 Failure in the sheet to perpendicular member fasteners in a direction perpendicular to the span of the sheeting

The sheet to perpendicular member (purlin) fasteners carry shear load in a direction perpendicular to the corrugations as they transfer force into the 'flanges' of the diaphragm beam. These forces are not usually large enough to cause failure but nevertheless, this is a condition that must be checked. These forces do not necessarily give rise to a simple mode of fastener failure because the situation is complicated by local distortions of the ends of the corrugation profiles in the vicinity of the fasteners. Fig. 2.16(a) shows the local forces due to the shear flow in the profile and fig. 2.16(b) illustrates how the upwards web force results in a prying action which tends to reduce the failure load per fastener. This effect is more pronounced in tall profiles of height above 60 or 70 mm.

For the above reasons, a conservative approach to this failure mode is indicated and, in particular, it is recommended that the calculated strength for this failure mode should be 25% greater than the calculated strength of the diaphragm. This recommendation is included in the following expression which takes the form of a necessary condition that failure should not occur in the sheet to perpendicular member fasteners at the upper and lower edges of the panel, namely:

$$\frac{0.8\, b\, F_p}{p} \geqslant V^* \tag{2.8}$$

where b = depth of diaphragm in a direction parallel to the corrugations,
V^* = design strength of panel (i.e. lowest strength obtained when all other failure modes are considered),
p = pitch of sheet to purlin fasteners,
and the other symbols have been defined above.

(a)

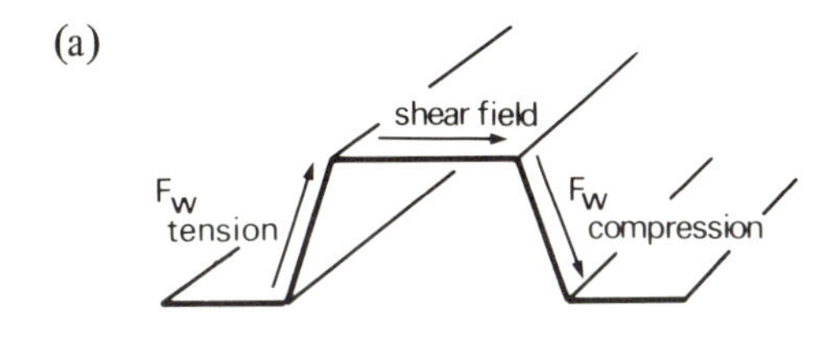

(b)

Fig. 2.16 Forces and deformations at sheet to perpendicular member fasteners: (a) local web forces, (b) local distortion near fasteners.

2.7.6 Failure of the edge member in compression or in combined compression and bending

In fig. 2.3, the lower perpendicular member is in compression carrying a maximum force of Va/b and the left hand rafter is in compression carrying a maximum force V. The other two edge members carry similar forces in tension. In a typical practical situation each of these edge members has a primary function in carrying vertical load and the stresses arising from stressed skin action are usually small when compared with those arising from this primary function. Nevertheless, the stresses from stressed skin action may affect the design of these members and the combined stresses must be considered.

2.8 Expressions for diaphragm flexibility (cantilever panel, sheeting perpendicular to span)

The flexibility of a diaphragm is obtained by considering each of the component flexibilities in turn and summing them to give the total movement of the assembly.

Thus expressions have been derived whereby the flexibility c may be calculated as the sum of the following components:

$c_{1.1}$ = flexibility due to distortion of the sheeting profile,
$c_{1.2}$ = flexibility due to shear strain in the sheet,
$c_{2.1}$ = flexibility due to movement at the sheet to perpendicular member fasteners,
$c_{2.2}$ = flexibility due to movement in the seams,
$c_{2.3}$ = flexibility due to movement in the sheet to parallel member fasteners (four sides fastened) or flexibility due to movement at the perpendicular member to parallel member (purlin to rafter) connections (two sides fastened),
c_3 = flexibility due to axial strain in the edge members (treated as an equivalent shear flexibility.

Each of these will now be considered in turn.

2.8.1 Flexibility due to distortion of the sheeting profile

A typical example of distortion of the sheeting profile is shown in fig. 2.17. The shear flexibility due to this distortion is a most important component and depends crucially on how the sheet ends are fastened to the supporting members. For

Fig. 2.17 Example of profile distortion.

trapezoidal profiles the usual alternatives are to fix with a single fastener through every trough or through alternate troughs. The deformations at the sheet ends with each of these alternatives are shown in fig. 2.18 and it is immediately clear that, due to the lateral movement in the intermediate trough, fastening in alternate troughs is likely to produce distortional flexibility an order of magnitude greater than when every trough is fastened. It is important to bear this in mind when determining fastener specifications as fixing in every trough may not be necessary from strength considerations alone.

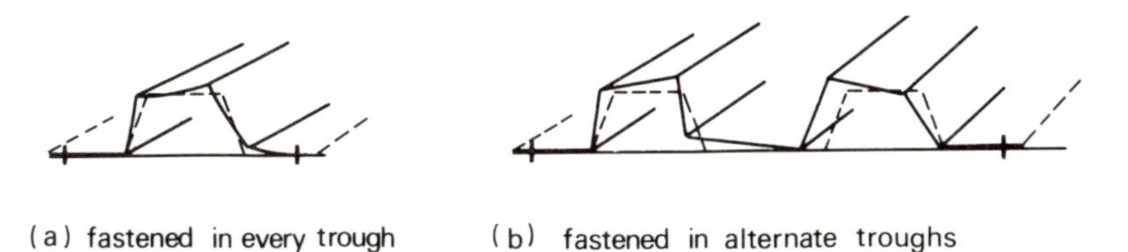

Fig. 2.18 Profile distortion with alternative fastener arrangements: (a) fastened in every trough, (b) fastened in alternate troughs.

The expression for the distortional flexibility $c_{1.1}$ (mm/kN) of a panel is

$$c_{1.1} = \frac{a\,d^{2.5}\,\alpha_1\,\alpha_4\,\bar{K}}{E\,t^{2.5}\,b^2} \tag{2.9}$$

where a = width of panel in a direction perpendicular to the corrugations (mm),
b = depth of panel in a direction parallel to the corrugations (mm),
d = pitch of corrugations (mm),
E = modulus of elasticity (kN/mm^2),
t = net sheet thickness excluding galvanising and coatings (mm),
$\bar{K}$ = non dimensional sheeting constant (see below),
α_1, α_4 = non-dimensional factors (see below).

The non-dimensional sheeting constant $\bar{K}$ is a function of the shape of the profile and the arrangement of fasteners to the supporting structure. For a trapezoidal profile, the value of $\bar{K}$ can be expressed in terms of the parameters (h/d), (l/d) and θ and which are defined in fig. 2.19. It is useful to define two distinct values of $\bar{K}$, namely $\bar{K}_1$ for profiles fastened in every trough (fig. 2.18(a) and $\bar{K}_2$ for profiles

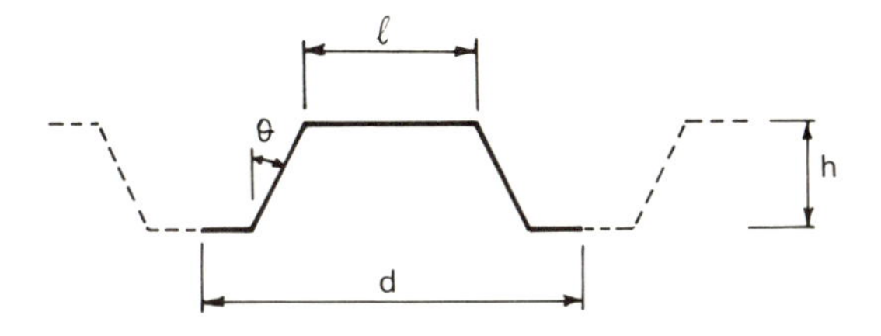

Fig. 2.19 Basic profile dimensions.

fastened in alternate troughs (fig. 2.18(b)) and these values are tabulated for the complete range of trapezoidal profiles in tables 9.6 and 9.7 so that the appropriate value for a given application can be obtained by linear interpolation. The factor α_1 takes account of the fact that fixings to intermediate supporting members will prevent free distortion of the profile so that the flexibility is reduced. The factor α_4 takes account of the fact that if the full depth of the panel has to be made up of several sheet lengths, the end laps will increase the flexibility. There is a range of practical details leading to various combinations of values of $\bar{K}$, α_1 and α_4 and these are summarised in table 9.1. It may be noted that in a built-up profile which contains a flat sheet, such as that shown in fig. 2.20, distortion cannot take place and $c_{1.1}$ = zero.

Fig. 2.20 Built-up profile with no distortional flexibility.

2.8.2 Flexibility due to shear strain in the sheet

When a shear force is applied to a profiled sheet, each rectangular face of the profile will be subject to shear strain tending to distort the rectangle into a parallelogram. The shear flexibility $c_{1.2}$ (mm/kN) due to this cause may be expressed approximately as

$$c_{1.2} = \frac{2a\,(1+\nu)\,[1+(2h/d)]}{E\,t\,b} \tag{2.10}$$

where, in addition to the symbols defined in 2.8.1 above,
ν = Poisson's ratio.

2.8.3 Flexibility due to movement at the sheet to perpendicular member fasteners

This component is due to movement in the sheet to perpendicular member fasteners in a direction parallel to the member. Typical fasteners for fixing the sheeting to these members are self-drilling self-tapping screws or shot-fired pins. The expression for this component of flexibility, $c_{2.1}$ (mm/kN), therefore contains the experimentally obtained value for slip in these fasteners. Thus

$$c_{2.1} = \frac{2\,a\,s_p\,p}{b^2} \tag{2.11}$$

where s_p = slip (flexibility) per sheet to perpendicular member (purlin) fastener per unit load (mm/kN),
p = pitch of sheet to perpendicular member (purlin) fasteners (mm).

2.8.4 Flexibility due to movement in the seams

The expression for this component is

$$c_{2.2} = \frac{2\, s_s s_p\, (n_{sh} - 1)}{2\, n_s\, s_p + \beta_1\, n_p\, s_s} \tag{2.12}$$

where n_s = number of seam fasteners per sidelap (see below),
n_p = total number of perpendicular members (purlins),
n_{sh} = number of sheet widths per panel,
s_s = slip (flexibility) per seam fastener per unit load (mm/kN),
β_1 = factor given in table 9.5 which depends on n_f and also on whether the profiled metal cladding is fixed as sheeting or decking as shown in figs. 2.4 and 2.10,
n_f = number of sheet to perpendicular member fasteners per member per sheet width.

Typical arrangements of seams showing how n_s, n_f, etc. are calculated are shown in fig. 2.10.

2.8.5 Flexibility due to movement in the sheet to parallel member fasteners

This component of flexibility is only applicable if the sheeting is fastened to the supporting structure on four sides. If the sheeting is fastened on two sides only the expression given in section 2.8.6 applies. The relevant expression for $c_{2.3}$ (mm/kN) is simply

$$c_{2.3} = \frac{2 s_{sc}}{n_{sc}} \tag{2.13}$$

where n_{sc} = total number of sheet to shear connector fasteners per parallel member (rafter),
s_{sc} = slip (flexibility) per sheet to shear connector fastener per unit load (mm/kN).

2.8.6 Flexibility due to movement at the perpendicular member to parallel member (purlin to rafter) connections

This component of flexibility is only applicable if the sheeting is fastened to the supporting structure on two sides. When this is the case, force from the parallel members (rafters) has to pass through the connections into the perpendicular members (purlins) and thence into the sheeting. The effect is concentrated at the ends of the perpendicular members (purlins). The relevant expression for the component of flexibility, $c_{2.3}$ (mm/kN) is

$$c_{2.3} = \frac{2}{n_p}\left(s_{pr} + \frac{s_p}{\beta_2}\right) \tag{2.14}$$

where, in addition to symbols defined previously,

s_{pr} = movement of perpendicular member to parallel member connection per unit load (mm/kN),

β_2 = factor given in table 9.5 which depends on n_p.

Values of s_{pr} are obtained from simple tests such as that shown in fig. 2.14. Many such tests have been carried out on a wide range of practical connections and these are summarised in table 9.12. From this table it will usually be possible to estimate a value of s_{pr} for a given connection without any necessity for further testing.

2.8.7 Flexibility due to axial strain in the edge members

For simplicity, it is convenient, though by no means essential, to treat the effect of axial strain in the edge members (which is strictly speaking a bending effect) as an equivalent shear flexibility. For cantilever panels, as considered in this chapter, the equivalence is exact. For diaphragm beams, which will be considered in a later chapter, a degree of approximation is involved. Thus, the expression for the equivalent shear flexibility c_3 (mm/kN) due to axial strain in the perpendicular edge members (the upper and lower members in fig. 2.3) is

$$c_3 = \frac{2a^3}{3EAb^2} \qquad (2.15)$$

where A = the cross-sectional area of a single edge member (mm^2)

2.8.8 Summation of component flexibilities

The flexibility c (mm/kN) of the complete diaphragm is obtained by summation of the component flexibilities, thus

$$c = c_{1.1} + c_{1.2} + c_{2.1} + c_{2.2} + c_{2.3} + c_3 \qquad (2.16)$$

2.9 Modifications to design expressions for sheeting spanning parallel to span of diaphragm

In order to amend the design expressions given in sections 2.7 and 2.8 to deal with a cantilever diaphragm with the sheeting spanning parallel to the span of the diaphragm, it is merely necessary to recognise the equivalence of the two arrangements shown in fig. 2.21, the apparent shear strain γ being the same in both cases. In fig. 2.21 it should be carefully noted that in both cases the dimension b is measured along the corrugations and a is measured at right angles to them. This is an important convention that is preserved throughout the book.

The procedures derived previously give the design strength V_0* and the flexibility c_0 of the diaphragm in fig. 2.21(b). It follows directly that the required design strength in fig. 2.21(a) is simply

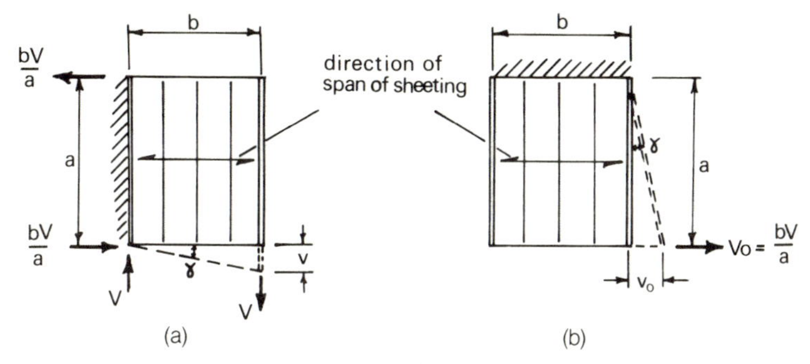

Fig. 2.21 Equivalent cantilever panels: (a) required arrangement with sheeting parallel to span, (b) equivalent panel with sheeting spanning perpendicular to span.

$$V^* = \frac{a}{b} V_0^* \tag{2.17}$$

Also, the required flexibility c is by definition equal to v/V whereas the readily calculated value given by equation 2.16 is $c_0 = v_0/V_0$. But equivalence of forces gives $V = (a/b)V_0$ and equivalence of shear strains gives $v = (b/a)v_0$. It then follows directly that

$$c = \frac{b^2}{a^2} c_0 \tag{2.18}$$

The above modification must be made to the value of $(c_{1.1} + c_{1.2} + c_{2.1} + c_{2.2} + c_{2.3})$ but it must not be applied to c_3 (flexibility due to axial strain in the edge mem-

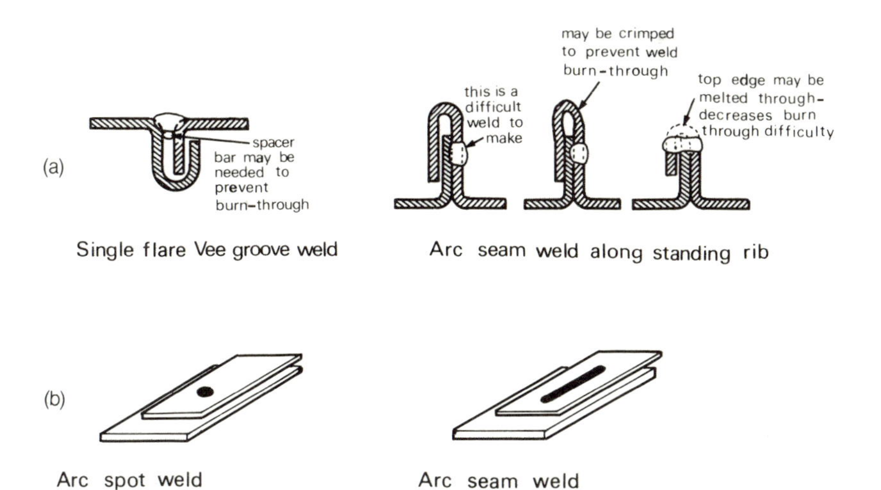

Fig. 2.22 Weld types for welded diaphragms: (a) seam welds, (b) welds to supporting structure.

bers), since this component is independent of the direction of span of the sheeting. Therefore, for sheeting spanning parallel to the span of the diaphragm

$$c = \frac{b^2}{a^2}(c_{1.1} + c_{1.2} + c_{2.1} + c_{2.2} + c_{2.3}) + c_3 \qquad (2.19)$$

where $c_{1.1}$, etc. are calculated for the identical diaphragm orientated with the sheeting spanning perpendicular to the span of the diaphragm.

2.10 Welded diaphragms

There is little experience with welded diaphragms in Britain, or indeed in most parts of the world, but they have been extensively used in the U.S.A., particularly in California, in order to accommodate the large lateral forces associated with earthquakes. The design expressions given previously are of direct application to welded diaphragms as the internal force distributions are essentially unchanged. The use of welding, however, does give rise to some different constructional details and it is, of course, necessary to know the properties of the welds.

The types of weld most frequently used in welded diaphragms are shown in fig. 2.22. They are made through the welded sheet without any advance preparation. Galvanising or paint coatings are not normally removed prior to welding. The strength of these welds can therefore be quite variable. The qualifications and experience of the welders and correct welding procedures are of particular importance as also is the inspection of the work. The fact that a welder may have satisfactorily passed a test for structural steel welding does not necessarily mean that he can produce sound welds on sheet steel. As in conventional structural welding, it is general good practice to require that the deposited filler metal should have a tensile strength at least equal to that of the members being joined. The most frequent failure modes of well-made welds then involve tearing of the parent metal and exhibit considerable ductility. The strength of these welds can readily be predicted from simple design expressions and these are given in table 9.11. In general, the flexibility is so small that it may be neglected in comparison with the flexibility due to profile distortion, i.e. $c_{2.1} = c_{2.2} = c_{2.3} = 0$. However, if a built-up section (such as that shown in fig. 2.20), or any other section in which there is no flexibility due to distortion of the corrugation profile is used, it is more conservative to include a nominal amount of weld flexibility although the diaphragm is likely to be so stiff that deflections are not significant. Suitable nominal flexibility values are: sheet to supporting structure welds, 0.01 mm/kN; seam welds, 0.015 mm/kN.

Effective control of welding current is absolutely essential in order to obtain consistently sound welds. The current required to produce arc spot welds or arc seam welds is considerably higher than for most conventional welds. As an example, when a typical 20 mm visible diameter arc spot weld was made in 1.3 mm thick galvanised sheet the current was 210 amps and the welding time was 10 seconds. There is a considerable body of opinion among welding experts that the best practical way to maintain uniformity in sheet steel welding is through regulation of the burn-off rate. In the above example, the burn-off rate was 450 mm/min. If too low a welding current (too slow a burn-off rate) is used an arc spot weld or arc seam weld may appear sound but have negligible strength. Further guidance regarding correct welding procedures for light gauge steel will be found in references 6.19 and 6.23. In making arc spot welds in sheet of 0.7 mm thickness or less, weld washers may be required. These are small pieces of steel sheet of about 1.5 mm thickness with punched holes somewhat smaller in diameter than the visible weld diameter as shown in fig. 2.23. These permit the weld to be made without burning the thin sheet.

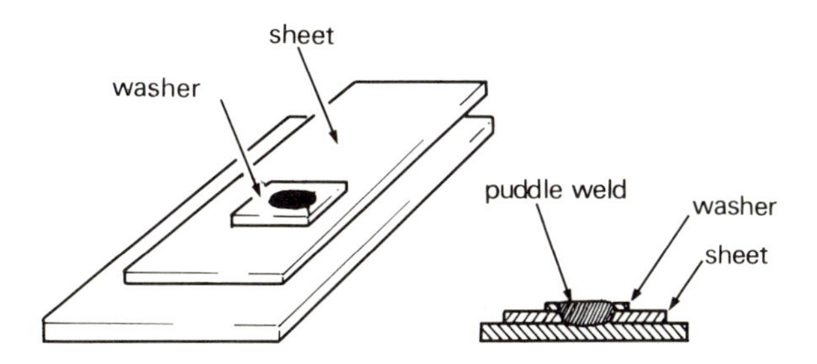

Fig. 2.23 Weld washer.

2.11 Aluminium diaphragms

The design expressions given previously are of direct application to diaphragms using aluminium rather than steel sheeting. Aluminium diaphragms tend to be more flexible than similar steel diaphragms, largely on account of the smaller value of Young's modulus (69 kN/mm^2) and also on account of the fact that fasteners through aluminium sheeting exhibit somewhat greater flexibility. Information on fasteners through aluminium sheeting is rather limited and it will usually be necessary to carry out tests to determine the relevant fastener properties before proceeding with a given design. However, in one study[7.4] nearly 200 tests on fasteners of various types in aluminium sheet of various thickness and surface treatments were summarised by the following values:

Sheet to purlin fasteners (e.g. 6.2 mm dia. self-drilling screws with neoprene washers)	characteristic strength $F_p = 3.0$ kN per mm thickness of sheet. slip per fastener = 0.45 mm/kN.
Seam fasteners: (e.g. 4.8 mm dia. aluminium blind rivets)	characteristic strength $F_p = 1.8$ kN per mm thickness of sheet. slip per fastener = 0.60 mm/kN.

For many applications the above values are conservative and can be used as the basis of design calculations. The main additional considerations in the diaphragm action of aluminium sheeting are summarised formally in reference 7.5.

2.12 Effect of bonded insulation

When metal roof cladding is fixed as decking with thermal insulation and water-proofing bonded to the upper surface of the profile, the effect is to cause a significant increase in the stiffness when the decking is fastened in alternate troughs but not when it is fastened in every trough.[1.66] In neither case does the insulation increase the strength of the diaphragm. In order to take advantage of this increase in stiffness, if so desired, the value of $c_{1.1}$ for the case of alternate troughs fastened may be multiplied by the following factor: for profile height $h \leqslant 50$ mm, 0.7; for profile height 50 mm $< h <$ 80 mm, 0.5.

2.13 Diaphragms in the vertical plane

Wall cladding can act as a vertical diaphragm and transmit loads from the plane of the roof down to the foundations. Figure 2.24 shows an example of this in which

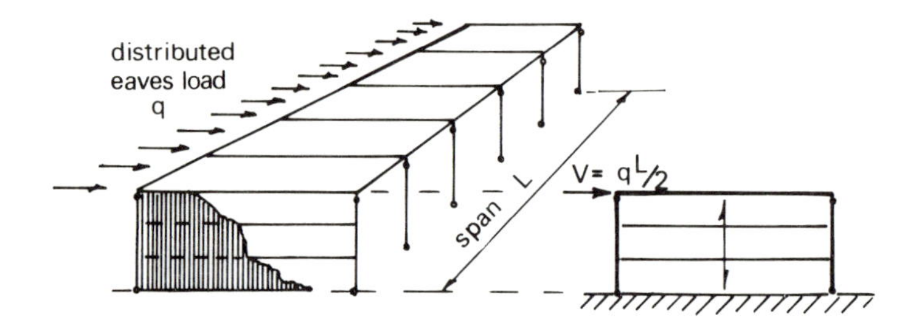

Fig. 2.24 Stressed skin action of gable cladding.

the stressed skin effect of the gable cladding acts in lieu of gable bracing. From the point of view of design, the gable acts as a cantilever diaphragm subject to an in-plane load at eaves level equal to the shear force V in the end panel of the roof. The design expressions are unchanged from those given previously. A similar purpose can also be served very efficiently by infilling light gable framing with masonry or brickwork though the detailed design of such infilled steelwork is outside the scope of the present work.

CHAPTER THREE

Design of panel assemblies

3.1 Assemblies of panels to form a complete diaphragm

Chapter 2 considered the design expressions for an individual panel or cantilever diaphragm, as shown in fig. 2.3. In this chapter, the additional factors present when individual panels are assembled to form a complete diaphragm are considered. Figure 3.1 shows a typical simple situation in which conventional wind bracing in the plane of the roof is replaced by diaphragm action. In the absence of joint rigidity the structure is not stable until construction of the diaphragm is complete.

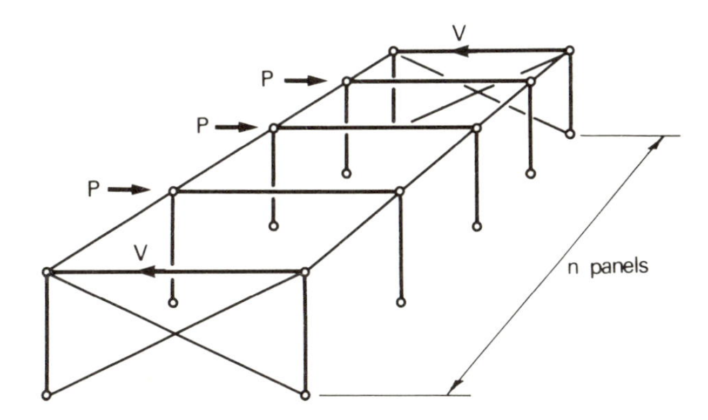

Fig. 3.1 Diaphragm action in flat roofed construction.

Before considering the influence of this assembly on the design expressions, it is convenient first to consider the basic response of a roof made up of n panels of known equal flexibility. As the entire load is carried by diaphragm action in the plane of the roof, the loads on the diaphragm are statically determinate. Thus if the design loads at each frame are equal to P and the flexibilities of the individual

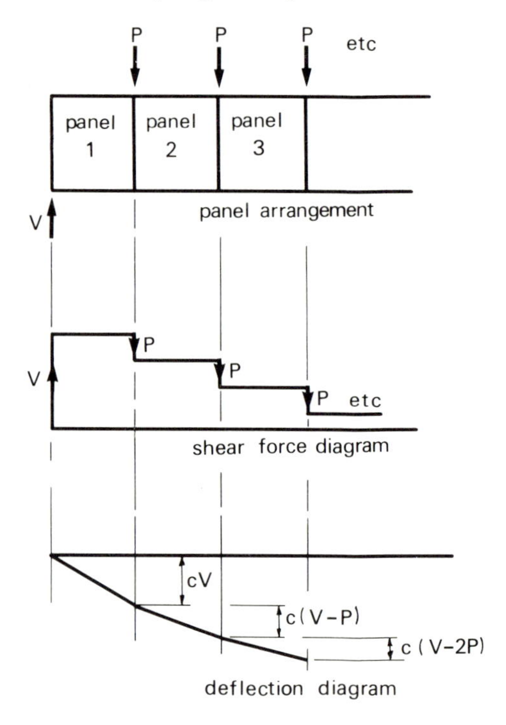

Fig. 3.2 Forces and deflections in flat roof diaphragms.

panels forming the complete diaphragm are c the situation is as shown in fig. 3.2. The maximum shear force $V = \frac{1}{2}[(n-1)P]$ is readily calculated and the design strength of the end panel must be adequate to accommodate this. The deflected shape of the roof diaphragm can also be calculated as follows:

shear deflection of panel 1 $= c\,V$
shear deflection of panel 2 $= c\,(V-P)$
shear deflection of panel m $= c\,[V-(m-1)P]$.

The deflection at any point is the sum of the individual panel deflections so that the total deflection at the mth panel is:

$$\Delta m = c\{mV - P[1 + 2 + \ldots + (m-1)]\}$$

$$= c\left[\frac{m(n-1)}{2} - \frac{m(m-1)}{2}\right]P$$

$$= c\,\frac{m}{2}\,(n-m)\,P \qquad (3.1)$$

and the maximum deflection when $m = n/2$ is given by

$$\Delta_{max} = \frac{cn^2P}{8}. \qquad (3.2)$$

3.2 Roofs of irregular plan

When a roof which is required to act as a diaphragm has an irregular plan form and/or parts of the roof at different levels it is necessary to divide the roof into zones so that each part of the building is stabilised by a rectangular diaphragm zone to resist horizontal forces applied in both the longitudinal and transverse directions. In the design calculations each zone is then treated as a separate diaphragm. Fig. 3.3 shows a typical roof plan of such a building in which the roof is divided into zones A, B, C, D. Zones A and C act as conventional diaphragms spanning between vertical bracings to resist both North/South and East/West loads. Zone D resists North/South loads only and acts as a cantilever off zone A. Zone B contains a relatively high proportion of roof lights but is in fact surplus to requirements and need not be designed as a diaphragm.

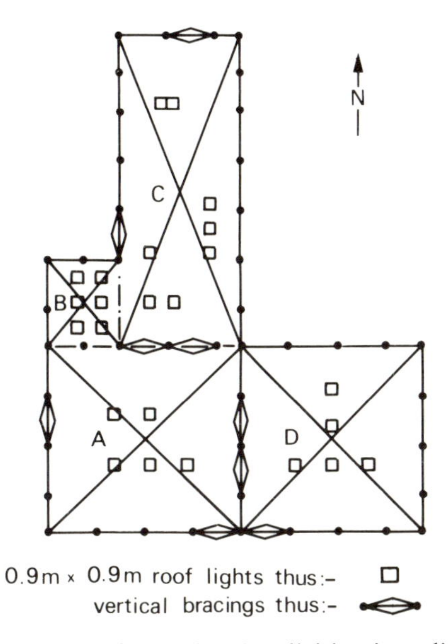

Fig. 3.3 Irregular roof plan showing division into diaphragms.

3.3 Design expressions for complete diaphragms

The typical design situation is shown in fig. 3.4 where a distributed load of intensity q per unit length at eaves level gives rise to point loads $P = qa$ at each rafter (perpendicular member) and a maximum shear force in the diaphragm of $V = \frac{1}{2}[(n-1)P] = \frac{1}{2}[(n-1)qa]$. The case quoted assumes that the framing members in the longitudinal sides of the building carry the distributed side loads back to the lines of the rafters so that an individual panel is loaded only at the node points. This is not an essential restriction and a treatment for point loads within the side of a panel will be considered in chapter 5. The design for strength is based on the capacity of the end panel to sustain a shear force V and, in the main, the design

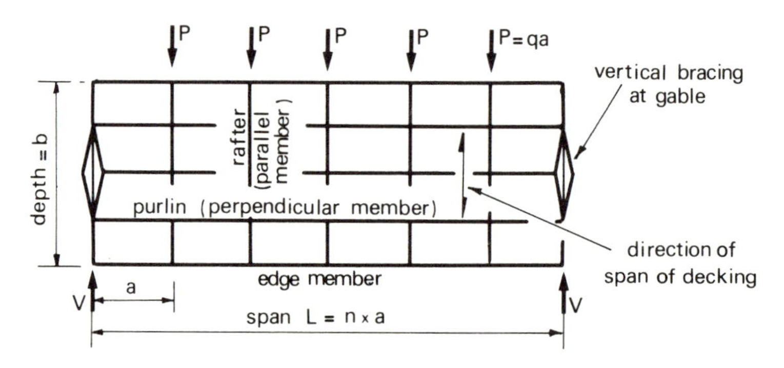

Fig. 3.4 Diaphragm with sheeting spanning perpendicular to span.

expressions given in chapter 2 for a cantilever diaphragm subject to a shear force V apply equally here. There are however, two further conditions as follows:

3.3.1 Strength condition at intermediate rafter

The connections at the intermediate rafters must be adequate to transmit the applied load P into the sheeting. Thus, if shear connectors are provided on these rafters or if there are other direct connections between the sheeting and the rafters,

$$P_{ult} = (q_a)_{ult} = n'_{sc} F_{sc} \tag{3.3}$$

where n'_{sc} = total number of fasteners between sheeting and each intermediate rafter,
F_{sc} = design strength in an individual fastener (kN).

It should be noted that the shear connectors at the gables must be designed for the much larger shear force $V = [\frac{1}{2}(n-1)] P$ and therefore they will in general contain a much larger number n_{sc} of fasteners where

$$n_{sc} = [\tfrac{1}{2}(n-1)]\, n'_{sc} \tag{3.4}$$

The expressions for flexibility in the shear connectors given in section 3.3.4 make the assumption that fasteners are provided on the above basis. If no intermediate shear connectors are provided so that indirect shear transfer takes place through the purlin to rafter connections and sheet to purlin fasteners, either

$$P_{ult} = (q_a)_{ult} = \beta_2 n_p F_p \tag{3.5}$$

or

$$P_{ult} = (q_a)_{ult} = n_p F_{pr} \tag{3.6}$$

where n_p = total number of purlins within the depth of the panel,
F_p = design strength of an individual sheet to purlin fastener (kN),
β_2 = factor given in table 9.5 which depends on n_f,
n_f = number of sheet to purlin fasteners per member per sheet width,
F_{pr} = design strength of an individual purlin to rafter connection (kN).

3.3.2 Maximum force in edge members

In fig. 3.4, the purlins carry the axial forces due to bending action while the sheeting carries the shear. The maximum axial force is therefore in the outermost purlins (edge members) at mid-span and is given to a sufficient degree of accuracy by the expression

$$\frac{qL^2\alpha_3}{8b} \tag{3.7}$$

where α_3 is a factor given in table 9.3 which takes account of the fact that the internal purlins also assist in carrying bending moment. The derivation of α_3 is given in references 1.20 and 1.57. The design of the purlins must be checked to ensure that they are adequate to carry the combined stresses from stressed skin action and their primary function of carrying vertical load in the roof.

3.3.3 Expressions for flexibility

As with the cantilever diaphragms considered in chapter 2, the flexibility c of an individual panel within a complete diaphragm beam is obtained as the sum of components $c_{1.1}, c_{1.2}, \ldots$, etc. Thus

$$c = c_{1.1} + c_{1.2} + c_{2.1} + c_{2.2} + c_{2.3} + c_3\,. \tag{3.8}$$

The expressions for each of the components in the above equation are given in section 9.5 such that when the resulting flexibility c is substituted into the equation

$$\Delta_{\max} = \frac{cn^2P}{8} \tag{3.9}$$

the correct central deflection is obtained. This approach leaves the expressions given in chapter 2 for cantilever diaphragms substantially unchanged but requires major amendments to $c_{2.3}$ and c_3 as follows:

3.3.4 Flexibility due to movement at the gables and intermediate rafters

There are three alternative cases to consider depending on whether shear connectors are provided and, if so, whether they are provided at the gables only or at the gables and intermediate rafters. If shear connectors or their equivalent are provided at the gables and each intermediate rafter, so that the sheeting in each panel is fastened to the supporting structure on four sides, the expression for $c_{2.3}$ (mm/kN) is

$$c_{2.3} = \frac{4(n+1)\,s_{sc}}{n^2 n'_{sc}} = \frac{2(n^2-1)\,s_{sc}}{n^2\;n_{sc}} \tag{3.10}$$

where s_{sc} = slip (flexibility) per sheet to shear connector fastener per unit load (mm/kN),

and the other symbols have been previously defined.

If shear connectors are provided at the gables only, it is reasonable to assume that the movement at the gables will be small relative to the movement at the intermediate rafters. The expression for $c_{2.3}$ is then given by

$$c_{2.3} = \frac{4(n-1)}{n^2 n_p}\left(s_{pr} + \frac{s_p}{\beta_2}\right) \tag{3.11}$$

where, in addition to symbols defined previously,

s_p = slip (flexibility) per sheet to purlin fastener per unit load (mm/kN),
s_{pr} = movement of purlin to rafter connection per unit load (mm/kN),
β_2 = factor given in table 9.5 which depends on n_f.

The strictly correct expression for an end panel, when used in conjunction with the above expression for intermediate panels, is

$$c_{2.3} = \frac{s_{sc}}{n_{sc}} + \frac{4(n-1)}{n^2 n_p}\left(s_{pr} + \frac{s_p}{\beta_2}\right) \tag{3.12}$$

Finally, if no shear connectors are provided at the gables either, the reasoning for intermediate panels remains unchanged. However, the correct expression for the end panel then becomes

$$c_{2.3} = \left(\frac{1}{n_p} + \frac{4(n-1)}{n^2 n_p}\right)\left(s_{pr} + \frac{s_p}{\beta_2}\right) \tag{3.13}$$

3.3.5 Flexibility due to axial strain in the edge members

If the bending flexibility of the purlins is replaced by an equivalent shear flexibility it is found that the resulting shear flexibility does not vary greatly over the span and it is sufficiently accurate for all practical purposes to take an average value. Thus

$$c_{2.3} = \frac{n^2 a^3 \alpha_3}{4.8\, E\, A\, b^2} \tag{3.14}$$

where E = Young's modulus (kN/mm^2),
A = cross-sectional area of a single edge member (mm^2),
α_3 = factor for internal purlins (table 9.3).

3.3.6 Flexibility due to shear strain in the sheet

The expression given in section 9.5 is identical to that given in section 9.3 and explained in section 2.8.2 except for an additional factor α_2. This factor is given in table 9.3 and takes account of the fact that as intermediate purlins assist in carrying the bending moment there is a consequent reduction is the shear force over the outer parts of diaphragm. The derivations of α_2 and the related factor α_3 assume a linear variation of bending strain over the depth of the diaphragm and are given in references 1.20 and 1.57.

3.4 Modification to design expressions for sheeting spanning parallel to span of diaphragm

The design situation for this case is shown in fig. 3.5 where a distributed load of intensity q per unit length at eaves level gives rise to point loads $P = qb$ at each rafter and a maximum shear force in the diaphragm of

$$V = \frac{(n-1)P}{2} = \frac{(n-1)qb}{2} \tag{3.15}$$

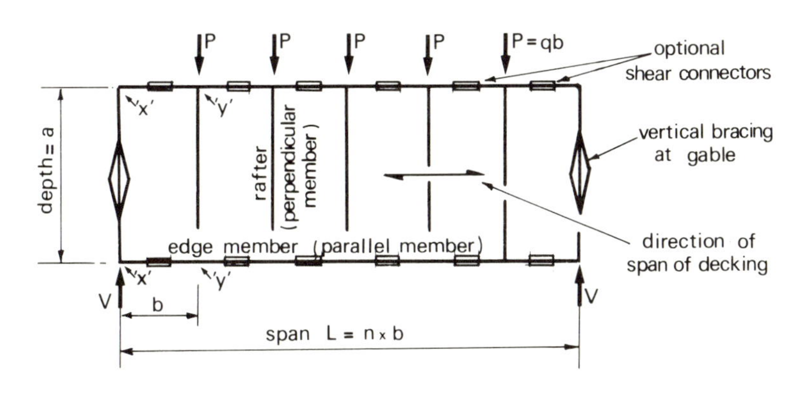

Fig. 3.5 Diaphragm with sheeting spanning parallel to span.

The design for strength is again based on the capacity of the end panel to sustain a shear force V and, in the main, the design expressions given in chapter 2 for a cantilever diaphragm apply here also. There is only one further condition which is discussed in section 3.4.1 below. The maximum force in the edge members is as given in section 3.3.2 for sheeting spanning perpendicular to the span of the diaphragm though in this case the factor α_3 is always equal to unity as there are no internal members which assist the edge members to carry bending forces.

3.4.1 Strength condition in indirect shear transfer

If the shear connectors shown in fig. 3.5 are omitted so that the sheeting is fastened to the supporting structure on two sides only, shear forces have to pass from the edge member into the sheet via the sheet to rafter connections. This 'complementary' shear force is greatest in the end panel where the relevant fasteners are at 'x' and 'y' in fig. 3.5. As 'y' is common to two panels, and as there may not be a sheet lap at 'y' it is conservative to include only half of the fastener capacity at this point in the design expression so that

$$V_{\text{ult}} = \frac{a}{b}\,(1.5\beta_2 F_p) \tag{3.16}$$

or

$$V_{\text{ult}} = \frac{a}{b}\,(1.5\,F_{pr}) \tag{3.17}$$

It should be noted that, even if the shear connectors are omitted, the stability of the structure requires the provision of continuous edge members.

3.4.2 Design expression for flexibility

The basic approach to the flexibility calculation for this case is unchanged and the design expressions, which are given in full in section 9.6, require little further comment. The only point of any complexity concerns the value of $c_{1.1}$, the flexibility due to distortion of the corrugation profile, bearing in mind that the sheeting may be continuous over more than one panel and that the fastener spacings on rafters where there is an end lap may be different from the spacings on rafters over which the sheeting is continuous. The various practical possibilities are covered by an empirical factor α_5 which is given in tables 9.2 and 9.4.

3.5 Other design criteria

In general, stressed skin design requires no modification to the basic construction of a roof employing profiled metal sheet. It merely takes advantage of, and possibly enhances, a basic strength and stiffness that is always present in any case. It follows that the majority of other design criteria such as the provision of thermal and acoustical insulation, vapour barriers, waterproofing, etc. are unaffected by the use of the roof cladding as a diaphragm. In this section some relevant points that may raise questions in the minds of designers are clarified.

3.5.1 Thermal stresses

The fear has arisen in the minds of some designers that, because a stressed skin roof may be more heavily fastened than a conventional roof, more frequent expansion joints may be necessary. This is not the case. In the direction perpendicular to the span of the sheeting there is no possibility of a build up of thermal stresses as 'concertina action' in the profile dissipates these, no matter how frequently the sheeting is fastened. In the direction parallel to the span of the sheeting end laps occur at the same frequency as in conventional construction and no additional fasteners are required so that the problem is not in any way aggravated. The only factor of note is that stressed skin action demands continuity of the edge members and provision should be made for expansion joints in these at the intervals that are usual in conventional steelwork construction. Expansion joints in the edge members will usually define diaphragm boundaries and it is necessary to bear this in mind when providing vertical bracing to transmit diaphragm forces to the foundations.

3.5.2 Combined normal and shear loads

In addition to in-plane shear loads due to diaphragm action, it is usual for diaphragms to be subject to loads acting in a direction normal to the plane of the sheeting.

These loads may be either downward (e.g. dead and imposed loads) or upward (e.g. wind suction). Some tests on diaphragm panels under combined shear and upward normal load are described in reference 1.46.

3.5.3 Effect of combined loading on diaphragm flexibility

Downward normal loads tend to prevent the free distortion of the profile under shear and hence reduce the flexibility of the diaphragm. The effect of upward normal load is not so obvious but tests have shown that such loads do not increase the shear flexibility. It is therefore recommended that no account of normal loads should be taken in calculating the diaphragm flexibility.

3.5.4 Effect of combined loading on diaphragm strength

Since the sheeting is designed for its primary purpose as cladding, the stress in bending is the prime consideration and in the European recommendations the in-plane shear stress is limited to 25% of this bending stress. When this provision is met, it may be shown that the maximum principal stress in the sheeting cannot be more than 6% greater than the bending stress under normal loads alone. It is therefore considered unnecessary to reduce the design strength of the sheeting in bending in order to take account of this relatively small amount of in-plane shear.

Seam fasteners and sheet to shear connector fasteners are usually unaffected by uniformly distributed loads acting normally to the plane of the sheeting. As the usual modes of failure involve these fasteners and as the European recommendations require other modes to have a 25% greater design shear strength, it is unlikely that there are any significant interaction problems and there is no need to reduce the diaphragm shear strength on account of combined loading.

3.5.5 Repeated loading of diaphragms

Tests on diaphragms subjected to repeated loading are described in reference 1.46. Both experimental and theoretical results for repeated loading of a complete clad building are given in reference 2.44. It is concluded that no allowance need be made for dynamic effects (e.g. due to wind and crane loads) in determining the design strength of a diaphragm. There may be an increase in flexibility but this is likely to be small unless the repeated loading is unusually severe. Further consideration of this topic is given in section 13.5.

3.5.6 Insulation positioned between the sheeting and the purlins

When thermal insulation is positioned between the sheeting and the purlins, sheet to purlin fasteners must pass through the insulation and the requirement that the sheeting shall be connected directly and tightly to the supporting member may be violated. On occasions, therefore, such a detail may prevent the use of stressed skin design. However, the insulation is often relatively thin and it has been shown[7.4] that

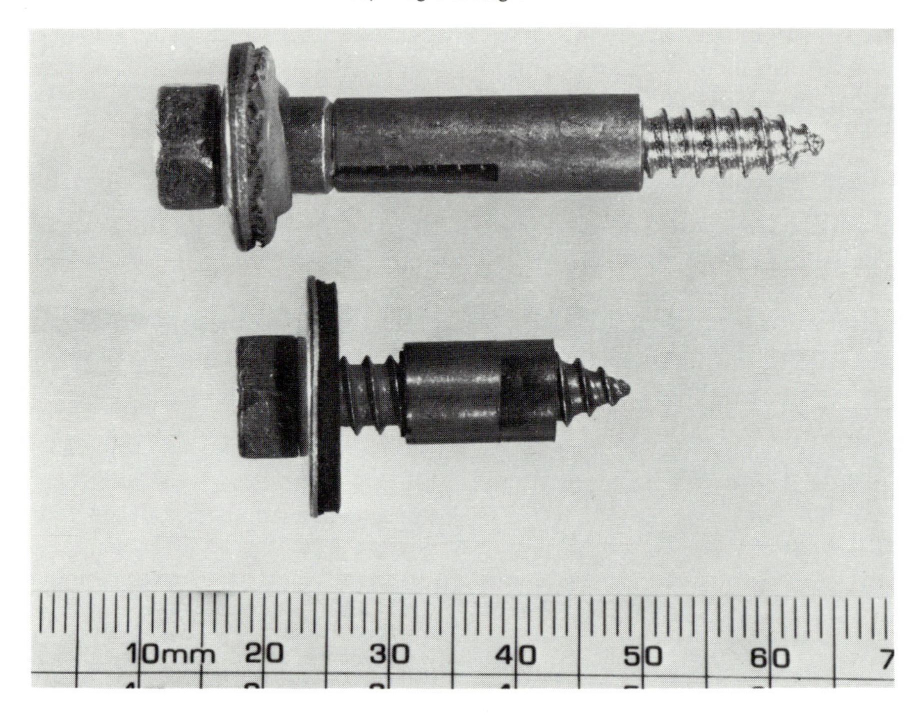

Fig. 3.6 Sheet to purlin fasteners with ferrules.

in such a case the use of sheet to purlin fasteners with ferrules, as shown in fig. 3.6, allows stressed skin action to take place without significant loss of strength or stiffness.

In tests on an aluminium diaphragm with 12.9 mm thick expanded polyurethane insulation bonded beneath the aluminium, 6.2 mm diameter self-tapping screw sheet to purlin fasteners were provided with 7.9 mm outside diameter ferrules 12.2 mm long. The calculated failure load was achieved and the stiffness was increased. The diaphragm effect of the insulation outweighed any additional flexibility that may have been introduced by using the steel ferrules.

CHAPTER FOUR

Interaction of panels and stiff frames

4.1 Introduction

A typical rigid-jointed steel frame clad with profiled steel sheeting is shown in fig. 4.1. Such a structure has two distinct load-carrying systems. Part of the load is carried by frame action in the conventional way and part is carried by diaphragm action in the cladding. The distribution of load between the frames and the cladding is dependent on their relative stiffnesses. The elastic analysis of a complete stressed skin structure is therefore a matter of satisfying the requirements of com-

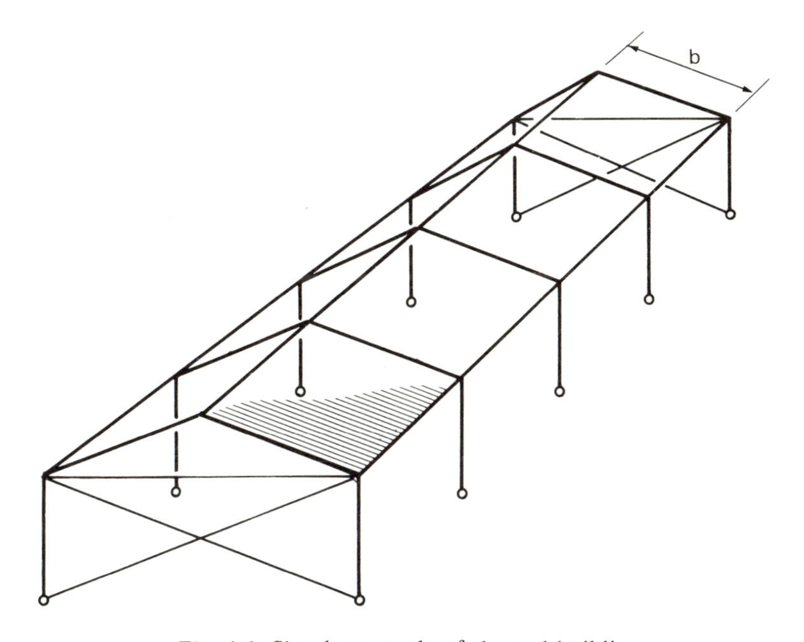

Fig. 4.1 Simple example of sheeted building.

patability between the frames and the sheeting and this requires an analysis which considers the complete (three-dimensional) structure. In practice, stressed skin structures of the type shown in fig. 4.1 are often designed by plastic theory although for reasons which will be discussed later, an elastic analysis is also required.

For relatively simple structures with uncomplicated loading conditions, manual elastic and plastic analyses are readily carried out. For more complex structures a computer analysis is required but it should be emphasised at this stage that this does not require special programming. The elastic analysis of a complete clad structure can be carried out without difficulty using any program suitable for plane frame analysis.

An important general principle is that the stressed skin action of the cladding serves to restrain joint movements and the associated stresses. It has no effect at all on the 'no sway' distribution of forces in the frames. It follows that in structures of rectangular cross section with flat roofs, stressed skin action is of no benefit in resisting uniform vertical loading but it is of great benefit in resisting side loading. In pitched roof structures such as the one shown in fig. 4.1, stressed skin action is likewise of considerable benefit in resisting side load. The benefits under uniform vertical load however depend on the angle of the roof pitch. For small roof pitches of 6° to 10° they are likely to be too small to be of practical value but as the roof pitch increases above about 10° the benefits of stressed skin action start to become appreciable.

Before proceeding to consider computer techniques it is convenient to first consider the manual methods, as these are not only important in their own right, but they also provide an essential insight into the real behaviour of rigid-framed structures.

4.2 Manual elastic analysis of clad structures

As an illustration of the principles involved, consider the rectangular rigid-jointed structure shown in fig. 4.2 which has two gable frames (assumed to be prevented from swaying by cross-bracing) and three intermediate sway frames. The roof is clad with profiled steel sheets forming individual panels of flexibility c. Any general

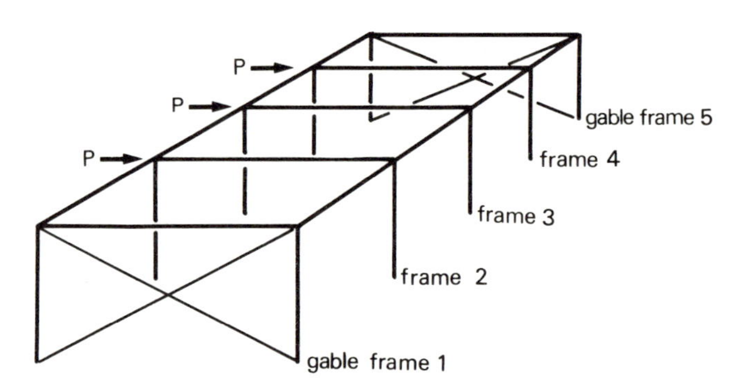

Fig. 4.2 Sheeted rectangular portal frame structure.

system of loading on the individual frames can be split into sway and no-sway cases as shown in fig. 4.3. It is the sway force P (implied eaves restraint reversed) which is reduced by stressed skin action. The forces P shown in fig. 4.2 may be assumed to have been derived from a more general loading case by calculating this implied restraint.

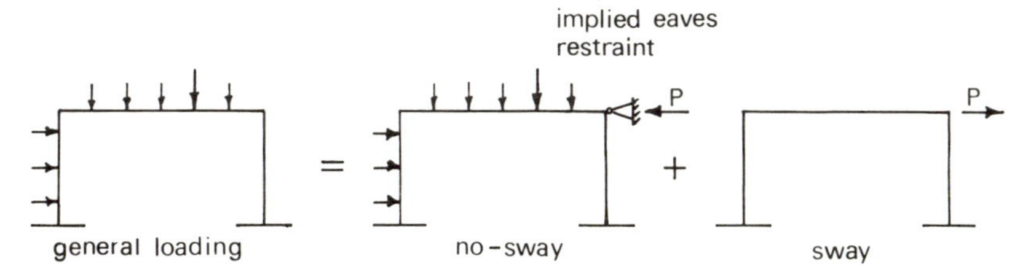

Fig. 4.3 Sway and no-sway forces on rectangular portal frames.

It is convenient to define the frame flexibility k (fig. 4.4a), the shear flexibility c of the sheeting panel (fig. 4.4b) and the relative flexibility $\psi = c/k$. If, at each intermediate frame, the applied force P is divided into a force R_i carried by the sheeting and a force $P - R_i$ carried by the frame, the forces and deflections of the components of the building are then as shown in fig. 4.5. The forces R_2 and R_3

Fig. 4.4 Definitions of frame and panel flexibilities: (a) frame, (b) sheeting panel.

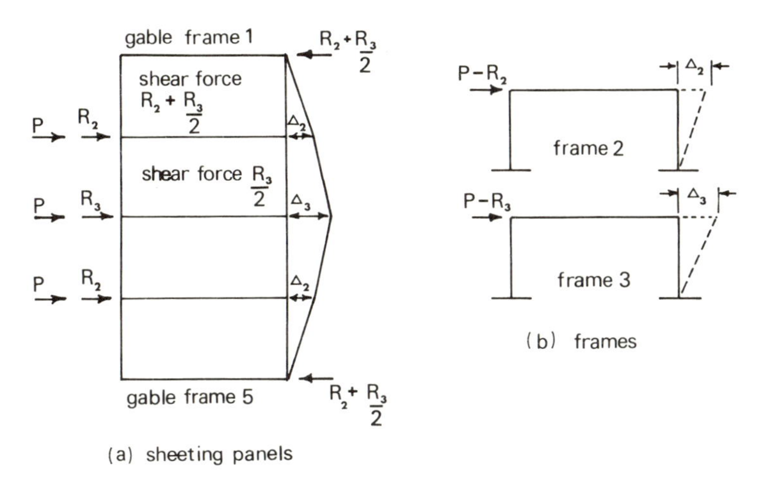

Fig. 4.5 Forces and deflections of components of building: (a) sheeting panels, (b) frames.

between the frames and the sheeting panels are statically indeterminate and must be found by considering the compatability of the deflections Δ_2 and Δ_3.

Thus

$$\left.\begin{aligned} \Delta_2 &= k(P-R_2) = c\left(R_2+\frac{R_3}{2}\right) \\ \Delta_3 &= k(P-R_3) = \Delta_2+\frac{cR_3}{2} \end{aligned}\right\} \quad (4.1)$$

which gives two simultaneous equations in the two unknowns R_2 and R_3. Solving these equations using $\psi = c/k$ gives

$$R_2 = P\left(\frac{\psi+2}{\psi^2+4\psi+2}\right),\ R_3 = P\left(\frac{2}{\psi^2+4\psi+2}\right) \quad (4.2)$$

from which the maximum shear force in the sheeting can be determined as

$$R_2+\tfrac{1}{2}R_3 = P\left(\frac{\psi+3}{\psi^2+4\psi+2}\right) \quad (4.3)$$

The frame forces can also be determined as

$$\left.\begin{aligned} \text{force on frame 2} &= P-R_2 = P\left(\frac{\psi^2+3\psi}{\psi^2+4\psi+2}\right) = \eta_2 P \\ \text{force on frame 3} &= P-R_3 = P\left(\frac{\psi^2+4\psi}{\psi^2+4\psi+2}\right) = \eta_3 P. \end{aligned}\right\} \quad (4.4)$$

η_2 and η_3 can be seen to be reduction factors on the bare frame forces, bending moments and deflections and are dependent solely on the value ψ of the relative flexibility of the panels and frames. Clearly, it is not possible to solve all such problems from first principles because the number of simultaneous equations increases as the number of frames increases. Values of η have therefore been tabulated by computer for various buildings up to 12 frames long and for a whole range of relative flexibilities. They are given in table 9.13 in chapter 9. Using this table, the forces applied to the sheeting at each frame i are given by

$$R_i = P(1-\eta_i) \quad (4.5)$$

and by summing such forces from the middle of the building the shear forces in the sheeting may be calculated.

4.2.1 One frame only loaded

The diaphragm action of sheeting or decking is especially effective if one frame carries a significant point load. This case can, of course, be considered separately and added to the forces arising from uniform loading using the principle of superposition. When only one frame is loaded, the sheeting panels serve not only to transmit a proportion of the load to the gables but also to distribute the load between the other frames of the building. The calculations therefore require consideration of compatability between the frames and the sheeting panels over the whole length of the building as for the case of all frames loaded. As before, the reduction factors for one frame only loaded have been tabulated by computer and are given in table 9.14. They are in the form of an additional factor by which the factor η for all frames loaded should be divided. This additional factor is strictly applicable to the case of the central frame loaded which is the worst case. It can be applied to other frames and the results will usually be adequate for all practical purposes.

4.2.2 Manual analysis of pitched roof portal frame buildings

The general case of loading on a pitched roof portal frame, as shown in fig. 4.6(a) can again be split up into a no-sway case (fig. 4.6(b) and a sway case (fig. 4.6(c)).

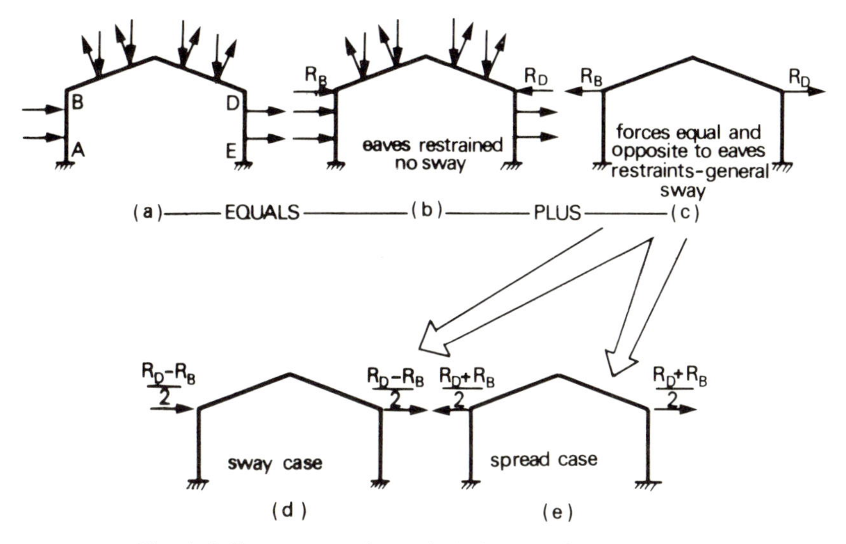

Fig. 4.6 Forces on a sheeted pitched roof portal frame.

The latter case may be further sub-divided into the antisymmetrical case of sway alone (fig. 4.6(d)) and the symmetrical case of spread alone (fig. 4.6(e)). The sheeting serves to reduce the sway and spread moments but has no effect on the no-sway moments. The bending moments in the clad frame can therefore be found by applying the procedure described above for rectangular frames first to the sway case and then to the spread case. Thus:

$$\begin{aligned}\text{Bending moment} &= \text{No-sway bending moment}\\ \text{in clad frame} &\quad + (\eta_{sw} \times \text{sway bending moment})\\ &\quad + (\eta_{sp} \times \text{spread bending moment})\end{aligned} \tag{4.6}$$

It may be noted that the manual procedures for the stressed skin analysis of both rectangular and pitched roof frames follow a basic philosophy that is closely allied to that used in the moment-distribution method of analysis. Moment-distribution may therefore be seen to be the preferred method of manual analysis for stressed skin structures and, using the tables of reduction factors 9.13 and 9.14, there is a surprisingly small amount of extra work required to obtain the solution for all cases where the frames in a building are single span and of uniform construction.

The analysis requires the definition of sway and spread flexibilities and it is convenient to define these with reference to horizontal loads as shown in fig. 4.7.

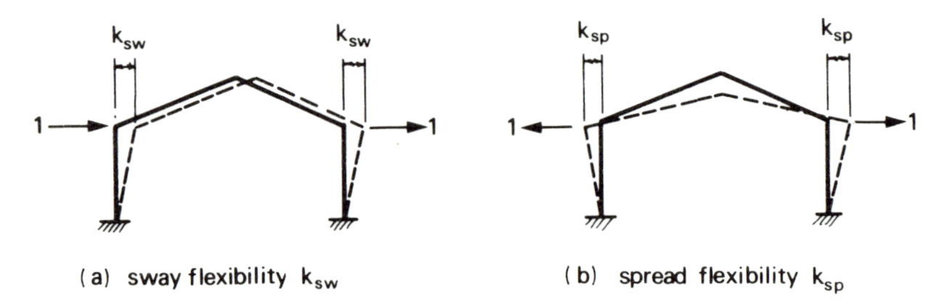

Fig. 4.7 Definitions of frame flexibility for pitched roof portal frames: (a) sway flexibility k_{sw}, (b) spread flexibility k_{sp}.

These frame flexibilities must then be combined with equivalent horizontal shear flexibilities of the roof panels which are defined in fig. 4.8 as $c_h = \Delta/V$. The depth of the panel used in the calculations is the depth of one roof slope (b in fig. 4.1) and the in-plane flexibility c is calculated in the usual way. In the plane of the sheeting the applied shear force is $V/\cos\theta$ and the shear displacement is $\Delta\cos\theta$ so that it follows that

$$c = \frac{\Delta\cos^2\theta}{V} \tag{4.7}$$

and

$$c_h = c\sec^2\theta \tag{4.8}$$

For the sway case, the relative flexibility of the panel to the frame is $\psi_{sw} = c_h/k_{sw}$ and this value is used in the table of reduction factors (table 9.13) to give the factors

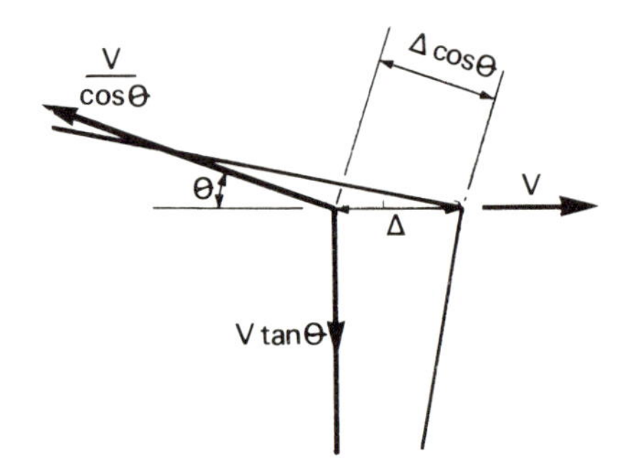

Fig. 4.8 Determination of equivalent horizontal shear flexibility of panels.

η_{sw} by which the bare frame sway moments are reduced. The corresponding force on the sheeting panel is given by

$$\tfrac{1}{2}(R_D - R_B)(1 - \psi_{sw}) \sec \theta \qquad (4.9)$$

where R_D and R_B are defined in fig. 4.6(d). For the spread case, a similar procedure is followed. The relative flexibility is given by $\psi_{sp} = c_h/k_{sp}$ and from this value the reduction factors η_{sp} follow directly as before. Worked examples of the above methods of calculation are given in chapter 7.

4.3 Computer analysis of clad structures

For complex structures with several bays or irregular construction or irregular loading, manual methods of analysis become unworkable and it is necessary to use a computer. Fortunately, it is not necessary to use special programs and the elastic analysis of complete clad structures can be readily undertaken using any program suitable for the analysis of plane frames. Suitable programs are available for almost all computers used by structural engineers.

Although the analysis is applicable to complex structures it is convenient to describe it with reference to the pitched roof portal structure shown in fig. 4.1. The gables are assumed to be rigid in their own planes and each intermediate frame is a plane, rigid-jointed frame with either pinned or fixed feet. The individual frames are connected together by complete sheeting panels whose flexibility is summarised by the single quantity c. As these cladding panels provide, in effect, a simple coupling between adjacent frames, precisely the same coupling can be obtained by moving the individual plane frames close together, and by replacing the shear panels by 'springs' of the same flexibility. Thus fig. 4.9 shows a mathematical model which accurately simulates the stressed skin behaviour of the structure shown in fig. 4.1. Figure 4.9 shows the individual frames slightly apart for illustrative purposes. Computationally there is no reason why they cannot be coincident and if the frames are moved into coincidence the entire three-dimensional structure reduces to a plane

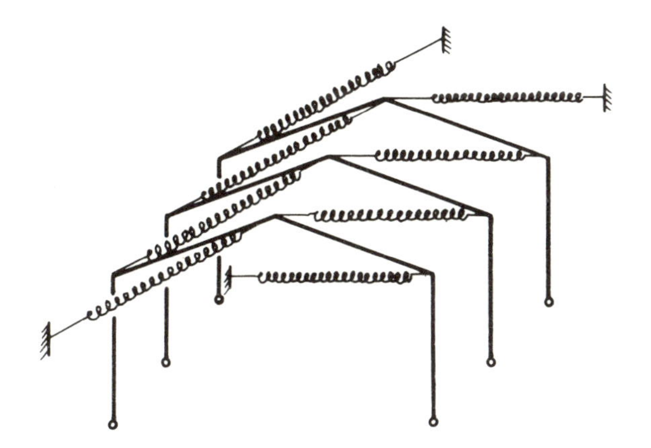

Fig. 4.9 Mathematical model of simple sheeted building.

frame. Admittedly, it is a rather unusual plane frame in that it has a number of joints with precisely the same co-ordinates and a number of members in precisely the same positions but the computer does not know this and it is possible to use any available plane frame program to analyse the complete structure.

Flexible end gables can be simulated in the same way. This allows the case to be analysed where the gables are not diagonally braced and the loads in the roof sheeting are transferred back to sheeted end gables which themselves act as shear diaphragms.

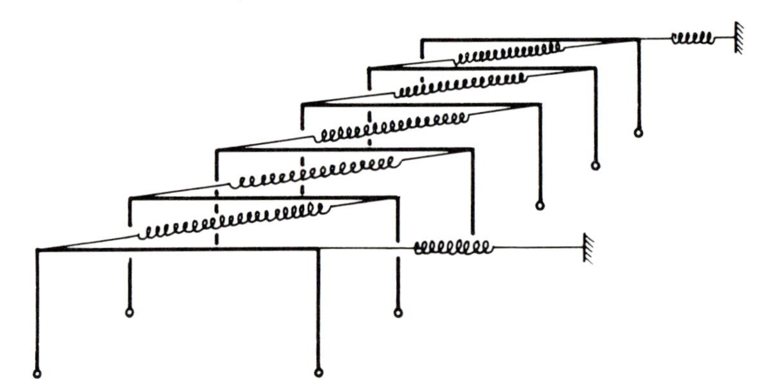

Fig. 4.10 Mathematical model of building with flexible gables.

Figure 4.10 illustrates how a simple rectangular building with flexible end gables can be analysed as a plane frame. As most plane frames do not have specific facilities for inserting springs of a given flexibility a spring with flexibility c can be treated as a prismatic member with properties:

$$\left.\begin{array}{ll}\text{second moment of area} & = 0 \\ \text{area of cross-section} & = A \\ \text{Young's modulus} & = E \\ \text{length} & = L\end{array}\right\} \text{where } A = \frac{L}{cE} \tag{4.10}$$

Examples of computer analyses obtained on this basis are given in chapters 7 and 12.

4.4 Manual plastic analysis of clad structures

The plastic methods of structural analysis make the basic assumption that the behaviour of the structure prior to collapse is ductile so that full redistribution of load can take place before the structure collapses as a mechanism. Usually the designer is concerned with the analysis of a single plane frame which fails by the formation of plastic hinges and he appeals to the well-established requirements for ductility of plastic hinges in structural steel sections. When the influence of the cladding is considered, an additional factor emerges. Fig. 4.11 shows the plastic collapse of a complete sheeted building subject to vertical loading. It is immediately apparent that before the complete structure can collapse it is necessary for all of the intermediate frames to form mechanisms and, in addition, for the sheeting panels at the ends of the building to yield. As it is not known at what stage in the

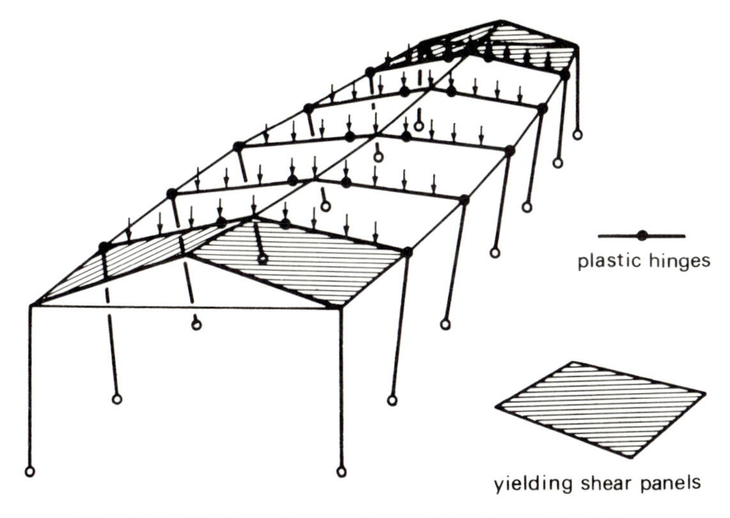

Fig. 4.11 Plastic collapse of complete sheeted building.

process of loading to failure that yield will occur in the sheeting panels, it is a fundamental requirement that the failure of an individual panel should be ductile. As it is fundamental to the philosophy of stressed skin design followed in this book, and adopted in the European recommendations, that this should be so, this requirement poses no great problem.

A typical load-deflection curve for an individual panel loaded up to failure is shown in fig. 4.12. The required yield plateau before the load starts to fall away will always be present provided that failure takes place in a line of fasteners by tearing of the sheeting at the fasteners. The provisions of chapters 2 and 3 and the design expressions given in chapter 9 serve to ensure that this occurs. It follows that failure of a clad building will usually involve a three-dimensional plastic collapse of the complete structure and indeed such a failure has been obtained experimentally

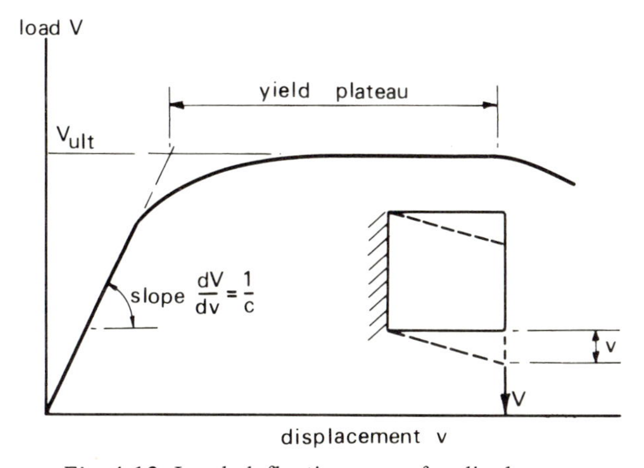

Fig. 4.12 Load–deflection curve for diaphragm.

Fig. 4.13 Inside view of sheeted building at collapse.

in a full scale test on a complete building. Fig. 4.13 shows an interior view of the test building after collapse. Plastic hinges in the rafters and at the eaves were clearly evident in each intermediate frame as also was the failure in the sheet to shear connector fasteners in the most highly stressed panels. The calculation of the plastic collapse load of a complete clad building can be undertaken by any of the methods available for unclad buildings. For illustrative purposes one example of the use of the work equation method will be given but graphical methods are equally applicable.

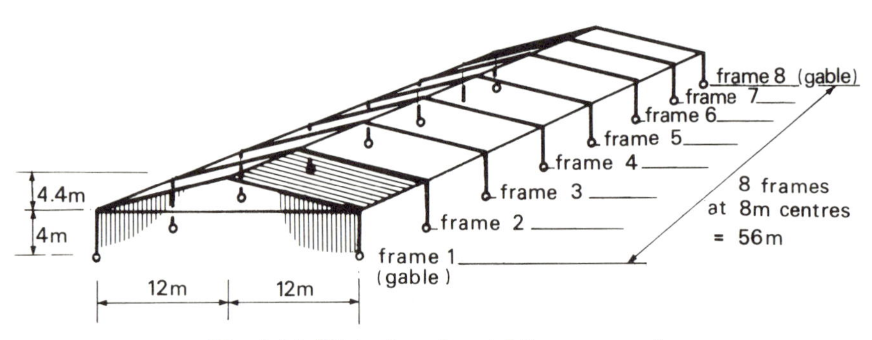

Fig. 4.14 Pitched roof portal frame example.

Figure 4.14 shows a typical portal frame structure which is assumed to be subject to the following loading using the partial load factors specified in the European recommendations: characteristic dead load 4 kN/m per frame with $\gamma = 1.33$, characteristic imposed load 7 kN/m per frame with $\gamma = 1.5$, basic design load = $(0.9 \times 1.33 \times 4) + (1.50 \times 7) = 15.29$ kN/m in plan and design load for plastic design = 1.12 X 15.29 = 17.12 kN/m in plan. The frames are of uniform section with pinned bases. The relevant properties of the frames and cladding panels are: frame (457 X 191 X 67 kg/m U.B.) M_{pl} = 359.9 kNm, sheeting panels flexibility c = 0.10 mm/kN and design strength V^* = 180 kN. It is assumed that the frames collapse in symmetrical mechanisms with the plastic hinges in the rafters forming at a purlin position 3 m from the apex. Taking account of the symmetry of the problem, the collapse mechanism for one quarter of the complete structure is shown in fig. 4.15. As this is a rigid-plastic collapse mechanism, all of the deformation is confined to the plastic hinges and the yielding gable panel. The intermediate

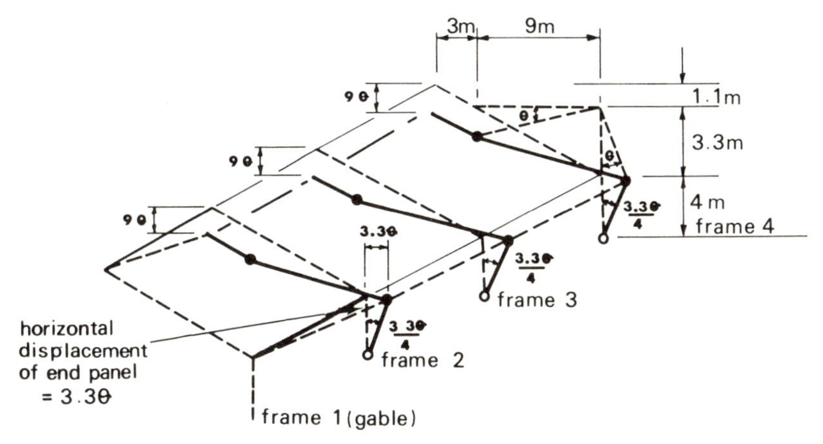

Fig. 4.15 Collapse mechanism for one quarter of structure.

panels do not deform and the intermediate frames have identical deformations. If γ_{pl} is the plastic multiplying factor which must have a value greater than unity for a structure of adequate strength, the work equation is

$$3 \times 17.12 \times \gamma_{pl} \left[(3 \times 9\theta) + \left(9 \times \frac{9\theta}{2}\right) \right] =$$

$$\left[3 \times 359.9 \times \left(2 + \frac{3.3}{4}\right)\theta \right] + (180 \times 3.3\theta \cos 20.14^\circ) \quad (4.11)$$

i.e. $\gamma_{pl} = 1.04$ (4.12)

The above calculation is the strictly correct application of plastic theory to the problem. However, the following reasoning allows the analysis to be reduced to that of a single frame which is much more convenient.

At collapse, each of the intermediate frames must have the same distribution of internal forces which must therefore be in equilibrium with the same set of external loads. These loads include the restraint provided by the sheeting panels and it follows that at collapse the ultimate strength of the two end panels is equally divided between the intermediate frames. Thus, in the above example, each intermediate frame is subject to an eaves force in the plane of the roof of 2 X 180/6 = 60 kN. The horizontal component of this force is 60 cos 20.14° = 56.33 kN so that

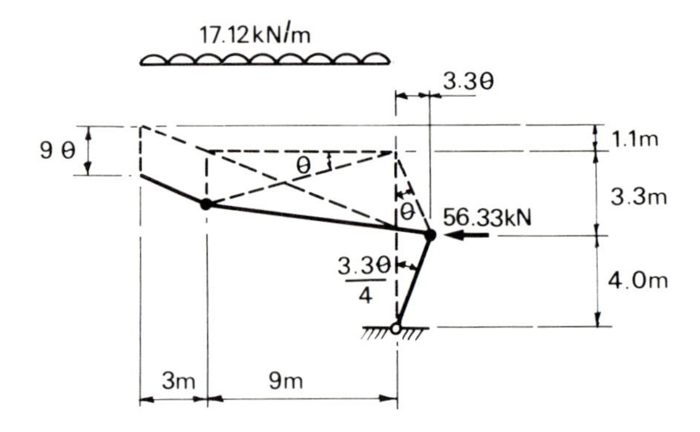

Fig. 4.16 Forces on an individual frame at collapse.

the forces on an individual frame at collapse are as shown in fig. 4.16. The work equation for the individual frame is therefore

$$17.12\,\gamma_{pl}\left[(3 \times 9\theta) + \left(9 \times \frac{9\theta}{2}\right)\right] = 359.9\left(2 + \frac{3.3}{4}\right)\theta + (56.33 \times 3.3\theta) \quad (4.13)$$

i.e.
$$\gamma_{pl} = 1.04 \text{ as before.} \quad (4.14)$$

It may be noted that if the last term in the above equation is omitted, it becomes the work equation for the bare frame which gives

$$\gamma_{pl} = 0.880 \quad (4.15)$$

so that the bare frame is not satisfactory. A consideration of stressed skin action merely adds a single extra term to the work equation for the bare frame. The plastic design of clad structures using conventional manual methods is therefore possible in many practical instances provided that the usual fundamental requirements are satisfied. These fundamental requirements can be summarised in two statements: the full plastic collapse load must be achieved without the possibility of any form of premature failure; there must be no possibility of damage to the building at the working loads.

Considering a stressed skin structure, the most important considerations can be further detailed as follows:

(a) The stability of columns and lateral stability of beams must be considered as in any conventional plastic design.
(b) The sheeting failure must be ductile and will be so provided that the principles given in the European recommendations and outlined in earlier chapters are observed. It should be noted in this connection that the use of aluminium blind rivets as seam fasteners can lead to brittle failure and should usually be avoided unless tests prove that the particular combination of sheeting and fastener to be used fails consistently in a ductile manner.
(c) The type of failure that occurs then depends critically on the relative strengths and stiffnesses of the sheeting and frames. If the sheeting is relatively flexible and

strong so that plastic hinges form first in the frames and only at a late stage of loading does yield occur in the sheeting panels there is no problem.
(d) Usually, however, the sheeting panels prove to be relatively stiff but not very strong so that first yield takes place in the sheeting and plastic hinges in the frames form later. For this reason it is considered mandatory to carry out an elastic analysis in order to ensure that yield at the sheeting fasteners does not occur at the working loads. For the purposes of this serviceability check, it is considered sufficient to establish that under the unfactored characteristic loads (strictly the loads defined in the relevant standard or code of practice as being applicable to the serviceability limit state) the maximum shear load in any panel is less than its design strength. The nature of this serviceability check takes advantage of the non-linear behaviour of diaphragms. If the calculated force in a given panel is only a little less than its calculated design strength, the actual force will be significantly less than that calculated using an elastic analysis as some favourable redistribution will already have taken place.

4.5 Plastic analysis of clad structures by computer

The plastic analysis of stressed skin structures is readily possible on the same plane frame basis that was described in section 4.3 for elastic analysis. The requirement is for a computer program for the plastic analysis of plane frames that is capable of dealing with both bending members forming plastic hinges and also members carrying axial load only and yielding in tension or compression. Unfortunately, such programs are not readily available to the profession, although if a program for the elastic-plastic analysis of plane frames is available it is possible, with a little ingenuity, to use it for the elastic-plastic analysis of stressed skin structures. It is necessary to model the flexibility and strength of each shear panel by replacing it by a cranked pair of bending members with the same flexibility and strength.

A program for the elastic-plastic analysis of stressed skin structures has been written by the first author and, at the time of writing, is available to the profession at the University of Salford. It is anticipated that, in time, it may also be available through one or more commercial outlets. Obviously, such a program is an essential tool for the efficient design of complex clad structures.

4.6 The danger of ignoring stressed skin action in conventional construction

Regardless of whether the design of a clad building is elastic or plastic and whether the design takes into account the stiffening effect of cladding or not, it is likely that the relative strengths and stiffnesses of the frames and sheeting panels are such that, under increasing load, first yield will take place in the sheeting panels. This is particularly the case in relatively tall, steel-framed structures where a major design factor is lateral loading due to wind and where the relative displacement between the gable frame and adjacent frame can seriously embarrass the cladding. In such structures, yield or even failure of the sheeting panels could occur at the working loads. As has been pointed out earlier, stressed skin action is present whether the designer acknowledges it or not. The methods of stressed skin design allow an analysis to be made of such cases so that the forces in the sheeting may be investigated. The authors believe that this is the correct way to proceed whether or not it is intended to take account of stressed skin action in the design of the frames.

A number of tall rectangular buildings have been analysed in order to investigate the condition of typical roof sheeting panels at the working loads. One of these theoretical investigations of an actual building has been reported in detail by Bryan and El-Dakhakhni.[2.7] The important results are repeated here as they provide a forceful illustration of the relevance of stressed skin design to tall sway frame structures. These results have been recalculated since they were first published in 1968 and the figures presented below show significant differences from those given previously. This reflects the influence of the improved calculation methods developed in the intervening years. The steel-framed building in question was 80 ft. wide, 309 ft. long and 50 ft. high. A diagrammatic representation of the main frames is shown in fig. 4.17 and the plan of the building is given in fig. 4.18. The transverse

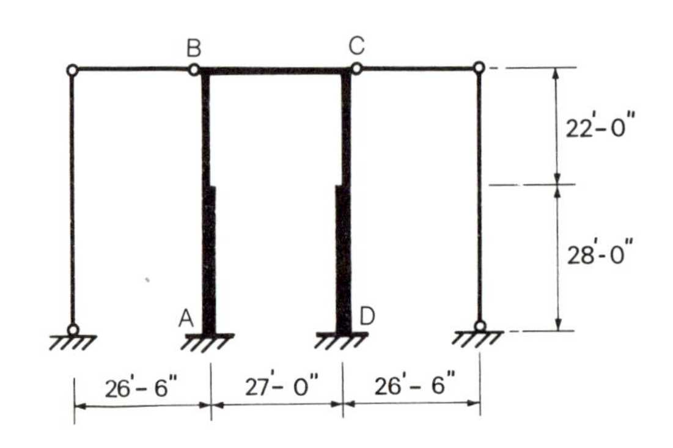

Fig. 4.17 Idealised steel frame.

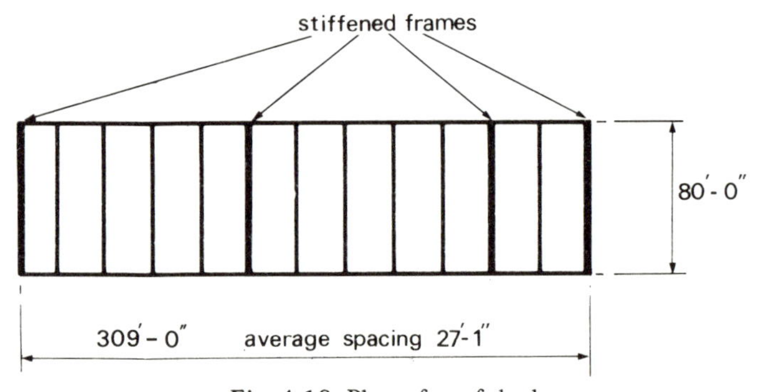

Fig. 4.18 Plan of roof deck.

strength of the building depended on the rigid jointed portal frame ABCD in fig. 4.17 and the outer pinned frames did not contribute to this strength. Referring to fig. 4.18, there were rigid partition walls across the building at frames 6 and 11, so that the greatest length of building to be considered was the portion between these frames. In this portion, there were four intermediate frames and the average width of a panel of sheeting was 27.05 ft.

In the bare frame analysis, the bending moments due to wind loads far exceeded those due to any other type of loading. In order to simplify the example, only wind bending moments are therefore considered. Figure 4.19 shows these calculated

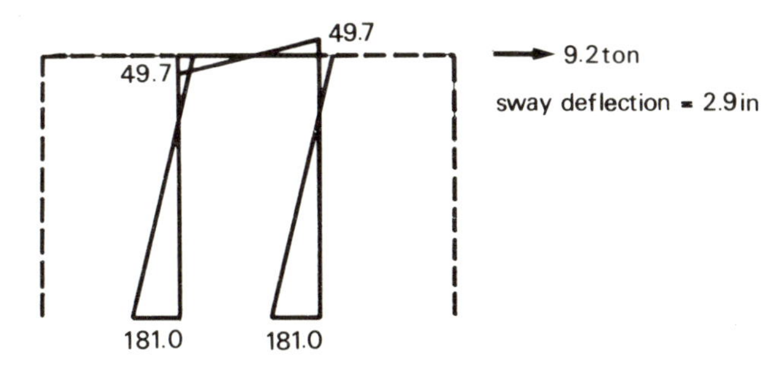

Fig. 4.19 Bare frame bending moments in ton-ft.

bending moments in the bare steel frame under working loads; the calculated sway deflection is 2.90 in. The calculated shear flexibility of a panel of sheeting using the design expressions given in chapter 9 is 0.0743 in/ton giving a relative flexibility of 0.236. The reduction factor ψ for the most highly stressed frames (8 and 9) is therefore 0.432 so that the maximum bending moments and deflections in any frame of the structure are those shown in fig. 4.20. Clearly the bare frame analysis for this structure gives a completely erroneous picture of the true behaviour of the sheeted building.

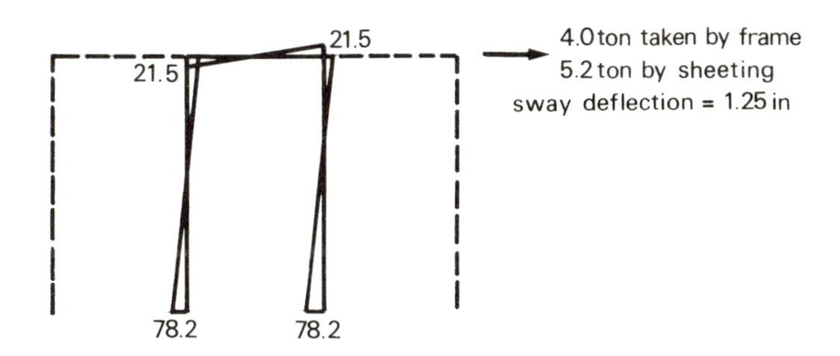

Fig. 4.20 Clad frame bending moments in ton-ft.

The sheeting on this structure was fastened on two sides only, with no provision of shear connectors or their equivalent, and the calculated ultimate shear load for this case (based on tests on the actual fasteners) is 5.88 tons. However, the calculated shear force in the most highly stressed panels is 11.7 tons so that stressed skin analysis predicts that the sheeting fasteners will fail under wind loads well below the working value. Indeed, tearing of the sheeting at these fasteners may be expected at wind speeds with quite low return periods. Obviously this does not endanger the structure, since the steelwork was designed on the basis of bare frames, but it could well cause trouble in keeping the building watertight. This is a typical pattern of behaviour in tall rectangular-framed buildings and is particularly critical when the sheeting is fastened on two sides only, which will almost always be the case when no consideration is given to stressed skin effects. In such structures the calculated sway moments and deflections are likely to be completely fictitious and the forces in the sheeting panels large enough to demand serious consideration.

CHAPTER FIVE

Irregular diaphragms

5.1 Introduction

This chapter is somewhat more involved than the other chapters in Part I and may be omitted on first reading unless the reader has a specific irregular building in mind. In particular, it may be noted that an approximate treatment of significant openings is given in section 6.7 and this will suffice for many practical situations. The procedures described in the previous chapters are applicable to the great majority of diaphragms which are rectangular in plan and regular in construction. Occasionally it may be necessary to design a diaphragm for which the design expressions given previously are not applicable. It is then necessary to resort to detailed analysis for which two procedures are available, namely finite element analysis or plane frame simulation. These techniques will be described in sections 5.2 and 5.3 respectively. Alternatively, irregular diaphragms may be designed by testing and the appropriate test procedures are reviewed in section 5.4.

There are, however, two common situations which are of practical importance and which have been subjected to detailed study. The first of these is the problem of diaphragms containing significant openings such as those required for roof lights or to accommodate large flues. A typical test on such a diaphragm is shown in fig. 5.1. For diaphragms containing distributions of openings within certain practical limitations a design procedure is available which makes detailed analysis unnecessary. This is described in section 5.5. The second situation of practical importance is when a point load occurs in the plane of the diaphragm and its line of action does not coincide with the line of a framing member. Two typical cases of this type are shown in fig. 5.2. In fig. 5.2(a), the flat roof of a single-storey building is acting as a diaphragm carrying wind loads back to the stiffened gables. The wind forces arise as a series of point loads at eaves level and only alternate point loads coincide with a framing member. The question arises whether the diaphragm can accommodate the intermediate point loads without any additional stiffening members. Figure 5.2(b)

Fig. 5.1 Test on a diaphragm with a significant opening.

shows the light gauge steel folded plate roof of a small factory building in which the runway beam carrying a small hoist is suspended from the lower fold-line members. Here the designer must check whether the plate elements forming the roof can accommodate the point loads from the runway beam. Design expressions for the additional local forces due to point loads are given in section 5.6.

5.2 Finite element analysis of diaphragms

Figure 5.3 is typical of a structure for which a finite element analysis may be required. The MACE unit is a light gauge steel hipped plate structure which was originally conceived as being suitable for system-built nursery schools. Under uniform vertical load, forces from the roof sheeting pass directly into the framing members and thence to the foundations. Under asymmetric loading, however, the stability of the structure depends on stressed skin action in the trapezoidally shaped roof panels and it was considered necessary to carry out an analysis in order to investigate the forces in the fasteners. Further details of the design of this structure are given in references 3.17 and 3.18.

For the investigation under wind load it was necessary to consider the problem shown in fig. 5.4 where a trapezoidal diaphragm is subjected to an in-plane distributed load. As this problem is symmetrical about a vertical centre line, it is sufficient to consider one half of the diaphragm for which a suitable finite element model is shown in fig. 5.5. A number of investigations of diaphragms using finite

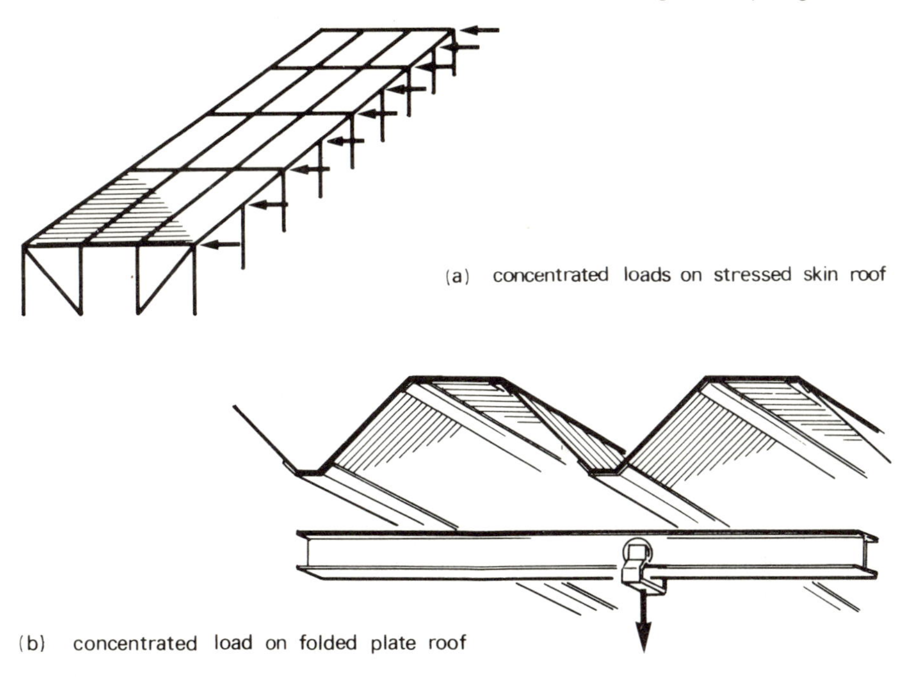

Fig. 5.2 Examples of concentrated loads on light gauge steel diaphragms: (a) concentrated loads on stressed skin roof, (b) concentrated load on folded plate roof.

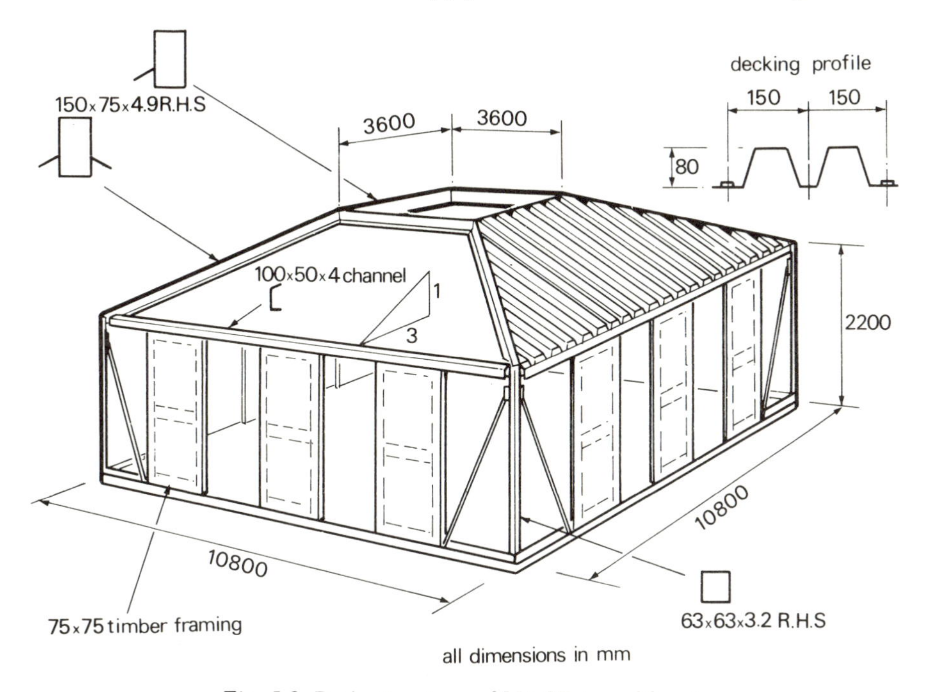

Fig. 5.3 Basic structure of MACE type 30 unit.

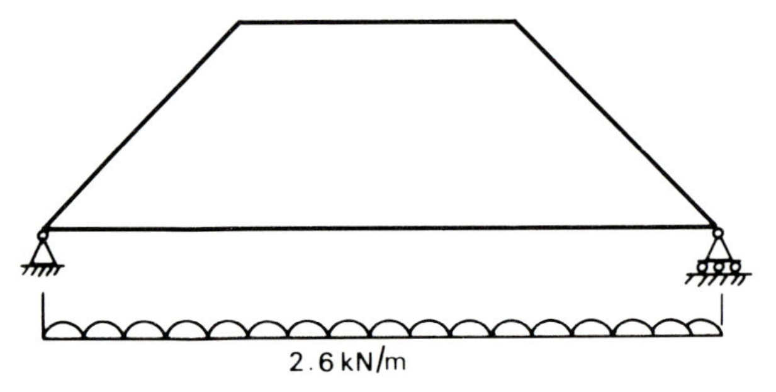

Fig. 5.4 Analytical problem for wind load analysis.

elements have been reported[1.51, 1.58, 1.86, 2.23, 3.19] and in each case it has been found sufficient to consider the diaphragm as a plane assembly of plates, prismatic finite elements and fasteners. Thus, the problem shown in fig. 5.5 requires the following element types.

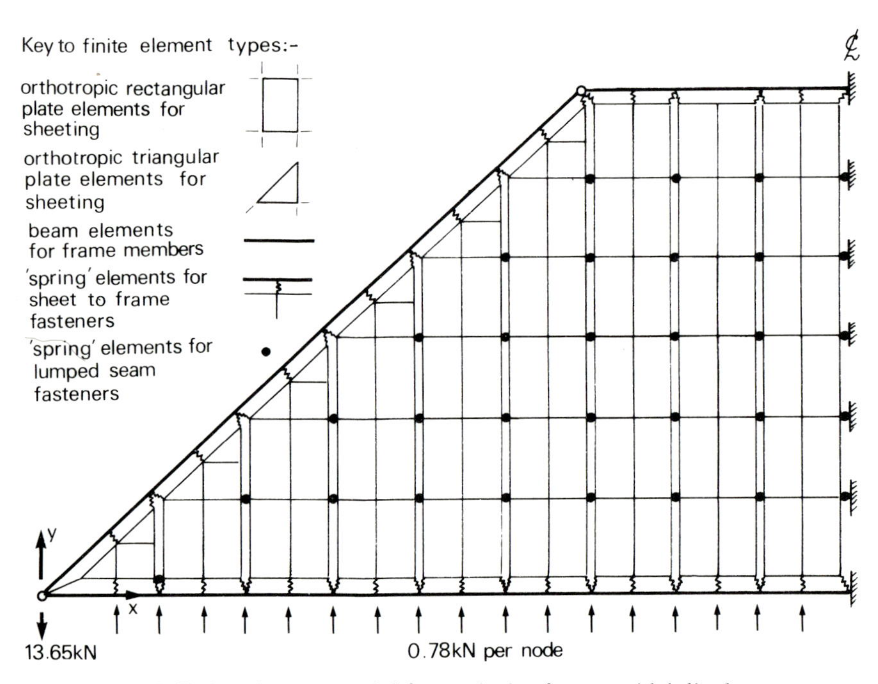

Fig. 5.5 Finite element model for analysis of trapezoidal diaphragm.

5.2.1 Orthotropic rectangular plate elements

As these elements are subject to a plane stress distribution, that is predominantly pure shear, simple elements with two degrees of freedom at each node are adequate. These elements are therefore orthotropic forms of the simplest rectangular plane stress elements, details of which will be found in any elementary text book on finite element analysis. Crucial to the analysis is the derivation of the appropriate elastic properties for inclusion in the elasticity matrix which has the form:

$$D = \frac{1}{1-\nu_{xy}\nu_{yx}}\begin{bmatrix} E_x & \nu_{xy}E_x & 0 \\ \nu_{yx}E_y & E_y & 0 \\ 0 & 0 & (1-\nu_{xy}\nu_{yx})G_{\text{eff}} \end{bmatrix} \quad (5.1)$$

where E_x and E_y are the effective values of Young's modulus along the axes of orthotropy and ν_{xy} and ν_{yx} the corresponding values of Poisson's ratio. It may be noted that

$$\nu_{xy}E_x = \nu_{yx}E_y \quad (5.2)$$

so that there are four elastic constants to be determined in such a way that the behaviour of profiled metal sheeting subject to in-plane load is accurately represented by an equivalent orthotropic plate. The determination of E_x, E_y, ν_{xy} and ν_{yx} presents no difficulty[1.51, 1.58, 2.23] due regard being given to the very low stiffness transverse to the corrugations, due to 'concertina' action.

A perfectly adequate value for G_{eff} can be derived from the expressions for $c_{1.1}$ and $c_{1.2}$ given in chapters 2 and 9 as follows:

$$G_{\text{eff}} = E\Bigg/\left[\frac{d^{2.5}\,\alpha_1\,\alpha_4\,\bar{K}}{t^{1.5}\,b} + 2\,(1+\nu)\left(1+\frac{2h}{d}\right)\right] \quad (5.3)$$

where E and ν here are Young's modulus and Poisson's ratio of the material of the sheeting, the other symbols being defined in chapter 9. The profile constant $\bar{K}$ reflects the contribution made to the shear flexibility by distortion of the profile of the sheeting and is tabulated for a wide range of sheeting profiles in tables 9.6 and 9.7. There is a great increase in $\bar{K}$ when the fastener pitch at the ends of the sheet changes from every corrugation to alternate corrugations; this is because alternate corrugations open and close as shown in fig. 5.6. This form of shear distortion is directly related to the very low value of E_x, the effective value of Young's modulus transverse to the corrugations, and can appear again in any finite element analysis in which there are unrestrained nodes at the ends of the corrugations. *In any finite element analysis of shear diaphragms, it is therefore essential to avoid any unrestrained nodes at the sheet ends*. There is then only one element between adjacent sheet to purlin fasteners and the value of G_{eff} is obtained from the above equation using the value of $\bar{K}$ appropriate to the number of corrugations between these fasteners. Additional deformation of the type shown in fig. 5.6 is inhibited by the horizontal stiffness of the fasteners and correct results are obtained. This places a restriction on the number of finite elements that can be used to model a given situation. However, the element suggested above, and indeed any practical plane stress element, is capable of modelling a case of pure shear precisely and as the stress field approximates to a case of pure shear and the behaviour is dominated by shear displacements this is not a serious problem.

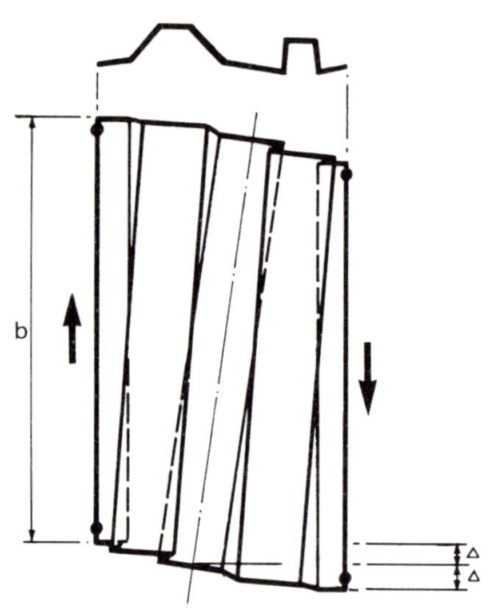

Fig. 5.6 Concertina-like deformations with fasteners in alternate troughs.

The question of the correct modelling of the shear stiffness of profiled steel sheeting has been discussed in some detail because it is not at all obvious and yet it is of fundamental importance in any analysis. As finite element programs for diaphragm analysis are now being offered to the profession (notably in the U.S.A.) the whole matter is of considerable practical importance.

5.2.2 Orthotropic triangular plate elements

Triangular elements are only required as infil pieces in non-rectangular diaphragms. It is strongly recommended that they are not used in any other situation as, for a given number of degrees of freedom, their performance is inferior to rectangular elements. The triangular elements to be used are therefore dictated by requirements of compatibility with adjacent rectangular elements and this necessitates the use of the simple uniform stress element with two degrees of freedom per node. The derivation of this element will be found in any elementary text book on finite element analysis. The considerations regarding the choice of elastic constants are identical to those discussed above for rectangular elements.

5.2.3 Fastener elements

A distinctive feature of the finite element analysis of shear diaphragms is the modelling of individual fasteners as discrete elements of zero size. Thus fig. 5.5 includes fastener elements representing the stiffness of both the seam fasteners and the sheet to frame fasteners. In other applications, similar elements may also represent the flexibility of fasteners to shear connectors and purlin to rafter connections.

The influence of these fastener elements may best be appreciated by considering them as a pair of springs as shown in fig. 5.7 having equal stiffness in two orthogonal

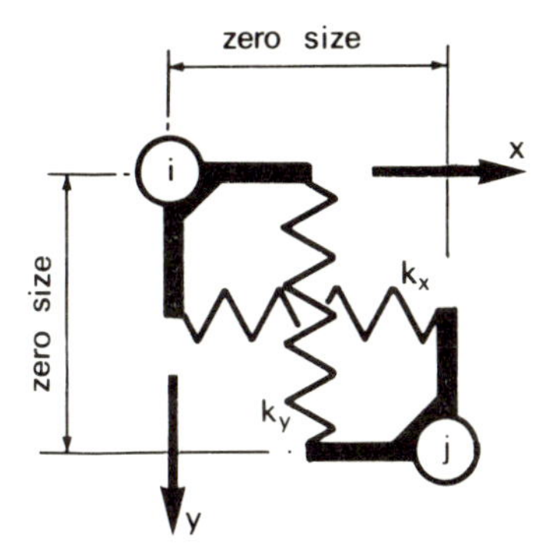

Fig. 5.7 Finite element simulation of fastener.

directions but no rotational stiffness. As the elements are of zero size, the joints *i* and *j* in fig. 5.7, though shown apart for clarity, are in fact coincident. Because the influence of these fasteners on the analysis is of fundamental significance it is essential that they be correctly modelled and, as fastener elements are not generally available with existing finite element packages, it follows that the finite element analysis of light gauge steel shear diaphragms requires purpose-written programs. It may be noted that it is essential to model sheet to frame member fasteners precisely since adjacent fasteners tend to have quite different values of force and displacement. However, the fasteners in a given seam or line of shear connectors (i.e. in a line of fasteners parallel to the corrugations) tend to have very similar values of force and displacement and there is little loss of accuracy when these fasteners are 'lumped' to form equivalent fasteners at convenient node positions. This has been done in fig. 5.5.

5.2.4 Beam elements

Beam elements representing the frame members are conventional elements used for plane frame analysis having three degrees of freedom per node.

5.2.5 Available programs

Computer programs for the finite element analysis of diaphragms have been written and used in the U.S.A. (Cornell University),[1.51,1.58] Australia (University of Melbourne),[2.17,2.23] and England (University of Salford).[1.61,1.86,3.19] The American and British programs include data generators whereby the considerable quantity of data required for the analysis may be generated automatically for many regular configurations and these two programs are available for commercial use. If a suitable data generator is not available, and this is always the case in irregular situations, data preparation becomes a major task and is prone to error. This is a considerable disincentive towards the use of finite element analysis unless it is considered essential. The American program is specifically designed to carry out non-linear analysis where non linearity is confined to the fasteners. In commercial terms this is expensive and in practical terms it is considered to be unnecessary so that consideration here is confined to linear analysis.

5.2.6 Results of finite element analysis

Finite element analysis gives a wealth of information regarding the distributions of internal force and displacement which cannot be obtained in any other way. In the analysis of the diaphragm shown in fig. 5.5 the results of particular interest were the bottom flange displacements and the sheet to edge member fastener forces and these are shown in fig. 5.8. The seam fastener forces were found to be relatively insignificant.

It is clear that these distributions of force and displacement could hardly have been predicted by any simplified method of calculation. Of particular interest to the designers were the high fastener forces in the top flange at the change of direction of the members and directly opposite this point in the bottom flange. The maximum calculated fastener force was 2.42 kN which should be compared with the ultimate capacity of an individual fastener of approximately 4.0 kN. The critical fasteners were therefore safe but, as a single highly stressed fastener represents a potential weakness, fasteners in the critical regions were increased from alternate corrugation troughs to every corrugation.

5.3 Simplified computer analysis

This section describes an alternative computer analysis whereby irregular diaphragms may be analysed using a conventional plane frame analysis program of the type available on most computer installations. A typical diaphragm, whether regular or irregular, becomes an almost trivial computation problem so that data preparation is no longer a significant factor. In describing this approach, it is convenient to first describe the analysis of a simple diaphragm and then to show how this may be extended to a typical irregular case. A typical simple diaphragm is shown in fig. 5.9 and its full finite element equivalent is shown in fig. 5.10. Although fig. 5.10 is shown in three dimensions for clarity, the computational problem is set up as though the members are co-planar.

A number of such diaphragms were analysed in developing the design expressions discussed in chapter 2 and given in chapter 9 and certain consistent features were apparent as follows:

(a) In deriving suitable equivalent orthotropic properties for the finite elements representing the profiled steel sheeting, the only significant property is the shear stiffness.

(b) The variation of force between individual seam fasteners in a given line is not greatly significant and the experimental evidence confirms that these will tend to be equalised by non-linear behaviour long before failure of the diaphragm takes place. Consequently there seems to be little advantage in modelling seam fasteners individually when a combined stiffness and strength for the complete seam can be used.

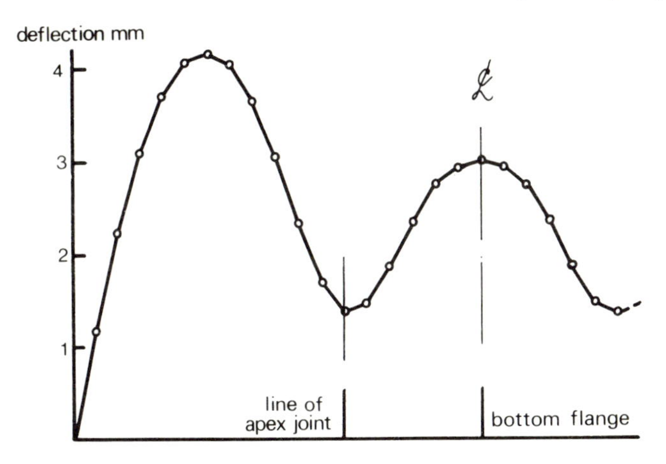

(a) in plane displacements of bottom flange

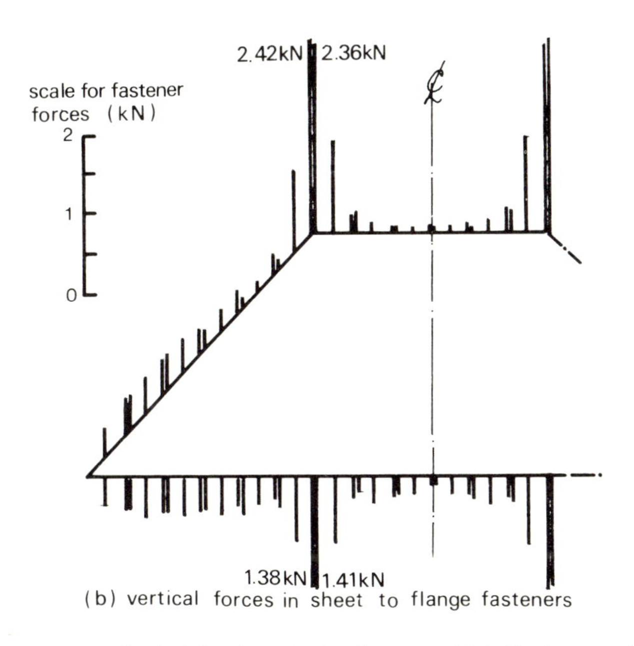

(b) vertical forces in sheet to flange fasteners

Fig. 5.8 Results of wind load analysis of trapezoidal diaphragm: (a) in-plane displacements of bottom flange, (b) vertical forces in sheet to flange fasteners.

(c) The arguments advanced in (b) apply equally to a line of shear connector fasteners or any other fasteners in a line parallel to the corrugations.

(d) Forces perpendicular to the direction of the corrugations on sheet to purlin fasteners are very small internally and form a regular pattern on the outermost purlins consistent with a linear increase in purlin axial force.

(e) Forces parallel to the direction of the corrugations on sheet to purlin fasteners are

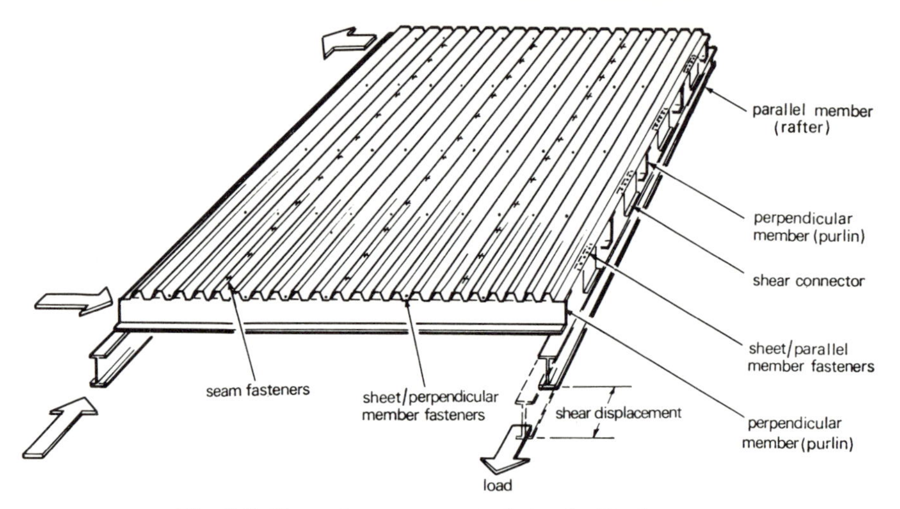

Fig. 5.9 General arrangement of simple diaphragm.

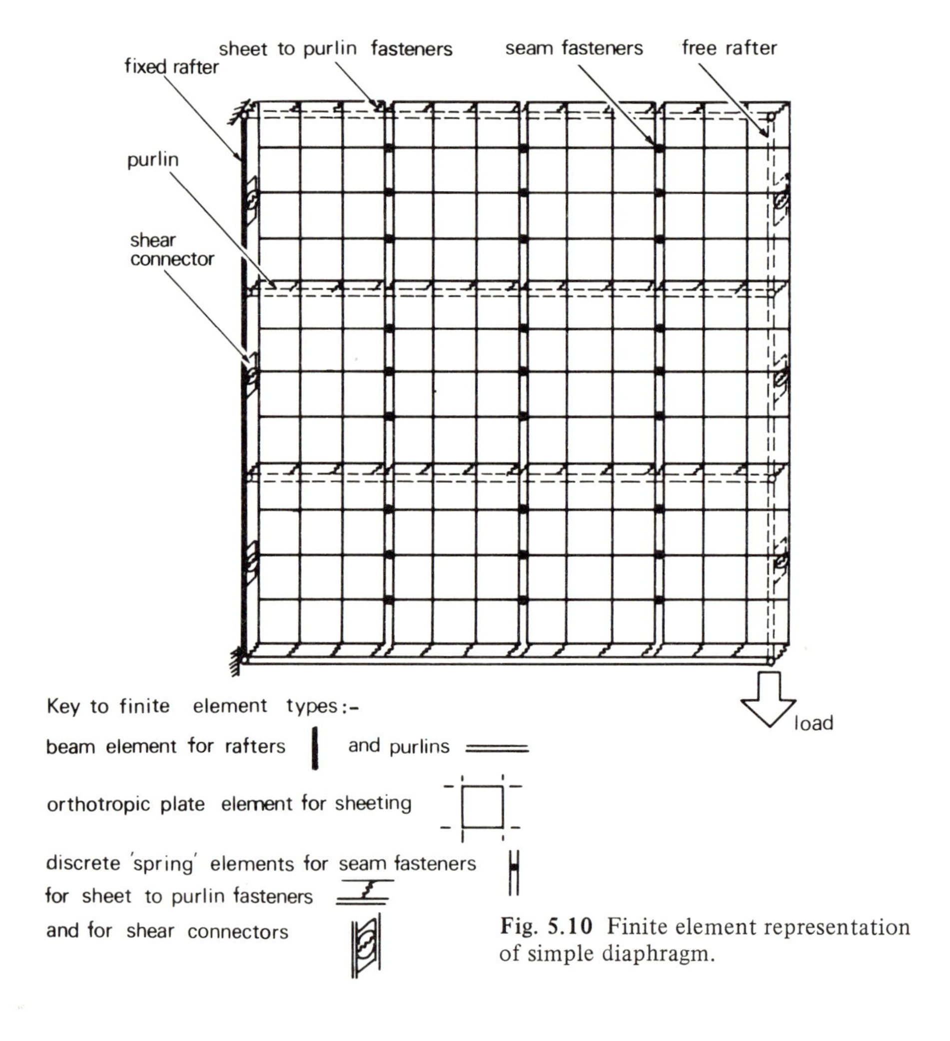

Fig. 5.10 Finite element representation of simple diaphragm.

significant and it is necessary to model each fastener precisely. However, the distributions of vertical force associated with each purlin are very similar and there would be no significant loss of accuracy if the purlins and sheet to purlin fasteners were lumped together within the depth of the diaphragm while preserving the precise arrangements of fasteners along the purlins.

The preceding considerations suggest that a suitable greatly simplified mathematical model for a diaphragm can be developed in which only the important features are retained and those with second-order significance omitted. A suitable mathematical model for the typical diaphragm mentioned earlier is shown in fig. 5.11. The seam fasteners and shear connector fasteners are treated as single lumped elements and the shear flexibility of the sheeting is simulated by a series of bars forming a truss.

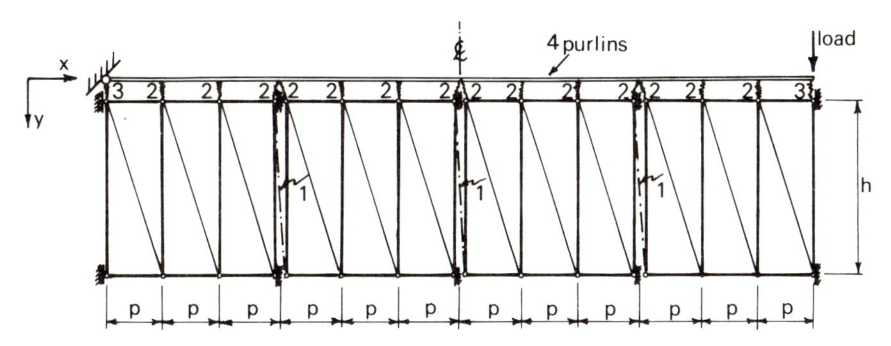

Fig. 5.11 Mathematical model of complete diaphragm.

In contrast to the full finite element treatment the spring elements shown in fig. 5.11 are given finite length so that they can be modelled by prismatic members thus eliminating the need for special programming. Fig. 5.11 therefore represents a plane frame that can be analysed by any conventional program. This model cannot be readily made to include the forces and displacements associated with overall bending of the diaphragm and therefore no attempt is made to include for any strains in the direction of the x axis. Each small truss representing a single sheet width is restrained against lateral movement and at the conclusion of the analysis the deflections due to flexibility components $c_{2.1}$ (due to lateral movement in the sheet to purlin fasteners) and c_3 (due to axial strain in the purlins) are added to the computed deflections. The purlin is given appropriate minor axis bending stiffness and the remaining members have axial stiffness only. Those shown by heavy lines are made sufficiently stiff for their axial strain to be neglected so that the shear flexibility of the sheet is dependent on the properties of the diagonal members only. It then follows, by equating the shear displacement of a piece of sheeting to that of its equivalent truss, that the required cross-sectional area, A, of a given diagonal member simulating a panel of sheeting is

$$A = \frac{btG_{\text{eff}}l^3}{pEh^2} \tag{5.4}$$

in which b = depth of diaphragm represented by the truss assembly,
E = Young's modulus of diagonal member,
G_{eff} = effective shear modulus of steel sheet,
h = depth of assembly representing the sheeting,
l = length of diagonal member,
p = pitch of sheet to purlin fasteners,
t = net thickness of steel sheet.

For regular diaphragms it has been shown[1.103] that the results obtained using the equivalent truss shown in fig. 5.11 are virtually identical to those obtained using the full finite element representation in fig. 5.10 and that for such diaphragms the full analysis is quite unnecessary.

It is also shown in reference 1.103 that further simplifications to the above model can be made. In particular, the results are symmetrical about the vertical centre line so that it is only necessary to analyse half of the diaphragm and if all displacements in the x direction are suppressed by restraining the joints a number of the truss members can also be omitted. This leads to the simplified model shown in fig. 5.12.

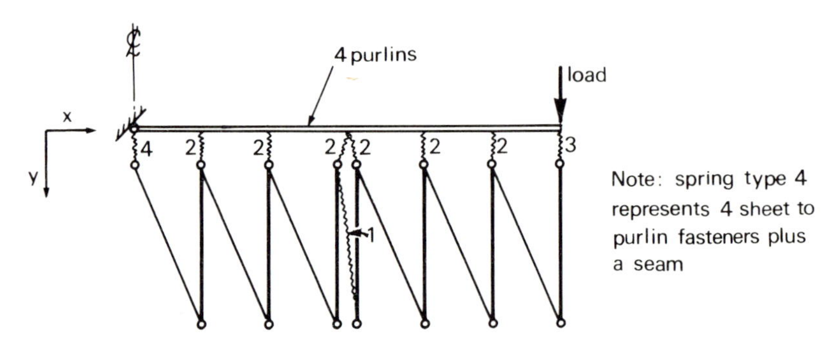

Fig. 5.12 Simplified model with x-displacement inhibited.

5.3.1 Application of simplified computer analysis to irregular diaphragms

The simplified analysis described above is of particular application to irregular diaphragms which necessitate a detailed analysis but for which the data preparation for a finite element analysis presents a formidable obstacle. Fig. 5.13 shows such a case in the form of a finite element representation of a SEAC Mark 3 roof deck with a significant opening. This arrangement was tested[1.46] as part of a series of tests to establish the SEAC Mark 3 system before the finite element analysis was available. A suitable mathematical model for one half of this diaphragm is shown in

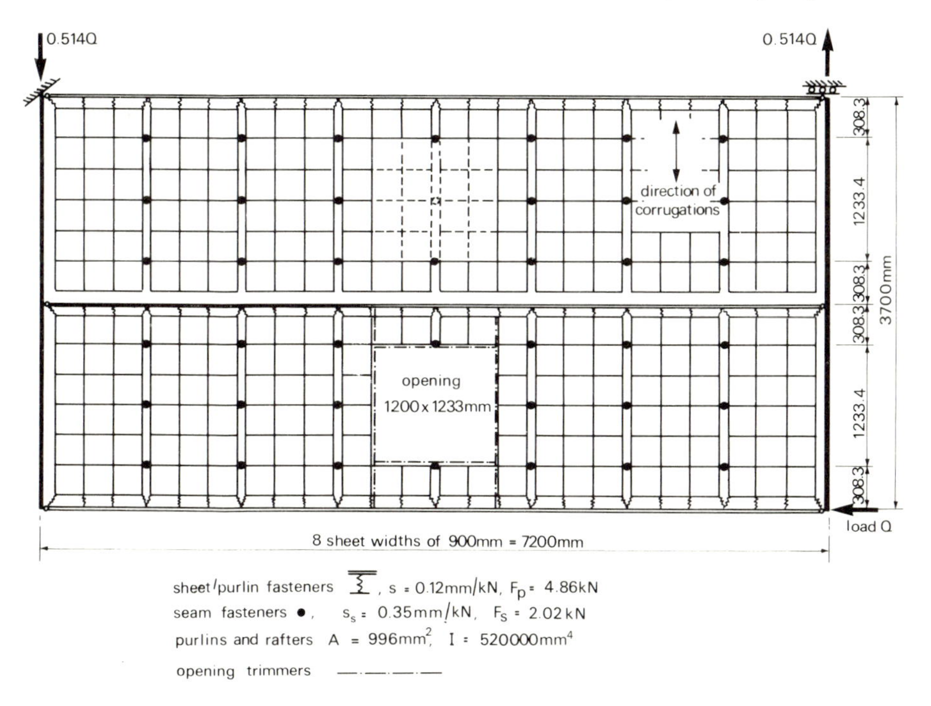

Fig. 5.13 Finite element representation of diaphragm with opening.

fig. 5.14. The upper beam member simulates both the upper and middle purlins of the actual diaphragm and therefore has twice the cross-sectional area and flexural rigidity of the lower beam member. Similarly, the upper row of springs representing the sheet to purlin fasteners has twice the strength and stiffness of the lower row.

It may be noted that in fig. 5.13 the load is applied in a direction perpendicular to the span of the sheeting so that the cantilever diaphragm is spanning in a direction parallel to the span of the sheeting. As the simulation in fig. 5.14 only considers movements parallel to the direction of the corrugations, the applied load perpendicular to the corrugations is replaced by a statically equivalent load in the direction in which the diaphragm is free to move. For the diagonal members simulating the sheeting the required cross-sectional area may be obtained as before. For the outer regions, where the sheet is not cut by the opening, the effective shear modulus G_{eff} is that appropriate to the full depth of the diaphragm (3700 mm). However, G_{eff} is strongly influenced by the length of the sheet so that above and below the opening different values of G_{eff} are applicable and corresponding values of cross-sectional area must be calculated. The dimensions parallel to the corrugations chosen for the analysis are shown in fig. 5.14. These are quite arbitrary and are chosen for convenience rather than to relate to the original diaphragm. It may be noted here that the members simulating the areas of sheet above and below the opening are given the same depth as the corresponding members in the remainder of the diaphragm which results in simplified data preparation though it produces an arrangement that is difficult to represent to scale.

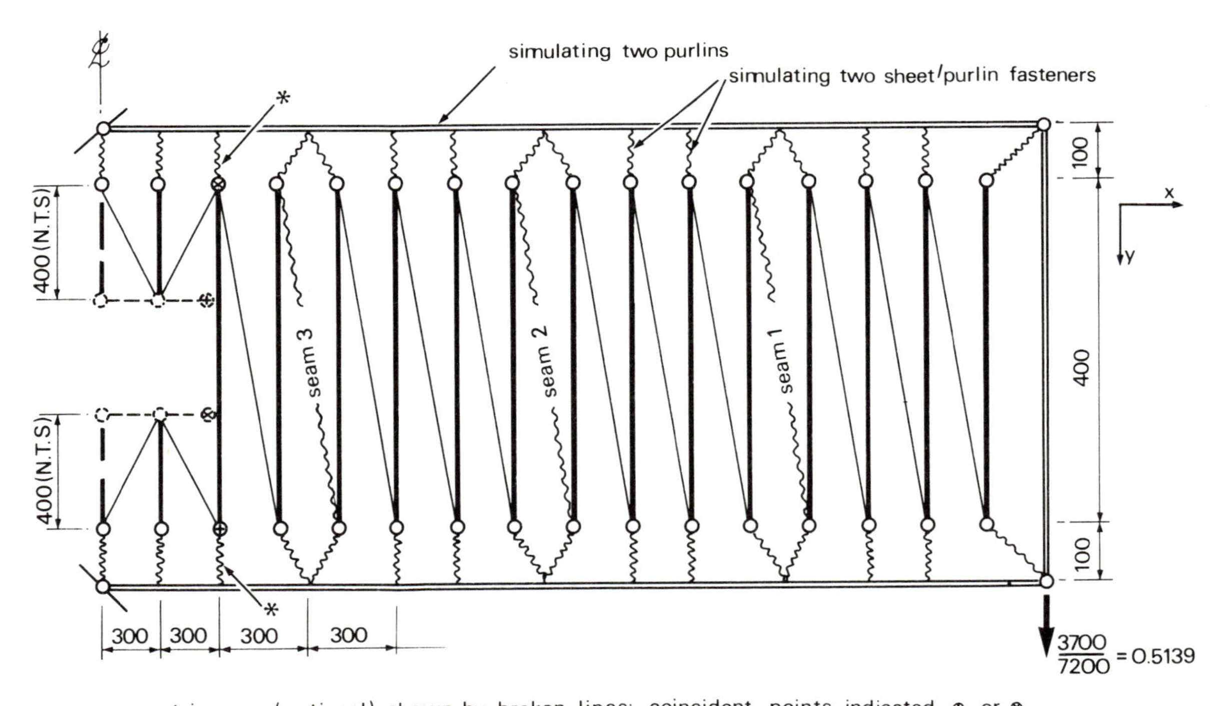

trimmers (optional) shown by broken lines: coincident points indicated ⊕ or ⊗, an increase in the strength and stiffness of the sheet/purlin fasteners indicated * can be used to simulate the extra fasteners to the trimming member parallel to the corrugations: as before, all displacements in the X direction are suppressed.

Fig. 5.14 Simulation of diaphragm with opening.

The way in which an opening is framed may have a significant effect on the local forces in its vicinity and, in the theoretical investigation of the SEAC diaphragms, the opportunity was taken to consider its influence. Two analyses were therefore undertaken; the first was with minimal trimmers simply framing the upper and lower edges of the opening and the second was with full trimmers as shown by broken lines in fig. 5.13. Consequently, the arrangement of trimmers shown in fig. 5.14 (not to scale) may be considered to be optional as the analysis remains valid with or without them. These trimmers are connected to the effectively rigid members which complete the truss, whereas in practice they would be connected to further trimming members running parallel to the corrugations that would in turn be connected to the purlins as shown in fig. 5.13. The sheets at the edges of the opening would be fastened to these further trimming members thus reducing the forces in the sheet to purlin fasteners marked with an asterisk in fig. 5.14. The arrangement shown in which the fasteners marked with an asterisk are given increased stiffness and strength to represent these additional fasteners is considered to be an effective compromise though not a completely accurate representation of the complex effect of a full system of trimmers.

Figure 5.15 shows the comparison of the internal force distributions when the diaphragm is analysed by the full finite element and the approximate truss methods. The comparison includes the distribution along each of the three purlins of the fastener forces normal to that purlin, three distributions of purlin bending moments and the average seam fastener force. Evidently the approximate method results in identical distributions of force and moment along each of the two upper purlins, whereas the finite element analysis reveals minor differences in these distributions. Nevertheless, taken as a whole, the agreement between them is remarkably good and, for practical purposes, the approximate truss analogy is perfectly adequate. The force distributions in fig. 5.15 indicate a number of interesting features typical of diaphragms containing large openings:

(a) Perhaps most important is that at the edge of the opening the minor axis purlin bending moments rise by an order of magnitude compared with the moments present in the absence of an opening. Clearly minor axis bending stresses in the purlins are a significant design consideration and it is important that they should be predicted with reasonable accuracy.
(b) There is a tendency for high local sheet to purlin fastener forces to arise at the edge of the opening. Here they are a little larger than the peak forces at the seams though this is not always the case.
(c) Finally there is a significant increase in the seam fastener and sheet to purlin fastener forces in the seam adjacent to the opening. However, non-linear analysis indicates that this increase is quickly dissipated by redistribution of forces prior to failure so that this effect is not considered significant.

A comparison of deflections is given in table 5.1. It can be seen that the approximate method agrees quite well with the more complete finite element method for the diaphragm with no opening and for the case of minimum trim but less well for the case of full trim. Reference 1.46 states that the experimental flexibility of the

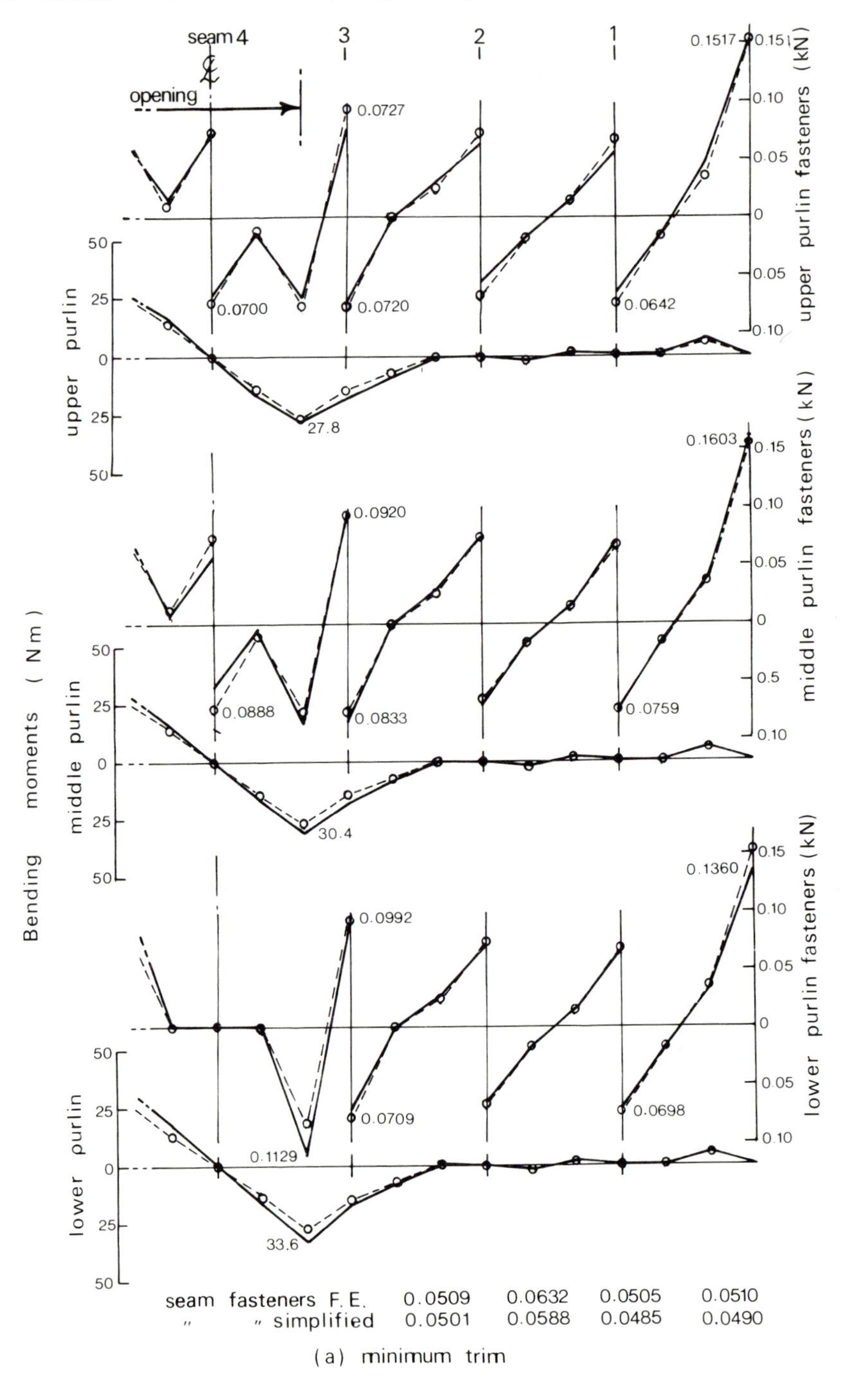

Fig. 5.15 Comparison of analyses of diaphragm with opening: (a) minimum trim,

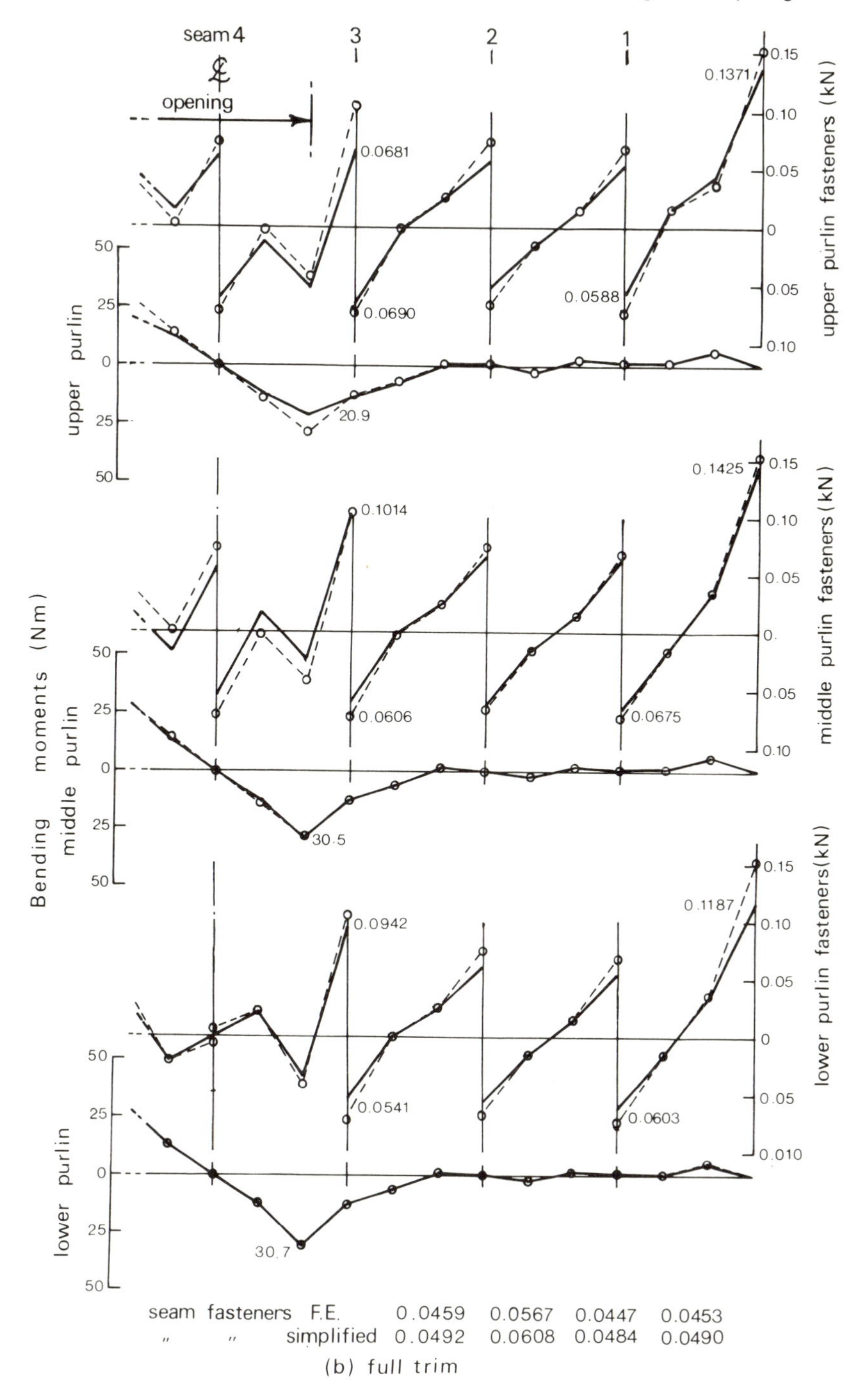
seam 4
3
2
1
opening
0.1371
0.0681
0.0690
0.0588
20.9
0.15
0.10
0.05
0
0.05
0.10
upper purlin fasteners (kN)
50
25
0
25
50
upper purlin
Bending moments (Nm)
0.1425
0.1014
0.0606
0.0675
30.5
middle purlin fasteners (kN)
middle purlin
0.1187
0.0942
0.0541
0.0603
30.7
0.010
lower purlin fasteners (kN)
lower purlin
seam fasteners F.E. 0.0459 0.0567 0.0447 0.0453
" " simplified 0.0492 0.0608 0.0484 0.0490
(b) full trim

(b) full trim.

Table 5.1 Comparison of panel flexibilities (mm/kN)

Diaphragm type	Finite element results	Approximate method
Basic panel – no openings	0.356	0.351
One hole – minimum trim	0.497	0.470
One hole – full trim	0.414	0.465

basic diaphragm with no openings was 0.35 mm/kN which agrees well with the theoretically obtained values. The effect of one opening was stated to be very approximately to increase the shear flexibility by 50%. The theoretical results for minimum trim are broadly in line with this statement. Ultimate loads for the experimental diaphragms are not given as they are considered to be unreliable. Under very high shear loads the diaphragms deflected to such an extent that the test frame exerted a restraint.

5.4 Design by testing

If resort is made to testing, it is essential that light gauge steel diaphragms are tested full size. This makes any experimental work very expensive. Furthermore, tests give only limited information because it is generally only possible to measure loads and deflections. It is not usually possible to obtain meaningful strain gauge readings for such a complex assembly of light gauge steel sections and fasteners. For this reason, testing should be seen as a confirmation of theoretical predictions and therefore primarily as a research tool. In the present state of the art, testing for the purpose of confirming the behaviour of a prototype design should only be undertaken in exceptional circumstances.

Notwithstanding the above comments, design by testing was, for many years, the accepted method in the U.S.A.[1.15] and the appropriate test procedures are well established and documented. There are two acceptable arrangements known as the 'cantilever test' as shown in fig. 5.16 and the simple beam test as shown in fig. 5.17. The beam arrangement is more expensive and cumbersome and has not been used in Europe so that the European recommendations[1.99] only consider the cantilever test. As the presence or absence of the centre bay of the beam test has no effect on the shear strength and shear flexibility, merely affecting the axial forces in the edge members and the corresponding deflections due to axial strain, there seems to be no virtue in making the arrangement more expensive than is absolutely necessary. Hence, further consideration will be confined to the cantilever test.

Figure 5.18 shows a typical cantilever diaphragm test in progress at the University of Salford. The test can be carried out with the load applied either perpendicular or parallel to the direction of span of the sheeting. In either case it is essential that the length in the direction of the corrugations reflects the actual size of the prototype. Ideally the width perpendicular to the corrugations should also be the same as the panel width of the prototype but this is not essential. However, the

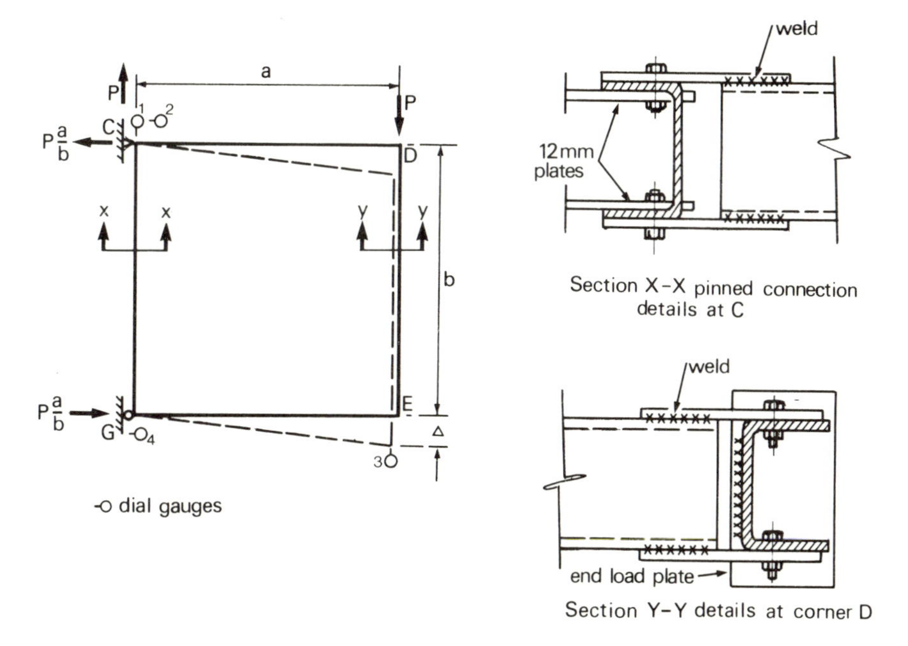

Fig. 5.16 Arrangement for cantilever test.

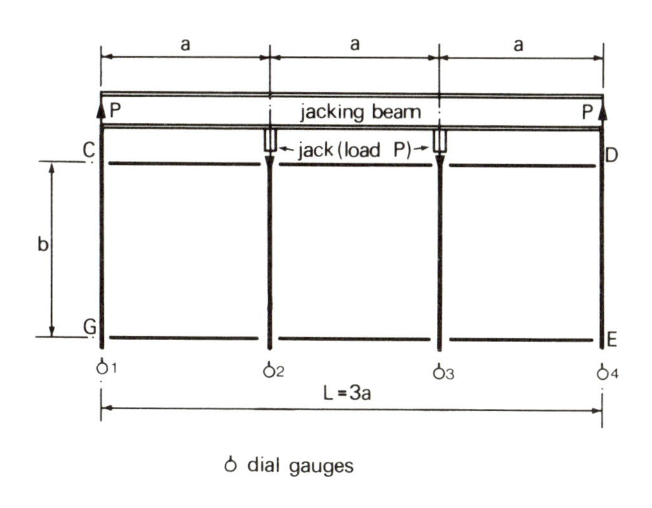

Fig. 5.17 Arrangement for simple beam test.

width of the test panel should not be less than four sheet widths. The cantilever frame in fig. 5.16 has a fixed side CG and a free side DE which must be supported on frictionless rollers. A restraining force may be necessary to prevent uplift at corner E. The corners of the frame require pinned connections and some suitable details taken from the American code are shown in fig. 5.16. It is important that provision

Fig. 5.18 Cantilever diaphragm test in progress.

should be made for measuring the body rotation of the test rig and that allowance should be made for this in interpreting the results. The four dial gauges shown in fig. 5.16 serve this purpose and if they measure displacements δ_1, δ_2, δ_3 and δ_4 respectively, the shear deflection Δ of the diaphragm itself is given by

$$\Delta = \delta_3 - \left[\delta_1 + \frac{a}{b}(\delta_2 - \delta_4)\right] \tag{5.5}$$

The details of the test diaphragm should be representative of the most unfavourable details likely to be adopted in the prototype. In particular it should be noted that, in most constructions, load is applied to the sheeting through rafters or supporting members which are themselves eccentric to the sheeting. The test arrangement should reflect the actual eccentricities of the prototype structure. The shear load is usually applied by means of a hydraulic jack. If testing under combined loading is required (e.g. shear in conjunction with normal load due to wind or snow) the loads normal to the plane of the sheeting may be applied by means of weights (downward load) or by means of jacks or pressure bags (upward load) provided these do not offer any restraint to the shear mode.

Prior to the sheeting being fixed, the test frame should be subjected to a preliminary test up to a deflection well in excess of the value expected during the test in order to verify that it has negligible stiffness. Diaphragms are usually more flexible on the first loading than on subsequent loadings due to 'bedding down' of the fasteners and for this reason it is important not to preload the diaphragm before commencing the formal test. A suitable test procedure is to first load the diaphragm in at least three increments up to the characteristic (working) load, maintaining this load for at least fifteen minutes in order to observe whether any creep occurs. The deflection is measured after each load increment. The diaphragm is then unloaded and the percentage recovery noted. The diaphragm is then loaded to either the full test value or failure in at least six increments. After each increment, the deflections are again measured and an examination made for signs of damage or distress. At the full test value of the load or as the failure load is approached the load increments should be maintained for at least fifteen minutes before the deflections are measured. A more formal set of test procedures together with requirements for recovery are given in the European recommendations for stressed skin design.[1.99]

5.5 Diaphragms with openings

The layout of a typical diaphragm containing significant openings is shown in fig. 5.19. One of the most important effects of an opening or line of openings in the

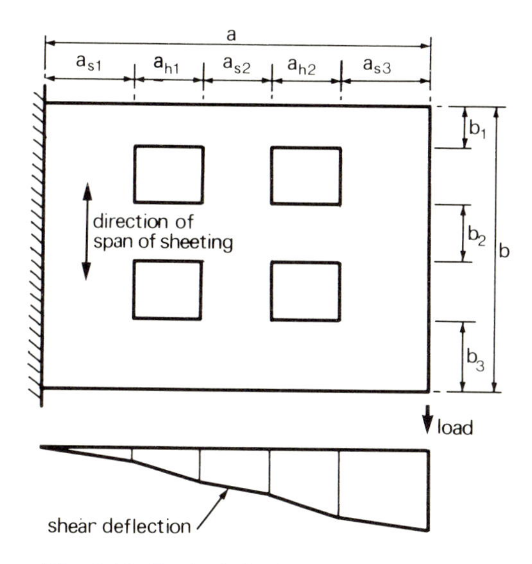

Fig. 5.19 Typical diaphragm with openings.

direction of span of the sheeting is to cause a sudden discontinuity in the shear deflection as shown in the lower part of the figure. This arises not only because an opening removes material but even more important is that it breaks the sheet into shorter lengths. Because the effective shear modulus of profiled steel sheet is proportional to the length measured parallel to the corrugations, short lengths of sheet have considerable shear flexibility. Purlins with relatively low minor axis bending stiffness tend to be constrained to follow this discontinuous profile and significant minor axis bending moments may occur. High local forces in the sheet to purlin fasteners may also be induced and the situation may be further complicated by the tendency of light gauge steel purlins to twist.

Another complication occurs when an opening or openings cuts a seam between adjacent sheet widths. If an opening divides a given length of seam containing uniformly spaced seam fasteners into two unequal lengths the strengths of the two portions are in approximately the same ratio as the lengths. The shear force in the panel will, however, divide itself according to the shear stiffness of the regions above and below the opening and these will be dominated by the stiffness in profile distortion which is proportional to the length squared. Consequently the shear force will not, in general, be divided in the same ratio as the strength and there exists the possibility of premature yield or even failure of the stiffer region.

A single small opening cutting a seam and dividing it into two regions of unequal length could, therefore, have an effect on the strength of the panel with respect to seam failure that is quite disproportionate to the size of the opening. Although in the majority of such cases, the situation will be considerably improved by the favourable redistribution of forces prior to failure, the possibility of a premature failure due to this cause must be considered in any generally applicable design method. This rules out any simple approach based on the percentage area of openings. Some further preliminary consideration of the effect of openings on the internal force distribution has also been given in section 5.3 and it follows that a suitable design approach must give due consideration to the following factors:

(a) Reduction in seam strength due to removal of material and the division into regions of disparate strength and stiffness.
(b) Local high values of purlin minor axis bending moment and sheet to purlin fastener force.
(c) Increase in the shear flexibility of the panel as a whole.

The following procedure is based on the application of these requirements to the design expressions given in chapter 9. It was first given in reference 1.108 where a full justification will be found.

5.5.1 A design procedure for light gauge steel diaphragms with openings

The equations given below are valid provided that the following conditions are satisfied:

(a) Openings occur singly or in bands running parallel to the corrugations.
(b) The opening or band of openings has a total depth which is less than one third of the depth of the diaphragm.
(c) Openings are spaced so that in a direction normal to the corrugations the clear distance between openings or bands of openings is at least equal to the width of the largest adjacent opening.

The arrangement shown in fig. 5.19 satisfies the above conditions provided that: $\Sigma_i\, b_i \geqslant (2b)/3, a_{s1} \geqslant a_{h1}, a_{s2} \geqslant a_{h1}, a_{s2} \geqslant a_{h2}$ and $a_{s3} \geqslant a_{h2}$. These conditions may be considered to represent good practice and should be satisfied wherever possible. They have the effect of producing an absolute limit on the total area of openings of no more than 16.7% of the area of the diaphragms. However, other arrangements of openings may be satisfactory although a comprehensive analysis of the diaphragm will usually be necessary in order to justify the design.

As a general rule, when diaphragms contain openings of significant size, the sheeting should be fastened to the supporting structure through every trough of the corrugations unless the diaphragm is only lightly loaded. Furthermore it should be considered normal good practice to frame large openings on all four sides and to carry the side framing members back to the adjacent purlins or other supporting members. The ends of the corrugations cut by an opening should always be fastened to a framing member, preferably through every trough of the profile.

The method of calculating the strength and stiffness of a diaphragm such as that shown in fig. 5.19 is as follows. The symbols used are those defined in chapter 9 augmented by fig. 5.19.

(a) Calculate the design strength V_{ult} and the flexibility c according to the design expressions given in chapter 9, ignoring the effect of the opening(s).
(b) Assume that the calculated design shear force V_{ult} divides itself between the regions above and below the openings according to the relative distortional stiffness of the sheeting. Thus for a given region j

$$V_j = \frac{c_h}{c_j} V_{ult} = \frac{\bar{K} b_j^2}{\sum_i \bar{K} b_i^2} V_{ult} \tag{5.6}$$

where

$$c_j = \frac{a d^{2.5} \bar{K}}{E t^{2.5} b_j^2} \tag{5.7}$$

Check that whenever seams are cut by openings, each region j has sufficient strength to accommodate the calculated shear force V_j. For this purpose the strength of a region of a seam may be conservatively taken to be

$$V_{j\,ult} = \frac{\beta_1}{\beta_3} n_{pj} F_p + n_{sj} F_s + n_{tj} F_t \tag{5.8}$$

where, within the region considered,

n_{pj} = number of sheet to purlin fasteners which pass through both sheets,
n_{sj} = number of seam fasteners,
n_{tj} = number of fasteners to framing members which pass through both sheets,
F_p = design strength of an individual sheet to purlin fastener,
F_s = design strength of an individual seam fastener,
F_t = design strength of an individual fastener to a framing member,
$\beta_1 \beta_3$ = factors which reflect the influence of the distribution of force in the sheet to purlin fasteners, see table 9.5 and section 9.2.7.

If in any region $V_{j\,ult} < V_j$, V_{ult} should be reduced by multiplying by the smallest value of $V_{j\,ult}/V_j$ found, or alternatively the seams may be strengthened in order to ensure no reduction of strength.

(c) Calculate the factor α_h according to

$$\alpha_h = \frac{1}{a}\sum_j a_{sj} + \frac{1}{a}\sum_k a_{hk}\frac{\bar{K}b^2}{\sum_i \bar{K}b_i^2} \qquad (5.9)$$

where $\Sigma_i \bar{K}b_i^2$ is taken over the sheeted regions within the width a_h of the band of openings. The factor $\bar{K}$ depends on the frequency of fastening at the ends of each individual length of sheet and should therefore reflect the fastening conditions of the diaphragm as a whole or the particular section of sheeting between openings or between an opening and the edge of the diaphragm as appropriate. In a diaphragm which is otherwise fastened to the supporting structure through alternate troughs, fasteners to the framing members which pass through every trough of the profile can have an important beneficial effect.

(d) In the calculation of the flexibility of the complete diaphragm, replace $c_{1.1}$ by $\alpha_h c_{1.1}$ to give an estimate of the flexibility of the diaphragm with openings.

(e) Evaluate the flexibility discontinuity $(c_h - c_s)$ according to the following equation where the quantities must be in consistent units of kN and mm.

$$c_h - c_s = \frac{1000d^{2.5}\bar{K}}{E\,t^{2.5}}\left[\frac{\bar{K}}{\sum_i \bar{K}b_i^2} - \frac{\alpha_1}{b^2}\right]\text{mm/kN/m} \qquad (5.10)$$

(f) Check the maximum minor axis purlin bending moment according to

$$M^{\max} = 0.007\,(c_h - c_s)\,I^{0.75}\ \text{kN mm/kN} \qquad (5.11)$$

where $M^{\max}$ is the maximum minor axis bending moment *per unit shear force* and I is the second moment of area of the purlin about its minor axis (in mm^4). At the calculated design load of the diaphragm this should be within the elastic range. Violation of this condition must be taken as an indication that the diaphragm is too flexible in the vicinity of the opening.

(g) Check the maximum sheet to purlin fastener force according to

$$F_a^{\max} = 0.015\,(c_h - c_s)I^{0.25}\ \text{kN/kN (alternate troughs fastened)}$$

or

$$F_e^{\max} = 0.010\,(c_h - c_s)I^{0.25}\ \text{kN/kN (every trough fastened)} \qquad (5.12)$$

where $F_a^{\max}$ and $F_e^{\max}$ are maximum fastener forces per purlin *per unit shear force.* These equations give the maximum force per purlin in line with the edge of an opening. The total force may be assumed to be taken by the sheet to purlin fasteners together with any fasteners to the framing member. Thus for satisfactory performance under shear force V,

$$n_pF_p + n_tF_t \geqslant V\,n_p\begin{bmatrix} F_a^{\max} \\ & \text{as appropriate} \\ F_e^{\max} \end{bmatrix} \qquad (5.13)$$

where n_t is the number of fasteners to the framing members at or in line with one side of the opening or line of openings under consideration. If this condition is violated, extra sheet to framing member fasteners may be inserted. An example of the use of this design procedure is given in chapter 7.

5.6 Diaphragms subject to in-plane point loads

Two instances of diaphragms subject to in-plane point loads have already been given as fig. 5.2. The first effect of such loads is to increase the shear forces, bending moments and deflections of the diaphragms and account must be taken of these in the usual calculations. The other effect is to induce local concentrations of force in the region of the point load in the form of edge member bending moments and sheet to edge member fastener forces and it is with the prediction of these that this section is concerned. Thus the basic problem is to calculate the local forces in the vicinity of the load P in fig. 5.20.

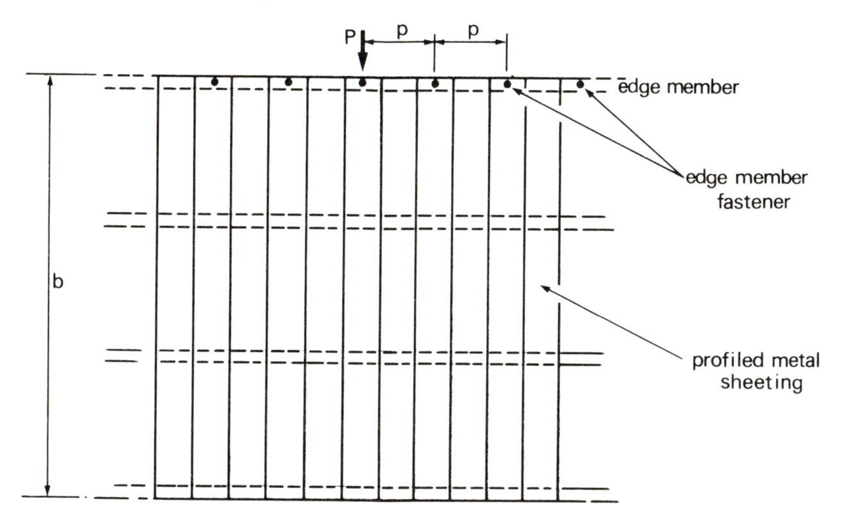

Fig. 5.20 In-plane point load on diaphragm.

In reference 1.109 it is shown that the prediction of the local forces admits of an explicit solution as follows. Comparison with finite element and test results show these expressions to be amply conservative. Maximum fastener force at the point of application of a load P is given by

$$F_{\max} = \frac{P}{4\alpha}\sqrt{\left(\frac{p}{s_p E I}\right)} \tag{5.14}$$

Maximum edge member bending moment in the plane of the diaphragm is given by

$$M_{\max} = \frac{P}{4\alpha}\left[1 + \frac{1}{4btG_{\text{eff}}}\sqrt{\left(\frac{EI}{s_p p}\right)}\right] \tag{5.15}$$

where $$\alpha = \sqrt{\left[\sqrt{\left(\frac{1}{4s_p p\,EI}\right)} + \frac{1}{4s_p pbtG_{\text{eff}}}\right]} \tag{5.16}$$

and where

b = depth of diaphragm in a direction parallel to the corrugations (mm),
EI = flexural rigidity of edge member (kN/mm^2),
G_{eff} = effective shear modulus of sheeting (kN/mm^2) (see section 5.2.1),
p = pitch of edge member fasteners (mm),
s_p = slip (flexibility) per edge member fastener per unit load (mm/kN),
t = net sheet thickness (mm).

If the point load causes tension in the sheet material in the vicinity of the load, the design strength for the most highly loaded fastener is obtained in the usual way and the values tabulated in table 9.9 can be used. If the sheet material is placed in compression as in fig. 5.20 there is the possibility of buckling of the sheet material behind the fastener so that the full fastener strength may not be attained. Figure 5.21 shows the deformation at the conclusion of a simple test to investigate this effect.

Fig. 5.21 Compressive failure of material behind fastener.

A number of tests similar to the one shown in fig. 5.21 indicated that the reduction in the failure load below that for a tension lap specimen was related to the ratio of the width l to the net thickness t of the fastened face and that design strengths adequate for all practical purposes could be obtained by multiplying the usual fastener design strength by the reduction factor given in table 5.2.

Table 5.2 Reduction factors for fastener strength when material behind fastener is in compression

Slenderness of fastened face of sheet (l/t)	Reduction factor for fastener capacity
Less than 80	1.0
100	0.95
120	0.90
140	0.85
160	0.80
180	0.75
200	0.70

Finally, it should be appreciated that the expressions given in equations (5.14) to (5.16) assume that the in-plane point load causing the increased local forces occurs at a position that is also remote from any other point load. If this is not the case a formal analysis may be considered necessary and for this the simplified computer analysis using the truss analogy as described in section 5.3 is an ideal tool.

CHAPTER SIX

Design tables for steel diaphragms

6.1 Introduction

In view of the increasing practical utilisation of light gauge steel diaphragms instead of wind bracing in flat roofed construction there is a demand for suitable design tables whereby the strength and stiffness of a given diaphragm can be easily obtained. Because there are many design parameters in a diaphragm, the construction of design tables involves a number of assumptions which result in tables which are not of universal application but which, nevertheless, can be used in many practical situations. Tables similar to those given in this chapter were originally produced at the request of the Metal Roof Deck Association[1.126] and the choice of design parameters reflects typical British practice in metal roof deck construction. As the design tables were prepared by computer using a specially written program, tables based on alternative parameters can be readily produced as required.

As a consequence of the safe assumptions necessary for the presentation of design data in a generally useful tabular form, the design values obtained will usually be amply conservative. To obtain more exact values, the full design expressions must be used. However, in many instances, a conservative estimate of the diaphragm properties is all that is required and the tables have the additional advantage that their use does not require detailed technical knowledge.

6.2 Arrangements of diaphragms

The tables cover both basic arrangements as shown in plan in fig. 6.1. Within these two basic types of diaphragm there are sub-groupings depending on the fastener arrangements as shown in fig. 6.2. The main alternatives are that individual panels within the diaphragms may be fastened to the supporting structure on four sides (direct shear transfer) or two sides (indirect shear transfer). Direct shear transfer usually involves the provision of 'shear connectors' whereby the decking is fastened

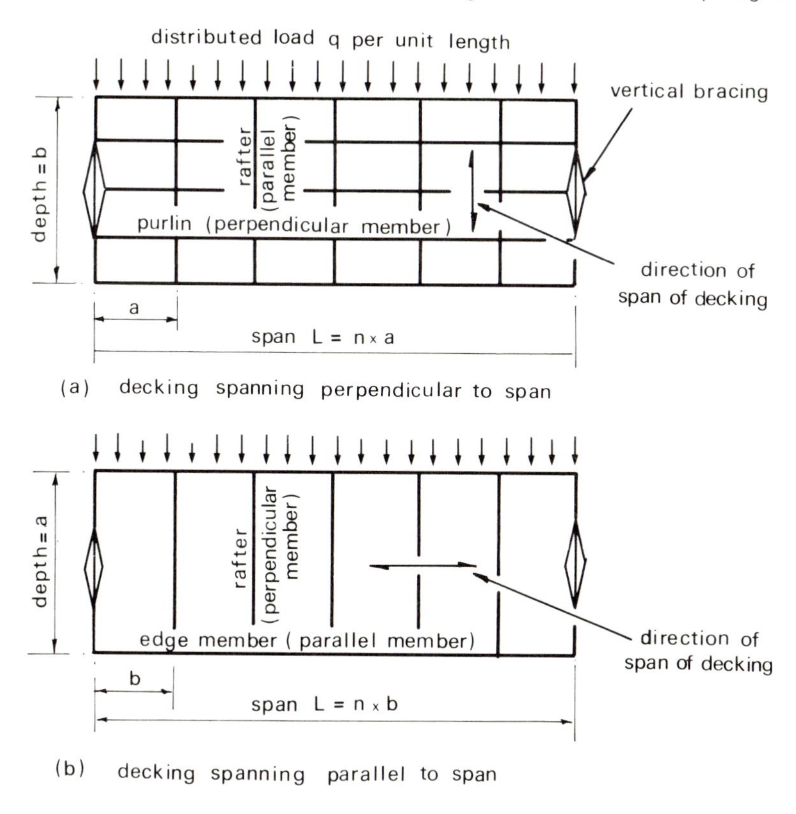

Fig. 6.1 Basic diaphragm arrangements: (a) decking spanning perpendicular to span, (b) decking spanning parallel to span.

directly to the parallel members through short connecting pieces which will usually be purlin off-cuts. In fig. 6.2, case (3), there is a further sub-division depending on whether or not shear connectors are provided at the gables. Gable shear connectors are desirable for efficient utilisation of the load-carrying capacity of the diaphragm but may be omitted in lightly loaded diaphragms.

The stiffness of a diaphragm is greatly influenced by the frequency of fasteners at the sheet ends. Three alternatives are considered. The two main alternatives are that the decking should be fastened to the supporting structure in every corrugation trough (stiffness k_1) or in alternate troughs (stiffness k_2) at the ends of every sheet. The third alternative is to use every trough fixing at the edges of the diaphragm and alternate trough fixing elsewhere (stiffness k_3).

6.3 Design expressions

The design expressions used were taken directly from chapter 9 and a computer program was written to tabulate strengths and stiffnesses for the range of diaphragm types and sizes. The strengths are not calculated explicitly but are given instead in

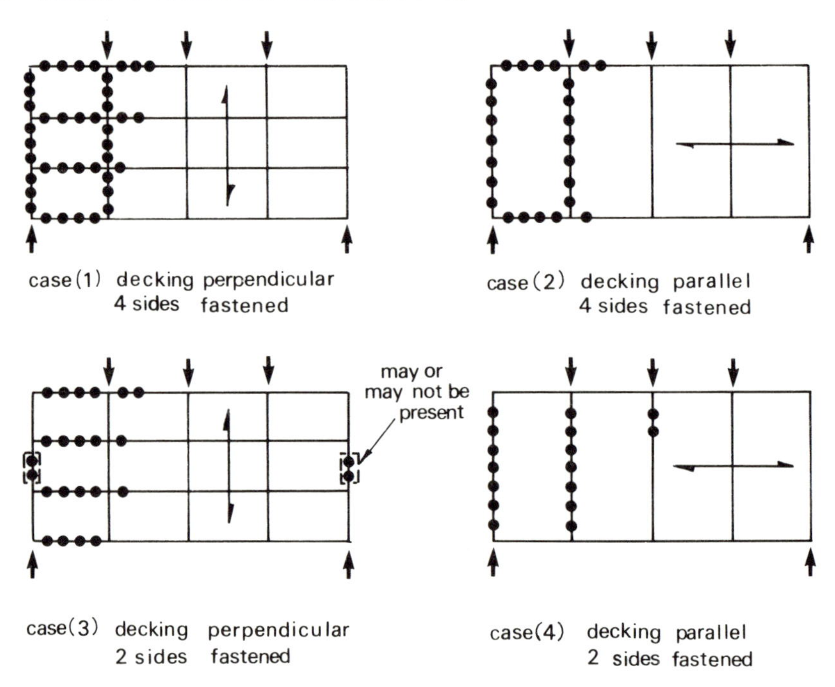

Fig. 6.2 Alternative fastener arrangements: case (1) decking perpendicular, 4 sides fastened, case (2) decking parallel, 4 sides fastened, case (3) decking perpendicular, 2 sides fastened, case (4) decking parallel, 2 sides fastened.

the form of a permissible distributed load per unit length q_{perm} in units of kN/m applied along the edge of the diaphragm as shown in fig. 6.1. This permissible load is derived with a load factor for wind of 1.4. In fig. 6.2, case (3), a further permissible load q_{perm2} is calculated for situations where the gable shear connectors are omitted. The stiffnesses k_1, k_2, k_3 defined above are given in the form of a distributed line load per mm deflection (kN/m/mm) so that the mid-span deflection of a given diaphragm can be obtained by dividing the applied load by the appropriate tabulated stiffness.

6.4 Practical considerations in the preparation of design tables

During the preparation of the design tables a number of practical considerations were discussed. One of these concerned whether or not the contribution to seam strength and stiffness of fasteners connecting two or more sheet thicknesses to the supporting structure should be ignored. One reason for neglecting the influence of these fasteners is because, in a small number of decking profiles used in current practice, the lap dimensions are such that it is difficult to meet the edge distance requirements given in section 2.5 and which are necessary to ensure that they achieve their full strength in shear. This problem is illustrated in fig. 6.3.

A second possible reason for ignoring these fasteners was that a number of

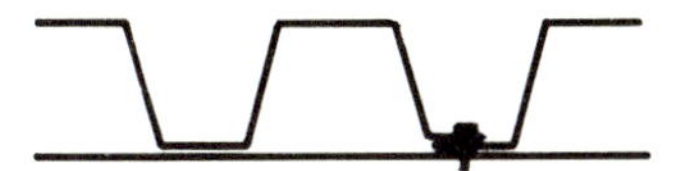

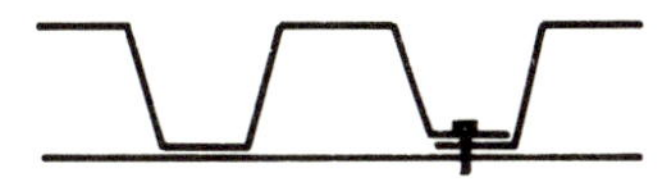

Fig. 6.3 Alternative lap details influencing strength of sheet to supporting member fasteners: (a) fastener has insufficient edge distance, (b) edge distance adequate for full strength.

profiles have an odd number of complete corrugations per sheet width and if these are fastened to the supporting structure through alternate corrugations there is a fastener present at the seam at only half of the supporting members. As the missing sheet to supporting member fasteners are likely to occur in a random pattern, it is difficult to make a rational allowance in the design expressions and it is argued that it is better to omit these fasteners from consideration altogether.

Finally, for the case of sheeting, where the seam fasteners are at the crests of the corrugations, the influence of the sheet to purlin fasteners is relatively small in any case. For these reasons, the design tables given in chapter 9 make the safe assumption that the seam strength and stiffness is dependent only on the strength and stiffness of the seam fasteners. However, as the majority of available decking profiles do provide adequate edge distances for sheet to supporting member fasteners and as many profiles and their fixing specifications do provide for these fasteners at all seams, it is desirable that alternative tables should be available whereby advantage may be taken of the significant contribution made by these fasteners to the seam strength. Accordingly, the computer program can either include or neglect the contribution of these fasteners and alternative design tables are available which include their influence.

A further point made by the Metal Roof Deck Association was that design to the available expressions could be complicated by the use of narrow make-up pieces of metal decking at the ends of diaphragms which did not accommodate an exact number of sheet widths. The effect of such make-up pieces on the design calculations is only of significance in the calculation of the strength for failure in the sheet to supporting member fasteners in the case of diaphragms fastened on two sides only. The relevant expressions for failure at the gables of the structure is

$$q_{\text{perm}2} = \frac{2\beta_2 n_p F_p}{\gamma L} \tag{6.1}$$

where $q_{\text{perm}2}$ = permissible distributed horizontal load on diaphragm,

n_p = number of purlins or supporting members,

F_p = design strength or an individual sheet to supporting member fastener,

γ = load factor for wind,

L = span of diaphragm,

β_2 = numerical factor which takes account of the distribution of sheet to purlin fastener forces along the purlin.

β_2 depends on the number of fasteners to each supporting member per sheet width as given in table 9.5. Evidently, if the possibility of a narrow make-up piece at the critical gable exists, it appears necessary to take $\beta_2 = 1.0$ with a consequent reduction in the permissible load and the Metal Roof Deck Association tables were conservatively prepared on this assumption. Subsequently, in order to investigate this effect further, a number of diaphragms with thin make-up strips were analysed using finite elements.[1.117] It was found that, even with such strips, it was more reasonable to take $\beta_2 = 1.25$ when the fasteners are in every corrugation trough and $\beta_2 = 1.1$ when they pass through alternate troughs.

When the gable shear connectors are provided, failure of the sheet to supporting member fasteners ceases to be critical at the gables but can be critical internally at the rafters. The relevant expression for the permissible load is then

$$q_{\text{perm}} = \frac{\beta_2 n_p F_p}{\gamma a} \tag{6.2}$$

where a is the length of the panel and the other quantities are defined above. Here the strictly correct values of β_2 are 1.0 for fasteners in alternate corrugations and 1.25 for fasteners in every corrugation. However, in the case of fasteners in alternate corrugations, similar considerations to those above apply and it seems more reasonable to take $\beta_2 = 1.1$ for this case as well. Finally, for the fastener specifications adopted, it was found that the influence of the factor β_2 was the sole consideration which caused the strength of a diaphragm with fasteners in every corrugation to be different from that for a diaphragm with fasteners in alternate corrugations. In order to simplify the design tables the logical conclusion was to take $\beta_2 = 1.1$ throughout, accepting the fact that many diaphragms will be oversafe on this basis, and to give only one value of q_{perm} applicable to all diaphragms whether fastened to the supporting members through every or alternate corrugation troughs.

6.5 Parameters for table construction

A typical decking profile of the type shown in fig. 6.4 was assumed. The net steel thickness of 0.65 mm was chosen after enquiries had revealed that over 90% of decks currently constructed in the United Kingdom have a nominal thickness of

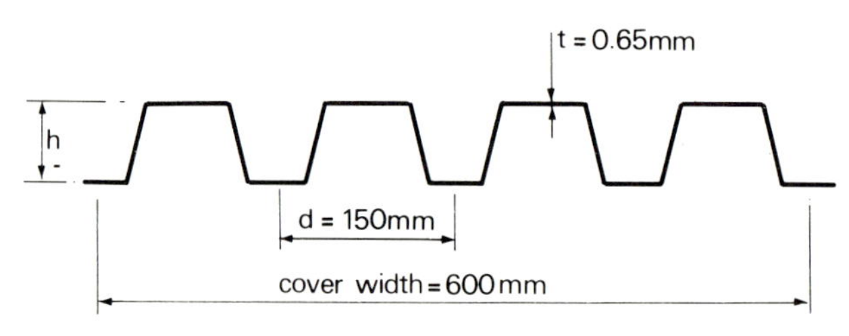

Fig. 6.4 Profile used in table construction.

0.70 mm which gives the above net value after deduction for coatings, etc. If the use of other thicknesses were to increase, there would be no difficulty in producing further tables as necessary. The cover width of 600 mm is a minimum value and the tables are conservative for larger values.

The profile height h is related to the spacing of the supporting members and a range of heights are used in practice. However, in general, the strength of a diaphragm is independent of the height and of the various flexibility components, only those associated with sheet deformation ($c_{1.1}$ and $c_{1.2}$) are influenced by the height. Conservative values for these quantities were obtained by assuming that decking profiles fell into two groups, namely, shallow decking with $h \leqslant 50$ mm and deep decking with $50 < h \leqslant 85$ mm and by basing the calculations on the most flexible profiles within the range of each group. A detailed examination of the profiles used in practice resulted in the choice of the following values for the profile constant $\bar{K}$ which is a fundamental parameter in the expression for the flexibility due to profile distortion ($c_{1.1}$): shallow decking, fasteners in every trough, $\bar{K} = 0.3$; shallow decking, fasteners in alternate troughs, $\bar{K} = 2.0$; deep decking, fasteners in every trough, $\bar{K} = 0.6$; deep decking, fasteners in alternate troughs, $\bar{K} = 5.0$. For the above profile depths, reasonable support members spacings were chosen as follows: shallow decking, supporting members at 3 m centres; deep decking, supporting members at 4.5 m centres. The maximum sheet length is not particularly critical and this was taken as 9 m. Likewise, variations in the length of the individual panels forming the complete diaphragm in the case of decking spanning perpendicular to the span do not have a great effect. It was found that the stiffness of a diaphragm decreases with an increase in the number of panels and therefore relatively small panel lengths with a maximum length of 5 m were used in the calculations. In the case of decking spanning parallel to the span and with two sides only fastened, the support member spacing is important and the design tables will often be very conservative for this case.

The fasteners were assumed to be conventional mechanical types such as self-drilling, self-tapping screws and blind rivets. The appropriate properties were taken to be as follows: sheet to perpendicular member fasteners, design strength = 3.56 kN, flexibility = 0.35 mm/kN; sheet to shear connector fasteners, design strength = 3.56 kN, flexibility = 0.35 mm/kN; seam fasteners, design strength = 1.51 kN, flexibility = 0.35 mm/kN. The fastener specifications were as follows:

(a) For diaphragms attached on four sides: seam fastener spacing = 300 mm; sheet to perpendicular member fastener spacing either 150 mm or 300 mm (either every or alternate troughs); number of sheet to parallel member fasteners (where applicable) = number of perpendicular members + half of the number of seam fasteners. This latter requirement served to ensure that the sheet to parallel member fasteners were always less critical than the seam fasteners.
(b) For diaphragms attached on two sides: seam fastener spacing 450 mm; sheet to perpendicular member fasteners as above; purlin to rafter connections were assumed to be strong enough to resist a load of 9 kN at the level of the top flange and to have a flexibility of 0.5 mm/kN.

Finally, in order to complete the calculation, it is necessary to include the area A

of the edge member which controls the bending component of the total displacement. This area can vary between very wide limits and in order to preserve the conservative basis of the tables, the smallest area likely in practice of 500 mm^2 was used in the calculations. Unfortunately, the bending component of deflection is by no means negligible in many diaphragms and the use of a minimum area can result in considerable overestimation of the deflections in certain instances. Examples of this overestimation are to be found in sections 7.3 and 7.4 where results from the design tables are compared with the full calculation for two specific diaphragms.

6.6 Design tables

The foregoing considerations result in a total of eight tables incorporating all combinations of the following alternatives: decking spanning perpendicular or parallel to the span of the diaphragm, individual panels fastened to the supporting structure on four or two sides and shallow or deep profiles. The resulting tables are given as tables 9.15 to 9.22 inclusive in chapter 9. In each case the tables give the permissible load q_{perm} and the alternative stiffnesses k_1, k_2, and k_3 in kN/m/mm as described in section 6.3. When the correct table has been found, the value of q_{perm} (or q_{perm2}, if appropriate) should be read off for the appropriate depth and span. This gives the permissible distributed load considering strength of the diaphragm. Then, depending on the fastener arrangement at the sheet ends, the appropriate value of k_1, k_2, or k_3 should be read off. If the permissible in-plane deflection of the diaphragm is Δ_{max}, the permissible distributed load considering stiffness of the diaphragm is $k_1 \Delta_{max}$, $k_2 \Delta_{max}$ or $k_3 \Delta_{max}$ as appropriate. This value may be modified for the effects of insulation or openings as specified in clauses 2.12 and 6.7. The design criterion is then the smaller value of the permissible distributed load obtained after considering both strength and stiffness.

6.7 Approximate treatment of openings

Small randomly arranged openings totalling not more than 2% of the area of an individual panel may be ignored for the purpose of calculating diaphragm strength and stiffness. In conjunction with the design tables, an approximate treatment of the strength and stiffness of diaphragms containing more than 2% of openings may be used. The following requirements must be met:

(a) Openings must be bounded on all four sides by steel trimmers. These trimmers must be attached to the supporting structure.
(b) The decking must be fixed in every trough to opening trimmers running perpendicular to the span of the decking.
(c) In the direction perpendicular to the span of the decking, the uninterrupted width of sheeting on either side of an opening shall be equal to or greater than the width of the opening.
(d) In the direction parallel to the span of the decking, the total depth of the openings shall not exceed 25% of the depth of the diaphragm.

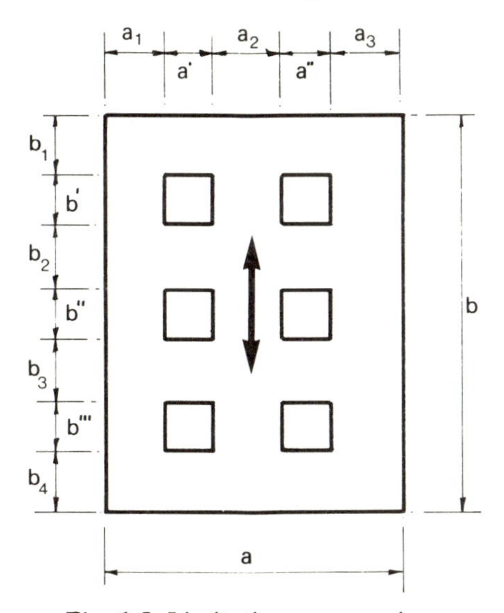

Fig. 6.5 Limitations on openings.

The above requirements are illustrated in fig. 6.5. Requirement (c) means that a_1 and a_2 must be greater than a' and a_2 and a_3 must be greater than a''. The total width of the opening must therefore be less than one half of the width of the panel. Requirement (d) states that $b' + b'' + b'''$ must be less than $b/4$. Hence requirements (c) and (d) together necessitate that the total area of the openings in any one panel must be less than $12\frac{1}{2}\%$ of the area of the panel. Strip openings, as shown in fig. 6.6, need not comply with the above requirements and can be conservatively treated by assuming the effective depth of the diaphragm to be the larger of the values b_1 and b_2.

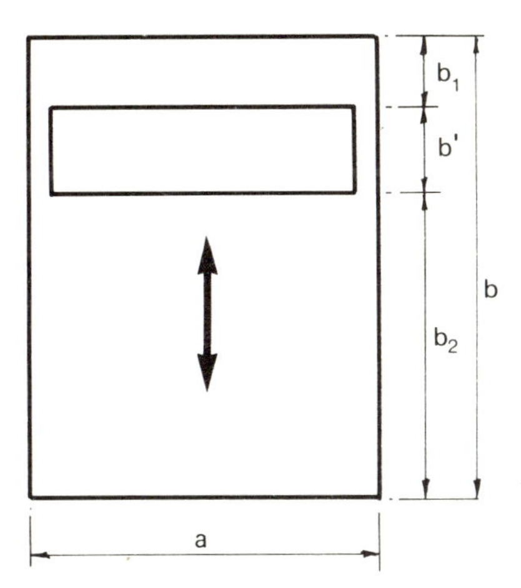

Fig. 6.6 Strip openings.

Openings which comply with the above requirements cause a reduction in the strength and stiffness of a diaphragm which may be conservatively estimated as follows:

6.7.1 Strength of diaphragms with openings

Openings divide the depth of a diaphragm into two or more portions. The seam strength of each separate portion is approximately proportional to its depth but the stiffness is approximately proportional to the depth squared. Hence, in general, the load attracted to each portion will not be in proportion to its strength. To take account of this, the tabulated permissible distributed load q_{perm} on a diaphragm with openings should be multiplied by a factor α which is the smallest value of α_i (see equation 6.3) which is obtained when all portions of decking are considered. Thus the reduction is calculated on the basis of a seam failure which is the mode of failure for diaphragms fastened on four sides. It may be conservative for diaphragms fastened on two sides when other failure modes are likely.

The general expression for α_i is (fig. 6.5)

$$\alpha_i = \frac{\beta_1 b_1{}^2 + \beta_2 b_2{}^2 + \ldots + \beta_n b_n{}^2}{b\,\beta_i b_i} \tag{6.3}$$

The factor β_i has the following values:

(a) If the decking is fastened in every trough, $\beta_i = 1.0$
(b) If the decking is fastened in alternate troughs, then
 (i) if the portion i under consideration is adjacent to the top or bottom edge of the panel (b_1 or b_4 in fig. 6.5), $\beta_i = 1.0$
 (ii) if the portion i is internal (b_2 or b_3 in the figure) $\beta_i = 3.3$ for shallow decking ($h \leqslant 50$ mm) or $\beta_i = 4.2$ for deep decking ($50 < h \leqslant 85$ mm).

It may be noted that within the restrictions operative on the approximate design method, the strength of a diaphragm may be reduced by up to 50%. An amply conservative rule is to double the number of seam fasteners in any seam interrupted by an opening in order to ensure that there is no reduction in strength. Alternatively, openings may be precluded from the end 25% of the span.

6.7.2 Stiffness of diaphragms with openings

The effect of openings is to cause a reduction in the stiffness of a diaphragm which may be conservatively estimated as follows: for shallow decking ($h \leqslant 50$ mm), k_1 is reduced by (4 times percentage area of openings)%, k_2 and k_3 are reduced by ($2\frac{1}{2}$ times percentage area of openings)%; for deep decking ($50 < h \leqslant 85$ mm), k_1 is reduced by (5 times percentage area of openings)%, k_2 and k_3 are reduced by (2 times percentage area of openings)%. In each case the percentage area of openings refers to the ratio of (area of opening) to (total area of panel).

The above percentage reductions in k_1, k_2 and k_3 are for openings in all panels of a diaphragm. If openings occur only in some panels, the percentage reduction is multiplied by the ratio (sum of the shear forces in panels with openings/sum of the shear forces in all panels) considered over half the span of the diaphragm.

6.8 Cantilevered diaphragms

Tables 9.15 to 9.22 are set out for diaphragms spanning between two lines of bracing as shown in fig. 6.1. They may nevertheless be used for cantilevered diaphragms as shown in fig. 6.7 in which case the tables should be entered for a span equal to twice that of the cantilevered span. It should be noted that provision must also be made to resist the edge member forces P shown in fig. 6.7.

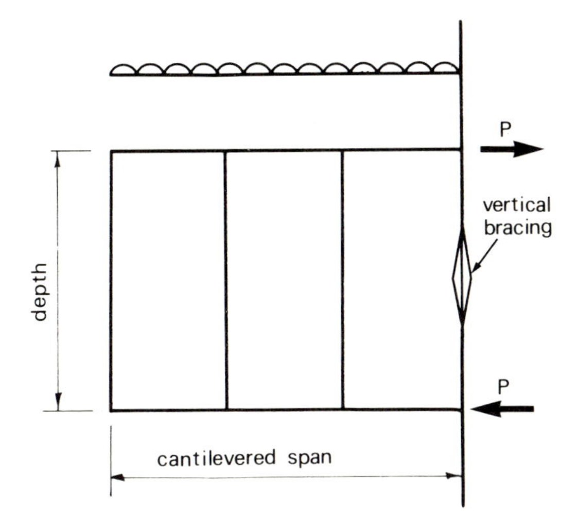

Fig. 6.7 Cantilevered diaphragm.

CHAPTER SEVEN

Design examples

7.1 Cantilevered diaphragm fastened on four sides, sheeting perpendicular to span of diaphragm

Figure 7.1 shows details of a panel which was tested for demonstration purposes at the University of Salford on a number of occasions with remarkably consistent results. The properties of this panel will be calculated in detail according to the design expressions and compared with the experimental results.

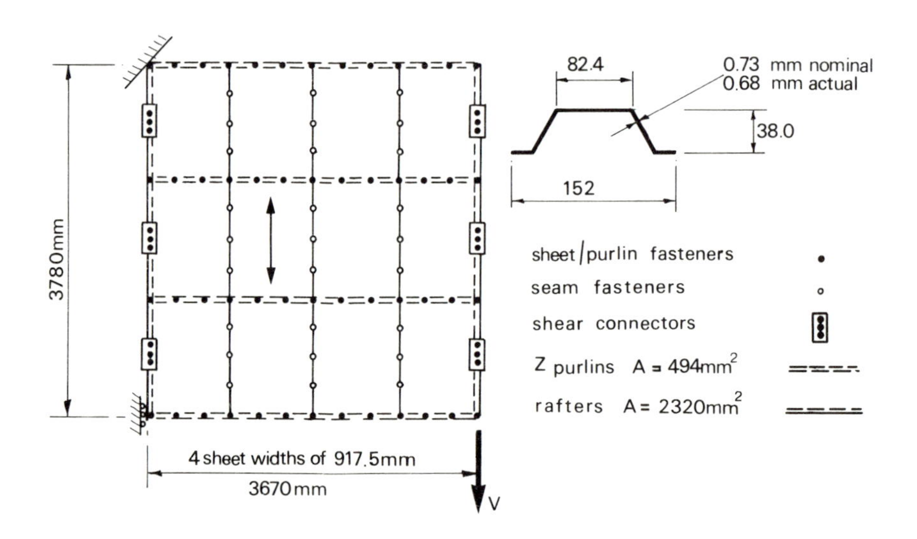

Fig. 7.1 Dimensions and details of panel A2 (alternate corrugations fastened).

7.1.1 Calculation of strength according to section 9.3

It should be noted that the fastener strengths used in the calculations are characteristic strengths based on fastener tests carried out at the same time as the diaphragm tests. They are the average value less about twice the standard deviation of the test results. These characteristic strengths are then further reduced by dividing by the material factor $\gamma_m = 1.11 = 1/0.9$. It follows that the calculated strength of a given diaphragm is always conservative and will usually be exceeded by the test results.

(a) Seam strength

n_f = number of sheet to purlin fasteners per member per sheet width = 4 fixed as decking with seams in troughs $\therefore \beta_1 = 1.04$ (table 9.5) and $\beta_3 = 1.0$ (note 9.2.8)

n_p = total number of purlins = 4

n_s = number of seam fasteners per side lap = 9

F_p = design strength of an individual sheet to purlin fastener = 0.9 × 4.03 = 3.63 kN

F_s = design strength of an individual seam fastener = 0.9 × 1.48 = 1.33 kN

$\therefore V_{ult} = n_s F_s + (\beta_1/\beta_3) n_p F_p = (9 \times 1.33) + (1.04 \times 4 \times 3.63) = 27.08$ kN

(b) Strength of fasteners to shear connectors

Note each individual shear connector shown in fig. 7.1 incorporates 3 fasteners with the same properties as the sheet to purlin fasteners.

n_{sc} = total number of sheet to shear connector fasteners per rafter = 9

F_{sc} = design strength of an individual sheet to shear connector fastener = 0.9 × 4.03 = 3.63 kN

$\therefore V_{ult} = n_{sc} F_{sc} = 9 \times 3.63 = 32.67$ kN

(c) Calculated design shear capacity V^*

The minimum of the above values of V_{ult} is 27.1 kN which gives the design strength of the diaphragm. The predicted failure mode is a seam failure. Thus $V^* = 27.1$ kN.

(d) General requirement for shear buckling

b = depth of diaphragm = 3780 mm

d = pitch of corrugations = 152 mm

E = modulus of elasticity = 207 kN/mm^2

t = net sheet thickness = 0.68 mm (0.73 mm minus coatings)

u = perimeter length = 192.7 mm

I_y = second moment of area of a single corrugation = 27 240 mm^4

ν = Poisson's ratio = 0.3

The requirement is that $(14.4/b) D_x^{\frac{1}{4}} D_y^{\frac{3}{4}} (n_p - 1)^2 \geqslant V^*$

$$D_x = \frac{Et^3 d}{12(1-\nu^2)u} = \frac{207 \times 0.68^3 \times 152}{12 \times 0.91 \times 192.7} = 4.70 \text{ kN mm}^2/\text{mm}$$

$$D_y = \frac{E I_y}{d} = \frac{207 \times 27\,240}{152} = 37\,100 \text{ kN mm}^2/\text{mm}$$

$\therefore (14.4/b) D_x^{\frac{1}{4}} D_y^{\frac{3}{4}} (n_p - 1)^2 = (14.4/3780) \times 4.70^{\frac{1}{4}} \times 37\,100^{\frac{3}{4}} \times 3^2 = 135.0$ kN

As this is greater than $V^* = 27.1$ kN, the requirement is satisfied.

(e) General requirement for sheet to purlin fasteners
p = pitch of sheet to purlin fasteners = 304 mm
The requirement is that $0.8\ bF_p/p \geqslant V^*$

$$\therefore \frac{0.8\ bF_p}{p} = \frac{0.8 \times 3780 \times 3.63}{304} = 36.1 \text{ kN}$$

As this is greater than $V^* = 27.1$, the requirement is satisfied.
(f) Maximum axial force in edge purlin
The value of this force is $V^*a/b = (27.1 \times 3670)/3780 = 26.3$ kN.
It can be shown that this is well within the capacity of the purlins used.

7.1.2 Calculation of flexibility according to section 9.3

It is first necessary to determine the sheeting constant for distortional flexibility $\bar{K}_2$ for the profile used (fastened in alternate troughs).
d = pitch of corrugations = 152.0 mm
h = height of profile = 38.0 mm
l = width of crest = 82.4 mm
θ = inclination of web to vertical = 30°
$\therefore h/d = 0.250$, $l/d = 0.542$; from table 9.7, $\bar{K}_2 = 1.49$

(a) Flexibility due to profile distortion
a = length of diaphragm = 3670 mm
b = depth of diaphragm = 3780 mm
E = modulus of elasticity = 207 kN/mm^2
t = net sheet thickness = 0.68 mm
α_1 = 0.85 (single sheet length, fasteners in alternate corrugations throughout. Hence use table 9.1, case (2) and table 9.3)
α_4 = 1.0

$$c_{1.1} = \frac{a\, d^{2.5}\, \alpha_1\, \alpha_4\, \bar{K}_2}{E\, t^{2.5}\, b^2} = \frac{3670 \times 152^{2.5} \times 0.85 \times 1.0 \times 1.49}{207 \times 0.68^{2.5} \times 3780^2} = 1.1740 \text{ mm/kN}$$

(b) Flexibility due to shear strain
ν = Poisson's ratio = 0.3

$$c_{1.2} = \frac{2a\,(1+\nu)\,[1+(2h/d)]}{E\,t\,b} = \frac{2 \times 3670 \times 1.3 \times [1 + (2 \times 38.0/152.0)]}{207 \times 0.68 \times 3780}$$

$$= 0.0269 \text{ mm/kN}$$

(c) Flexibility due to deformation in sheet to purlin fasteners
p = pitch of sheet to purlin fasteners = 304 mm
s_p = slip per sheet to purlin fastener per unit load = 0.2 mm/kN

$$c_{2.1} = \frac{2a\, s_p\, p}{b^2} = \frac{2 \times 3670 \times 0.2 \times 304}{3780^2} = 0.0312 \text{ mm/kN}$$

(d) Flexibility due to deformation in seam fasteners

n_f = number of sheet to purlin fasteners per member per sheet width = 4 fixed as decking with seams in troughs ∴ β_1 = 1.04 (table 9.5)

n_p = total number of purlins = 4

n_s = number of seam fasteners per sidelap = 9

n_{sh} = number of sheet widths in panel = 4

s_s = slip per seam fastener per unit load = 0.25 mm/kN

$$c_{2.2} = \frac{2\, s_s\, s_p\, (n_{sh} - 1)}{2n_s\, s_p + \beta_1\, n_p\, s_s} = \frac{2 \times 0.25 \times 0.2 \times 3}{(2 \times 9 \times 0.2) + (1.04 \times 4 \times 0.25)} = 0.0647 \text{ mm/kN}$$

(e) Flexibility in connections to rafters (shear connectors)

n_{sc} = total number of sheet to shear connector fasteners per rafter = 9

s_{sc} = slip per sheet to shear connector fastener per unit load = 0.20 mm/kN

$$c_{2.3} = \frac{2\, s_{sc}}{n_{sc}} = \frac{2 \times 0.20}{9} = 0.0444 \text{ mm/kN}$$

(f) Equivalent shear flexibility due to axial strain in purlins

A = cross-sectional area of purlin = 494 mm^2

$$c_3 = \frac{2a^3}{3EAb^2} = \frac{2 \times 3670^3}{3 \times 207 \times 494 \times 3780^2} = 0.0226 \text{ mm/kN}$$

(g) Total shear flexibility

$$c = c_{1.1} + c_{1.2} + c_{2.1} + c_{2.2} + c_{2.3} + c_3$$
$$= 1.1740 + 0.0269 + 0.0312 + 0.0647 + 0.0444 + 0.0226$$
$$= 1.364 \text{ mm/kN}$$

7.1.3 Comparison with test results

The values of strength and stiffness obtained above are compared with the corresponding experimental values in table 7.1. To complete the comparison, the relevant values from a comprehensive finite element analysis are also included. The calculated strength values reflect the conservative statistical treatment of fastener strength and the material factor of 1.11. Calculated strengths will always err on the safe side for this reason. It will also be noted that the calculated flexibility is significantly greater than the observed flexibility. This seems to be typically the case in the relatively small diaphragms that are amenable to test when the diaphragms are

Table 7.1 Calculated and observed behaviour of diaphragm A_2

	Strength (kN)		Flexibility (mm/kN)
Calculated values	27.1		1.364
Finite element analysis	yield	15.0	1.343
	approx. ult.	26.7	
Test results	34		0.93

fastened to the edge purlins in alternate corrugations. The error is on the safe side and is due to conservative assumptions in the derivation of the expression for $c_{1.1}$ as well as effects associated with the relatively small size of the test rig.

Similar problems do not exist in the case of diaphragms fastened in every corrugation. In the corresponding test on diaphragm A_1 which was similar in all respects to the diaphragm described above except that the number of sheet to purlin fasteners was increased to provide fastening in every trough, the comparison of flexibility values is as given in table 7.2. As this diaphragm was not tested to failure, no strength values are given.

Table 7.2 Calculated and observed behaviour of diaphragm A_1

	Flexibility (mm/kN)
Calculated value	0.253
Finite element analysis	0.260
Test results	0.256

7.2 Welded cantilever diaphragm fastened on four sides, sheeting parallel to span of diaphragm

Figure 7.2 shows details of a 10 ft. × 12 ft. (3.05 m × 3.66 m) welded diaphragm which was tested and analysed by Nilson[1.58] in the U.S.A. The properties of the panel will again be calculated and compared with experimental and finite element results.

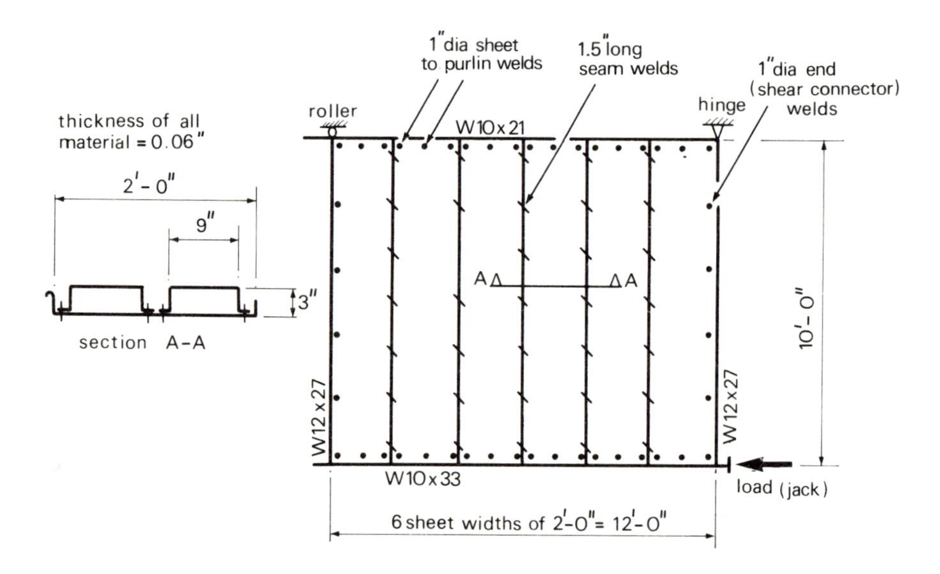

Fig. 7.2 Dimensions and details of 10 ft. × 12 ft. welded diaphragm tested by Nilson.

7.2.1 Calculation of strength according to section 9.4

As this diaphragm was constructed with imperial dimensions and Nilson's calculations are given in imperial units, it is convenient here also to work in imperial rather than S.I. units while giving the significant results in dual units.

(a) Weld strength
The sheet to purlin and the equivalent of the shear connector welds were 1 in. (25 mm) diameter puddle welds. Nilson does not give the ultimate strength of the sheeting used but for the purpose of this exercise it will be assumed to have been 50 kip/in.^{2} (0.345 kN/mm^2). The theoretical weld strength is then derived from table 9.11 as follows:
effective weld diameter $d_e = d_w - t = 1.0 - 0.06 = 0.94$ in.
$d_e/t = 0.94/0.06 = 15.67$; $11.6/\sqrt{\sigma_u} = 19.80$
$\therefore d_e/t < 11.6/\sqrt{\sigma_u}$ and the revelant expression for the characteristic strength is

$F'_p = 1.4\ t\ d_e \sigma_u = 1.4 \times 0.06 \times 0.94 \times 50 = 3.95$ kip (17.6 kN)

and the corresponding design strength is

$F_p = 0.9 \times 3.95 = 3.55$ kip (15.8 kN)

Similarly, the seam welds were $1\frac{1}{2}$ in. (38 mm) long and the relevant characteristic strength F'_s is calculated as

$F'_s = 0.55\ L_w t\ \sigma_u = 0.55 \times 1.5 \times 0.06 \times 50 = 2.48$ kip (11.0 kN)

and the corresponding design strength is

$F_s = 0.9 \times 2.48 = 2.23$ kip (9.9 kN)

(b) Seam strength

a = length of diaphragm in the direction perpendicular to the corrugations = 144 in.
b = length of diaphragm in the direction parallel to the corrugations = 120 in.
n_f = number of sheet to purlin fasteners per member per sheet width = 3 fixed as decking with seams in the troughs $\therefore \beta_1 = 1.0$ (table 9.5) and $\beta_3 = 1.0$ (note 9.2.8)
n_p = total number of purlins = 2
n_s = number of seam fasteners per sidelap = 7

$\therefore V_{ult} = (a/b)[n_s F_s + (\beta_1/\beta_3) n_p F_p] = (144/120)[(7 \times 2.23) + (2 \times 3.55)] = 27.3$ kip (121 kN)

(c) Strength in fasteners to shear connectors

n_{sc} = total number of shear connectors per rafter = 6

Note Strictly, in fig. 7.2, there are only 4 shear connector fasteners. However, in this particular case, the test rig allowed negligible flexibility in the purlin to rafter connections so that the end sheet to purlin fasteners were carrying effectively the same load as the shear connector fasteners and it is more correct to take $n_{sc} = 6$. The details of the shear connector fastener are not given by Nilson but as it appears that these were also 1 in diameter puddle welds, the same design value as for the sheet to purlin fasteners has been adopted, namely $F_{sc} = 3.55$ kip.

$V_{ult} = (a/b)(n_{sc} F_{sc}) = (144/120)(6 \times 3.55) = 25.6$ kip (114 kN)

(d) Calculated design shear capacity V^*

The minimum of the above calculated values of V_{ult} is the design shear capacity, $V^* = 25.6$ kip (114 kN).

(e) General requirement for shear buckling
d = pitch of corrugations = 12 in.
E = modulus of elasticity = 30 000 kip/in^2
t = net sheet thickness = 0.06 in.
u = perimeter length = 12 in.
(conservatively neglecting the stiffening effect of the welded hat section for bending about an axis parallel to the corrugations)
I_y = second moment of area of a single corrugation = 3.06 in.^{4}
ν = Poisson's ratio = 0.3
The requirement is that $(14.4/b^2)a\, D_x^{\frac{1}{4}}\, D_y^{\frac{3}{4}}\,(n_p - 1)^2 \geqslant V^*$

$$\therefore D_x = \frac{E\,t^3\,d}{12(1-\nu^2)u} = \frac{30\,000 \times 0.06^3 \times 12}{12 \times 0.91 \times 12} = 0.5934 \text{ kip in.}^2/\text{in.}$$

$$D_y = E\,I_y/d = (30\,000 \times 3.06)/12 = 7650 \text{ kip in.}^2/\text{in.}$$

$$\therefore (14.4\ a/b^2)\ D_x^{\frac{1}{4}}\ D_y^{\frac{3}{4}}\ (n_p - 1)^2 = (14.4 \times 144/120^2) \times 0.5934^{\frac{1}{4}} \times 7650^{\frac{3}{4}} \times 1$$
$$= 103.4 \text{ kip (460 kN)}$$

As this is greater than $V^* = 25.6$ kip, the requirement is satisfied.
(f) General requirement for sheet to purlin fasteners
p = pitch of sheet to purlin fasteners = 12 in.
The requirement is that $(0.8\,aF_p)/p \geqslant V^*$

$$\therefore \frac{0.8\,a\,F_p}{p} = \frac{0.8 \times 144 \times 3.55}{12} = 34.1 \text{ kip (152 kN)}$$

As this is greater than $V^* = 25.6$ kip, the requirement is satisfied.
(g) Maximum axial force in edge members
The maximum force in the edge members parallel to the direction of span is $V^*b/a = (25.6 \times 120)/144 = 21.3$ kip (95 kN) and in the edge members running perpendicular to the direction of span is $V^* = 25.6$ kip (114 kN). As heavy perimeter members were provided in the test rig, these forces are not significant.

7.2.2 Calculation of the flexibility according to section 9.4

(a) Flexibility due to profile distortion
For the built up section shown in fig. 7.2 there is no distortion of the profile. The shear is taken entirely in the lower plate and the welded hat section serves only to stiffen the section against shear buckling.
(b) Flexibility due to shear strain
a = length of diaphragm in the direction perpendicular to the corrugations = 144 in.
b = depth of diaphragm in the direction parallel to the corrugations = 120 in.
E = modulus of elasticity = 30 000 kip/in.^{2}
t = net sheet thickness = 0.06 in.
ν = Poisson's ratio = 0.3

$$c_{1.2} = \frac{2a\,(1+\nu)}{E\,t\,b} = \frac{2 \times 144 \times 1.3}{30\,000 \times 0.06 \times 120} = 0.001\,733 \text{ in./kip}$$

(c) Flexibility due to deformation in sheet to purlin fasteners

p = pitch of sheet to purlin fasteners = 8 in. (3 per 2′0″ panel)

s_p = slip per sheet to purlin fastener per unit load = 0.001 in./kip

Note The above value of s_p is given by Nilson. In diaphragms constructed of profiled steel sheet where there is significant distortional flexibility, the influence of movement in the welds can reasonably be ignored. Here the diaphragm is extremely stiff and if a reasonably accurate estimate of the flexibility is required it is necessary to include an allowance, albeit approximate, for flexibility in the welded connections.

$$c_{2.1} = \frac{2as_pp}{b^2} = \frac{2 \times 144 \times 0.001 \times 8}{120^2} = 0.000\,160 \text{ in./kip}$$

(d) Flexibility due to deformation in seam fasteners

n_f = number of sheet to purlin fasteners per member per sheet width = 3 fixed as decking with seams in troughs ∴ $\beta_1 = 1.0$ (table 9.5)

n_p = total number of purlins = 2

n_s = number of seam fasteners per sidelap = 7

n_{sh} = number of sheet widths per panel = 6

s_s = slip per seam fastener per unit load = 0.002 in./kip

Note The above value of s_s is given by Nilson. The remarks noted above with respect to s_p apply here also.

$$c_{2.2} = \frac{2\, s_s\, s_p\, (n_{sh} - 1)}{2\, n_s\, s_p + \beta_1\, n_p s_s} = \frac{2 \times 0.002 \times 0.001 \times 5}{(2 \times 7 \times 0.001) + (1.0 \times 2 \times 0.002)}$$

$$= 0.001\,111 \text{ in./kip}$$

(e) Flexibility in connections to rafters (shear connectors)

n_{sc} = total number of shear connectors per rafter = 6

s_{sc} = slip per sheet to shear connector fastener per unit load = 0.001 25 in./kip

$\therefore c_{2.3} = (2\, s_{sc})/n_{sc} = (2 \times 0.001\,25)/6 = 0.000\,417$ in./kip

(f) Total flexibility in true shear

$$c' = (b^2/a^2)(c_{1.1} + c_{1.2} + c_{2.1} + c_{2.2} + c_{2.3})$$
$$= (120^2/144^2)(0 + 0.001\,733 + 0.000\,160 + 0.001\,111 + 0.000\,417)$$
$$= 0.002\,376 \text{ in./kip}$$

(g) Equivalent shear flexibility due to axial strain in edge members

A = cross-sectional area of edge members = 7.97 in.^{2}

$$c_3 = \frac{2b^3}{3EAa^2} = \frac{2 \times 120^3}{3 \times 30\,000 \times 7.97 \times 144^2} = 0.000\,232 \text{ in./kip}$$

(h) Total shear flexibility

$$c = c' + c_3 = 0.002\,376 + 0.000\,232 = 0.002\,608 \text{ in./kip}$$

7.2.3 Comparison with test results

The values of strength and stiffness obtained above are compared with the corresponding experimental and finite element values in table 7.3. The calculated strength

Table 7.3 Calculated and observed behaviour of welded diaphragm

	Strength (kip)		Flexibility (in/kip)
Calculated values		25.6	0.0026
Finite element analysis	yield	17.5	0.0033
	approx. ult.	27.0	
Test results		38.6	0.0033

values again reflect the conservative treatment of fastener strength and the material factor of 1.11. As a consequence of the use of a box profile and welded connections, the flexibility is extremely small. This means that secondary effects play a more important role and the accurate prediction of deflection by an approximate analysis is not easy. This is reflected in the values in the above table. However, as the flexibility is so small it is not so important to predict it accurately and the value calculated above is adequate for all practical purposes.

7.3 Flat-roofed building with pinned frames, sheeting spanning perpendicular to span of diaphragm (including the effect of significant openings)

The building shown in fig. 7.3 is assumed to be situated in Coventry. The roof sheeting is fixed as decking with seams in the troughs and is delivered in double-span lengths. There are shear connectors to all rafters so that each diaphragm is fastened on four sides. The following calculations will be carried out:

(a) Calculation of the wind load on the diaphragm.
(b) Check whether the strength of the diaphragm is adequate.
(c) Determination of the maximum deflection.
(d) Comparison with approximate values given by design tables.
(e) Investigation of the effect of significant openings.
(f) Check whether the decking would be adequate as a diaphragm if the sheeting were fastened on two sides only.

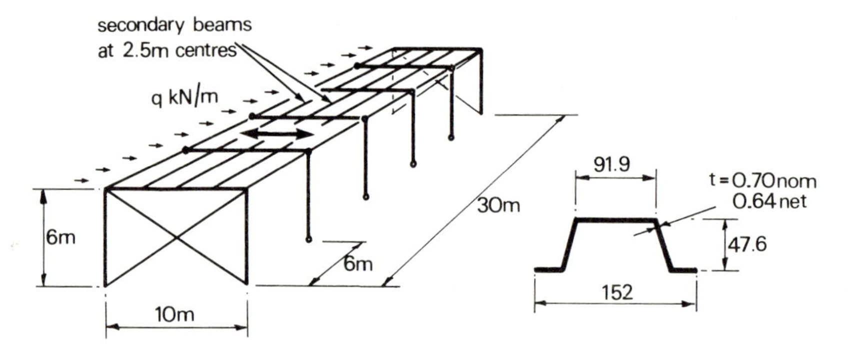

Fig. 7.3 Design example – flat roofed building with pinned frames.

The fastening specification of the roof deck is as follows: sheet to purlin fasteners, 6.3 mm self-drilling, self-tapping screws in every corrugation throughout; sheet to shear connector fasteners, 6.3 mm self-drilling, self-tapping screws with steel washers (a total of 24 per rafter); seam fasteners, 4.8 mm diameter monel metal blind rivets at 300 mm centres.

7.3.1 Determination of wind load on diaphragm

From *CP3*, chapter V, Part 2 (1972), the basic wind speed for Coventry is 44 m/s; $S_1 = 1.0$; $S_2 = 0.67$ (category 3, class B, height = 6 m); $S_3 = 1.0$. Hence, design wind speed, $V_s = 44.0 \times 1.0 \times 0.67 \times 1.0 = 29.5$ m/s and dynamic pressure = 0.533 kN/m^2. For a building of given dimensions, the force coefficient = 1.12 (*CP3*, chapter V, Part 2, table 10) and hence the line load q on the diaphragm is given by $q = (1.12 \times 0.533 \times 6.0)/2 = 1.79$ kN/m. Maximum shear force $V_{max} = qL/2 = (1.79 \times 30)/2 = 26.85$ kN. For a load factor of 1.7, design shear force $V_{des} = 26.85 \times 1.7 = 45.65$ kN.

7.3.2 Determination of design strength according to section 9.5

(a) Seam strength

n_f = number of sheet to purlin fasteners per member per sheet width = 6
fixed as decking with seams in troughs $\therefore \beta_1 = 1.22$ (table 9.5) and $\beta_3 = 1.0$ (note 9.2.8)

n_p = total number of purlins = 5

n_s = number of seam fasteners per sidelap = 32

F_p = design strength of individual sheet to purlin fastener = $0.9 \times 6.5 \times 0.64 =$ 3.74 kN

F_s = design strength of individual seam fastener = $0.9 \times 2.8 \times 0.64 = 1.61$ kN
(see clause 2.5 and table 9.8)

$$\therefore V_{ult} = n_s F_s + \frac{\beta_1}{\beta_3} n_p F_p = (32 \times 1.61) + \left[\frac{1.22}{1.0} \times 5 \times 3.74\right] = 74.33 \text{ kN}$$

(b) Strength in fasteners to shear connectors

n_{sc} = total number of sheet to shear connector fasteners per rafter = 24

F_{sc} = design strength of individual sheet to shear connector fastener = 3.74 kN

$\therefore V_{ult} = n_{sc} F_{sc} = 24 \times 3.74 = 89.76$ kN

(c) Calculated design shear capacity V^*

The minimum of the above values of V_{ult} gives the design strength of the diaphragm as $V^* = 74.33$ kN. This is well in excess of the 45.65 kN required.

(d) General requirement for shear buckling

b = depth of diaphragm = 10 000 mm

d = pitch of corrugations = 152 mm

E = modulus of elasticity = 207 kN/mm^2

t = net sheet thickness = 0.64 mm

u = perimeter length = 227.6 mm

I_y = second moment of area of single corrugation = 54 280 mm^4
ν = Poisson's ratio = 0.3

The requirement is that $\frac{14.4}{b} D_x^{\frac{1}{4}} D_y^{\frac{3}{4}} (n_p - 1)^2 \geqslant V^*$

$$D_x = \frac{E t^3 d}{12(1-\nu^2)u} = \frac{207 \times 0.64^3 \times 152}{12 \times 0.91 \times 227.6} = 3.318 \text{ kN mm}^2/\text{mm}$$

$$D_y = \frac{E I_y}{d} = \frac{207 \times 54\,280}{152} = 73\,920 \text{ kN mm}^2/\text{mm}$$

$$\therefore \frac{14.4}{b} D_x^{\frac{1}{4}} D_y^{\frac{3}{4}} (n_p - 1)^2 = \frac{14.4}{10\,000} \times 3.318^{\frac{1}{4}} \times 73\,920^{\frac{3}{4}} \times 4^2 = 139.4 \text{ kN}$$

As this is greater than V^* = 74.33 kN, the requirement is satisfied.
(e) General requirement for sheet to purlin fasteners
p = pitch of sheet to purlin fasteners = 152 mm
α_3 = 0.80 (using $n_p = 5$ in table 9.3)

The requirement is that $\frac{0.8\, b\, F_p}{p\, \alpha_3} \geqslant V^*$

$$\therefore \frac{0.8\, b\, F_p}{p\, \alpha_3} = \frac{0.8 \times 10\,000 \times 3.74}{152 \times 0.8} = 246.1 \text{ kN}$$

As this is greater than V^* = 74.33 kN, the requirement is satisfied. The panel is therefore satisfactory in all respects with regard to the required load.
(f) Maximum axial force in edge purlin
q = distributed load on diaphragm at unit load factor = 1.79×10^{-3} kN/mm
L = span of diaphragm = 30 000 mm
α_3 = 0.80 (from table 9.3 with $n_p = 5$)
∴ Maximum axial force in longitudinal edge purlin at unit load factor

$$= \frac{qL^2 \alpha_3}{8b} = \frac{1.79 \times 10^{-3} \times 30\,000^2 \times 0.80}{8 \times 10\,000} = 16.1 \text{ kN}$$

It is necessary to check the design of the edge purlin for this force together with any horizontal or vertical bending moments.

7.3.3 Calculation of maximum deflection according to section 9.5

To determine the sheeting constant $\bar{K}_1$ using table 9.6
d = pitch of corrugations = 152.0 mm
h = height of profile = 47.6 mm
l = width of crest = 91.9 mm
θ = inclination of web to vertical = 13.1°
$\therefore h/d = 0.313$, $l/d = 0.605$; $\bar{K}_1 = 0.324$

(a) Flexibility due to profile distortion

a = length of panel = 6000 mm
b = depth of diaphragm = 10 000 mm
E = modulus of elasticity = 207 kN/mm²
t = net sheet thickness = 0.64 mm
n_b = number of sheet lengths within depth of diaphragm = 2
α_1 = 1.0 (3 purlins per sheet length in table 9.3)
α_4 = $1 + 0.3\, n_b = 1.6$ (table 9.1, case 5)

$$c_{1.1} = \frac{a\, d^{2.5}\, \alpha_1\, \alpha_4\, \bar{K}_1}{E\, t^{2.5}\, b^2} = \frac{6000 \times 152^{2.5} \times 1.0 \times 1.6 \times 0.324}{207 \times 0.64^{2.5} \times 10\,000^2} = 0.1306 \text{ mm/kN}$$

(b) Flexibility due to shear strain

ν = Poisson's ratio = 0.3
α_2 = 0.67 (using $n_p = 5$ in table 9.3)

$$c_{1.2} = \frac{2\, a\, \alpha_2\, (1 + \nu)\, [1 + (2h/d)]}{E\, t\, b}$$

$$= \frac{2 \times 6000 \times 0.67 \times 1.3\, [1 + (2 \times 47.6/152.0)]}{207 \times 0.64 \times 10\,000} = 0.0128 \text{ mm/kN}$$

(c) Flexibility due to deformation in sheet to purlin fasteners

p = pitch of sheet to purlin fasteners = 152 mm
s_p = slip per sheet to purlin fasteners per unit load = 0.25 mm/kN
α_3 = 0.8 (From table 9.3 with $n_p = 5$)

$$c_{2.1} = \frac{2a\, s_p\, p\, \alpha_3}{b^2} = \frac{2 \times 6000 \times 0.25 \times 152 \times 0.8}{10\,000^2} = 0.0036 \text{ mm/kN}$$

(d) Flexibility due to deformation in seam fasteners

n_f = number of sheet to purlin fasteners per member per sheet width = 6 fixed as decking with seams in troughs ∴ $\beta_1 = 1.22$ (table 9.5)
n_p = total number of purlins = 5
n_s = number of seam fasteners per sidelap = 32
n_{sh} = number of sheet widths in panel = 8
s_s = slip per seam fastener per unit load = 0.28 mm/kN (table 9.10)

$$c_{2.2} = \frac{2\, s_s s_p\, (n_{sh} - 1)}{2\, n_s s_p + \beta_1\, n_p s_s} = \frac{2 \times 0.28 \times 0.25 \times (8 - 1)}{(2 \times 32 \times 0.25) + (1.22 \times 5 \times 0.28)}$$

$$= 0.0553 \text{ mm/kN}$$

(e) Flexibility in connections to rafters (shear connectors)

n = number of panels within diaphragm assembly = 5
n_{sc} = total number of sheet to shear connector fasteners per rafter = 24 (see data)
s_{sc} = slip per sheet to shear connector fastener per unit load = 0.25 mm/kN

$$c_{2.3} = \frac{4\,(n+1)\,s_{sc}}{n^2\,n_{sc}} = \frac{4 \times 6 \times 0.25}{5^2 \times 24} = 0.0100\text{mm/kN}$$

(f) Flexibility due to axial strain in purlins

A = cross sectional area of purlin = 965 mm^2

α_3 = 0.80 (using $n_p = 5$ in table 9.3)

$$c_3 = \frac{n^2\,a^3\,\alpha_3}{4.8\,E\,A\,b^2} = \frac{5^2 \times 6000^3 \times 0.80}{4.8 \times 207 \times 965 \times 10\,000^2} = 0.0451 \text{ mm/kN}$$

Note The above value of c_3 is averaged over the panels forming the complete diaphragm

(g) Total shear flexibility

$c = c_{1.1} + c_{1.2} + c_{2.1} + c_{2.2} + c_{2.3} + c_3$

$= 0.1306 + 0.0128 + 0.0036 + 0.0553 + 0.0100 + 0.0451$

$= 0.2574$ mm/kN

(h) Mid-span deflection

The maximum deflection v_{max}, at mid-span of the diaphragm is

$$v_{max} = \frac{n^2}{8} c\,(qa) = \frac{5^2 \times 0.2574 \times 1.79 \times 6}{8} = 8.64 \text{ mm}$$

7.3.4 Comparison with values given in the design tables

The values of strength and deflection given by the detailed calculation above are $q_{perm} = (1.79 \times 74.33)/45.65 = 2.915$ kN/m, $v_{max} = 8.64$ mm. These may be compared directly with the values given in the appropriate design table (table 9.15) and it is interesting to make the comparison as follows.

Entering the table with depth = 10 000 mm and span-depth ratio = 3.0 gives, for a load factor of 1.7 (the design tables assume a load factor of 1.4 for wind) $q_{perm} = 2.397 \times 1.4/1.7 = 1.97$ kN/mm, $k_1 = 0.167$ kN/mm. From this, the maximum deflection is found as $v_{max} = 1.79/0.167 = 14.4$ mm.

It will be recalled from chapter 6 that the design tables are based on a number of safe assumptions and the above results are indicative of this. In particular, the calculations for seam strength ignore the influence of sheet to purlin fasteners and, as seam failure is the usual failure mode, the tabulated strengths are usually very conservative. Furthermore, the edge member area assumed is very much on the low side and this usually results in a considerable over-estimate of the bending component of deflection. It is this factor that is primarily responsible for the considerable difference between the above values of deflection.

7.3.5 The effect of significant openings

It will now be assumed that the diaphragm is required to have the pattern of openings shown in fig. 7.4 and that no additional fasteners are to be provided other than

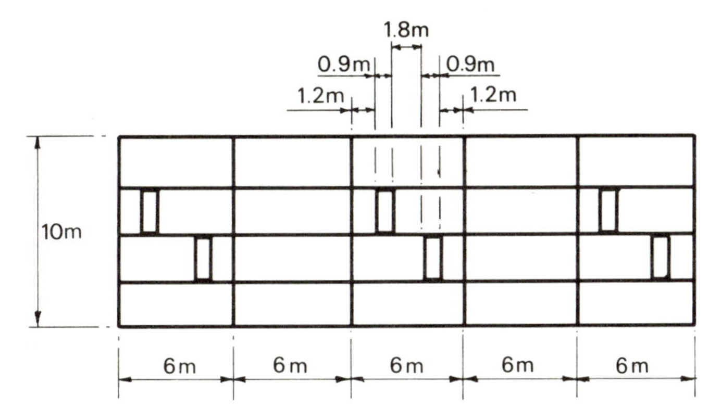

Fig. 7.4 Required pattern of openings.

those to members trimming the openings. Design procedures for dealing with openings in diaphragms have been given in section 5.5. The underlying theory and other considerations are described in chapter 14. There is also consideration of an approximate treatment in section 6.7. These procedures will now be applied to the diaphragm in fig. 7.4.

Detailed calculation according to section 5.5.
The first step in the design procedure involves the calculation of the design strength V^* and the flexibility c of the diaphragm in the absence of the openings. This has already been done and the relevant quantities are $V^* = 74.33$ kN, $c = 0.2574$ mm/kN. It may also be noted at this stage that the required design shear capacity of the end panel is $V_{des} = 45.65$ kN.

The reduction in the design strength of the end panel as a result of the opening is calculated by considering the distribution of load in each strip containing open-

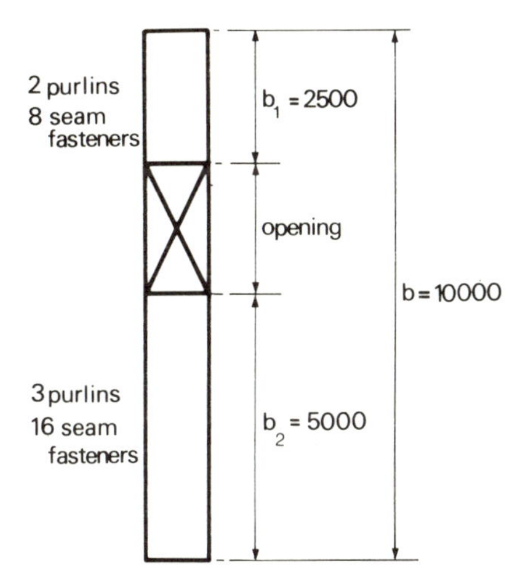

Fig. 7.5 Strip of diaphragm containing an opening.

ings as shown in fig. 7.5. Only one such strip need be considered here as the alternative strip is identical to the one shown when inverted. The load carried by the strip above the opening is

$$V_{ult}\left(\frac{b_1^2}{\Sigma b_i^2}\right) = V_{ult}\left(\frac{2500^2}{2500^2 + 5000^2}\right) = 0.2\ V_{ult}$$

The seam strength of this strip is taken as

$$2\frac{\beta_1}{\beta_3}F_p + 8F_s = \left(2 \times \frac{1.22}{1.0} \times 3.74\right) + (8 \times 1.61) = 22.0\ \text{kN}$$

so that the design strength with respect to failure of the upper strip is $V_{ult} = 22.0/0.2 = 110$ kN. The load carried by the strip below the opening is

$$V_{ult}\left(\frac{b_2^2}{\Sigma b_i^2}\right) = V_{ult}\left(\frac{5000^2}{2500^2 + 5000^2}\right) = 0.8\ V_{ult}$$

The seam strength of this strip is taken as

$$3\frac{\beta_1}{\beta_3}F_p + 16\,F_s = \left(3 \times \frac{1.22}{1.0} \times 3.74\right) + (16 \times 1.61) = 39.4\ \text{kN}$$

so that the design strength with respect to failure of the lower strip is $V_{ult} = 39.4/0.8 = 49.3$ kN.

It follows that the opening reduces the calculated strength from 74.33 kN to the above value but this is still above the required design strength of 45.65 kN so that the diaphragm with openings is satisfactory as regards strength. It may also be noted that the above calculation is extremely conservative. With good detailing, full redistribution of internal force can be possible and the actual design load could be as much as 22.0 + 39.4 = 61.4 kN. The openings also increase the flexibility $c_{1.1}$ of the panels in which they occur. The modification factor for $c_{1.1}$ for these panels is given by

$$\alpha_h = \frac{1}{a}\sum_j a_{sj} + \frac{1}{a}\sum_k a_{hk}\frac{\bar{K}\,b^2}{\sum_i \bar{K}\,b_i^2}$$

where the remaining symbols are defined in fig. 7.6. Now $\Sigma_j\, a_{sj} = 1200 + 1800 + 1200 = 4200$ mm and $\Sigma_k\, a_{hk} = 900 + 900 = 1800$ mm,

$$\text{giving } \alpha_h = \frac{4200}{6000} + \frac{1800}{6000}\left(\frac{10\,000^2}{2500^2 + 5000^2}\right) = 1.660$$

so that the flexibility of the panels containing openings is given by

$$\begin{aligned} c &= \alpha_h\, c_{1.1} + c_{1.2} + c_{2.1} + c_{2.2} + c_{2.3} + c_3 \\ &= (1.660 \times 0.1306) + 0.0128 + 0.0036 + 0.0553 + 0.0100 + 0.0451 \\ &= 0.3436\ \text{mm/kN} \end{aligned}$$

The panel shears under the unfactored loads are shown in fig. 7.7 and it follows that the central deflection is given by

$$v_{max} = (21.48 \times 0.3436) + (10.74 \times 0.2574) = 10.14\ \text{mm}$$

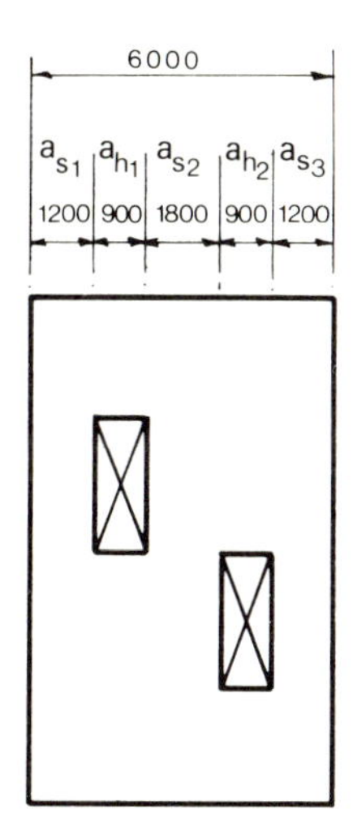

Fig. 7.6 Notation for panel with openings.

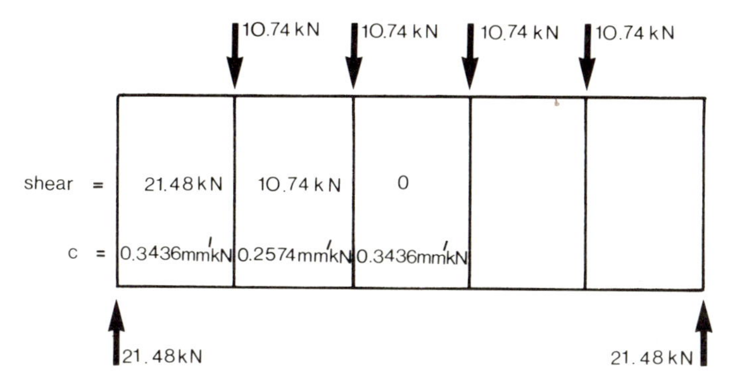

Fig. 7.7 Diaphragm shears and flexibilities.

Thus the percentage increase in deflection due to the presence of the openings is about 17%. The resulting deflection is quite permissible.

In addition to the calculations carried out above, it is necessary in most cases to check also the additional local forces induced by the discontinuity in the shear deflection profile in the vicinity of the opening. For this calculation it is necessary to know the properties of the members supporting the sheeting which are assumed to have the section shown in fig. 7.8. The procedure for this is also given in section 5.5 and is as follows. The local flexibility properties in the vicinity of the opening are

$$c_s = \frac{1000 d^{2.5} \bar{K}_1}{E\, t^{2.5}} \frac{\alpha_1}{b^2} = \frac{1000 \times 152^{2.5} \times 0.324}{207 \times 0.64^{2.5}} \times \left(\frac{1.0}{10\,000^2}\right)$$

$$= 0.013\,61 \text{ mm/kN}$$

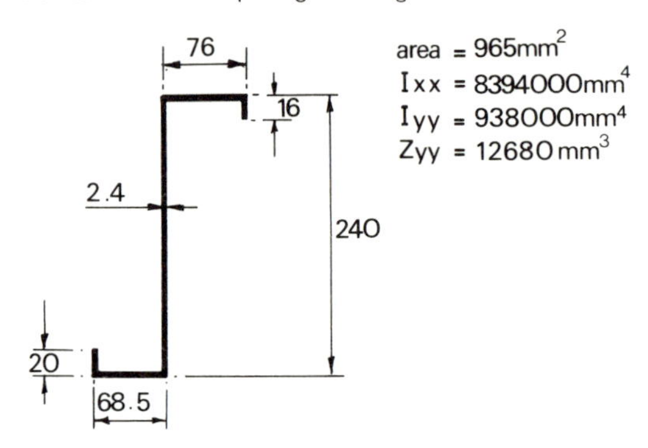

Fig. 7.8 Properties of member supporting sheeting.

$$c_h = \frac{1000\, d^{2.5}\, \bar{K}_1}{E\, t^{2.5}} \left(\frac{1}{\Sigma\, b_i^2}\right) = 0.01361 \left(\frac{10\,000^2}{2500^2 + 5000^2}\right) = 0.043\,55 \text{ mm/kN}$$

$$\therefore M_{max} = 0.007\,(c_h - c_s)\, I^{\frac{3}{4}}\, V^* = 0.007 \times (0.029\,94) \times 938\,000^{\frac{3}{4}} \times 49.3$$
$$= 311.4 \text{ kN mm}$$

It follows that the maximum minor axis bending stresses induced at the design load are of the order of $M_{max}/Z_{yy} = 311.4/12\,680 = 0.025$ kN/mm² and are not significant.

Similarly, $F_{max} = 0.01\,(c_h - c_s)\, I^{\frac{1}{4}}\, V^* = 0.01 \times 0.029\,94 \times 938\,000^{\frac{1}{4}} \times 49.3$
$= 0.46$ kN

The above value of F_{max} is the maximum force per purlin at the design load in line with the edge of the opening. The total force to be carried is thus 5×0.46 kN $= 2.3$ kN and, if this is carried entirely in the sheet to purlin fasteners, the available capacity is $5 \times 3.74 = 18.7$ kN which is ample. It follows that the diaphragm with openings is satisfactory in all respects.

7.3.6 Approximate treatment of openings according to section 6.7

If side trimmers are provided, the diaphragm with openings just satisfies the requirements for the approximate calculation described in section 6.7.

(a) Reduction factor for strength
As the decking is fastened to the supporting structure through every trough, the factors β_i in the expression for the reduction factor for strength are all equal to unity.

$$\text{Thus } \alpha_1 = \frac{\Sigma\, b_i^2}{b b_1} = \frac{2500^2 + 5000^2}{10\,000 \times 2500} = 1.25$$

$$\alpha_2 = \frac{\Sigma b_i^2}{bb_2} = \frac{2500^2 + 5000^2}{10\,000 \times 5000} = 0.625$$

Taking the smaller of the above two values gives $V_{ult} = 0.625 \times 74.33 = 46.5$ kN which may be compared with the value of 49.3 kN obtained when the calculation is carried out in more detail.

(b) Reduction factor for stiffness

As the height h of the profile is 47.6 mm, it is shallow within the terms of section 6.7 and the percentage reduction in stiffness is 4 $\times$ (percentage area of openings) = $4[(2 \times 0.9 \times 2.5)/(6 \times 10)] \times 100 = 30\%$ in the panels containing the openings. Thus the predicted flexibility of these panels is $0.2574/0.7 = 0.3677$ mm/kN by the approximate method compared with 0.3436 mm/kN found by the more exact calculation.

7.3.7 Diaphragm fastened on two sides only

If the shear connectors are omitted from the intermediate rafters in fig. 7.3 we have the case of diaphragms fastened on two sides only though still preserving shear connectors at the gables where the highest shear force has to be transferred. The effect of this on the calculations is as follows. *Note* In this calculation it is assumed that the sheeting is supported on Z purlins which are fastened to the rafters by stiffened cleats (detail 17 in table 9.12).

(a) Seam strength

No change.

(b) Strength in fasteners to gable shear connectors

No change.

(c) Strength in sheet to purlin connections adjacent to internal rafters

q_{des} = design value of distributed load on diaphragm = $1.79 \times 1.7 = 3.04$ kN/m

a = length of panel = 6000 mm

n_p = total number of purlins = 5

F_p = design strength of individual sheet to purlin fastener = 3.74 kN

F_{pr} = design strength of individual purlin to rafter connection = 6.0 kN (detail 17 from table 9.12). Value taken conservatively between elastic and ultimate loads.

n_f = number of sheet to purlin fasteners per member per sheet width = 6

$\therefore \beta_2 = 1.40$ (table 9.5)

$\therefore$ Required design force at rafter = $(qa)_{des} = 3.04 \times 6 = 18.24$ kN

Capacity of row of fasteners = $\beta_2\, n_p\, F_p = 1.40 \times 5 \times 3.74 = 26.18$ kN

Capacity of row of purlin to rafter connections = $n_p F_{pr} = 5 \times 6.0 = 30.0$ kN

Thus, as both $\beta_2 n_p F_p$ and $n_p F_{pr}$ are greater than $(qa)_{des}$, the design is satisfactory for strength when the diaphragm is fastened on two sides only internally. It is at the same time quite obvious that it would not be satisfactory in the absence of the gable shear connectors.

(d) Calculated design shear capacity V^*

When the diaphragm is fastened on two sides only, the design shear capacity is reduced according to the above calculation to $V^* = (45.65 \times 26.18)/18.24 =$ 65.5 kN

(e) General requirements for shear buckling and sheet to purlin fasteners
These are clearly still satisfied.

(f) Maximum axial force in edge purlin
No change.

(g) Changes in flexibility components
Only component $c_{2.3}$ is altered when the shear connectors to the intermediate rafters are removed.

n = number of panels within diaphragm assembly = 5
s_p = slip per sheet to purlin fastener per unit load = 0.25 kN/mm
s_{pr} = movement of purlin to rafter connection per unit load = 0.38 mm/kN

$$c_{2.3} = \frac{4(n-1)}{n^2\, n_p}\left(s_{pr} + \frac{s_p}{\beta_2}\right) = \frac{4 \times 4}{25 \times 5}\left(0.38 + \frac{0.25}{1.40}\right) = 0.0715 \text{ mm/kN}$$

(h) Total shear flexibility

$$\begin{aligned} c &= c_{1.1} + c_{1.2} + c_{2.1} + c_{2.2} + c_{2.3} + c_3 \\ &= 0.1306 + 0.0128 + 0.0036 + 0.0553 + 0.0715 + 0.0451 \\ &= 0.3189 \text{ mm/kN} \end{aligned}$$

(i) Mid-span deflection

$$v_{max} = \frac{n^2 c}{8}(qa) = \frac{5^2 \times 0.3189 \times 1.79 \times 6}{8} = 10.7 \text{ mm}$$

(j) Comparison with values given in design tables
The values of strength and deflection given by the detailed calculation above are $q_{perm} = (1.79 \times 65.45)/45.65 = 2.57$ kN/m, $v_{max} = 10.7$ mm. Values of strength and deflection given by design table 9.17 are (depth = 10 m; span-depth ratio = 3, load factor = 1.7) $q_{perm1} = 1.598 \times (1.4/1.7) = 1.316$ kN/m, $k_1 = 0.113$ kN/m/mm. $\therefore v_{max} = 1.79/0.113 = 15.8$ mm

7.4 Flat-roofed building with sheeting spanning parallel to span of diaphragm (with both pinned and rigid-jointed frames)

The building shown in fig. 7.9 is to be designed to carry an unfactored wind load of 2.45 kN/m at eaves level. The roof sheeting is fixed as decking with seams in the troughs and is delivered in double span (9 m) lengths. Fixings to the longitudinal edge members are provided so that the diaphragms are fastened on four sides. The following calculations will be carried out:

(a) With pinned frames, check whether the strength of the diaphragm is adequate.
(b) With pinned frames, determination of the maximum deflection.
(c) Comparison of (a) and (b) with approximate values given by design tables.
(d) Consideration of conventional design in which the frames carry all the wind load.
(e) Analysis with rigid frames combined with stressed skin action.
(f) Consideration of the influence of non-rigid gables.

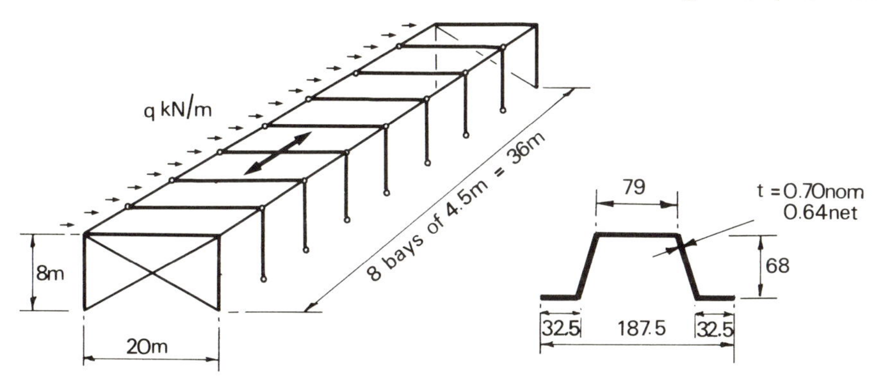

Fig. 7.9 Design example, flat roofed building with sheeting parallel to span.

The fastening specification for the roof deck is as follows: sheet to purlin fasteners, 4.5 mm cartridge-fired pins in every corrugation throughout; sheet to longitudinal edge member fasteners, 4.5 mm cartridge-fired pins at 500 mm centres (i.e. 9 per panel); seam fasteners, 4.8 mm diameter monel metal blind rivets at 300 mm centres.

7.4.1 Determination of design strength according to section 9.6

(a) Maximum shear force in diaphragm

Maximum shear force $V_{max} = qb(n-1)/2 = (2.45 \times 4.5 \times 7)/2 = 38.6$ kN

$\therefore$ for a load factor of 1.7, design shear force $V_{des} = 38.6 \times 1.7 = 65.6$ kN.

(b) Seam strength

a = length of diaphragm perpendicular to the corrugations = 20 000 mm

b = depth of diaphragm parallel to the corrugations = 4500 mm

n_f = number of sheet to purlin fasteners per member per sheet width = 5

$\therefore \beta_1 = 1.13; \beta_3 = 1.0$

n_s = number of seam fasteners per sidelap = 14

F_p = design strength of individual sheet to purlin fastener = $0.9 \times 4.6 \times 0.64$ = 2.65 kN

F_s = design strength of individual seam fastener = $0.9 \times 2.8 \times 0.64 = 1.61$ kN

$$\therefore V_{ult} = \frac{a}{b}\left(n_s F_s + \frac{\beta_1}{\beta_3} F_p\right) = \frac{20\,000}{4500}\left[\left(14 \times 1.61\right) + \left(\frac{1.13}{1.0} \times 2.65\right)\right] = 113.5 \text{ kN}$$

(c) Strength in fasteners to longitudinal edge members (shear connectors)

n_{sc} = total number of shear connector fasteners per member per panel = 9

F_{sc} = design strength of individual shear connector fastener = 2.65 kN

$\therefore V_{ult} = (a/b)\, n_{sc}\, F_{sc} = (20\,000/4500)\,(9 \times 2.65) = 106.0$ kN

(d) Calculated design shear capacity V^*

The minimum of the above values of V_{ult} gives the design strength of the diaphragm as $V^* = 106.0$ kN. This is well in excess of the 65.6 kN required.

(e) General requirement for shear buckling

d = pitch of corrugations = 187.5 mm
E = modulus of elasticity = 207 kN/mm^2
t = net sheet thickness = 0.64 mm
u = perimeter length = 286.8 mm
I_y = second moment of area of single corrugation = 141 250 mm^4
ν = Poisson's ratio = 0.3

The requirement is that $28.8a/b^2\, D_x^{\frac{1}{4}}\, D_y^{\frac{3}{4}} \geqslant V^*$

$$D_x = \frac{E\,t^3\,d}{12(1-\nu^2)u} = \frac{207 \times 0.64^3 \times 187.5}{12 \times 0.91 \times 286.8} = 3.249 \text{ kN mm}^2/\text{mm}$$

$$D_y = \frac{E\,I_y}{d} = \frac{207 \times 141\,250}{187.5} = 155\,940 \text{ kN mm}^2/\text{mm}$$

$$\therefore \frac{28.8a}{b^2} D_x^{\frac{1}{4}}\, D_y^{\frac{3}{4}} = \frac{28.8 \times 20\,000}{4500^2} \times 1.343 \times 7847 = 299.7 \text{ kN}$$

As this is greater than V^* = 106.0 kN, the requirement is satisfied.

(f) General requirement for sheet to purlin fasteners

p = pitch of sheet to purlin fasteners = 187.5 mm

The requirement is that $0.8\, a\, F_p/p \geqslant V^*$

$$\therefore \frac{0.8\, a\, F_p}{p} = \frac{0.8 \times 20\,000 \times 2.65}{187.5} = 226.1 \text{ kN}$$

As this is greater than V^* = 106.0 kN, the requirement is satisfied. The panel is therefore satisfactory in all respects with regard to the required load.

(g) Maximum axial force in edge purlin

q = distributed load on diaphragm at unit load factor = 2.45×10^{-3} kN/mm
L = span of diaphragm = 36 000 mm

$\therefore$ Maximum axial force in longitudinal edge member at unit load factor

$$= \frac{qL^2}{8a} = \frac{2.45 \times 10^{-3} \times 36\,000^2}{8 \times 4500} = 88.2 \text{ kN}$$

It is necessary to include for this force in the design of the edge member.

7.4.2 Calculation of maximum deflection according to section 9.6

To determine the sheeting constant $\bar{K}_1$ using table 9.6

d = pitch of corrugations = 187.5 mm
h = height of profile = 68 mm
l = width of crest = 79 mm
θ = inclination of web to vertical = 17.7°

$\therefore h/d = 0.363,\ l/d = 0.421;\ \bar{K}_1 = 0.317$

(a) Flexibility due to sheet distortion

a = length of panel = 20 000 mm
b = depth of panel = 4500 mm
E = modulus of elasticity = 207 kN/mm^2
t = net sheet thickness = 0.64 mm
n_l = number of sheet lengths within length of diaphragm = 8/2 = 4
α_5 = 0.8 (for $n_l = 4$ in table 9.4; see also case 3 in table 9.2)
m = number of panels within sheet length = 2

$$c_{1.1}\frac{\alpha_5}{m} = \frac{a\,d^{2.5}\,\alpha_5\,\bar{K}_1}{E\,t^{2.5}\,b^2\,m} = \frac{20\,000 \times 187.5^{2.5} \times 0.8 \times 0.317}{207 \times 0.64^{2.5} \times 4500^2 \times 2} = 0.8888 \text{ mm/kN}$$

(b) Flexibility due to shear strain

ν = Poisson's ratio = 0.3

$$c_{1.2} = \frac{2a\,(1+\nu)\,[1+(2h/d)]}{E\,t\,b} = \frac{2 \times 20\,000 \times 1.3 \times [1 + (2 \times 68/187.5)]}{207 \times 0.64 \times 4500}$$
$$= 0.1505 \text{ mm/kN}$$

(c) Flexibility due to deformation in sheet to purlin fasteners

p = pitch of sheet to purlin fasteners = 187.5 mm
s_p = slip per sheet to purlin fastener per unit load = 0.025 mm/kN (see table 9.9)

$$c_{2.1} = \frac{2\,a\,s_p\,p}{b^2} = \frac{2 \times 20\,000 \times 0.025 \times 187.5}{4500^2} = 0.0093 \text{ mm/kN}$$

(d) Flexibility due to deformation in seam fasteners

n_f = number of sheet to purlin fasteners per member per sheet width = 5 fixed as decking with seams in troughs $\therefore \beta_1 = 1.13$ (table 9.5)
n_s = number of seam fasteners per sidelap = 14
n_{sh} = number of sheet widths in panel = 27
s_s = slip per seam fastener per unit load = 0.28 mm/kN (table 9.10)

$$c_{2.2} = \frac{s_s\,s_p\,(n_{sh}-1)}{n_s\,s_p + \beta_1 s_s} = \frac{0.28 \times 0.025 \times (27-1)}{14 \times 0.025 + 1.13 \times 0.28} = 0.2731 \text{ mm/kN}$$

(e) Flexibility in connections to edge members (shear connectors)

n_{sc} = total number of shear connector fasteners per member per panel = 9
s_{sc} = slip per shear connector fastener per unit load = 0.025 mm/kN

$$c_{2.3} = \frac{2\,s_{sc}}{n_{sc}} = \frac{2 \times 0.025}{9} = 0.0056 \text{ mm/kN}$$

(f) Total flexibility in true shear

$$c' = \frac{b^2}{a^2}\left(c_{1.1}\frac{\alpha_5}{m} + c_{1.2} + c_{2.1} + c_{2.2} + c_{2.3}\right)$$
$$= \left(\frac{4500}{20\,000}\right)^2 (0.8888 + 0.1505 + 0.0093 + 0.2731 + 0.0056)$$

$= 0.0672$ mm/kN

(g) Flexibility due to axial strain in edge members
A = cross-sectional area of edge member = 1000 mm^2
n = number of panels within diaphragm assembly = 8

$$c_3 = \frac{n^2 b^3}{4.8 EA a^2} = \frac{8^2 \times 4500^3}{4.8 \times 207 \times 1000 \times 20\,000^2} = 0.0147 \text{ mm/kN}$$

(h) Total shear flexibility
$c = c' + c_3 = 0.0672 + 0.0147 = 0.0819$ mm/kN
(i) Mid-span deflection

$$\Delta_{max} = \frac{n^2}{8} c\,(qa) = \frac{8^2 \times 0.0819 \times 2.45 \times 4.5}{8} = 7.22 \text{ mm}$$

(j) Comparison with values given in design tables
The values of strength and deflection given by the detailed calculations above are $q_{perm} = 2.45 \times 106.0/75.0 = 3.46$ kN/m, $\Delta_{max} = 7.22$ mm. Strictly speaking, the approximate design tables are not applicable to decks with a corrugation pitch other than 150 mm but, for the case in question, the consequences of the different pitch are not great. The values of strength and deflection given by table 9.20 are (for depth = 20 m, span–depth ratio = 1.8, load factor = 1.7), $q_{perm} = 4.01 \times 1.4/1.7 = 3.30$ kN/m, $k_1 = 0.213$ kN/m/mm. $\therefore \Delta_{max} = 2.45/0.213 = 11.5$ mm.

Once again, the calculation of deflection given by the approximate tables is shown to be very conservative. The strength values are not directly comparable as the diaphragm under consideration has different fastener strengths from those assumed in the construction of the design tables.

7.4.3 Conventional design in which the frames carry the entire wind load

When both vertical and horizontal loads on the bare frames are considered with appropriate load factors, a suitable elastic design based on considerations of strength alone for a pinned base frame uses a uniform section of 533 mm × 165 mm U.B. × 66 kg/m. Using this section, it may be shown that the horizontal deflection of the frame under a side load of 1 kN (i.e. the frame flexibility k) is 2.64 mm/kN, as shown in fig. 7.10. Under the unfactored side load, the horizontal deflection is $2.45 \times 4.5 \times 2.64 = 29.1$ mm, i.e. height/274. This deflection is rather high and would normally be reduced by increasing the size of the frame members.

7.4.4 Combination of rigid frames and diaphragm action

The effective shear flexibility c of an individual panel has already been shown in section 7.4.2 to be 0.0819 mm/kN. Thus the relative flexibility of a panel and frame is given by $\psi = c/k = 0.0819/2.64 = 0.0310$. The reduction of sway moment and deflection in a sheeted frame depends on this value of ψ, the number of frames

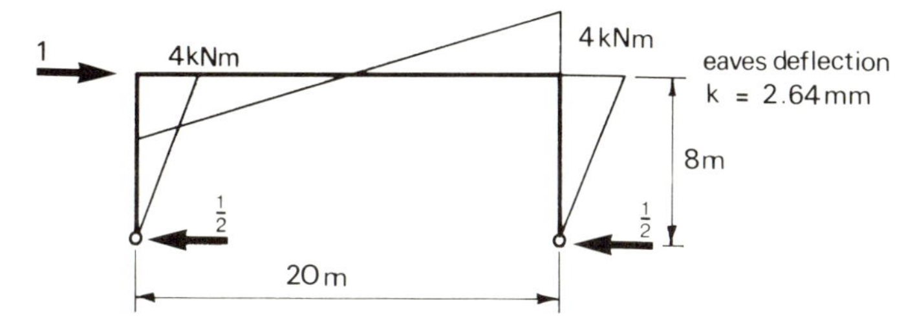

Fig. 7.10 Behaviour of bare frame under unit eaves load.

in the building and on the position of the frame in the building. The appropriate reduction factors are tabulated in table 9.13. For the particular case of a building with a total of 9 frames, the reduction factors to be applied to the side loads on the frames are as shown in table 7.4.

Table 7.4 Reduction factors for frame forces in example structure

Frame number	2	3	4	5
Reduction factor η	0.091	0.155	0.192	0.204

Hence, for unfactored loads, the horizontal deflection of the centre frame (which is, of course, the most critical) is $0.204 \times 29.1 = 5.9$ mm which is quite satisfactory. In addition, the bending moments reduce to 20.4% of their previous values. It is also readily possible to calculate the forces in the diaphragm in the combined case. At a given frame, η times the applied side load goes into the frame so that $(1 - \eta)$ times the side load goes into the diaphragm. The applied loads and resulting shears for the diaphragm in question at the design loads are therefore shown in fig. 7.11. In fig. 7.11 the maximum shear of 32.64 kN may be compared with the value of 38.6 kN when the diaphragm acts alone.

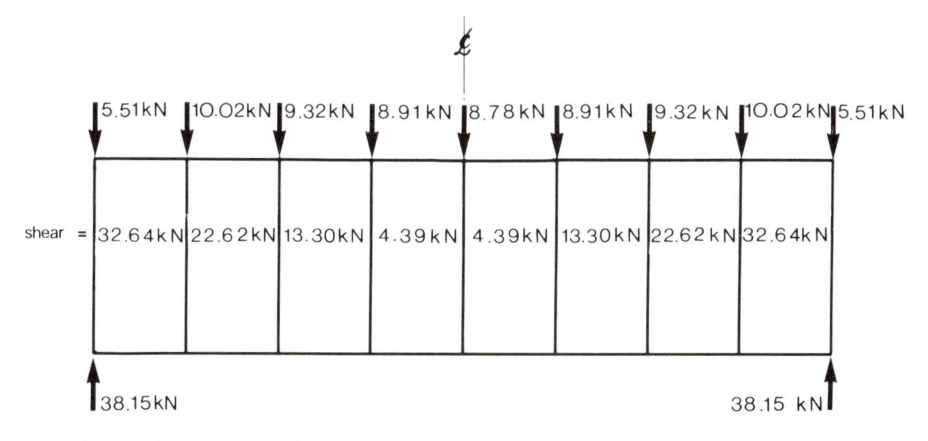

Fig. 7.11 Forces and shears in diaphragm when interacting with frames.

7.4.5 Influence of non-rigid gables

If the gable is itself a sheeted frame, it will act as a diaphragm under the action of the maximum shear force V_{max} arising in the roof. In such a case where there is also interaction with the frames, V_{max} is statically indeterminate and depends not only on the flexibility k of the frames and c of the panels of roof sheeting but also on the flexibility c_g of the gable panel. The relevant quantities k, c and c_g can be calculated in the usual way. For the analysis of the complete assembly it is then easiest to analyse the complete structure as a complex plane frame using a computer as described in chapter 4. For the frame in question, symmetry indicates that it is only necessary to analyse half of the frame and a suitable mathematical model is shown in fig. 7.12.

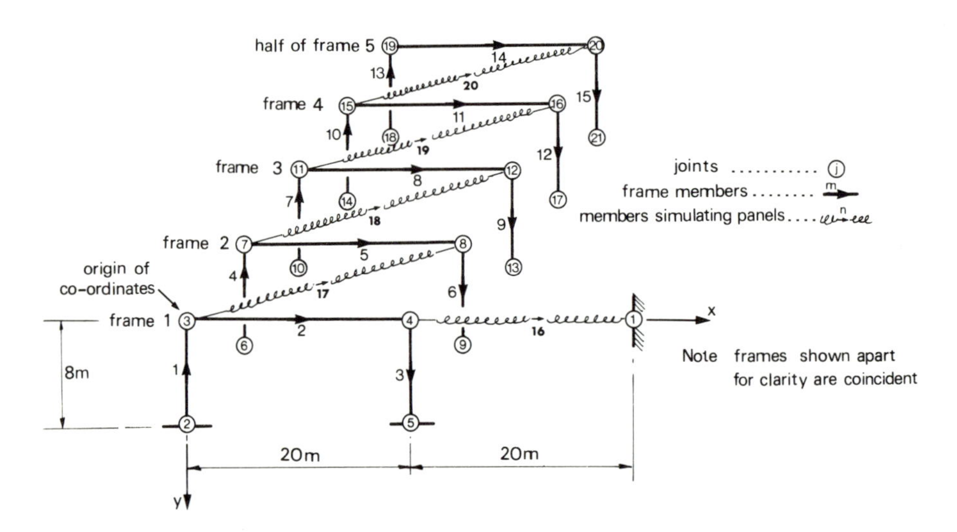

Fig. 7.12 Mathematical model for half of sheeted building.

For the purposes of an illustrative analysis, it will be assumed that the properties of the gable shear panel are as follows: flexibility $c_g = 0.135$ mm/kN, design strength $V_{ult} = 170$ kN, and it will also be assumed that the gable frame is rigid jointed and identical to the intermediate frames. The equivalent area of a prismatic member 20 m long providing the same stiffness as the gable shear panel is given by $A_g = L/(c_g\ E) = 20000/(0.135 \times 207) = 715.7\ \text{mm}^2$. Similarly, the area of the prismatic members replacing the roof sheeting is given by $A = 20\,000/(0.0819 \times 207) = 1180\ \text{mm}^2$.

Plane frame analysis can be carried out using any one of a large number of different readily available computer programs and, naturally, the form of the data and output varies considerably from program to program. For illustration, the results of a computer run of the above example using a program written by the first author are given below. These results include a repeat of the input data together with, for checking purposes, the member lengths and inclinations calculated from the joint co-ordinates. The program concerned is also capable of performing elastic-plastic analysis with the shear panels represented as yielding ties and the format of the output to some extent reflects this capability and also other available facilities that are not used in this example. Although the data is set up so that a full elastic-plastic analysis is possible, only the elastic analysis is considered here. An example of elastic-plastic analysis up to plastic collapse will be given in connection with the next example. The output is quite fully annotated so that no further explanation is considered necessary. The relevant results, extracted from this output, are given in table 7.5. These may be compared with those given earlier for a rigid gable. Where relevant, table 7.5 quotes average values for the two eaves joints of a frame.

Table 7.5 Summarised results of computer analysis

Frame number	Sidesway (mm)	Eaves moment (kNm)	Panel force (kN)
1 (gable)	4.355	6.59	
2	6.916	10.46	27.04
3	8.722	13.19	18.63
4	9.805	14.83	10.90
5	10.225	15.46	3.628

Computer output for section 7.4.5

```
      21  JOINTS    15  MEMBERS     5  YIELDING TIES

  MODE =  0

    5  LOADED JOINTS          1  LOAD CASES          0  MEMBERS WITH UDL

  YOUNGS MODULUS          207.00

  LOAD FACTOR       1.000
```

	NUMBER	DEGREES OF FREEDOM		CO-ORDINATES x	y
JOINT DATA	1	0	0	0.400000E 05	0.000000E 00
JOINT DATA	2	1	1	0.000000E 00	0.800000E 04
JOINT DATA	3	3	111	0.000000E 00	0.000000E 00
JOINT DATA	4	3	111	0.200000E 05	0.000000E 00
JOINT DATA	5	1	1	0.200000E 05	0.800000E 04
JOINT DATA	6	1	1	0.000000E 00	0.800000E 04
JOINT DATA	7	3	111	0.000000E 00	0.000000E 00
JOINT DATA	8	3	111	0.200000E 05	0.000000E 00
JOINT DATA	9	1	1	0.200000E 05	0.800000E 04
JOINT DATA	10	1	1	0.000000E 00	0.800000E 04
JOINT DATA	11	3	111	0.000000E 00	0.000000E 00
JOINT DATA	12	3	111	0.200000E 05	0.000000E 00
JOINT DATA	13	1	1	0.200000E 05	0.800000E 04
JOINT DATA	14	1	1	0.000000E 00	0.800000E 04
JOINT DATA	15	3	111	0.000000E 00	0.000000E 00
JOINT DATA	16	3	111	0.200000E 05	0.000000E 00
JOINT DATA	17	1	1	0.200000E 05	0.800000E 04
JOINT DATA	18	1	1	0.000000E 00	0.800000E 04
JOINT DATA	19	3	111	0.000000E 00	0.000000E 00
JOINT DATA	20	3	111	0.200000E 05	0.000000E 00
JOINT DATA	21	1	1	0.200000E 05	0.800000E 04

	NUMBER		END 1	END 2	CRITICAL SECTIONS							
MEMBER	1	DATA	2	3	0	0	TYPE	1	L =	8000.000	INCL =	-90.000
MEMBER	2	DATA	3	4	2	2	TYPE	1	L =	20000.000	INCL =	0.000
MEMBER	3	DATA	4	5	0	0	TYPE	1	L =	8000.000	INCL =	90.000
MEMBER	4	DATA	6	7	0	0	TYPE	1	L =	8000.000	INCL =	-90.000
MEMBER	5	DATA	7	8	2	2	TYPE	1	L =	20000.000	INCL =	0.000
MEMBER	6	DATA	8	9	0	0	TYPE	1	L =	8000.000	INCL =	90.000
MEMBER	7	DATA	10	11	0	0	TYPE	1	L =	8000.000	INCL =	-90.000
MEMBER	8	DATA	11	12	2	2	TYPE	1	L =	20000.000	INCL =	0.000
MEMBER	9	DATA	12	13	0	0	TYPE	1	L =	8000.000	INCL =	90.000
MEMBER	10	DATA	14	15	0	0	TYPE	1	L =	8000.000	INCL =	-90.000
MEMBER	11	DATA	15	16	2	2	TYPE	1	L =	20000.000	INCL =	0.000
MEMBER	12	DATA	16	17	0	0	TYPE	1	L =	8000.000	INCL =	90.000
MEMBER	13	DATA	18	19	0	0	TYPE	2	L =	8000.000	INCL =	-90.000
MEMBER	14	DATA	19	20	2	2	TYPE	2	L =	20000.000	INCL =	0.000
MEMBER	15	DATA	20	21	0	0	TYPE	2	L =	8000.000	INCL =	90.000

YIELDING TIES

MEMBER	16	DATA	1	4	0	0	TYPE	3	L =	20000.000	INCL =	180.000
MEMBER	17	DATA	3	8	0	0	TYPE	4	L =	20000.000	INCL =	0.000
MEMBER	18	DATA	7	12	0	0	TYPE	4	L =	20000.000	INCL =	0.000
MEMBER	19	DATA	11	16	0	0	TYPE	4	L =	20000.000	INCL =	0.000
MEMBER	20	DATA	15	20	0	0	TYPE	4	L =	20000.000	INCL =	0.000

MEMBER PROPERTIES

GROUP	A	I	MP
1	8360.00	350829952.00	398310.00
2	4180.00	175414976.00	199155.00
3	715.70	0.00	170.00
4	1180.00	0.00	106.00

LOAD VECTORS

JOINT	3	1	LOADS	5.5125
JOINT	7	1	LOADS	11.0250
JOINT	11	1	LOADS	11.0250
JOINT	15	1	LOADS	11.0250
JOINT	19	1	LOADS	5.5125

DISPLACEMENTS AT JOINTS

		X	Y	ROTATION
JOINT	2	0.00000E 00	0.00000E 00	0.69061E-03
JOINT	3	0.45384E 01	-0.30440E-02	0.32066E-03
JOINT	4	0.41719E 01	0.30445E-02	0.28449E-03
JOINT	5	0.00000E 00	0.00000E 00	0.63998E-03
JOINT	6	0.00000E 00	0.00000E 00	0.10791E-02
JOINT	7	0.70796E 01	-0.48339E-02	0.49664E-03
JOINT	8	0.67521E 01	0.48339E-02	0.46433E-03
JOINT	9	0.00000E 00	0.00000E 00	0.10339E-02
JOINT	10	0.00000E 00	0.00000E 00	0.13485E-02
JOINT	11	0.88389E 01	-0.60961E-02	0.61751E-03
JOINT	12	0.86047E 01	0.60961E-02	0.59439E-03
JOINT	13	0.00000E 00	0.00000E 00	0.13162E-02
JOINT	14	0.00000E 00	0.00000E 00	0.15080E-02
JOINT	15	0.98785E 01	-0.68532E-02	0.68847E-03
JOINT	16	0.97313E 01	0.68532E-02	0.67393E-03
JOINT	17	0.00000E 00	0.00000E 00	0.14876E-02
JOINT	18	0.00000E 00	0.00000E 00	0.15691E-02
JOINT	19	0.10277E 02	-0.71462E-02	0.71551E-03
JOINT	20	0.10172E 02	0.71463E-02	0.70515E-03
JOINT	21	0.00000E 00	0.00000E 00	0.15546E-02

MEMBER FORCES

				END 1			END 2	
			AXIAL	SHEAR	MOMENT	AXIAL	SHEAR	MOMENT
MEMBER	1	VECTOR 1	-0.65854E 00	-0.83959E 00	-0.46566E-09	0.65854E 00	0.83959E 00	-0.67167E 04
MEMBER	2	VECTOR 1	0.31710E 02	0.65854E 00	0.67167E 04	-0.31710E 02	-0.65854E 00	0.64541E 04
MEMBER	3	VECTOR 1	0.65863E 00	-0.80676E 00	-0.64541E 04	-0.65863E 00	0.80676E 00	-0.11642E-08
MEMBER	4	VECTOR 1	-0.10458E 01	-0.13219E 01	0.46566E-09	0.10458E 01	0.13219E 01	-0.10575E 05
MEMBER	5	VECTOR 1	0.28330E 02	0.10458E 01	0.10575E 05	-0.28330E 02	-0.10458E 01	0.10340E 05
MEMBER	6	VECTOR 1	0.10458E 01	-0.12925E 01	-0.10340E 05	-0.10458E 01	0.12925E 01	-0.46566E-09
MEMBER	7	VECTOR 1	-0.13188E 01	-0.16590E 01	0.37253E-08	0.13188E 01	0.16590E 01	-0.13272E 05
MEMBER	8	VECTOR 1	0.20264E 02	0.13188E 01	0.13272E 05	-0.20264E 02	-0.13188E 01	0.13104E 05
MEMBER	9	VECTOR 1	0.13188E 01	-0.16380E 01	-0.13104E 05	-0.13188E 01	0.16380E 01	-0.13970E-08
MEMBER	10	VECTOR 1	-0.14826E 01	-0.18599E 01	0.93132E-09	0.14826E 01	0.18599E 01	-0.14879E 05
MEMBER	11	VECTOR 1	0.12745E 02	0.14826E 01	0.14879E 05	-0.12745E 02	-0.14826E 01	0.14773E 05
MEMBER	12	VECTOR 1	0.14826E 01	-0.18467E 01	-0.14773E 05	-0.14826E 01	0.18467E 01	-0.18626E-08
MEMBER	13	VECTOR 1	-0.77300E 00	-0.96861E 00	-0.13970E-08	0.77300E 00	0.96861E 00	-0.77489E 04
MEMBER	14	VECTOR 1	0.45439E 01	0.77300E 00	0.77489E 04	-0.45439E 01	-0.77300E 00	0.77112E 04
MEMBER	15	VECTOR 1	0.77300E 00	-0.96390E 00	-0.77112E 04	-0.77300E 00	0.96390E 00	-0.23283E-08
MEMBER	16	VECTOR 1	0.30903E 02	0.00000E 00	0.00000E 00	-0.30903E 02	0.00000E 00	0.00000E 00
MEMBER	17	VECTOR 1	-0.27037E 02	0.00000E 00	0.00000E 00	0.27037E 02	0.00000E 00	0.00000E 00
MEMBER	18	VECTOR 1	-0.18626E 02	0.00000E 00	0.00000E 00	0.18626E 02	0.00000E 00	0.00000E 00
MEMBER	19	VECTOR 1	-0.10898E 02	0.00000E 00	0.00000E 00	0.10898E 02	0.00000E 00	0.00000E 00
MEMBER	20	VECTOR 1	-0.35800E 01	0.00000E 00	0.00000E 00	0.35800E 01	0.00000E 00	0.00000E 00

7.5 Pitched roof structure subject to vertical load

The structure shown in fig. 7.13 has already been considered in section 4.4 as an example of manual plastic analysis of a complete clad structure. Here the full range of alternative analyses will be considered as follows:

1. Elastic analysis of bare frame
2. Manual elastic analysis of clad frame
3. Computer elastic analysis of clad frame

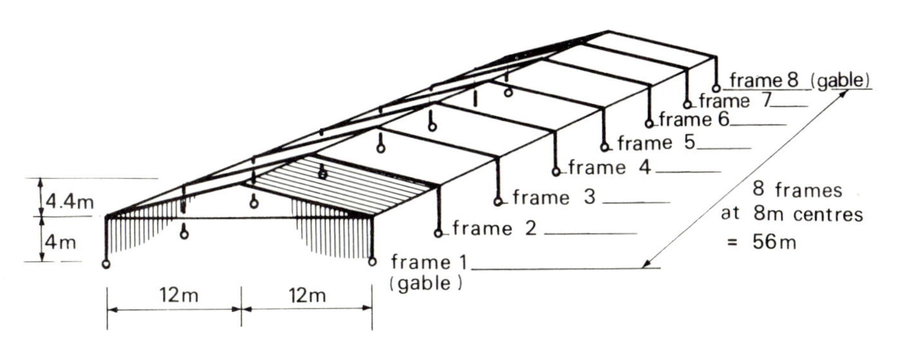

Fig. 7.13 Design example, pitched roof structure.

4. Plastic analysis of bare frame
5. Manual plastic analysis of clad frame
6. Computer plastic analysis of clad frame.

The frames are subject to the following vertical line loads using the partial load factors specified in the European recommendations: characteristic dead load 4 kN/m per frame with $\gamma = 1.33$, characteristic imposed load 7 kN/m per frame with $\gamma = 1.5$, basic design load $= (0.9 \times 1.33 \times 4) + (1.50 \times 7) = 15.29$ kN/m in plan, design load for plastic design $= 1.12 \times 15.29 = 17.12$ kN/m in plan. The frames are of uniform section with pinned bases. The relevant properties of the frames and cladding panels are - frame (457 X 191 X 67 kg/m U.B.): area = 85.4 cm^2, I = 29337 cm^4, yield moment M_y = 316.8 kNm, full plastic moment M_{pl} = 359.9 kNm; diaphragms: flexibility c = 0.10 mm/kN, design strength V^* = 180 kN. It may be noted that, according to the European recommendations, the material factor for steel is equal to unity so that the yield moment is also the design moment for elastic design.

7.5.1 Elastic analysis of bare frame

This analysis is carried out partly for comparison purposes and partly because some of the results will be utilised later in the analysis of the clad structure. The analysis will not be given in detail, but relevant results will be presented as though they had been obtained by the method of moment distribution.

Thus, the complete bending moment diagram shown in fig. 7.14(c) is obtained as a combination of the no-sway analysis shown in fig. 7.14(a) and the sway analysis shown in fig. 7.14(b). In the no-sway analysis the joints are assumed to be fixed in position but free to rotate and it is important to realise that this part of the analysis cannot be changed in any way by stressed skin action. The no-sway analysis implies horizontal eaves forces of 235.6 kN necessary to prevent frames from spreading and, in the final distribution of bending moment shown in fig. 7.14(c), it is a condition of équilibrium that these forces are exactly balanced by the forces implied in the sway distribution of bending moment shown in fig. 7.14(b). The sway distribution of moments is usually obtained by considering an arbitrary sway and then finding what proportion of this arbitrary sway is necessary to satisfy equilibrium and it is in this part of the total analysis that the forces and bending moments can be significantly reduced by stressed skin action. For later use, the eaves deflections implied in this sway analysis are also calculated.

The final distribution of bending moment shown in fig. 7.14(c) is obtained as the sum of (a) and (b) and implies the sway deflections of (b) at the joints of the structure only. The maximum bending moment is at the eaves and has a value of 474.9 kNm. This is much higher than the design moment of 316.8 kNm and the design can in no way be justified by an elastic analysis of the bare frames.

7.5.2 Manual elastic analysis of clad frame

This analysis follows the procedures described in section 4.2. From the sway analysis of the bare frame, the spread flexibility k_{sp} defined in fig. 4.7(b) may be obtained as k_{sp} = 43.53/235.6 = 0.185 mm/kN. As the in-plane flexibility of the diaphragms is c = 0.10 mm/kN and the roof slope is 20.14°, it follows from equation 4.8 that the equivalent horizontal flexibility is c_h = 0.10 $\sec^2$ 20.14° = 0.1134 mm/kN. The relative flexibility ψ_{sp} is therefore given by $\psi_{sp} = c_h/k_{sp}$ = 0.1134/0.185 = 0.614. There is a total of eight frames in the building and therefore, from table 9.13, the reduction factors η for frame bending moments, etc. are as shown in table 7.6.

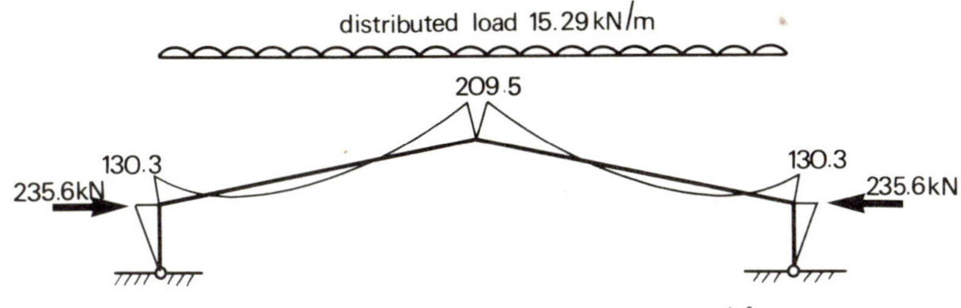

(a) no sway distribution of bending moments and forces

all bending moments in kNm

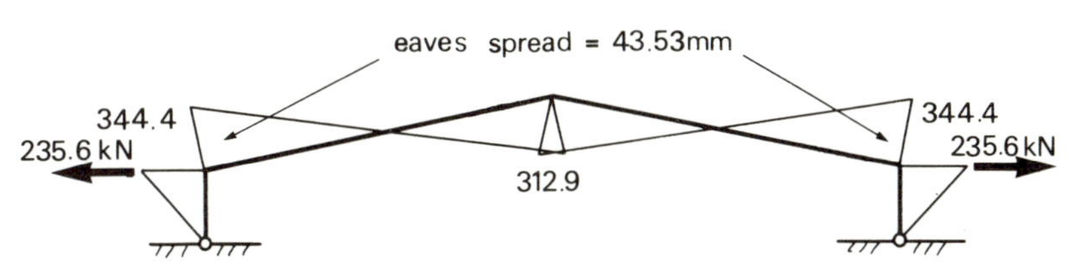

(b) sway distribution of bending moments and forces

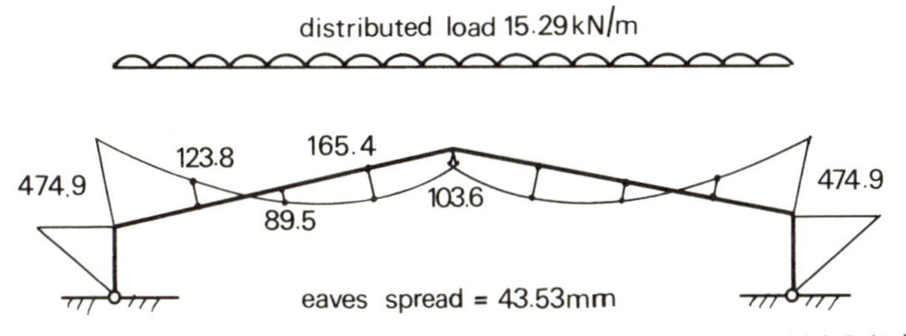

(c) final distribution of moments as a combination of (a) & (b)

Fig. 7.14 Moment distribution for pitched roof frame: (a) no-sway distribution of bending moments and forces, (b) sway distribution of bending moments and forces, (c) final distribution of moments as a combination of (a) and (b).

Table 7.6 Reduction factors for frame forces in pitched roof structure

Frame number	2	3	4
Reduction factor η	0.526	0.762	0.853

The bending moments in the frames of the clad structure may now be obtained as the no-sway moment + η times the sway moment. The corresponding deflections may be found similarly. Thus:

for frames 2 and 7

no-sway	M_{eaves} =	−130.3	M_{apex} =	−209.5
η_2 X sway		−181.2		+164.6
		−311.5 kNm		−44.9 kNm

Eaves deflection = 43.53 X 0.526 = 22.9 mm

for frames 3 and 5

no-sway	M_{eaves} =	−130.3	M_{apex} =	−209.5
η_3 X sway		−262.4		238.4
		−392.7 kNm		28.9 kNm

Eaves deflection = 43.53 X 0.762 = 33.2 mm

for frames 4 and 5

no-sway	M_{eaves} =	−130.3	M_{apex} =	−209.5
η_4 X sway		−293.8		266.9
		−424.1 kNm		57.4 kNm

Eaves deflection = 43.53 X 0.853 = 37.1 mm

It follows that stressed skin action reduces the maximum bending moment from 474.9 kNm to 424.1 kNm, a reduction of 10.7%, but elastic design is still not possible.

The forces in the diaphragms follow in similar way, as before, by considering the implied propping forces in the analysis. At frames 2 and 7, the horizontal propping force implied is 235.6 $(1 - \eta_2)$ = 111.7 kN. Therefore the force taken by diaphragm action is, in the plane of the roof, 111.7 sec 20.14° = 119.0 kN. Similarly, at frames 3 and 6, the force entering the diaphragm is 59.7 kN and at frames 4 and 5 it is 36.9 kN. It follows that the diaphragm forces on each half of the roof structure are as shown in fig. 7.15. The forces shown in fig. 7.15 are those arising as a result

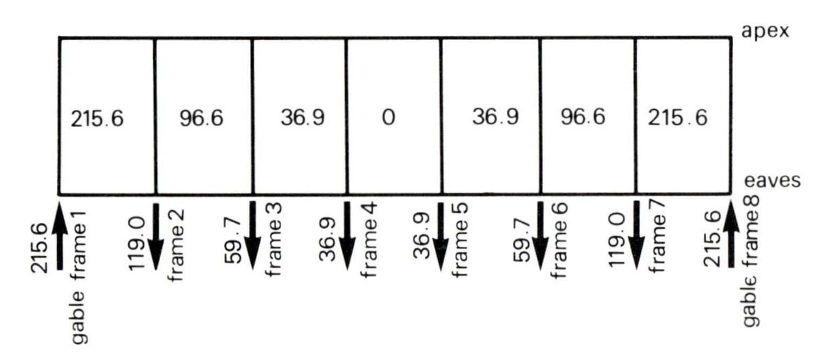

Fig. 7.15 Forces (kN) on roof diaphragms of pitched roof structure.

of the factored design loads and the maximum diaphragm force of 215.6 kN is greater than the design strength Q_{ult}. However, the characteristic (unfactored) load per frame is 11.0 kN and so the maximum shear force in the diaphragms at the characteristic load is 215.6 X 11.0/15.29 = 155.1 kN. It follows that, although elastic design of the clad structure is not permissible on two counts, the above calculation is valid as a serviceability check on a plastic design. The maximum diaphragm force under the characteristic loads is less than the design strength of 180 kN.

7.5.3 Computer elastic analysis of clad frame

Under symmetrical vertical load, the structure is symmetrical about two axes and it is only necessary to analyse one quarter of the complete structure as shown in fig. 7.16. As a condition of symmetry, it is necessary for the apex to be free to move downwards without rotation or lateral movement. If symmetry is to be utilised, it is necessary that the computer program is capable of accommodating such partial constraints. The properties of the diaphragms have already been given, and so the area of the prismatic members replacing them is $A = L/cE = 12781/(0.1 \times 207) = 617.45\ \text{mm}^2$. The data and output now follow and have the same format as before. In this case the analysis will be continued through to plastic collapse but the elastic-plastic phase will be presented later. It may be noted that the frame members have been given unrealistically large cross-sectional areas in order to suppress the influence of axial strains in the frame. This is not necessary but has been done to improve the comparison with the results from the manual method of analysis given earlier. The influence of axial strains is quite significant and it is more accurate to include them. Avoiding their influence here must be seen as being for illustrative purposes only.

The important results extracted from this computer output are as follows. These may be compared with the results of the manual analysis given previously. There are inevitable slight differences as the manual analysis is based on linear interpolation from a table of factors which are themselves only given to three significant figures.

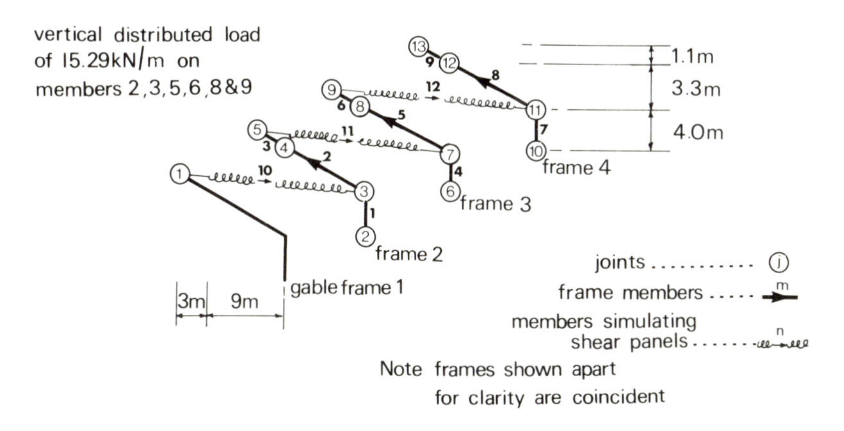

Fig. 7.16 Mathematical model of one quarter of a sheeted building.

Computer output for section 7.5.3

13 JOINTS 9 MEMBERS 3 YIELDING TIES

MODE = 0

0 LOADED JOINTS 1 LOAD CASES 6 MEMBERS WITH UDL

YOUNGS MODULUS 207.00

LOAD FACTOR 1.000

	NO.	DEG. OF FREEDOM		CO-ORDINATES x	CO-ORDINATES y
JOINT DATA	1	0	0	0.000000E 00	0.000000E 00
JOINT DATA	2	1	1	0.120000E 05	0.840000E 04
JOINT DATA	3	3	111	0.120000E 05	0.440000E 04
JOINT DATA	4	3	111	0.300000E 04	0.110000E 04
JOINT DATA	5	1	10	0.000000E 00	0.000000E 00
JOINT DATA	6	1	1	0.120000E 05	0.840000E 04
JOINT DATA	7	3	111	0.120000E 05	0.440000E 04
JOINT DATA	8	3	111	0.300000E 04	0.110000E 04
JOINT DATA	9	1	10	0.000000E 00	0.000000E 00
JOINT DATA	10	1	1	0.120000E 05	0.840000E 04
JOINT DATA	11	3	111	0.120000E 05	0.440000E 04
JOINT DATA	12	3	111	0.300000E 04	0.110000E 04
JOINT DATA	13	1	10	0.000000E 00	0.000000E 00

	NO.	END 1	END 2	CRITICAL SECTIONS		TYPE				
MEMBER DATA	1	2	3	0	0	1	L =	4000.000	INCL =	-90.000
MEMBER DATA	2	3	4	2	2	1	L =	9585.926	INCL =	200.136
MEMBER DATA	3	4	5	0	2	1	L =	3195.309	INCL =	200.136
MEMBER DATA	4	6	7	0	0	1	L =	4000.000	INCL =	-90.000
MEMBER DATA	5	7	8	2	2	1	L =	9585.926	INCL =	200.136
MEMBER DATA	6	8	9	0	2	1	L =	3195.309	INCL =	200.136
MEMBER DATA	7	10	11	0	0	1	L =	4000.000	INCL =	-90.000
MEMBER DATA	8	11	12	2	2	1	L =	9585.926	INCL =	200.136
MEMBER DATA	9	12	13	0	2	1	L =	3195.309	INCL =	200.136
YIELDING TIES										
MEMBER DATA	10	1	3	0	0	2	L =	12781.234	INCL =	20.136
MEMBER DATA	11	5	7	0	0	2	L =	12781.234	INCL =	20.136
MEMBER DATA	12	9	11	0	0	2	L =	12781.234	INCL =	20.136

9 CRITICAL SECTIONS

MEMBER PROPERTIES

GROUP	A	I	MP	K1	K2
1	90000.00	293369984.00	359900.00	0.00	0.00
2	617.45	0.00	180.00	0.00	0.00

DISTRIBUTED LOADS

VERTICAL ON MEMBER	2	0.15290E-01
VERTICAL ON MEMBER	3	0.15290E-01
VERTICAL ON MEMBER	5	0.15290E-01
VERTICAL ON MEMBER	6	0.15290E-01
VERTICAL ON MEMBER	8	0.15290E-01
VERTICAL ON MEMBER	9	0.15290E-01

Locations where displacements are to be output in elastic-plastic phase.

6 DISPLACEMENT LOCATIONS 3 1 5 1 7 1 9 1 11 1 13 1

INITIAL ELASTIC ANALYSIS (at unit load factor)

DISPLACEMENTS AT JOINTS

		X	Y	ROTATION
JOINT	2	0.00000E 00	0.00000E 00	0.91296E-02
JOINT	3	0.22845E 02	0.30595E-01	-0.11254E-02
JOINT	4	0.33607E 00	0.61887E 02	-0.19194E-02
JOINT	5	0.00000E 00	0.62944E 02	0.00000E 00
JOINT	6	0.00000E 00	0.00000E 00	0.12630E-01
JOINT	7	0.33241E 02	0.35015E-01	-0.32910E-03
JOINT	8	0.21303E 01	0.85212E 02	-0.48110E-02
JOINT	9	0.00000E 00	0.91116E 02	0.00000E 00
JOINT	10	0.00000E 00	0.00000E 00	0.13981E-01
JOINT	11	0.37255E 02	0.36719E-01	-0.20742E-04
JOINT	12	0.28241E 01	0.94197E 02	-0.59257E-02
JOINT	13	0.00000E 00	0.10197E 03	0.00000E 00

MEMBER FORCES

			END 1 AXIAL	END 1 SHEAR	END 1 MOMENT	END 2 AXIAL	END 2 SHEAR	END 2 MOMENT
MEMBER	1	VECTOR 1	0.14249E 03	-0.77845E 02	0.14901E-07	-0.14249E 03	0.77845E 02	-0.31138E 06
MEMBER	2	VECTOR 1	0.33673E 03	0.10698E 03	0.31138E 06	-0.28936E 03	0.22216E 02	0.94906E 05
MEMBER	3	VECTOR 1	0.28936E 03	-0.22216E 02	-0.94906E 05	-0.27357E 03	0.65282E 02	-0.44885E 05
MEMBER	4	VECTOR 1	0.16307E 03	-0.98371E 02	0.67055E-07	-0.16307E 03	0.98371E 02	-0.39348E 06
MEMBER	5	VECTOR 1	0.24402E 03	0.11924E 03	0.39348E 06	-0.19665E 03	0.99605E 01	0.13028E 06
MEMBER	6	VECTOR 1	0.19665E 03	-0.99604E 01	-0.13028E 06	-0.18086E 03	0.53027E 02	0.29650E 05
MEMBER	7	VECTOR 1	0.17101E 03	-0.10629E 03	0.44703E-07	-0.17101E 03	0.10629E 03	-0.42515E 06
MEMBER	8	VECTOR 1	0.19490E 03	0.12396E 03	0.42515E 06	-0.14752E 03	0.52348E 01	0.14392E 06
MEMBER	9	VECTOR 1	0.14752E 03	-0.52348E 01	-0.14392E 06	-0.13173E 03	0.48301E 02	0.58385E 05
MEMBER	10	VECTOR 1	-0.21459E 03	0.00000E 00	0.00000E 00	0.21459E 03	0.00000E 00	0.00000E 00
MEMBER	11	VECTOR 1	-0.95524E 02	0.00000E 00	0.00000E 00	0.95524E 02	0.00000E 00	0.00000E 00
MEMBER	12	VECTOR 1	-0.36235E 02	0.00000E 00	0.00000E 00	0.36235E 02	0.00000E 00	0.00000E 00

for frames 2 and 7 $M_{eaves} = -311.4$ kNm $M_{apex} = -44.9$ kNm
Eaves deflection = 22.8 mm

for frames 3 and 6 $M_{eaves} = -393.5$ kNm $M_{apex} = 29.7$ kNm
Eaves deflection = 33.2 mm

for frames 4 and 5 $M_{eaves} = -425.2$ kNm $M_{apex} = 58.4$ kNm
Eaves deflection = 37.3 mm

shear panel forces 214.6 kN, 95.5 kN, 36.2 kN, 0, 36.2 kN, 95.5 kN, 214.6 kN

7.5.4 Plastic analysis of bare frame

In order to make the analysis more easy to follow, without destroying any of its characteristics, it is assumed that the plastic hinge in the rafter forms at a purlin point distant 3 m from the apex in plan. The collapse mechanism of one half of one frame is then as shown in fig. 7.17. Noting that the design load for plastic design has been previously calculated as 17.12 kN/m in plan, the virtual work equation for this mechanism is readily written down as

$$17.12\,\gamma_{pl}\left[(3 \times 9\theta) + \left(9 \times \frac{9\theta}{2}\right)\right] = 359.9\left(2 + \frac{3.3}{4}\right)\theta$$

where γ_{pl} is a multiplying factor which must have a value greater than unity if the

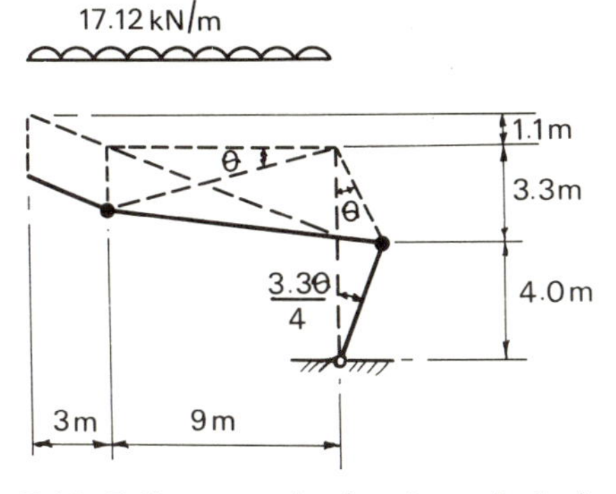

Fig. 7.17 Collapse mechanism for a single frame.

design is adequate. This gives $\gamma_{pl} = 0.880$. It follows that the bare frame is not satisfactory.

7.5.5 Manual plastic analysis of clad frame

The manual plastic analysis of the clad frame was considered in some detail in section 4.4 where it was shown that the plastic multiplying factor when cladding is taken into account is increased to $\gamma_{pl} = 1.04$. As the required serviceability check has already been carried out in section 7.5.2, it follows that the design is satisfactory when the influence of the cladding is considered.

7.5.6 Computer plastic analysis of clad frame

The data for this analysis has already been given in section 7.5.3. In the elastic-plastic phase, the behaviour of the frame is considered under increasing load as plastic hinges form in the frame at some or all of the locations identified by the figure 2 in the 4th and 5th columns of the member data. These locations are termed 'critical sections' and are numbered in order as shown in fig. 7.18. In addition, the

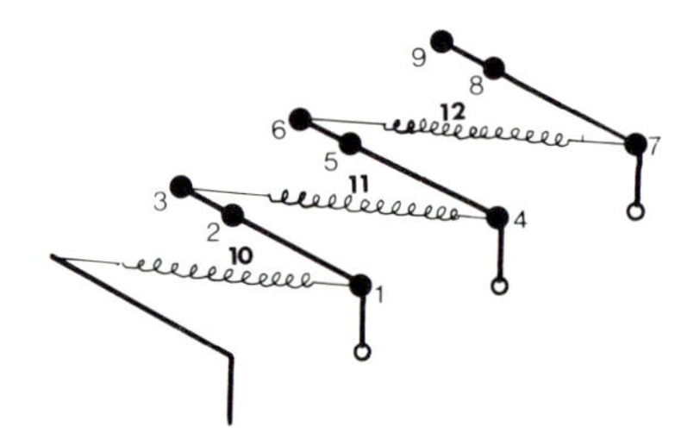

Fig. 7.18 Critical section numbers in elastic–plastic analysis.

springs or ties representing the cladding panels are allowed to yield when they reach the ultimate load of the panel in either tension or compression. Shear panels which may yield also have critical section numbers which follow sequentially after the plastic hinge section numbers. Thus in the structure under consideration, critical sections numbered 1 to 9 are potential plastic hinges and 10 to 12 are potential yielding shear panels. It is a facility of the program used that mid-span plastic hinges occurring in a member carrying a uniformly distributed load may be automatically located at the section of maximum bending moment but this facility was suppressed in this instance in order to allow comparison with the previous analysis.

The relevant computer analysis now follows. This is a continuation of the previously given elastic analysis and therefore starts with a uniformly distributed load on each frame of 15.29 kN/m. The program follows the behaviour of the structure as the load increases setting plastic hinges and allowing shear panels to yield as appropriate. At each stage, the load is output as a multiplying factor (load factor) on the starting load of 15.29 kN/m. The deflections at the eaves and apex of each frame in order are also output. As each plastic hinge forms the stability of the

ENTER ELASTIC-PLASTIC PHASE

12 CRITICAL SECTIONS. LAST 3 ARE YIELDING TIES

SET HINGE 10 LOAD FACTOR 0.838801E 00

DISPLACEMENTS AT FORMATION OF FIRST HINGE
0.1916E 02 0.5280E 02 0.2788E 02 0.7643E 02 0.3125E 02 0.8553E 02
STABILITY CRITERION 0.10000E 01

SET HINGE 7 LOAD FACTOR 0.845710E 00

DISPLACEMENTS FOR EACH LOAD SYSTEM AS SPECIFIED
0.1946E 02 .0.5362E 02 0.2818E 02 0.7725E 02 0.3155E 02 0.8636E 02

STABILITY CRITERION 0.96046E 00

SET HINGE 4 LOAD FACTOR 0.884080E 00

DISPLACEMENTS FOR EACH LOAD SYSTEM AS SPECIFIED
0.2178E 02 0.5996E 02 0.3090E 02 0.8470E 02 0.3533E 02 0.9667E 02

STABILITY CRITERION 0.72302E 00

SET HINGE 1 LOAD FACTOR 0.954116E 00

DISPLACEMENTS FOR EACH LOAD SYSTEM AS SPECIFIED
0.2972E 02 0.8167E 02 0.4188E 02 0.1147E 03 0.4777E 02 0.1306E 03

STABILITY CRITERION 0.28447E 00

SET HINGE 8 LOAD FACTOR 0.114653E 01

DISPLACEMENTS FOR EACH LOAD SYSTEM AS SPECIFIED
0.1115E 03 0.3046E 03 0.1236E 03 0.3376E 03 0.1295E 03 0.3536E 03

STABILITY CRITERION 0.20063E 00

SET HINGE 5 LOAD FACTOR 0.115560E 01

DISPLACEMENTS FOR EACH LOAD SYSTEM AS SPECIFIED
0.1172E 03 0.3201E 03 0.1295E 03 0.3536E 03 0.1357E 03 0.3704E 03

STABILITY CRITERION 0.10427E 00

SET HINGE 2 LOAD FACTOR 0.116523E 01

DISPLACEMENTS FOR EACH LOAD SYSTEM AS SPECIFIED
0.1294E 03 0.3536E 03 0.1424E 03 0.3889E 03 0.1490E 03 0.4067E 03

STABILITY CRITERION -0.37593E-06

MECHANISM CRITERION SATISFIED

CURRENT LIMITING BENDING MOMENTS

	MP	M-MAX	M-MIN
1	0.359900E 06	0.359900E 06	0.359900E 06
2	0.359900E 06	0.359900E 06	0.359900E 06
3	0.359900E 06	0.279138E 06	0.279138E 06
4	0.359900E 06	0.359900E 06	0.359900E 06
5	0.359900E 06	0.359900E 06	0.359900E 06
6	0.359900E 06	0.279138E 06	0.279138E 06
7	0.359900E 06	0.359900E 06	0.359900E 06
8	0.359900E 06	0.359900E 06	0.359900E 06
9	0.359900E 06	0.279138E 06	0.279138E 06
10	0.180000E 03	-0.180000E 03	-0.180000E 03
11	0.180000E 03	-0.119999E 03	-0.119999E 03
12	0.180000E 03	-0.599994E 02	-0.599994E 02

FAILURE LOAD = 1.1652 CYCLE 1

structure is examined and the analysis terminates when a mechanism is discovered. The distribution of bending moments and panel shears is available at each stage and in this case is given at collapse only.

The load factor at failure of 1.1652 given by the elastic-plastic analysis is of course the value obtained previously of 1.04 multiplied by the plastic multiplication factor of 1.12 which was not included in the loads in this instance. The final collapse mechanism (completed by symmetry) showing the order in which the critical sections yielded is shown in fig. 7.19. It is interesting to note that, as is

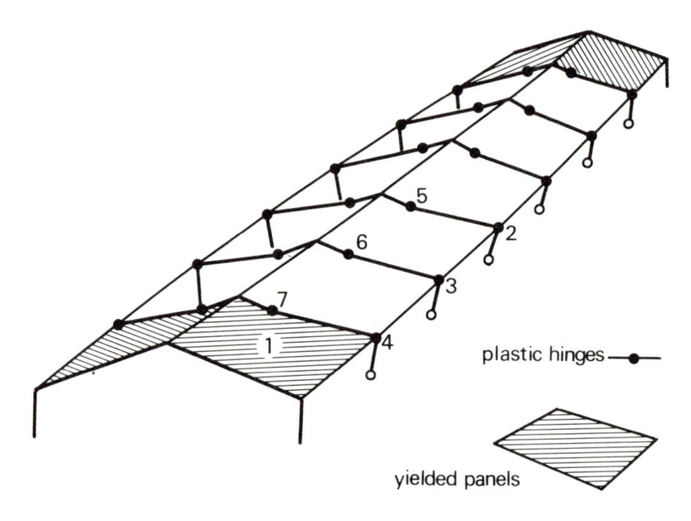

Fig. 7.19 Collapse mechanism for pitched roof structure showing the order in which the critical sections yielded.

usually the case, the gable shear panel yielded first and plasticity in the frames tended to spread outwards from the centre of the building. A closer study of the final distribution of internal forces indicates that the assumption inherent in the simplified manual method of analysis described in section 4.4 is justified. At collapse, the restraint from the sheeting panels has shared itself equally between the frames so that they are each subject to identical loading conditions.

7.6 Further examples of diaphragm calculations

The foregoing numerical examples cover the majority of the situations likely to be met with in practice. Further worked examples will be found in other parts of the book, namely: in section 12.8, the calculation of a sheeted pitched roof frame building including roof lights and diagonal wind bracing in the end bays; in chapter 17, typical calculations demonstrating the ability of decking to ensure lateral stability of the supporting beams and to replace gable and eaves bracing.

7.7 Folded plate roof

The full-scale testing of a folded plate roof is described in section 15.7. Here some of the basic design calculations will be given. Further details can be found in reference 3.25.

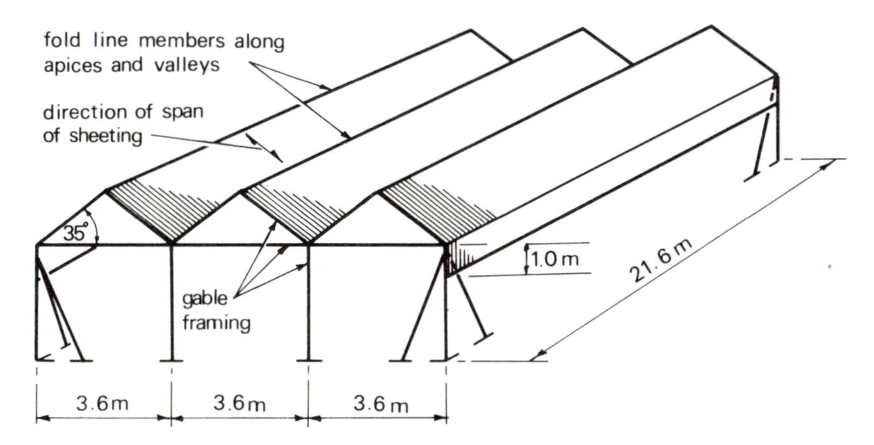

Fig. 7.20 General arrangement of folded plate roof.

The general arrangement of the tested structure is shown in fig. 7.20. The assumed loading is given in table 7.7. The design was carried out in accordance with the design expressions given in section 9.10. The principles involved are expounded in more detail in chapter 15. In order to correlate with the presentation of theoretical results given in section 15.7, the calculations will be carried out in terms of the unfactored loads and the load factor against collapse for each failure mode will be estimated.

Table 7.7 Unfactored design loads

Imposed load	0.75 kN/m^2
Dead load (insulation etc.)	0.23 kN/m^2
Self-weight	0.22 kN/m^2
Total load measured on plan	1.20 kN/m^2

7.7.1 Design of sheeting for bending

As shown in fig. 15.27, the profiled sheeting of the test structure was pressed out of flat sheet and had a curved profile. For the purpose of this example, the sheeting is assumed to have the equivalent trapezoidal profile shown in fig. 7.21. The calculated properties of this profile are: second moment of area $I = 174\,000$ mm^4/m, section modulus $Z = 9270$ mm^3/m, and the yield stress of the material was approximately 230 N/mm^2.

The loading conditions for the design of the sheeting in bending are shown in

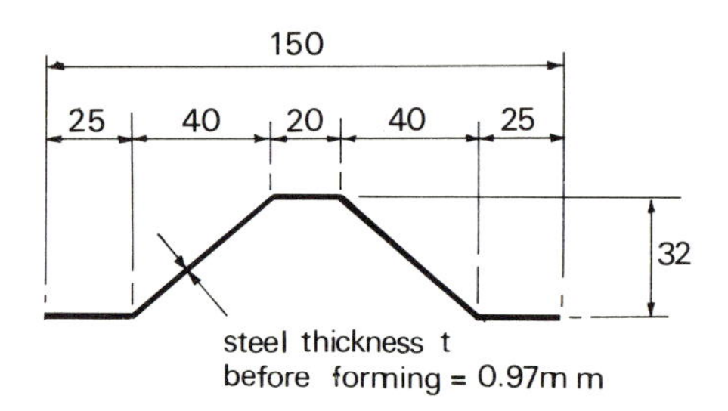

Fig. 7.21 Approximate pressed profile.

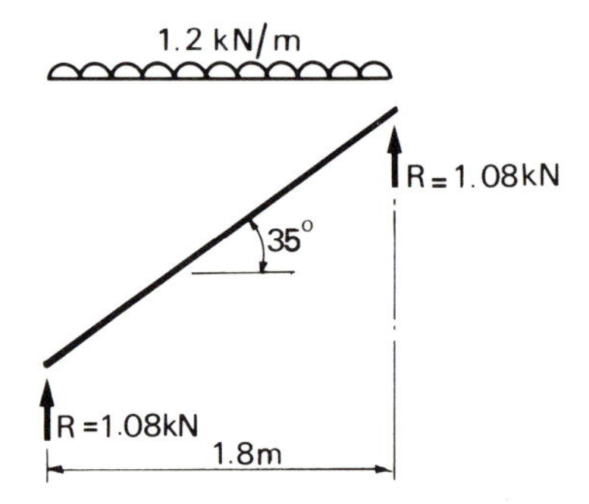

Fig. 7.22 Loading conditions per metre width of sheeting.

fig. 7.22. Thus, the maximum bending stress in the sheeting at mid-span is $(1.2 \times 10^3 \times 1.8) \times 1800/(8 \times 9270) = 52.4$ N/mm^2. Therefore the approximate load factor against failure in the sheeting, taking into account a 10% thinning of the section during pressing of the profile = $(0.9 \times 230)/52.4 = 3.9$.

7.7.2 In-plane loads on individual elements

The reactions R from the simply-supported sheeting shown in fig. 7.22 give rise to the statically determinate forces in the roof planes shown in fig. 7.23. It follows that the in-plane loads on individual roof elements are as follows: for typical members CD, DE, etc., in-plane load $= 2P = 2R$ cosec $35° = 3.77$ kN/m; for outermost roof plane BC, in-plane load $= P = R$ cosec $35° = 1.88$ kN/m; for downstand edge beam AB, in-plane load $= R = 1.08$ kN/m.

7.7.3 Design of fold-line members

The cross-section of the apex members is shown in fig. 7.24. The valley members were similar except that the lips were turned in the opposite direction. The details of the edge members at A and B in the downstand edge beam are shown in fig. 7.25. In each case, the yield stress may be taken as 250 N/mm^2.

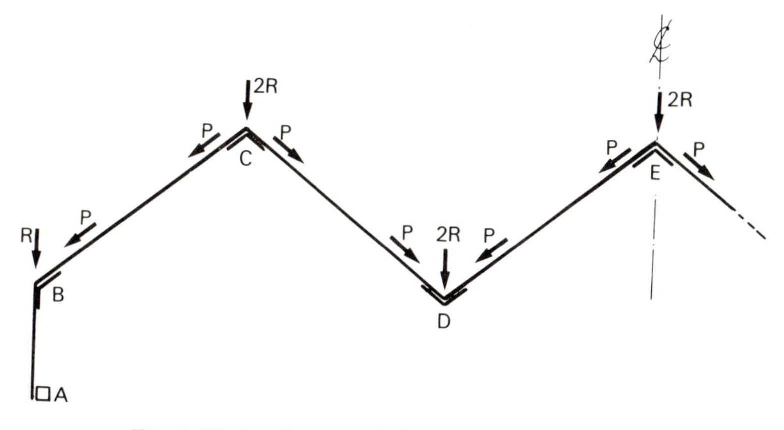

Fig. 7.23 Loads on roof elements per metre length.

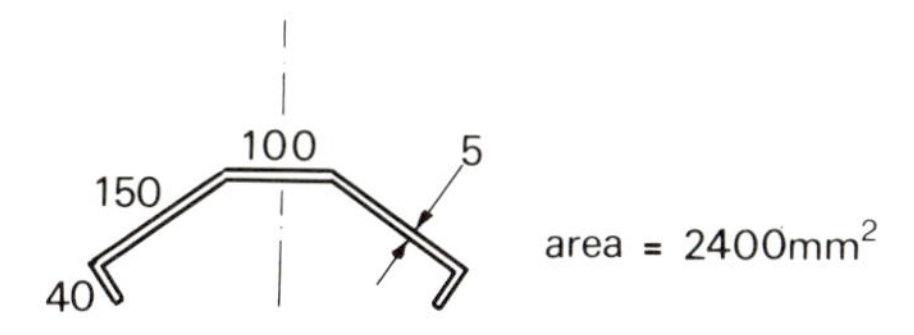

Fig. 7.24 Fold line member at apex.

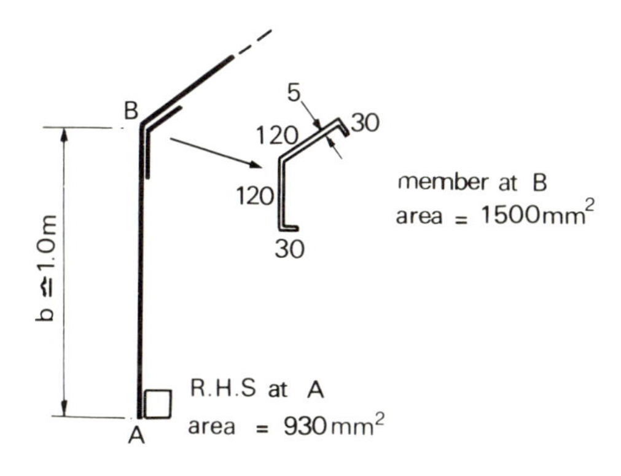

Fig. 7.25 Details of edge beam.

The design of the typical apex and valley members at D, E, . . ., etc., arises from a consideration of the equivalent plate girder shown in fig. 7.26 in which each flange has a cross-section equal to one half of the area of the typical fold-line member shown in fig. 7.24, i.e. 1200 mm^2. Thus, the maximum bending moment in a roof element $= (3.77 \times 21.6^2)/8 = 220$ kNm and the axial stress in flange members D, E, etc. $= (220 \times 10^5)/(1200 \times 2100) = 87.3$ N/mm^2. As the flange mem-

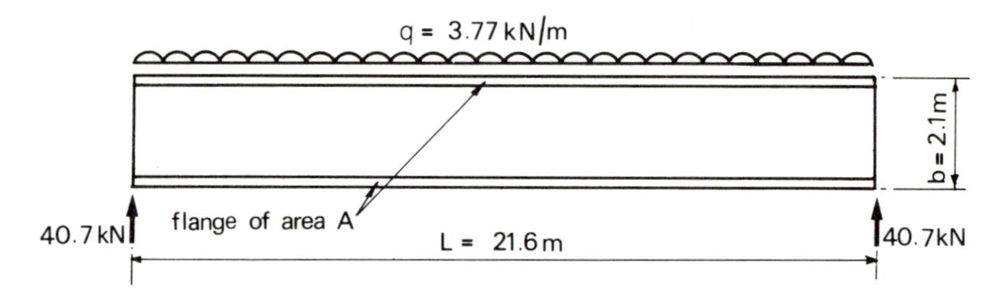

Fig. 7.26 Typical roof element (equivalent plate girder).

bers have continuous lateral support it may be shown that, according to the current British Standard for cold formed steel construction, the permissible compressive stress is 147 N/mm^2 and therefore that the implied load factor is equal to 147/(0.65 × 87.3) = 2.59. It follows similarly that the stresses in the members at A, B and C under the loads shown in fig. 7.23 are (compression positive):

$$\sigma_A = \left(-\frac{1.08 \times 10^6}{930 \times 1000}\right)\frac{21.6^2}{8} = -67.7 \text{ N/mm}^2$$

$$\sigma_B = \left(\frac{1.08 \times 10^6}{1500 \times 1000} - \frac{1.88 \times 10^6}{1500 \times 2100}\right)\frac{21.6^2}{8} = +7.1 \text{ N/mm}^2$$

$$\sigma_C = \left(\frac{1.88 \times 10^6}{2400 \times 2100} + \frac{3.77 \times 10^6}{2400 \times 2100}\right)\frac{21.6^2}{8} = +65.4 \text{ N/mm}^2$$

According to the current British Standard, the permissible stresses in the members at A and B are 155 N/mm^2 and 148 mm^2 respectively so that the load factors implied for the members at A, B and C are greater than the value calculated for the members at D, E, etc. These load factors are, of course, generous and there are two reasons for this. In the first place, it is a practical requirement for erection that the fold-line members should be stiff enough so that they do not deflect or twist excessively during the fixing of the sheeting. The members of the test structure were more than adequate in this respect but for this prototype structure it was prudent to be cautious. In the second place, it was desirable that the tested structure should fail in the sheeting rather than in the fold-line members and the excessive area of fold-line members ensured that this was so.

7.7.4 Design of typical plate element in shear

The maximum shear force in a typical element under the unfactored loads is (3.77 × 21.6)/2 = 40.7 kN. The typical roof element must be checked for this shear force for each of the possible failure modes in turn.

(a) Seam failure

The seam detail that was used in the tested structure is shown in fig. 7.27. This detail is intermediate between the two alternative possibilities that were considered

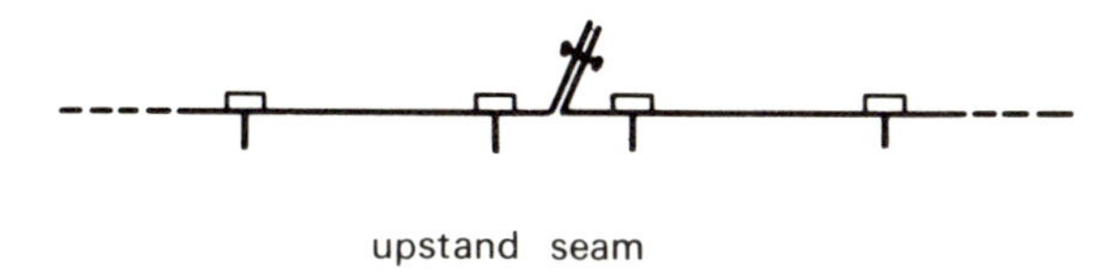

Fig. 7.27 Cross-section through seam.

in deriving the theoretical expression and which are shown in fig. 15.8. In fabricating the roof for the test, the sheet to flange fasteners were placed close to the seams so that the decking condition is probably the more representative of the two alternatives, although both are included in the calculations as representing limits to the actual behaviour.

The data for the seam strength calculation for the most highly stressed seam at the gable is as follows:

n_{sh} = number of sheet widths in plate element = 24
n_s = number of seam fasteners per seam = 22
F_s = ultimate strength of seam fastener = 2.71 kN (test result)
F_p = ultimate strength of sheet to flange fastener = 5.86 kN (test result)
n_f = number of fasteners per sheet width = 7
$\therefore$ for case of decking β_1 = 1.33 (table 9.5), β_3 = 1.0 (note 9.2.8)
for case of sheeting β_1 = 0.84 (table 9.5), β_3 = 6/7 = 0.857 (note 9.2.8)
$\therefore$ for case of decking,

$$V_{ult} = \left[(22 \times 2.71) + \frac{2 \times 1.33 \times 5.86}{1.0}\right]\left(\frac{24}{22}\right) = 82.0 \text{ kN}$$

$\therefore$ load factor = 82.0/40.7 = 2.02.
For case of sheeting,

$$V_{ult} = \left[(22 \times 2.71) + \frac{2 \times 0.84 \times 5.86}{0.857}\right]\left(\frac{24}{22}\right) = 77.6 \text{ kN}$$

$\therefore$ load factor against seam failure = 77.6/40.7 = 1.91
It follows that the predicted failure load at the critical seam is within the range 2.29 to 2.42 kN/m^2 with the likelihood of being nearer the higher figure. It should be noted that the above calculation is based on the average fastener ultimate strength and does not include the usual statistical and material factors. The usual design calculations would give values significantly lower than the above.

(b) Failure in fasteners to gable members
n_{sc} = number of sheet to gable fasteners = 14
F_{sc} = ultimate strength of sheet to gable fastener = 5.86 kN (test result)
$\therefore V_{ult} = n_{sc} F_{sc} + 2F_p = (14 \times 5.86) + (2 \times 5.86) = 93.76$ kN
$\therefore$ load factor against failure in gable fasteners = 93.76/40.7 = 2.30

(c) Shear buckling of sheeting
t = the net thickness of steel sheet = 0.97 mm
E = Young's modulus for steel = 210 kN/mm^2

ν = Poisson's ratio for steel = 0.25

b = depth of plate element = 2100 mm

D_x = the bending stiffness of steel sheet parallel to corrugations

$$= \left(\frac{\text{corrugation pitch}}{\text{developed length}} \frac{Et^3}{12(1-\nu^2)}\right) = \frac{150 \times 210 \times 0.97^3}{171 \times 12(1-0.25^2)}$$

$= 14.9$ kN mm^2/mm

D_y = the bending stiffness of steel sheet perpendicular to corrugations $= EI_y/d$ $= (210 \times 174\,000)/1000 = 36\,540$ kN mm^2/mm

The best estimate of the buckling load is therefore, using equation 10.47,

$$V_{ult} = \frac{36}{b} D_x^{\frac{1}{4}} D_y^{\frac{3}{4}} = \frac{36 \times 14.9^{\frac{1}{4}} \times 36540^{\frac{3}{4}}}{2100} = 89.1 \text{ kN}$$

∴ load factor against shear buckling = 89.1/40.7 = 2.19

It may be noted that the above calculation does not include the additional 25% reserve of safety usually specified for buckling failure (as in section 9.10).

(d) Failure in sheet to fold-line member fasteners

If we again neglect the additional 25% reserve of strength that is usually specified for these fasteners, the maximum shear force, V_{ult}, that can be sustained is given by $V_{ult} = bF_p/p$ where p = pitch of sheet of flange fasteners = 150 mm and the other quantities have already been defined.

∴ $V_{ult} = 2100 \times 5.86/150 = 82.04$ kN

∴ load factor against failure in flange fasteners = 82.04/40.7 = 2.02

7.7.5 Design of downstand edge girder for shear

The calculations for the downstand edge girder for shear may be carried out in the same way as those for the main roof elements. As the load factor is approximately 3 in this element it is not critical and the calculation will not be given in detail.

7.7.6 Summary of strength calculations

The strength calculations for the main roof elements are summarised in table 7.8. It follows that the probable load factor is between 1.91 and 2.02. The corresponding failure loads on the roof are these values multiplied by 1.2 kN/m^2 giving a range from 2.29 to 2.42 kN/m^2. The probable failure mode involves tearing at the fasteners in the seams adjacent to the gables in the interior plate elements. However, the possibility of failure in the sheet to flange fasteners or even a shear buckling failure cannot be excluded.

7.7.7 Calculation of deflections

For the purpose of predicting the deflection profile over the entire roof, taking account of the calculated stresses in the fold line members near the longitudinal

Table 7.8 Summary of strength calculations for folded plate roof

Modes of failure	Load factor
Bending failure of the sheeting	approximately 3.9
Failure of the fold-line members in axial tension or compression	2.59
Buckling of the sheeting	2.19
Failure of the sheet to flange fasteners	2.02
Failure of seam fasteners	1.91–2.02 (probably nearer 2.02)
Failure of sheet to gable fasteners	2.30

edges, it is convenient to separate the shear deflections from bending deflections. Thus the component of deflection $\Delta_{1.3}$ in section 9.10 is considered separately.

(a) Shear deflection of typical plate element

$$\text{Sheet distortion } \Delta_{1.1} = \frac{d^{2.5}\ \bar{K}\, q\, L^2}{8\, E\, t^{2.5}\, b^2} = \frac{150^{2.5} \times 0.0192 \times 21.6^2 \times 10^3 q}{8 \times 210 \times 0.97^{2.5} \times 2100^2}$$

$$= 0.359q \text{ mm}$$

Note that $\bar{K}$ = sheeting constant for distortional flexibility = 0.0192 and is based on a test result. The other quantities have been defined previously (see figs. 7.21 and 7.26).

$$\text{Shear strain } \Delta_{1.2} = \frac{(1+\nu)\,[1+(2h/d)]\,q\,L^2}{4\,E\,t\,b}$$

$$= \frac{1.25[1 + (2 \times 32/150)] \times 21.6^2 \times 10^3 q}{4 \times 210 \times 0.97 \times 2100} = 0.486q \text{ mm}$$

$$\text{Sheet to flange fasteners } \Delta_{2.1} = \frac{s_p p\, qL^2}{4b^2} = \frac{0.188 \times 150 \times 21.6^2 \times 10^3 q}{4 \times 2100^2}$$

$$= 0.746q \text{ mm}$$

where s_p = slip per sheet to flange fastener = 0.188 mm/kN (test result)

$$\text{Seam fasteners } \Delta_{2.2} = \frac{2\, s_s\, s_p\, (n_{sh} - 2) q\, L}{8(n_s s_p + \beta_1\, s_s)} = \frac{2 \times 0.110 \times 0.188 \times 22 \times 21.6q}{8\,[(22 \times 0.188) + (1.33 \times 0.110)]}$$

$$= 0.574q \text{ mm}$$

where s_s = slip per seam fastener = 0.110 mm/kN (test result)

It should be noted in the above expression that, where the number of seam fasteners varies in proportion to the shear force, the deflection due to seam slip is approximately twice that given in section 9.10. In the tested structure, the seam fasteners were progressively reduced towards the centre of the roof and therefore the factor 2 is introduced in the top line to take account of this.

$$\text{Slip at gable } \Delta_{2.3} = \frac{s_p\, s_{sc}\, q\, L}{2\,(2\,\beta_1\, s_{sc} + n_{sc}\, s_p)} = \frac{0.188 \times 0.188 \times 21.6q}{2[(2 \times 1.33 \times 0.188) + (14 \times 0.188)]}$$

$$= 0.122q \text{ mm}$$

Hence, the total shear deflection in the plane of a typical roof element is $(0.359 + 0.486 + 0.746 + 0.574 + 0.122)q = 2.287q$ mm.

(b) Bending deflection of typical interior plate element

$$\Delta_{1.3} = \frac{qL^4}{38.4\,EAb^2} = \frac{21.6^4 \times 10^9\, q}{38.4 \times 210 \times 1200 \times 2100^2} = 5.10q \text{ mm}$$

(c) Deflection at a typical interior fold line

For a fold line where two typical plate elements meet, the total in-plane deflection of each element is $(2.287 + 5.10) \times 3.77 = 27.8$ mm and it follows from a simple displacement diagram that the vertical deflection at a typical fold line is 27.8/ sin 35° = 48.5 mm.

(d) Non-typical deflections near edges of roof

When a plate element has flange members which carry axial stresses σ_T and σ_B in the top and bottom flanges respectively, it is easy to show that the bending component of mid-span deflection is:

$$\Delta_B = \frac{5L^2\,(\sigma_T - \sigma_B)}{48Eb}$$

The shear deflection of the downstand edge beam may be shown to be 14.4 mm. It then follows that the in-plane displacements of the members shown in fig. 7.23 are:

$$\text{member AB} \quad 14.4 + \frac{5 \times 21.6^2 \times 10^3\,(7.1 + 67.7)}{48 \times 210 \times 1000} = 31.7 \text{ mm}$$

$$\text{member BC } 2.287 \times 1.88 + \frac{5 \times 21.6^2 \times 10^3\,(65.4 - 7.1)}{48 \times 210 \times 2100} = 10.7 \text{ mm}$$

$$\text{member CD } 2.287 \times 3.77 + \frac{5 \times 21.6^2 \times 10^3\,(65.4 + 87.3)}{48 \times 210 \times 2100} = 25.4 \text{ mm}$$

member DE from (c) above = 27.8 mm

Hence, from a series of displacement diagrams the displacement pattern shown in fig. 15.28 may be determined. Figure 15.28 also shows the values of deflection calculated similarly but using values of fastener slip obtained after preloading to the working load. The appropriate reloading values of fastener flexibility are:

s = slip of sheet to flange fastener = 0.038 mm/kN (test result)

s_s = slip of seam fastener = 0.080 mm/kN (test result)

(e) Deflections under wind load

For testing purposes, wind load was simulated by a line load of 0.78 kN/m applied at eaves level. This load is carried by the downstand edge beam and the first plate element, the relevant in-plane components of force being shown in fig. 7.28. As

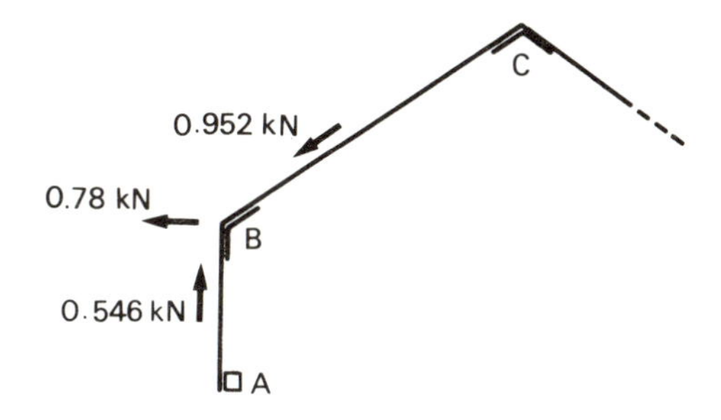

Fig. 7.28 Plate element forces per metre length under wind load.

these are less than the corresponding forces under vertical loads, only a deflection calculation is required.

The fold-line member stresses are:

$$\sigma_A = \left(+\frac{0.546 \times 10^6}{930 \times 1000}\right)\frac{21.6^2}{8} = 34.2 \text{ N/mm}^2$$

$$\sigma_B = \left(-\frac{0.546 \times 10^6}{1500 \times 1000} - \frac{0.952 \times 10^6}{1500 \times 2100}\right)\frac{21.6^2}{8} = -38.9 \text{ N/mm}^2$$

$$\sigma_C = \left(+\frac{0.952 \times 10^6}{2400 \times 2100}\right)\frac{21.6^2}{8} = 11.0 \text{ N/mm}^2$$

and the in-plane displacements are:

$$\text{member AB} \; -14.4 \times \frac{0.546}{1.08} + \frac{5 \times 21.6^2 \times 10^3 (-38.9 - 34.2)}{48 \times 210 \times 1000} = -24.2 \text{ mm}$$

$$\text{member BC} \; 2.287 \times 0.952 + \frac{5 \times 21.6^2 \times 10^3 (11.0 + 38.9)}{48 \times 210 \times 2100} = 7.7 \text{ mm}$$

$$\text{member CD} \; 0 + \frac{5 \times 21.6^2 \times 10^3 (11.0 + 0)}{48 \times 210 \times 2100} = 1.2 \text{ mm}$$

Hence, as before, the displacement pattern shown in fig. 15.32 may be determined.

CHAPTER EIGHT

Examples of actual buildings

8.1 Introduction

A large number of stressed skin buildings have been constructed throughout the world. In this chapter brief descriptions of only a few of these can be given, together with a note of some of the salient design features. The examples have been chosen to indicate something of the evolution of stressed skin design in the U.K.

8.2 SEAC Mark 3 Building System[1.46]

The 'South Eastern Architects Collaboration' was set up in England in 1963 to develop a system of construction suitable for a large range of building types such as schools, offices and libraries. The design was based on a modular component approach involving structural frames, roof and floor decks, cladding, staircases, etc. Progressively, the system was widened to include more components, using a dimensionally co-ordinated framework with a structural grid of 0.6 m. The heights of single storey buildings were in increments of 0.3 m up to 7.5 m. The maximum number of storeys in multi-storey construction was four and could be achieved by various combinations of the standard floor to ceiling heights of 2.4 m, 2.7 m and 3.0 m.

Initially, construction was based on rigid-jointed portal frames but, as the system became more complex with the introduction of longer spans, this concept became increasingly impractical. The difficulties were compounded by the need to produce calculations justifying the design for approximately 180 projects per annum with the inevitable peaks and troughs in the programme. These constraints led to the development, at no extra cost, of a pin-jointed frame solution in which wind forces were taken by conventional bracing. This simplified the details of the beam connections and removed the necessity for fixed column bases so that the columns could be designed for axial load only. Nevertheless, these advantages were offset by the need to build into the beams a variety of possible bracing connections and by the cost of the bracing members themselves.

At this point, profiled metal decking, which had been a feature of the system for some years, was again established as providing the cheapest deck and it was suggested that substantial savings could be effected if the conventional wind bracing were to be replaced by stressed skin action in the deck. This appeared to be extremely economical in that diaphragm action could be obtained in the majority of SEAC buildings at no extra cost and for buildings in higher wind load areas by adding a small number of extra fasteners. Accordingly, tender documents were prepared on a performance specification basis with both the shear and uplift forces defined. The winning deck tender incorporated a profiled steel deck of 38 mm depth and 0.81 mm thickness. The fastener specification was as follows:

sheet to beam fasteners:	3.7 mm diameter shot fired pins with 19 mm diameter X 3 mm thick galvanised steel washers in every corrugation trough at the sheet end and alternate troughs elsewhere.
seam fasteners:	4.1 mm diameter self-drilling, self-tapping screws at 450 mm centres or, for high wind loads, 250 mm centres.

Typical roof construction is shown in fig. 8.1. A typical layout for a complete building that could be achieved by this system is shown in fig. 8.2. Complex plan shapes were designed as a series of rectangular diaphragms as shown in section 3.2.

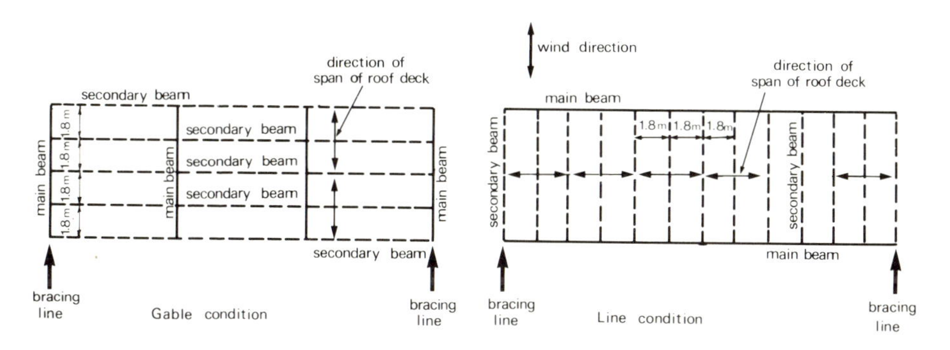

Fig. 8.1 Typical construction of SEAC Mark 3 roof decks.

To verify these proposals, which were made at an early stage in the history of the practical utilisation of stressed skin design, full scale tests were carried out at the University of Salford. These tests included assessment of both the effect of combined wind shear and wind suction and the effect of openings and are described in reference 1.46. The final feature of this development work was the production of detailed design charts relating span, depth and permissible in-plane line load for each of two alternative fixing specifications. These charts were found to substantially reduce the time spent on structural design. A typical example of a SEAC

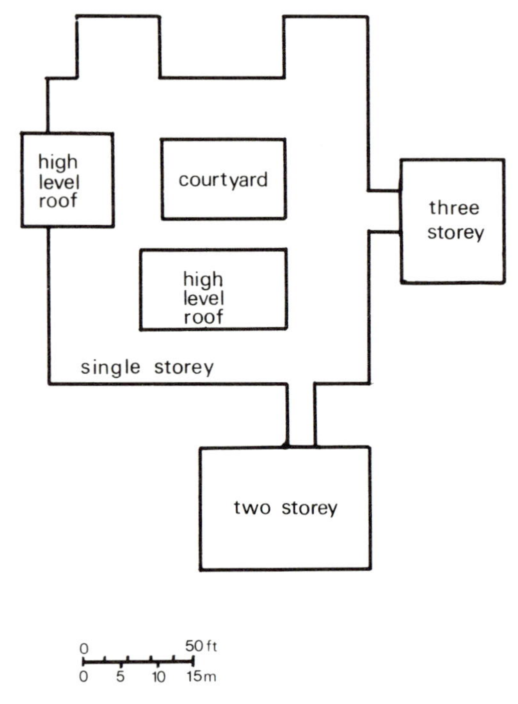

Fig. 8.2 Typical layout of a SEAC secondary school.

school built according to this system has already been shown in fig. 1.1. The direct cost saving in terms of structural steelwork for such single storey construction has been calculated as approximately 6.5%. To this has to be added the indirect saving in simplification of the system and the saving in professional time.

8.3 CLASP Mark 5 Building System

The 'Consortium of Local Authorities Special Programme' was set up in 1957 as a building system designed to meet certain specific problems including site labour shortages and ground movement from mining subsidence. By 1973, over 1500 CLASP buildings had been built in the U.K. alone. CLASP is in some respects similar to SEAC and has a structural grid of 0.9 m and vertical increments of 0.3 m. The structure is a lightweight pin-jointed steel frame which enables buildings to articulate during ground movement and from the start this system included the principle of a diaphragm roof. Initially a timber deck was used, fixed to the steel frame with bolts and toothed plates and the wind load was transferred to the ground through this deck and diagonal steel wall braces. With Mark 5 of the system it was found to be expedient to use a steel deck of 63.5 mm depth fastened to the supporting structure with 3 mm diameter fired pins at 152 mm centres at the sheet ends and 304 mm centres elsewhere. Seam fasteners were 4.1 mm diameter self-

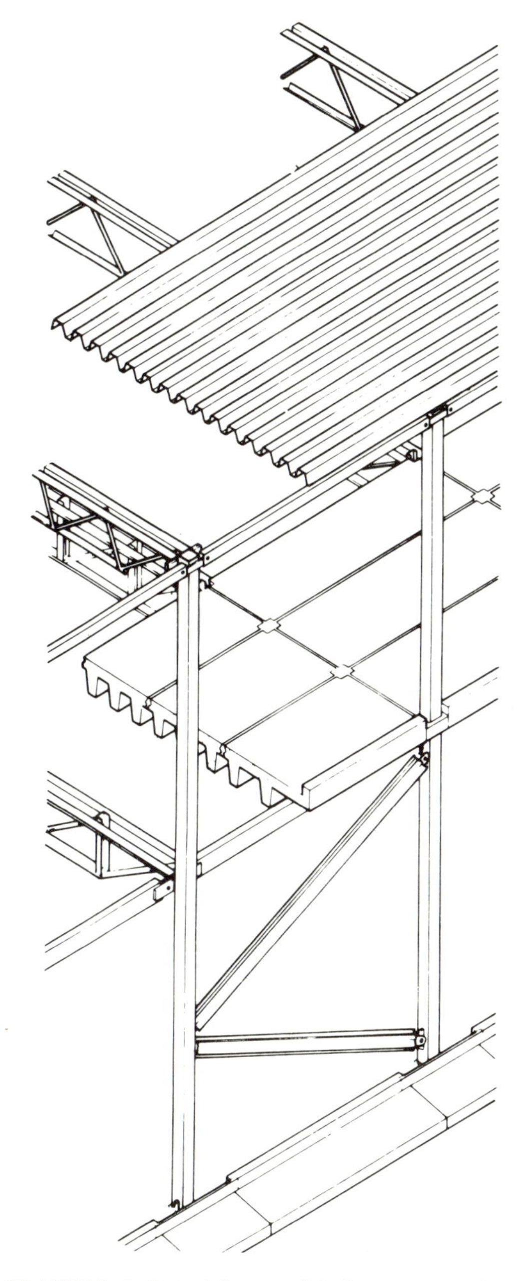

Fig. 8.3 CLASP Mark 5 steel frame with floor and roof diaphragms.

drilling, self-tapping screws at either 450 or 300 mm centres. Figure 8.3 shows a typical construction.

As with the SEAC system, the proposed diaphragms were first fully tested and then design charts were prepared in order to minimise the time spent on structural design. A typical CLASP structure has already been shown in fig. 1.2. The same structure under construction is shown in fig. 8.4. The design was carried out by the County Architect, Nottinghamshire County Council. Figure 8.4 shows clearly how a CLASP structure is erected in order to meet the requirements of temporary stability during construction. The floors and roof are built first, together with the diagonal braces. The side cladding is only added when the roof is complete. Dalestorth Primary School, the first building to be constructed using the CLASP Mark 5 system, is described in reference 1.56.

Fig. 8.4 CLASP computer building under construction.

8.4 New Covent Garden fruit and vegetable market[1.47, 1.60]

An aerial view of this structure is shown in fig. 8.5. It comprises twin buildings each 386 m long and 65.6 m wide which are placed 33.6 m apart and linked by amenity bridges. The roofs are believed to be the largest stressed skin structures in Europe. The length of the building is divided up by firebreak walls, creating, in effect, a series of buildings each about 52 m long. A central gallery with roof lights divides the roof into two parts longitudinally so that individual diaphragms each about 52 m long and 20 m deep span between the firebreak walls. As the total height of the roof is about 9 m, the diaphragm forces are substantial.

The roof construction was of 48 mm deep × 0.8 mm thick steel decking supported on channel purlins which in turn were supported on twin boom rectangular hollow section trusses at 4.72 m centres. The decking was fixed to these purlins by shot-fired pins at 152 mm centres. Seam fasteners were at 125 mm centres. As with

Fig. 8.5 Fruit and Vegetable Building, New Covent Garden, London. (*Photograph by Handford Photography*)

all of these relatively early examples of stressed skin construction, fastening to the supporting structure was on two sides only. No attempt was made to enhance stressed skin action by the provision of shear connectors or the like.

Construction was completed in 1974 and, at the time, it was felt that the acceptance of stressed skin design by the Greater London Council for a project of this size and importance represented a major step forward in the practical utilisation of the method.

8.5 Tablet factory at Beeston

Another example of a major structure stabilised entirely by stressed skin action is the tablet factory built at Beeston, Nottingham, in 1975. A photograph of the completed structure is shown in fig. 8.6 and a plan of the roof showing the major supporting members and the lines of vertical bracing is shown in fig. 8.7. The designers of the building were John Laing Associates Ltd. Figure 8.7 also shows the direction of span of the 47.5 mm deep decking which was supported on secondary members at 3 m centres. Fixing to the supporting structure was by fired pins at an average spacing of 250 mm. Seam fasteners were at 430 mm centres.

A particular feature of the stressed skin design of this structure was that provision was made so that a complete 36 m wide strip of roof cladding running in either direction could be removed without endangering the structure. As the primary and secondary supporting members were at the same level it was originally intended that the diaphragms should be fastened on all four sides. However, it subsequently

Fig. 8.6 Stressed skin roof of tablet factory.

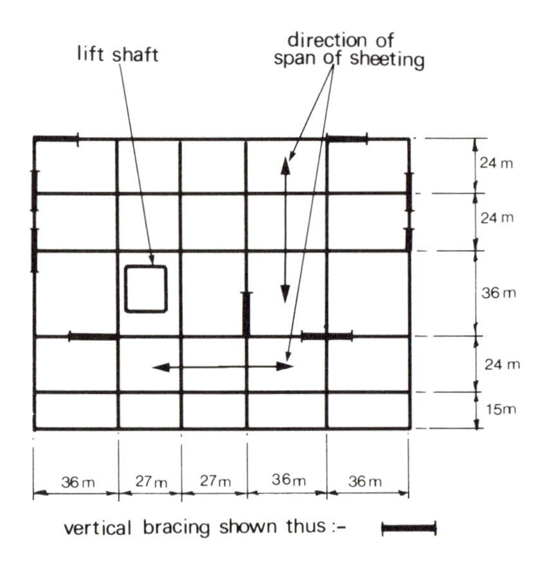

Fig. 8.7 Plan showing roof construction.

became apparent that this was not necessary and that the structure would be satisfactory with fastenings to the supporting members on two sides only.

8.6 Industrial warehouses at Queen's Drive, Nottingham

These buildings were constructed in 1979 and are typical of a number of structures designed by Peter Brett Associates in recent years that are stabilised by stressed skin action. A typical feature of these structures is a relatively deep roof deck spanning directly over the main beams at 5 m centres.

The Queen's Drive Project is a 14 000 sq. m industrial warehouse development consisting of two buildings situated on either side of a central service road. Figure 8.8 shows the leading dimensions and the position of bracings transferring the

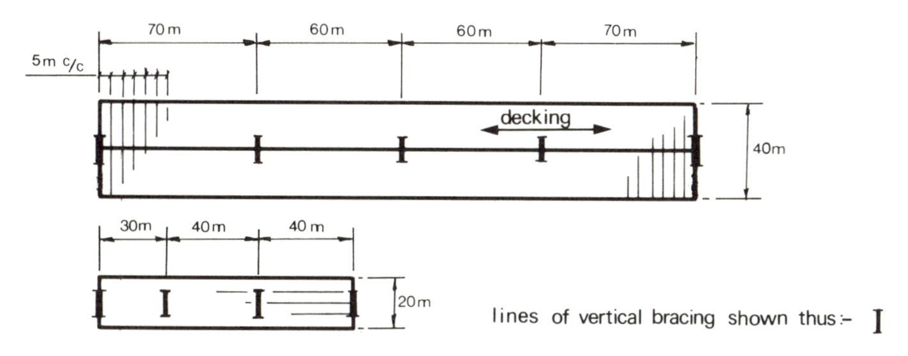

Fig. 8.8 Queen's Drive Project – general arrangement.

Fig. 8.9 Queen's Drive Project – completed structure.
(*Photograph by Jo Reid and John Peck*)

diaphragm forces to the foundations. The design allows for both high volume storage and for manufacturing processes to be carried out and includes internal office accommodation. Figure 8.9 shows part of the completed construction. The main steel frame of the buildings is designed on a 20 m X 5 m bay system, and includes site butt welded joints in order to achieve economy and to control the flat roof deflection. The roof deck is an 80 mm deep X 0.9 mm thick trapezoidal profile fastened to the supporting structure on four sides using 6 mm diameter self-drilling, self-tapping screws. Seam fasteners are 4.8 mm diameter blind rivets at 300 mm centres. Figure 8.10 shows block B under construction. A typical braced bay can be seen in the foreground. In the background, the edge members providing fastening on all four sides are just visible.

Fig. 8.10 Queen's Drive Project under construction.

8.7 Stuttgarter Neckarstadion - main stand

The structure, which is shown in fig. 8.11, was built for the world football championships in 1974. The main stand has a number of unusual features and does not include conventional wind bracing so that it depends on diaphragm action for its stability. The roof deck is 60 mm deep and 0.88 mm thick and spans over purlins at approximately 4.6 m centres. The purlins, in turn, span approximately 23 metres between main frames. Only part of the roof acts as a diaphragm and in this part the thickness of the decking was increased to 1.5 mm. Fastenings to the purlins were self-tapping screws (AM6) in every corrugation trough, i.e. at 167 mm centres. Seam fasteners were blind rivets at 90 mm centres.

Fig. 8.11 Aerial view of the Neckarstadion.

CHAPTER NINE

Summary of design expressions, tables of factors and symbols

9.1 Symbols required for diaphragm strength and flexibility

a = length of diaphragm in the direction perpendicular to the corrugations (mm)

A = cross-sectional area of longitudinal edge member (mm^2)

b = depth of diaphragm in the direction parallel to the corrugations (mm) (see note 9.2.1)

B_w = breadth of weld (mm)

c = overall shear flexibility of diaphragm (mm/kN)

$c_{1.1}$, $c_{1.2}$, etc. = component shear flexibilities (mm/kN)

d = pitch of corrugations (mm)

d_w = observed diameter of arc spot weld (mm)

d_e = effective diameter of arc spot weld (mm)

D_x, D_y = bending stiffness of profiled sheets per unit length perpendicular and parallel to the corrugations respectively (kN mm^2/mm) (see note 9.2.2)

E = modulus of elasticity of steel or aluminium (kN/mm^2)

F_p = design strength of individual sheet to perpendicular member (purlin) fastener (kN)

F_{pr} = design strength of an individual perpendicular member to parallel member (purlin to rafter) connection (kN)

F_s = design strength of individual seam fastener (kN)

F_{sc} = design strength of individual sheet to shear connector fastener or gable fastener in a folded plate (kN)

h = height of profile (mm)

I_y = second moment of area about the neutral axis for a single corrugation

k = frame flexibility (mm/kN)

$\bar{K}_1, \bar{K}_2$ = sheeting constants for distortional flexibility (see note 9.2.3)

l = width of corrugation crest (mm)
L = span of diaphragm between braced frames (mm)
L_w = length of weld (mm)
m = number of panels within sheet length
n = number of panels within length of diaphragm assembly
n_b = number of sheet lengths within depth of diaphragm
n_f = number of sheet to perpendicular member (purlin) fasteners per member per sheet width
n_l = number of sheet lengths within length of diaphragm
n_p = total number of perpendicular members (purlins)
n_s = number of seam fasteners per sidelap (excluding those which pass through both sheets and the supporting members)
n_{sc} = total number of sheet to shear connector fasteners per parallel member (rafter) or number of gable fasteners per gable in an element of a folded plate roof
n_{sh} = number of sheet widths per panel
p = pitch of sheet to perpendicular member (purlin) fasteners (mm)
q = distributed load on diaphragm (kN/mm)
s_p = slip (flexibility) per sheet to perpendicular member (purlin) fastener per unit load (mm/kN) (see note 9.2.4)
s_{pr} = movement of perpendicular member (purlin) to parallel member (rafter) connection per unit load (mm/kN) (see note 9.2.5)
s_s = slip (flexibility) per seam fastener per unit load (mm/kN) (see note 9.2.4)
s_{sc} = slip (flexibility) per sheet to shear connector fastener per unit load (mm/kN) (see note 9.2.4)
t = net sheet thickness excluding galvanising and coatings (mm)
u = perimeter length of a single corrugation
v = shear displacement of diaphragm (mm)
V = shear force in diaphragm (kN)
V^* = design shear capacity of diaphragm (kN)
V_{crit} = shear force on diaphragm to cause overall buckling (kN)
V_{ult} = strength associated with a given failure mode (kN) or ultimate load (kN)
w = vertical load per unit area in plan
$\alpha_1, \alpha_2, \alpha_3, \alpha_4, \alpha_5$ = correction factors to allow for intermediate purlins (perpendicular members) and number of sheet lengths (see note 9.2.6)
β_1, β_2 = factors to allow for number of sheet to perpendicular member (purlin) fasteners per sheet width (see note 9.2.7)
β_3 = (distance between outermost fasteners across sheet width) ÷ (sheet width) (see note 9.2.8)
γ = shear strain or load factor
γ_m = material factor. In the European recommendations, $\gamma_m = 1.0$ for steel members and 1.11 for fasteners
Δ = mid-span deflection of a diaphragm beam (mm)

η	= reduction factor for frame forces and deflections
θ	= inclination of web of profile to the vertical
ν	= Poisson's ratio for steel or aluminium
σ_u	= ultimate strength of plate material (kN/mm^2)
σ_{uw}	= ultimate strength of weld material (kN/mm^2)
ψ	= relative flexibility of shear panel and frame = c/k

9.2 Notes on symbols

9.2.1

Where the sheets overhang the supporting members at the sheet ends, the depth b of the panel may be taken to the ends of the sheets.

9.2.2

$$D_x = \frac{Et^3 d}{12(1-\nu^2)u}, \quad D_y = \frac{E\,I_y}{d}$$

9.2.3

The non-dimensional sheeting constants $\bar{K}_1$, $\bar{K}_2$ are a measure of the shear flexibility of the sheeting due to distortion of its profile. They have been systematically tabulated by computer for the complete range of trapezoidal and arc and tangent profiles and values can be obtained by linear interpolation from tables 9.6 to 9.8.

9.2.4

Slip values for sheeting fasteners have to be determined by testing. Some typical values are given in tables 9.9 and 9.10 and, where applicable, these may be used for the purposes of design.

9.2.5

Values for movement in perpendicular to parallel member connections are required when the diaphragm is fastened on two sides only. They must be determined by testing. Many tests have been carried out and the results of these tests are summarised in table 9.12. From this table it will normally be possible to estimate a suitable value of this movement for the purpose of design.

9.2.6

The effect of intermediate perpendicular members (purlins) is to reduce the shear flexibility of the diaphragm. Values of α_1, α_2 and α_3 for various numbers of purlins are given in table 9.3. When there are several sheet lengths within the depth of the diaphragm, the flexibility is increased. The factor α_4 which takes account of this effect, is given in table 9.1. When the sheeting spans parallel to the span of the diaphragm and is continuous over several panels, the flexibility is reduced. The factor α_5 is incorporated in tables 9.2 and 9.4 which take account of this.

9.2.7

The factors β_1 and β_2 allow for the distribution of forces in sheet to perpendicular member fasteners along the member. Values are given in table 9.5. There are two sets of values of β_1 according to whether the seam fasteners pass through the crests of the corrugations (sheeting, fig. 2.4 case 1) or through the troughs (decking, fig. 2.4 case 2).

9.2.8

$\beta_3 = (n_f - 1)/n_f$ for sheeting (seam fasteners in the crests, fig. 2.4, case 1); $\beta_3 =$ 1.0 for decking (seam fasteners in the troughs, fig. 2.4, case 2).

9.3 Design expressions, cantilever diaphragm, sheeting perpendicular (fig. 9.1)

(a) Seam strength

$$V_{ult} = n_s F_s + \frac{\beta_1}{\beta_3} n_p F_p \quad \text{(see 9.7.4 and 9.7.5)}$$

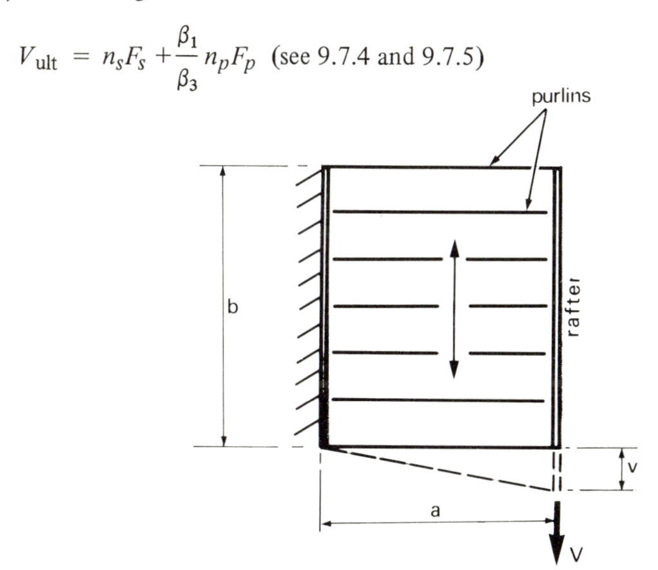

Fig. 9.1 Case considered in section 9.3.

(b) Strength in fasteners to shear connectors (4 sides fastened only)

$V_{ult} = n_{sc} F_{sc}$ (see 9.7.4)

(c) Strength at end sheet to perpendicular member (purlin) fasteners (2 sides fastened only)

$V_{ult} = \beta_2 \, n_p \, F_p$ or $V_{ult} = n_p \, F_{pr}$ (see 9.7.4 and 9.7.6)

(d) Design shear capacity V^*

V^* is the minimum of the values of V_{ult} above.

(e) General requirement for shear buckling

$$\frac{14.4}{b} D_x^{\frac{1}{4}} D_y^{\frac{3}{4}} (n_p - 1)^2 \geqslant V^*$$

(f) General requirement for sheet to perpendicular member (purlin) fasteners

$$\frac{0.8 \, bF_p}{p} \geqslant V^*$$

(g) Maximum axial force in longitudinal edge member (purlin)

The value of this force is V^*a/b. The capacity of the upper and lower edge members and their connections must be checked with respect to this force together with any bending due to vertical loads.

(h) Shear flexibility $c = v/V$

Shear flexibility due to		Expression	Flexibility mm/kN
Sheet deformation	profile distortion	$c_{1.1} = \dfrac{a\,d^{2.5}\,\alpha_1\,\alpha_4\,\bar{K}}{E\,t^{2.5}\,b^2}$ (see 9.7.1)	$c_{1.1} =$
	shear strain	$c_{1.2} = \dfrac{2a\,(1+\nu)[1+(2h/d)]}{Etb}$	$c_{1.2} =$
Fastener deformation	sheet to purlin fasteners	$c_{2.1} = \dfrac{2a\,s_p\,p}{b^2}$	$c_{2.1} =$
	seam fasteners	$c_{2.2} = \dfrac{2s_s s_p\,(n_{sh}-1)}{2n_s s_p + \beta_1 n_p s_s}$	$c_{2.2} =$
	connection to rafters	4 sides fastened $c_{2.3} = \dfrac{2s_{sc}}{n_{sc}}$ or 2 sides only fastened $c_{2.3} = \dfrac{2}{n_p}\left(s_{pr} + \dfrac{s_p}{\beta_2}\right)$	$c_{2.3} =$
Flange forces	axial strain in purlins	$c_3 = \dfrac{2a^3}{3EAb^2}$	$c_3 =$
Total shear flexibility		$c = c_{1.1} + c_{1.2} + c_{2.1} + c_{2.2} + c_{2.3} + c_3$	$c =$

9.4 Design expressions, cantilever diaphragm, sheeting parallel (fig. 9.2)

(a) Seam strength

$$V_{ult} = \frac{a}{b}\left[n_s F_s + \frac{\beta_1}{\beta_3} n_p F_p\right] \quad \text{(see 9.7.4 and 9.7.5)}$$

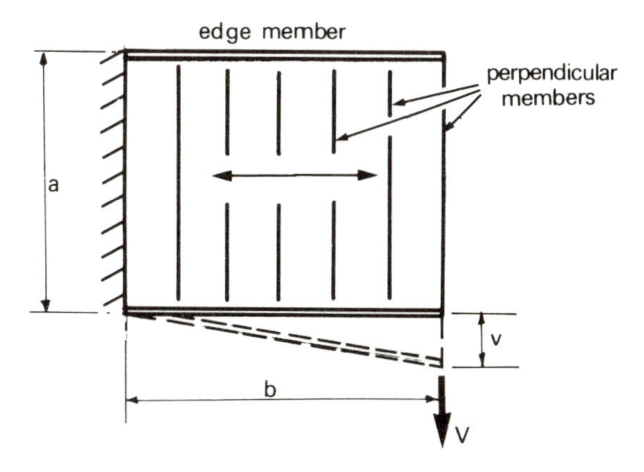

Fig. 9.2 Case considered in section 9.4.

(b) Strength in fasteners to shear connectors (4 sides fastened only)

$$V_{ult} = \frac{a}{b}(n_{sc}F_{sc}) \quad \text{(see 9.7.4)}$$

(c) Strength at end sheet to perpendicular member (purlin) fasteners (2 sides fastened only)

$$V_{ult} = \frac{a}{b}(\beta_2 n_p F_p) \text{ or } V_{ult} = \frac{a}{b}(n_p F_{pr}) \quad \text{(see 9.7.4 and 9.7.6)}$$

(d) Design shear capacity V^*
V^* is the minimum of the values of V_{ult} above.
(e) General requirement for shear buckling

$$\frac{14.4a}{b^2} D_x^{\frac{1}{4}} D_y^{\frac{3}{4}} (n_p - 1)^2 \geqslant V^*$$

(f) General requirement for sheet to perpendicular member (purlin) fasteners

$$\frac{0.8a\, F_p}{p} \geqslant V^*$$

(g) Maximum axial force in edge members
In the diaphragm above, the edge members parallel to the direction of span carry a

maximum axial force of V^*b/a and the perpendicular edge members carry a maximum axial force of V^*. The capacity of these members and their connections must be checked with respect to these forces and any bending due to vertical loads.

(h) Shear flexibility $c = v/V$

Shear flexibility due to		Expression	Flexibility mm/kN
Sheet deformation	profile distortion	$c_{1.1} = \dfrac{a\,d^{2.5}\,\alpha_1\,\alpha_4\,\bar{K}}{E\,t^{2.5}\,b^2}$ (see 9.7.1)	$c_{1.1} =$
	shear strain	$c_{1.2} = \dfrac{2a\,(1+\nu)\,[1+(2h/d)]}{Etb}$	$c_{1.2} =$
Fastener deformation	sheet to perpendicular member fasteners	$c_{2.1} = \dfrac{2\,a\,s_p\,p}{b^2}$	$c_{2.1} =$
	seam fasteners	$c_{2.2} = \dfrac{2s_s\,s_p\,(n_{sh}-1)}{2n_s\,s_p + \beta_1\,n_p s_s}$	$c_{2.2} =$
	connections to edge members	4 sides fastened $c_{2.3} = \dfrac{2s_{sc}}{n_{sc}}$ or 2 sides only fastened $c_{2.3} = \dfrac{2}{n_p}\left(s_{pr} + \dfrac{s_p}{\beta_2}\right)$	$c_{2.3} =$
Total flexibility in true shear		$c' = \dfrac{b^2}{a^2}(c_{1.1}+c_{1.2}+c_{2.1}+c_{2.2}+c_{2.3})$	$c' =$
Flange forces	axial strain in edge members	$c_3 = \dfrac{2b^3}{3EAa^2}$	$c_3 =$
Total shear flexibility		$c = c' + c_3$	$c =$

9.5 Design expressions, diaphragm beam, sheeting perpendicular (fig. 9.3)

In the design for strength, the end panel, carrying a shear force $V = (qa/2)\,(n-1)$ is generally critical but conditions at the internal rafters must also be checked.

(a) Seam strength

$$V_{\text{ult}} = n_s F_s + \frac{\beta_1}{\beta_3} n_p F_p \quad \text{(see 9.7.4 and 9.7.5)}$$

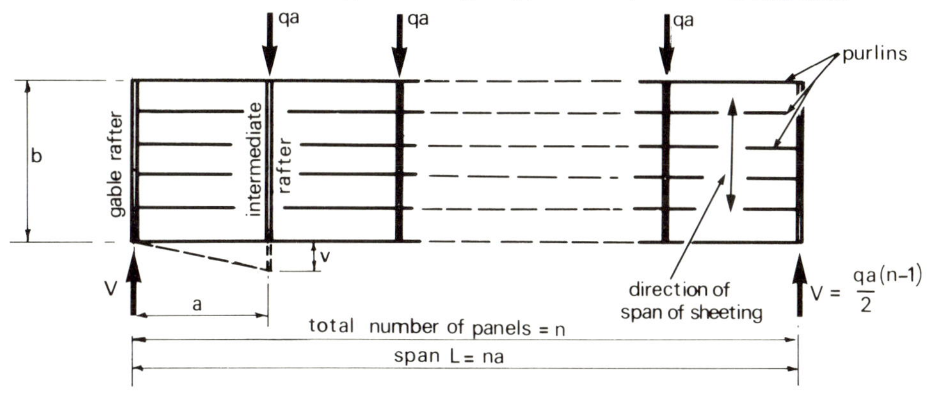

Fig. 9.3 Case considered in section 9.5.

(b) Strength in fasteners to shear connectors
for shear connectors to the gable rafter

$$V_{\text{ult}} = n_{sc}\, F_{sc} \quad \text{(see 9.7.4)}$$

for shear connectors to intermediate rafters, with number of fasteners n'_{sc}

$$(qa)_{\text{ult}} = n'_{sc}\, F_{sc} \text{ (see 9.7.4)}$$

(c) Strength at end sheet to purlin fasteners
with 2 sides only fastened and with *no* shear connectors to the gable rafter

$$V_{\text{ult}} = \beta_2\, n_p\, F_p \quad \text{or} \quad V_{\text{ult}} = n_p\, F_{pr} \quad \text{(see 9.7.4 and 9.7.6)}$$

with 2 sides only fastened internally but with shear connectors to the gable rafter

$$(qa)_{\text{ult}} = \beta_2\, n_p\, F_p \quad \text{or} \quad (qa)_{\text{ult}} = n_p\, F_{pr} \quad \text{(see 9.7.4 and 9.7.6)}$$

(d) Design shear capacity V^*
V^* is the minimum of the values of V_{ult} above.
(e) General requirement for shear buckling

$$\frac{14.4}{b} D_x^{\frac{1}{4}}\, D_y^{\frac{3}{4}}\, (n_p - 1)^2 \geqslant V^*$$

(f) General requirement for sheet to perpendicular member (purlin) fasteners

$$\frac{0.8bF_p}{p\,\alpha_3} \geqslant V^*$$

(g) Maximum axial force in longitudinal edge member (purlin)
The maximum value of this force occurs at mid-span and is approximately equal to $qL^2\alpha_3/8b$. The capacity of the upper and lower edge members and their connections must be checked with respect to this force together with any bending due to vertical loads.
(h) Shear flexibility $c = v/V$
The expression for flexibility obtained from the table below is a representative value applicable to each panel within the complete diaphragm.

Shear flexibility due to		Expression	Flexibility mm/kN
Sheet deformation	profile distortion	$c_{1.1} = \dfrac{a\,d^{2.5}\,\alpha_1\,\alpha_4\,\bar{K}}{E\,t^{2.5}\,b^2}$ (see 9.7.1)	$c_{1.1} =$
	shear strain	$c_{1.2} = \dfrac{2a\,\alpha_2\,(1+\nu)\,[1+(2h/d)]}{E\,t\,b}$	$c_{1.2} =$
Fastener deformation	sheet to purlin fasteners	$c_{2.1} = \dfrac{2a\,s_p\,p\,\alpha_3}{b^2}$	$c_{2.1} =$
	seam fasteners	$c_{2.2} = \dfrac{2s_s\,s_p\,(n_{sh}-1)}{2n_s\,s_p + \beta_1 n_p s_s}$	$c_{2.2} =$
	connection to rafters	4 sides fastened (n'_{sc} = number of fasteners to intermediate rafter) $c_{2.3} = \dfrac{4\,(n+1)\,s_{sc}}{n^2\,n'_{sc}}$ or 2 sides only fastened with gable shear connectors $c_{2.3} = \dfrac{4(n-1)}{n^2\,n_p}\left(s_{pr} + \dfrac{s_p}{\beta_2}\right)$ (see 9.7.3) double the above value when no gable shear connectors	$c_{2.3} =$
Flange forces	axial strain in purlins	$c_3 = \dfrac{n^2 a^3\,\alpha_3}{4.8\,E\,A\,b^2}$	$c_3 =$
Total shear flexibility		$c = c_{1.1} + c_{1.2} + c_{2.1} + c_{2.2} + c_{2.3} + c_3$	$c =$

Note For the load case shown, the mid-span deflection is given by $\Delta_{max} = (n^2/8)\,c(qa)$.

9.6 Design expressions, diaphragm beam, sheeting parallel (fig. 9.4)

In the design for strength, the end panels carrying a shear force $V = (qb/2)\,(n-1)$ are generally critical.

(a) Seam strength

$$V_{ult} = \frac{a}{b}\left(n_s F_s + \frac{\beta_1 F_p}{\beta_3}\right) \text{ (see 9.7.4 and 9.7.5)}$$

(b) Strength in fasteners to shear connectors (4 sides fastened)

$$V_{ult} = \frac{a}{b}\,(n_{sc} F_{sc}) \text{ (see 9.7.4)}$$

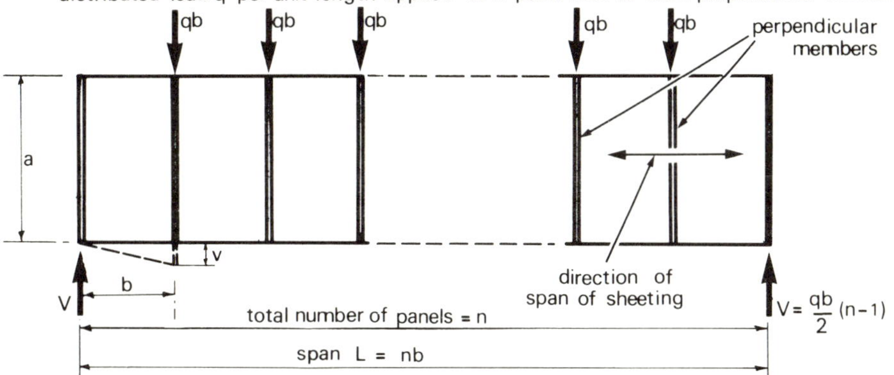

Fig. 9.4 Case considered in section 9.6.

(c) Strength at end sheet to perpendicular member fasteners (2 sides only fastened)

$$V_{\text{ult}} = \frac{a}{b}(1.5\,\beta_2 F_p) \text{ or } V_{\text{ult}} = \frac{a}{b}(1.5\,F_{pr}) \text{ (see 9.7.4 and 9.7.6)}$$

(d) Design shear capacity V^*

V^* is the minimum of the values of V_{ult} above.

(e) General requirement for shear buckling

sheeting fastened to supporting members in every corrugation trough

$$\frac{28.8a}{b^2}\,D_x^{\frac{1}{4}}\,D_y^{\frac{3}{4}} \geqslant V^*$$

sheeting fastened to supporting members in alternate troughs

$$\frac{14.4a}{b^2}\,D_x^{\frac{1}{4}}\,D_y^{\frac{3}{4}} \geqslant V^*$$

(f) General requirement for sheet to perpendicular member fasteners

$$\frac{0.8\,a\,F_p}{p} \geqslant V^*$$

(g) Maximum axial force in longitudinal edge member

The maximum value of this force occurs at mid-span and is approximately equal to $qL^2/(8a)$. The capacity of the upper and lower edge members and their connections must be checked with respect to this force together with any bending due to vertical loads.

(h) Shear flexibility $c = v/V$

The expression for flexibility obtained from the table below is a representative value applicable to each panel within the diaphragm.

Shear flexibility due to		Expression	Flexibility mm/kN
Sheet deformation	profile distortion	$c_{1.1} = \dfrac{a\, d^{2.5}\, \alpha_5\, \bar{K}}{E\, t^{2.5}\, b^2}$ (see 9.7.2)	$c_{1.1} =$
	shear strain	$c_{1.2} = \dfrac{2a\,(1+\nu)\,[1+(2h/d)]}{Etb}$	$c_{1.2} =$
Fastener deformation	sheet to perpendicular member fasteners	$c_{2.1} = \dfrac{2a\, s_p\, p}{b^2}$	$c_{2.1} =$
	seam fasteners	$c_{2.2} = \dfrac{s_s\, s_p\,(n_{sh}-1)}{n_s\, s_p + \beta_1\, s_s}$	$c_{2.2} =$
	connections to edge members	4 sides fastened $c_{2.3} = \dfrac{2\, s_{sc}}{n_{sc}}$ or 2 sides only fastened $c_{2.3} = s_{pr} + \dfrac{s_p}{\beta_2}$	$c_{2.3} =$
Total flexibility in true shear		$c' = \dfrac{b^2}{a^2}\,(c_{1.1} + c_{1.2} + c_{2.1} + c_{2.2} + c_{2.3})$	$c' =$
Flange forces	axial strain in edge members	$c_3 = \dfrac{n^2 b^3}{4.8E\, A\, a^2}$	$c_3 =$
Total shear flexibility		$c = c' + c_3$	$c =$

Note For the load case shown, the mid-span deflection is given by $\Delta_{max} = (n^2/8)\, c(qa)$.

9.7 Notes on design expressions for diaphragm strength and flexibility

9.7.1

In the expressions for $c_{1.1}$, $\bar{K}$ can take values $\bar{K}_1$ or $\bar{K}_2$ given in tables 9.6 to 9.8 according to whether the sheeting is fastened to the supporting structure through every or alternate corrugation troughs. The factors α_1 and α_4 take account of the influence of fasteners to intermediate purlins and also of the effect of several sheet lengths within the depth of the diaphragm. There are a number of practical possibilities giving rise to different combinations of values of $\bar{K}$, α_1 and α_4 and these are summarised in table 9.1.

The effect of insulation bonded to the top of roof decking is to cause a significant reduction in shear flexibility when the sheeting is fastened in alternate corrugations ($\bar{K} = \bar{K}_2$) but not when it is fastened in every corrugation ($\bar{K} = \bar{K}_1$). If it is wished to take this into account, the following multiplying factor may be applied to $c_{1.1}$ calculated for alternate corrugations: for profile height $h \leqslant 50$ mm, 0.7; for profile height $50 < h < 80$ mm, 0.5.

9.7.2

For sheeting spanning parallel to the span of the diaphragm in a diaphragm beam situation, and in the expression for $c_{1.1}$, $\bar{K}$ can take the values $\bar{K}_1$ or $\bar{K}_2$ given in tables 9.6 to 9.8 according to whether the sheeting is fastened to the supporting structure through every or alternate troughs. A further factor α_5 takes account of the effect of the sheeting having continuity over two or more spans. There are a number of practical possibilities giving rise to different combinations of values of $\bar{K}$ and α_5 and these are summarised in table 9.2.

9.7.3

For sheeting spanning perpendicular to the span of the diaphragm and for the case of fasteners on two sides only, it is good practice to provide shear connectors to the gable rafter although these are not provided at the intermediate rafters. (The *European Recommendations for the Stressed Skin Design of Steel Structures*[1.99] require such a provision.) For such a case, the expression given for $c_{2.3}$ in the design tables, namely

$$c_{2.3} = \frac{4\,(n-1)}{n^2\, n_p}\left(s_{pr} + \frac{s_p}{\beta_2}\right)$$

is strictly only correct for an intermediate panel, though it may also be used for an end panel in which case it will normally slightly under-estimate the flexibility. The correct expression for an end panel is

$$c_{2.3} = \frac{s_{sc}}{n_{sc}} + \frac{4\,(n-1)}{n^2\, n_p}\left(s_{pr} + \frac{s_p}{\beta_2}\right)$$

Likewise, when there are no shear connectors at the gable, the strictly correct expression for $c_{2.3}$ is

$$c_{2.3} = \left(\frac{1}{n_p} + \frac{4(n-1)}{n^2 n_p}\right)\left(s_{pr} + \frac{s_p}{\beta_2}\right)$$

9.7.4

The expressions for design strength which involve fastener failure are given in terms of the *design* strengths of the relevant fasteners which are equal to the characteristic strength divided by a material factor which, in the case of the European Recommendations, is equal to $1.11 = 1/0.9$. *Characteristic* strengths of various fasteners are given in tables 9.9, 9.10 and 9.11.

Table 9.1 Influence of various fastener arrangements on expression for $c_{1.1}$

	fastener positions			
	every corrugation	alternate corrugations	every corrugation at both sheet ends	every corrugation at one sheet end
one sheet length for full depth	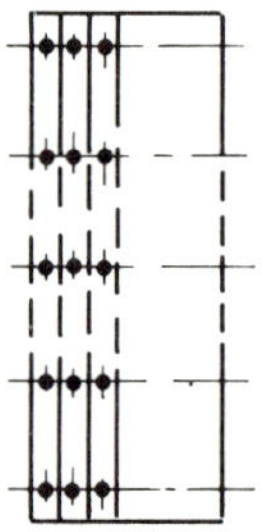 $\bar{K} = \bar{K}_1$ α_1 from table 9.3 $\alpha_4 = 1$ (1)	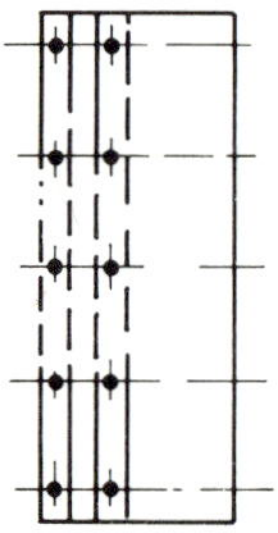 $\bar{K} = \bar{K}_2$ α_1 from table 9.3 $\alpha_4 = 1$ (2)	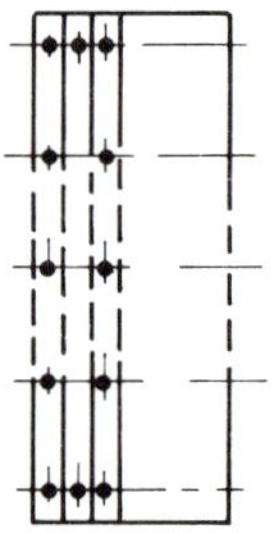 $\bar{K} = \bar{K}_1$ $\alpha_1 = 1$ $\alpha_4 = 1$ (3)	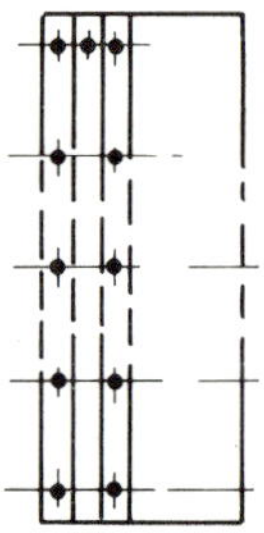 $\bar{K} = \bar{K}_2$ $\alpha_1 = 0.5$ $\alpha_4 = 1$ (4)
n_b sheet lengths in depth of panel	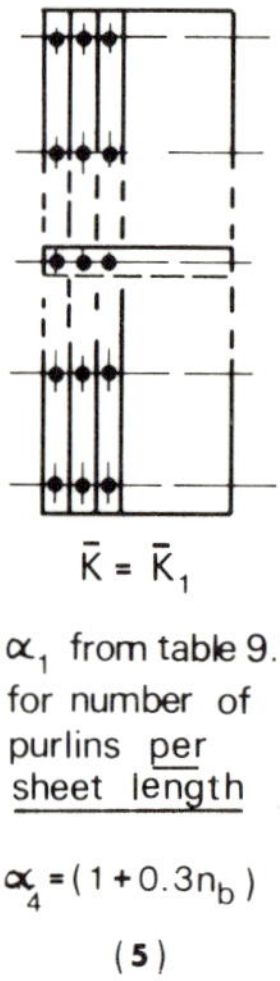 $\bar{K} = \bar{K}_1$ α_1 from table 9.3 for number of purlins <u>per sheet length</u> $\alpha_4 = (1 + 0.3n_b)$ (5)	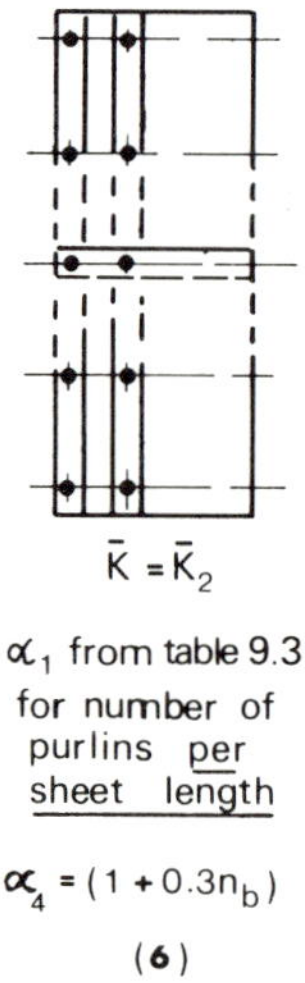 $\bar{K} = \bar{K}_2$ α_1 from table 9.3 for number of purlins <u>per sheet length</u> $\alpha_4 = (1 + 0.3n_b)$ (6)	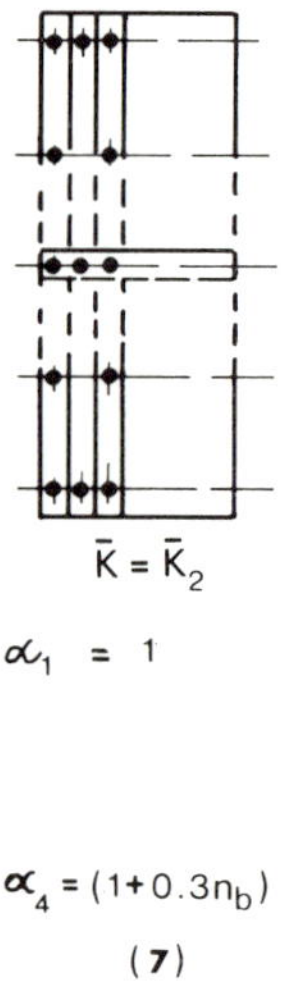 $\bar{K} = \bar{K}_2$ $\alpha_1 = 1$ $\alpha_4 = (1 + 0.3n_b)$ (7)	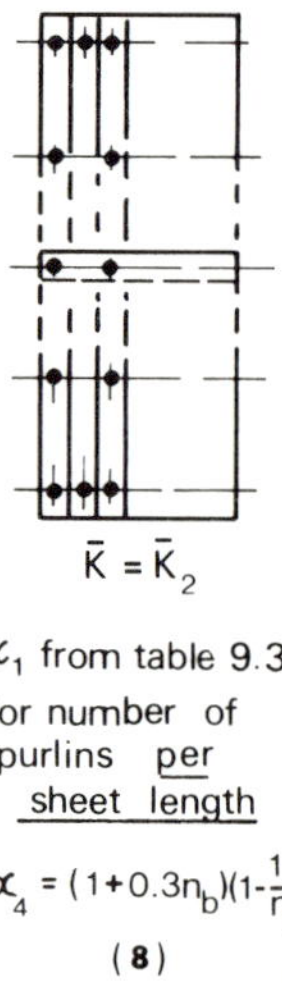 $\bar{K} = \bar{K}_2$ α_1 from table 9.3 for number of purlins <u>per sheet length</u> $\alpha_4 = (1 + 0.3n_b)(1 - \frac{1}{n_b})$ (8)

Notes to table 9.2

For the last case it is not possible to give a simple value for α_5. Instead,

$$c = \frac{b^2}{a^2}\left[\left(c'_{1.1}\,\frac{\alpha_5}{m} + c_{1.2} + c_{2.1} + c_{2.2} + c_{2.3}\right)_{\mathrm{E}}\left(\frac{n^2 - n_1^{\,2}}{n^2}\right) + (c'_{1.1} + c_{1.2} + c_{2.1} + c_{2.2} + c_{2.3})_{\mathrm{A}}\left(\frac{n_1^{\,2}}{n^2}\right)\right] + c_3$$

where $c'_{1.1}$ is the standard expression with $\alpha_5 = 1$. In the above expressions α_5 is given in table 9.4.

Table 9.2 Influence of sheet length on $c_{1.1}$ for sheeting spanning parallel to span of diaphragm

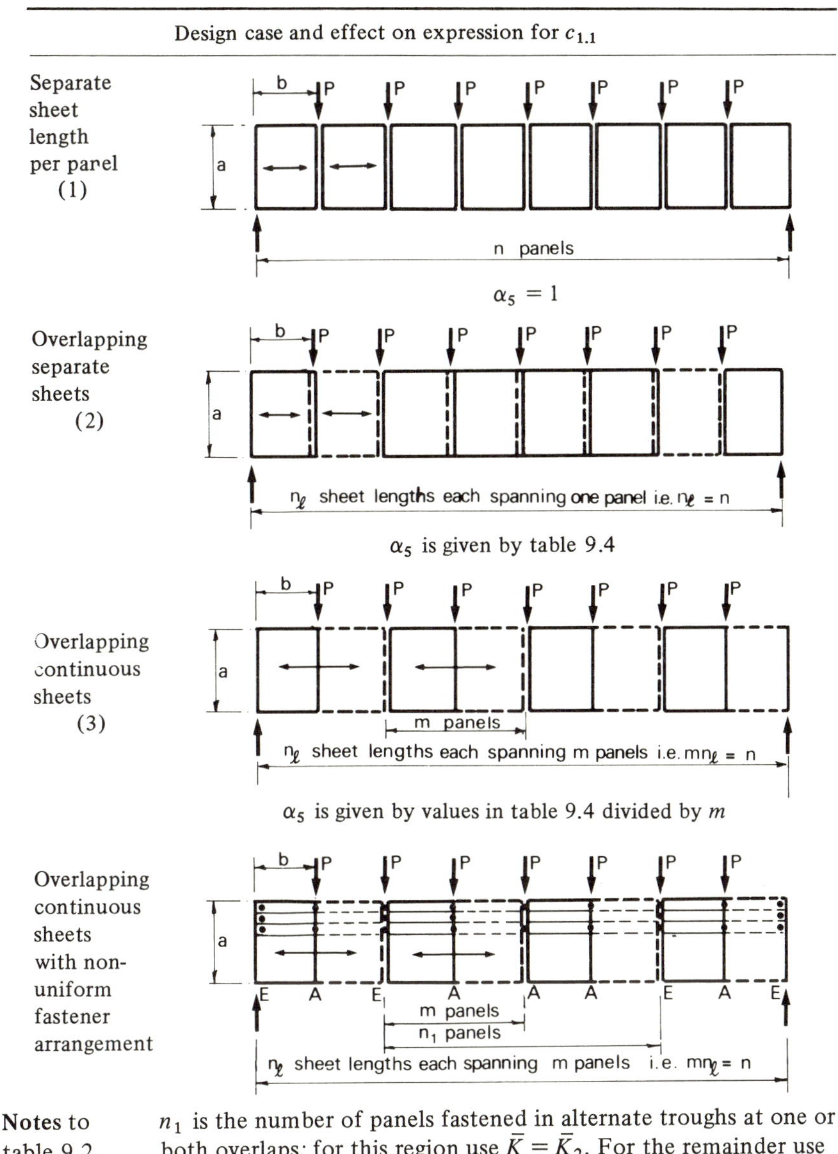

Notes to table 9.2. (cont. from p. 174)

n_1 is the number of panels fastened in alternate troughs at one or both overlaps; for this region use $\bar{K} = \bar{K}_2$. For the remainder use $\bar{K} = \bar{K}_1$.

E refers to every trough fixing over $(n - n_1)$ panels.

A refers to alternate trough fixings over n_1 panels.

Note For sheeting fastened in every trough at each sheet end (including overlaps) and in alternate troughs elsewhere, put $n_1 = 0$ in the above expression.

Note In cases (1), (2) and (3) in table 9.2, $\bar{K} = \bar{K}_1$ for fasteners in every connection or $\bar{K}_2$ for fasteners in alternate corrugations.

Table 9.3 Correction factors to allow for the effect of intermediate purlins

Total no of purlins per panel (or per sheet length for α_1)	Correction factors		
n_p	α_1	α_2	α_3
2	1	1	1
3	1	1	1
4	0.85	0.75	0.90
5	0.70	0.67	0.80
6	0.60	0.55	0.71
7	0.60	0.50	0.64
8	0.60	0.44	0.58
9	0.60	0.40	0.53
10	0.60	0.36	0.49
11		0.33	0.45
12		0.30	0.42
13		0.29	0.39
14		0.27	0.37
15		0.25	0.35
16		0.23	0.33
17		0.22	0.31
18		0.21	0.30
19		0.20	0.28
20		0.19	0.27

Table 9.4 Correction factors to allow for sheet continuity

Number of sheet lengths n_l	α_5
2	1.0
3	0.9
4	0.8
5 or more	0.7

Table 9.5 Factors to allow for the number of sheet to perpendicular member fasteners per sheet width

Total number of fasteners per sheet width n_f	Factor β_1 Case 1 – sheeting	Case 2 – decking	Factor β_2
2	0.13	1.0	1.0
3	0.30	1.0	1.0
4	0.44	1.04	1.11
5	0.58	1.13	1.25
6	0.71	1.22	1.40
7	0.84	1.33	1.56
8	0.97	1.45	1.71
9	1.10	1.56	1.88
10	1.23	1.68	2.04

Table 9.6 Values of $\bar{K}_1$ for fasteners in every trough

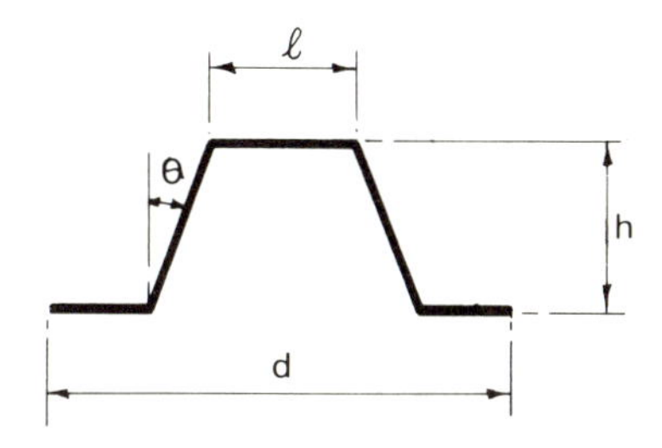

	h/d \ l/d	0.1	0.2	0.3	0.4	0.5	0.6	0.7	0.8	0.9
θ-0°	0.1	0.013	0.030	0.044	0.050	0.048	0.047	0.053	0.061	0.080
	0.2	0.044	0.107	0.145	0.165	0.165	0.171	0.203	0.256	0.323
	0.3	0.090	0.208	0.298	0.336	0.332	0.343	0.423	0.516	0.711
	0.4	0.151	0.350	0.491	0.560	0.554	0.568	0.689	0.877	1.24
	0.5	0.227	0.522	0.735	0.832	0.828	0.843	1.03	1.30	1.92
	0.6	0.310	0.727	1.03	1.16	1.16	1.15	1.41	2.04	3.93
	0.7	0.417	0.966	1.37	1.55	1.53	1.54	1.87	2.62	5.29
	0.8	0.536	1.24	1.77	1.97	1.96	1.95	2.39	3.39	6.87
θ-5°	0.1	0.014	0.032	0.044	0.049	0.047	0.046	0.051	0.061	0.092
	0.2	0.050	0.102	0.144	0.155	0.155	0.163	0.189	0.246	0.328
	0.3	0.113	0.206	0.288	0.310	0.320	0.326	0.391	0.506	0.860
	0.4	0.180	0.359	0.459	0.509	0.503	0.525	0.609	0.922	1.56
	0.5	0.315	0.533	0.711	0.759	0.746	0.797	0.917	1.43	2.58
	0.6	0.452	0.793	0.986	1.01	0.953	1.05	1.38	2.61	
	0.7	0.633	1.06	1.29	1.30	1.22	1.38	1.85	3.62	
	0.8	0.843	1.36	1.63	1.62	1.52	1.74	2.39	4.87	

Table 9.6 (*cont.*)

	h/d \ l/d	0.1	0.2	0.3	0.4	0.5	0.6	0.7	0.8	0.9
	0.1	0.015	0.033	0.045	0.047	0.045	0.045	0.049	0.061	0.095
	0.2	0.057	0.103	0.143	0.145	0.146	0.155	0.177	0.232	0.533
	0.3	0.130	0.204	0.277	0.291	0.305	0.311	0.364	0.490	
θ-10°	0.4	0.209	0.369	0.422	0.455	0.432	0.503	0.544	0.960	
	0.5	0.401	0.544	0.659	0.663	0.639	0.688	0.797	1.49	
	0.6	0.556	0.793	0.877	0.817	0.782	0.986	1.53		
	0.7	0.766	1.04	1.10	0.997	1.27	2.10			
	0.8	1.00	1.30	1.33	1.17	1.60	2.91			
	0.1	0.016	0.033	0.045	0.046	0.043	0.045	0.047	0.061	0.097
	0.2	0.065	0.104	0.141	0.133	0.135	0.145	0.165	0.217	
	0.3	0.147	0.201	0.261	0.251	0.248	0.290	0.323	0.472	
θ-15°	0.4	0.236	0.379	0.383	0.390	0.376	0.463	0.512		
	0.5	0.421	0.556	0.537	0.509	0.459	0.622	0.737		
	0.6	0.597	0.729	0.714	0.609	0.690	0.866			
	0.7	0.784	0.900	0.827	0.695	0.838	1.19			
	0.8	0.978	1.05	0.889	0.789	0.874				
	0.1	0.017	0.033	0.044	0.044	0.041	0.042	0.046	0.063	0.105
	0.2	0.070	0.107	0.134	0.124	0.124	0.132	0.157	0.245	
	0.3	0.161	0.226	0.248	0.234	0.231	0.232	0.344		
θ-20°	0.4	0.274	0.359	0.371	0.354	0.302	0.292	0.520		
	0.5	0.424	0.521	0.490	0.408	0.345	0.431			
	0.6	0.572	0.606	0.508	0.451	0.450				
	0.7	0.696	0.668	0.500	0.449					
	0.8	0.773	0.656	0.445	0.354					
	0.1	0.018	0.034	0.043	0.043	0.038	0.039	0.045	0.065	0.115
	0.2	0.076	0.110	0.127	0.117	0.113	0.120	0.145	0.203	
	0.3	0.170	0.201	0.222	0.206	0.201	0.186	0.481		
θ-25°	0.4	0.282	0.340	0.305	0.288	0.206	0.355			
	0.5	0.430	0.424	0.360	0.250	0.276				
	0.6	0.480	0.427	0.280	0.200					
	0.7	0.495	0.339	0.140						
	0.8	0.413	0.107							
	0.1	0.020	0.034	0.042	0.041	0.035	0.035	0.044	0.068	
	0.2	0.082	0.113	0.121	0.109	0.098	0.107	0.149		
	0.3	0.176	0.205	0.193	0.159	0.155	0.181			
θ-30°	0.4	0.271	0.275	0.219	0.169	0.166				
	0.5	0.331	0.281	0.159	0.122					
	0.6	0.333	0.152	0.109						
	0.7	0.159								
	0.1	0.021	0.034	0.041	0.039	0.032	0.033	0.043	0.076	
	0.2	0.085	0.110	0.111	0.106	0.082	0.111	0.184		
θ-35°	0.3	0.159	0.168	0.164	0.108	0.079	0.135			
	0.4	0.246	0.211	0.109	0.080					
	0.5	0.230	0.169							
	0.6	0.111								

	h/d \ l/d	0.1	0.2	0.3	0.4	0.5	0.6	0.7	0.8	0.9
	0.1	0.022	0.035	0.040	0.036	0.028	0.031	0.035		
	0.2	0.087	0.104	0.092	0.083	0.065	0.095			
θ-40°	0.3	0.157	0.146	0.110	0.055					
	0.4	0.168	0.092	0.034						
	0.5	0.063								
	0.1	0.024	0.035	0.039	0.032	0.026	0.029	0.049		
θ-45°	0.2	0.089	0.093	0.081	0.066	0.058				
	0.3	0.128	0.091	0.056						
	0.4	0.059								

Table 9.7 Values of $\bar{K}_2$ for fasteners in alternate troughs

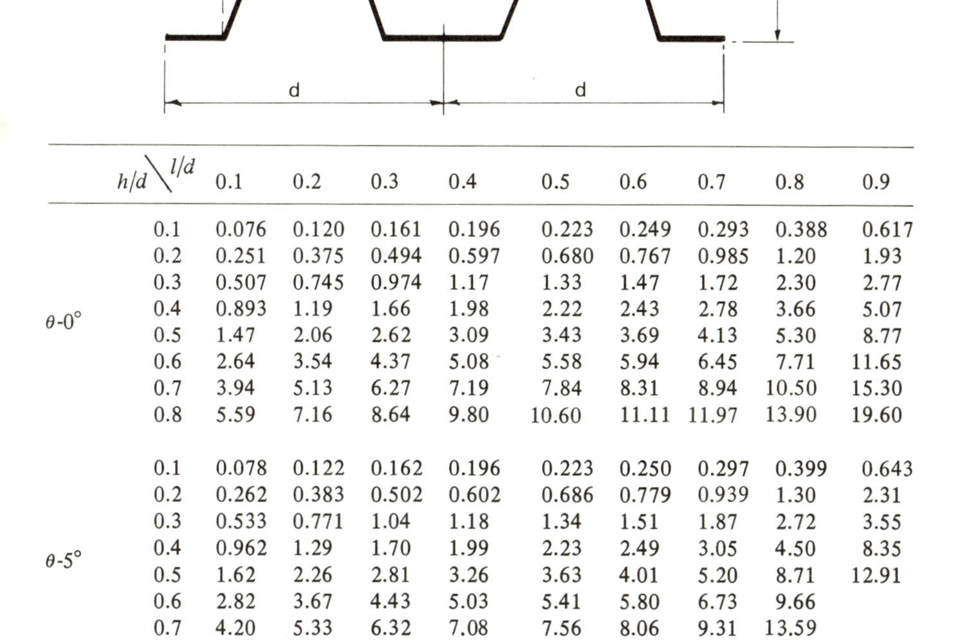

	h/d \ l/d	0.1	0.2	0.3	0.4	0.5	0.6	0.7	0.8	0.9
	0.1	0.076	0.120	0.161	0.196	0.223	0.249	0.293	0.388	0.617
	0.2	0.251	0.375	0.494	0.597	0.680	0.767	0.985	1.20	1.93
	0.3	0.507	0.745	0.974	1.17	1.33	1.47	1.72	2.30	2.77
θ-0°	0.4	0.893	1.19	1.66	1.98	2.22	2.43	2.78	3.66	5.07
	0.5	1.47	2.06	2.62	3.09	3.43	3.69	4.13	5.30	8.77
	0.6	2.64	3.54	4.37	5.08	5.58	5.94	6.45	7.71	11.65
	0.7	3.94	5.13	6.27	7.19	7.84	8.31	8.94	10.50	15.30
	0.8	5.59	7.16	8.64	9.80	10.60	11.11	11.97	13.90	19.60
	0.1	0.078	0.122	0.162	0.196	0.223	0.250	0.297	0.399	0.643
	0.2	0.262	0.383	0.502	0.602	0.686	0.779	0.939	1.30	2.31
	0.3	0.533	0.771	1.04	1.18	1.34	1.51	1.87	2.72	3.55
θ-5°	0.4	0.962	1.29	1.70	1.99	2.23	2.49	3.05	4.50	8.35
	0.5	1.62	2.26	2.81	3.26	3.63	4.01	5.20	8.71	12.91
	0.6	2.82	3.67	4.43	5.03	5.41	5.80	6.73	9.66	
	0.7	4.20	5.33	6.32	7.08	7.56	8.06	9.31	13.59	
	0.8	5.96	7.41	8.65	9.57	10.16	10.80	12.48	18.74	

	$h/d \backslash l/d$	0.1	0.2	0.3	0.4	0.5	0.6	0.7	0.8	0.9
θ-10°	0.1	0.080	0.124	0.163	0.197	0.224	0.252	0.303	0.417	0.697
	0.2	0.275	0.400	0.514	0.611	0.695	0.795	0.983	1.42	2.89
	0.3	0.578	0.813	1.12	1.20	1.36	1.56	2.02	3.15	
	0.4	1.03	1.40	1.74	2.00	2.24	2.64	3.49	6.12	
	0.5	1.88	2.48	3.03	3.46	3.86	4.57	6.50	14.50	
	0.6	2.99	3.78	4.45	4.32	5.25	6.00	8.47		
	0.7	4.44	5.46	6.31	6.87	7.33	8.47	13.39		
	0.8	6.29	7.56	8.58	9.22	9.83	11.64	25.46		
θ-15°	0.1	0.082	0.125	0.164	0.197	0.224	0.254	0.309	0.429	0.736
	0.2	0.287	0.412	0.524	0.619	0.706	0.720	1.07	1.63	
	0.3	0.613	0.842	1.19	1.22	1.41	1.69	2.40	4.15	
	0.4	1.11	1.44	1.77	2.04	2.38	3.12	5.60		
	0.5	1.91	2.45	2.94	3.36	4.01	6.22	9.22		
	0.6	3.14	3.86	4.43	4.83	5.48	7.94			
	0.7	4.64	5.54	6.21	6.72	7.96	16.43			
	0.8	6.52	7.60	8.36	9.10	12.01				
θ-20°	0.1	0.084	0.127	0.164	0.197	0.224	0.256	0.319	0.489	0.756
	0.2	0.302	0.424	0.534	0.627	0.714	0.834	1.13	1.98	
	0.3	0.656	0.879	1.11	1.25	1.44	1.82	2.85		
	0.4	1.17	1.53	1.83	2.08	2.52	3.59	8.75		
	0.5	1.94	2.43	2.84	3.27	4.24	8.30			
	0.6	3.28	3.92	4.43	5.10	7.84				
	0.7	4.79	5.57	6.25	8.02					
	0.8	6.66	7.59	8.84	20.2					
θ-25°	0.1	0.086	0.131	0.167	0.198	0.223	0.256	0.324	0.486	0.815
	0.2	0.317	0.437	0.543	0.634	0.727	0.883	1.27	2.52	
	0.3	0.600	0.915	1.11	1.29	1.54	2.12	4.50		
	0.4	1.26	1.60	1.90	2.25	3.01	6.27			
	0.5	2.06	2.61	3.03	3.92	7.71				
	0.6	3.41	4.05	4.82	8.80					
	0.7	4.99	5.97	9.95						
	0.8	7.10	10.09							
θ-30°	0.1	0.092	0.132	0.168	0.198	0.223	0.258	0.333	0.515	
	0.2	0.331	0.449	0.554	0.644	0.767	0.951	1.65		
	0.3	0.681	0.955	1.16	1.38	1.95	2.42			
	0.4	1.35	1.69	2.56	3.33	4.91				
	0.5	2.28	3.15	5.01	8.01					
	0.6	3.69	4.95	14.72						
	0.7	6.38								
θ-35°	0.1	0.096	0.134	0.169	0.198	0.223	0.262	0.351	0.566	
	0.2	0.347	0.463	0.564	0.656	0.777	1.09	2.09		
	0.3	0.984	1.00	1.21	1.47	2.23				
	0.4	1.46	1.85	2.39	4.43					
	0.5	2.57	3.66	8.73						
	0.6	5.90								
θ-40°	0.1	0.096	0.136	0.167	0.199	0.224	0.266	0.381	0.631	
	0.2	0.362	0.473	0.559	0.682	0.891	1.37			
	0.3	0.834	1.65	2.00	4.02					
	0.4	1.62	2.23	4.59						
	0.5	4.06								

	h/d \ l/d	0.1	0.2	0.3	0.4	0.5	0.6	0.7	0.8	0.9
θ-45°	0.1	0.098	0.138	0.166	0.196	0.227	0.273	0.409		
	0.2	0.385	0.493	0.593	0.710	1.01				
	0.3	0.925	1.15	1.62						
	0.4	2.13								

Table 9.8 Values of $\bar{K}$ for arc and tangent profiles

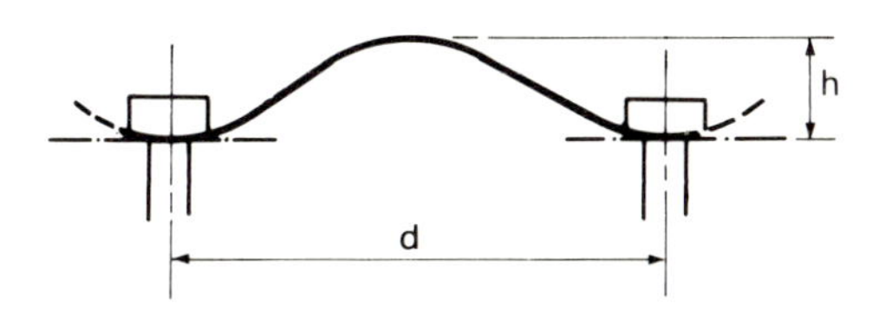

n_p \ h/d	0.1	0.2	0.25	0.3	0.4
2, 3	.017	.052	.079	.112	.204
4	.011	.035	.051	.070	.124
5	.009	.023	.034	.050	.098

(a) Values of the product $\alpha_1 \bar{K}_1$ for fasteners in every trough

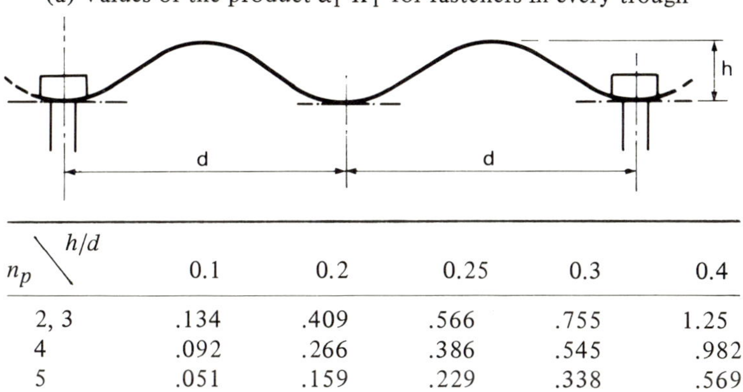

n_p \ h/d	0.1	0.2	0.25	0.3	0.4
2, 3	.134	.409	.566	.755	1.25
4	.092	.266	.386	.545	.982
5	.051	.159	.229	.338	.569

(b) Values of the product $\alpha_1 \bar{K}_2$ for fasteners in alternate troughs

Notes on table 9.8

1. It is considered that the above values of $\bar{K}$ for arc and tangent profiles lack the rigour of the previously given values for trapezoidal profiles. They are therefore offered as the best available values at the time of writing (1980).
2. The above tables include for the effect of intermediate purlins and therefore incorporate the factor α_1 in the expression for $c_{1.1}$. If the required design expression requires $\alpha_1 = 1$ use the value given above for number of purlins $n_p = 2$ or 3.
3. For fixing in every third corrugation use the value of $\alpha_1 \bar{K}_2$ given above multiplied by 2.7 and for every fourth corrugation multiply by 5.0.
4. Standard 3 in (75 mm) corrugated sheet to B.S. 3083 has $h/d = 0.25$.

Table 9.9 Typical characteristics of sheet to purlin or shear connector fasteners

Fastener type	Thickness of lapped plates		Characteristic strength (kN)	Characteristic strength per unit thickness (kN/mm)	Failure mode	Ultimate strength of thinner sheet (N/mm²)	Theoretical ultimate strength (kN)		Average flexibility (mm/kN)
	t_1 (mm)	t_2 (mm)					Baehre and Berggren	Strnad	
SELF-DRILLING, SELF-TAPPING SCREWS WITH STEEL WASHERS									
diameter = 7.9 mm	0.76	2.06	5.9	7.8	2	302	2.96	3.65	0.06
diameter = 6.3 mm	0.75	1.62	3.9	5.2	2	302	2.16	3.24	0.26
	0.75	2.05	5.1	6.8	2	302	2.70	3.13	0.08
diameter = 5.5 mm	0.53	2.06	2.0	3.8	2	292	1.59	1.69	0.03
	0.75	1.61	3.5	4.6	2	302	2.03	3.00	0.06
	0.75	2.07	4.1	5.5	2	302	2.56	2.88	0.04
	0.93	2.06	4.5	4.8	2	310	3.03	4.24	0.15
	1.23	2.06	8.4	6.8	1 or 2	347	3.92	5.17	0.40
diameter = 4.8 mm	0.77	2.06	3.8	5.0	2	302	2.54	2.83	0.05
SELF-DRILLING SELF-TAPPING SCREWS WITH NEO-PRENE WASHERS									
diameter = 7.9 mm	0.77	2.05	4.1	5.3	2	302	3.08	3.74	0.25
diameter = 6.3 mm	0.76	2.07	3.8	5.0	2	302	2.75	3.18	0.41
diameter = 5.5 mm	0.75	2.06	3.0	4.1	2	302	2.56	2.89	0.45
diameter = 4.8 mm	0.75	2.06	3.3	4.4	2	302	2.45	2.70	0.34
SELF-TAPPING SCREWS									
diameter = 5.5 mm	0.77	1.61	2.9	3.8	2	302	2.04	3.05	0.26
	0.77	2.03	3.2	4.2	2	302	2.66	2.24	0.24

CARTRIDGE-FIRED STEEL PINS								
diameter = 4.5 mm	0.75	6.4	3.5	4.6	2	302		0.025
diameter = 3.7 mm	0.76	6.3	3.7	4.9	2	302		0.025

Notes on table 9.9

1. Theoretical fastener strengths are calculated according to section 13.3 and are given for comparison purposes only.
2. Fastener strengths may be taken as being proportional to the ultimate strength of the thinner sheet. For sheets of strengths other than those used in the tests, the results may be adjusted accordingly.
3. Design strengths are equal to the characteristic strengths divided by the material factor γ_m (= 1.11 according to the European recommendations).
4. Failure modes: 1 = shear of fastener itself; 2 = bearing and tearing in thinner sheet (possibly accompanied by tilting of the fastener).

Table 9.10 Typical characteristics of seam fasteners

Fastener type	Thickness of lapped plates		Characteristic strength (kN)	Characteristic strength per unit thickness (kN/mm)	Failure mode	Ultimate strength of thinner sheet (N/mm^2)	Theoretical ultimate strength (kN)		Average flexibility (mm/kN)
	t_1 (mm)	t_2 (mm)					Baehre and Berggren	Strnad	
SELF-DRILLING, SELF-TAPPING SCREWS WITH STEEL WASHERS									
diameter = 5.5 mm	0.75	0.75	2.0	2.7	3	302	1.28	1.34	0.31
diameter = 4.8 mm	0.52	0.52	1.1	2.1	3	292	0.74	0.82	0.41
	0.76	0.76	2.0	2.7	3	302	1.25	1.27	0.24
	0.93	0.93	2.4	2.6	3	310	1.74	1.75	0.15
	1.23	1.23	3.7	3.0	1 or 3	347	3.11	2.58	0.06
SELF-DRILLING, SELF-TAPPING SCREWS WITH NEO-PRENE WASHERS									
diameter = 4.8 mm	0.75	0.75	1.8	2.4	3	302	1.22	1.26	0.36
STEEL BLIND RIVETS (open type)									
diameter = 6.4 mm	0.76	0.76	2.5	3.2	4	302	1.78		0.15
diameter = 4.8 mm	0.75	0.75	2.0	2.7	4	302	1.51		0.30
MONEL METAL BLIND RIVETS (open type)									
diameter = 6.4 mm	0.76	0.76	2.9	3.8	4	302	1.78		0.28
	1.00	1.00	4.0	4.0	4	302	3.37		0.19
diameter = 4.8 mm	0.51	0.51	1.4	2.7	4	292	0.89		0.35
	0.75	0.75	2.1	2.8	4	302	1.51		0.28
	0.92	0.92	2.7	2.9	4	310	2.11		0.25
	1.01	1.01	3.1	3.1	4	373	2.95		0.17
	1.23	1.23	3.8	3.1	4	347	3.83		0.22

ALUMINIUM ALLOY BLIND RIVETS (open type)								
diameter = 6.4 mm	0.75	0.75	2.6	3.4	4	302	1.75	0.06
	1.01	1.01	3.6	3.6	1	373	3.43	0.10
diameter = 4.8 mm	0.75	0.75	2.1	2.8	4	302	1.51	0.13
(sealed type, short break mandrel)								
diameter = 4.8 mm	0.75	0.75	2.6	3.4	4	302	1.51	0.14
	1.01	1.01	2.5	2.5	1	373	2.95	0.13
(sealed type, long break mandrel)								
diameter = 4.8 mm	0.75	0.75	2.4	3.1	4	302	1.53	0.10
	1.01	1.01	3.0	2.9	1	373	2.95	0.15
'BULB TITE' ALUMINIUM ALLOY BLIND RIVETS								
diameter = 7.1 mm	0.76	0.76	4.1	5.4	4	302	1.89	0.51
diameter = 6.4 mm	0.77	0.77	2.9	3.8	4	302	1.82	0.33
diameter = 4.8 mm	0.77	0.77	1.9	2.5	4	302	1.56	0.50
'FAB-LOK' STEEL FASTENERS WITH NEOPRENE WASHERS								
diameter = 7.7 mm	0.78	0.78	4.5	4.8	4	302	2.07	0.71

Notes on table 9.10

1. Theoretical fastener strengths are calculated according to section 13.3 and are given for comparison purposes only.
2. Fastener strengths may be taken as being proportional to the ultimate strength of the connected sheets. For sheets of strengths other than those used in the tests, the results may be adjusted accordingly.
3. Design strengths are equal to the characteristic strengths divided by the material factor γ_m (= 1.11 according to the European recommendations.
4. Failure modes: 1 = shear of fastener itself; 3 = inclination of screw followed by stripping of thread in formed sheet; 4 = crushing in combination with tilting and bearing.

Table 9.11 Characteristic weld strengths for welded diaphragms

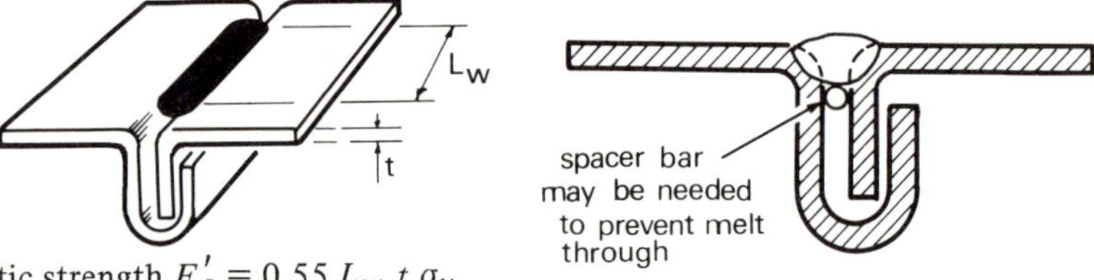

characteristic strength $F'_s = 0.55\, L_w\, t\, \sigma_u$

(a) single flare vee welds

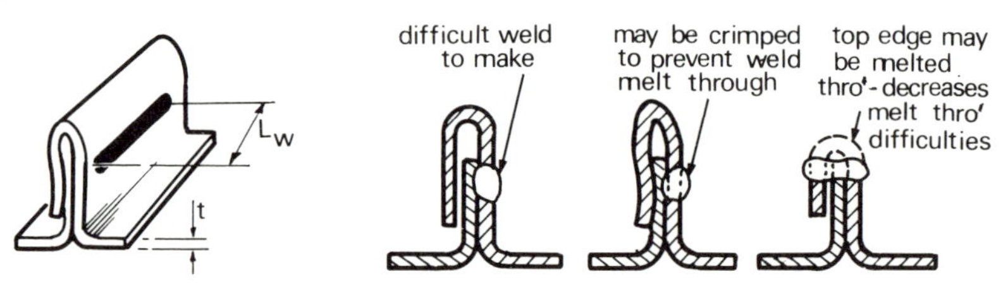

characteristic strength $F'_s = 0.55\, L_w t \sigma_u$

(b) arc seam welds

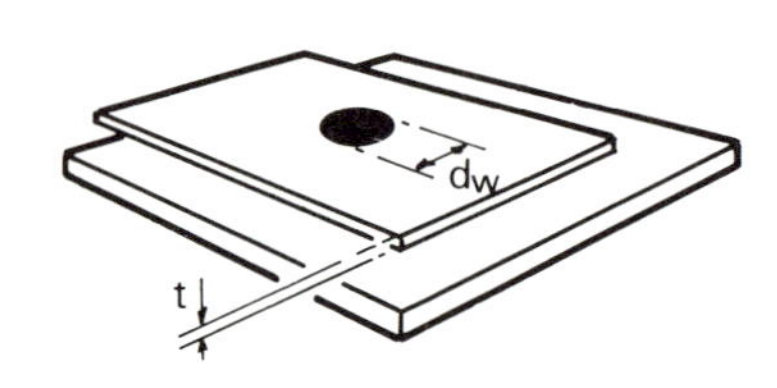

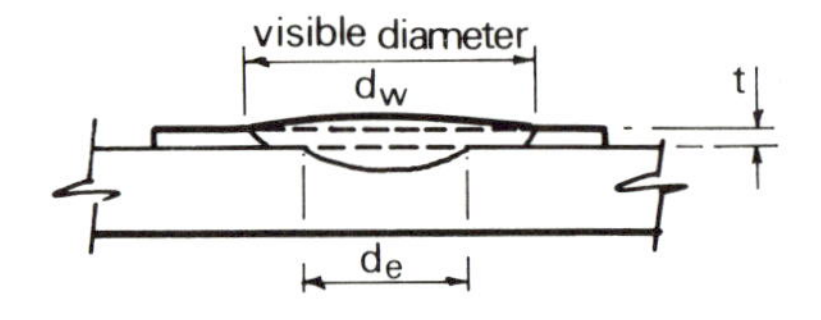

effective diameter $d_e = d_w - t$ (or $d_w - 2t$ for double sheet thickness)

The characteristic strength is the smaller of:

$$\begin{cases} F'_p = 1.4t\, d_e \sigma_u & \text{if } d_e/t < 11.6/\sqrt{\sigma_u} \\ F'_p = \left[2.1 - \dfrac{d_e\sqrt{\sigma_u}}{16.3t}\right] t\, d_e \sigma_u & \text{if } 11.6/\sqrt{\sigma_u} \leqslant d_e/t \leqslant 19.9/\sqrt{\sigma_u} \\ F'_p = 0.9t\, d_e \sigma_u & \text{if } d_e/t > 19.9/\sqrt{\sigma_u} \end{cases}$$

or $F'p = 0.35\,(0.7d_w - 1.5t)^2\, \sigma_{uw}$ where σ_{uw} = nominal tensile strength of filler metal.

(c) round puddle weld (arc spot weld)

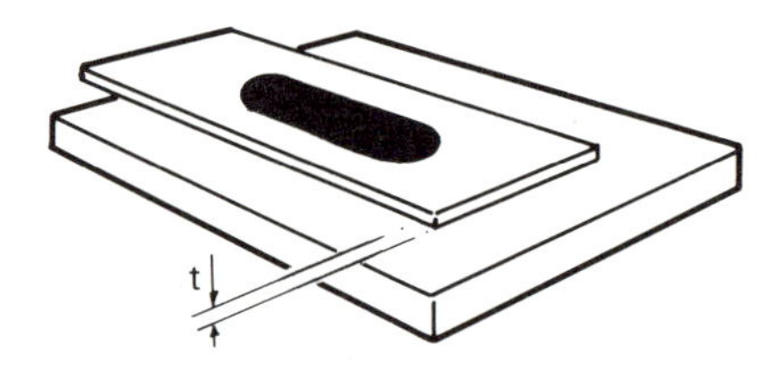

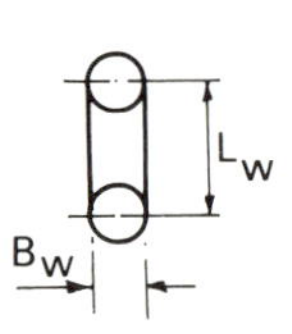

characteristic strength $F'_p = [0.52\, L_w + 2.0\, B_w]\; t\, \sigma_u$

(d) longitudinal puddle weld (arc spot weld)

Notes on table 9.11

1. (a) and (b) are seam connections, (c) and (d) are sheet to supporting structure connections.
2. In the above expressions, σ_u is the ultimate strength of the material of the thinner plate in kN/mm^2. Similar expressions based on the permissible tensile stress of the sheet material are given in reference 6.23.
3. The above strengths are based on a statistical interpretation of a large number of test results and incorporate a reserve of safety related to the variability of the test results.
4. The expressions given are for failure in or immediately adjacent to the weld. For welds in which there is a plate edge adjacent to the weld in the direction of the applied load the possibility of tearing of the plate should also be considered. In general, plate tearing is not relevant to stressed skin designs and the above expressions will usually be all that is required.
5. Design strengths are equal to the characteristic strengths divided by the material factor γ_m (= 1.11 according to the European recommendations).
6. Design charts for resistance spot welds are given in section 13.3.3.

Table 9.12 Strength and flexibility of various purlin to rafter connections

Purlin type	Connection number	Connection detail	Notes	Worst test results per purlin		
				Flexibility s_{pr} (mm/kN)	Elastic load (kN)	Ultimate load (kN)
102 × 51 R.S.C.	1	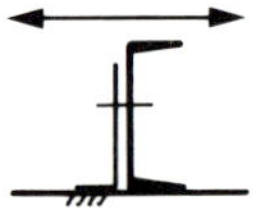	2 16 mm bolts	0.84	2.7	5.4
(89 × 64 × 7.8 angle cleat × 89 mm long)	2	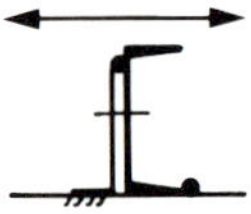	toes welded	0.11	10.7	22.2
152 × 76 R.S.C.	3	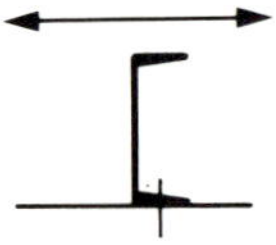	2 19 mm bolts	0.60	11.1	16.0
(76 × 64 × 6.2 angle cleat × 127 mm long)	4	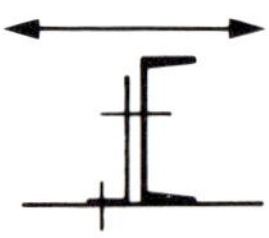	flange unbolted	1.2	5.8	8.0
	5	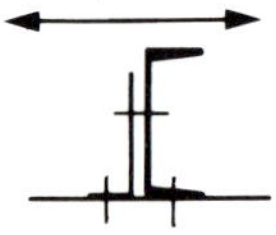	flange bolted	0.35	13.8	21.8
	6	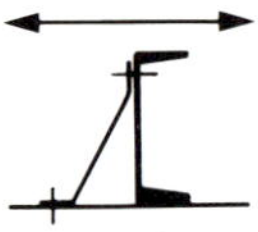	flange unbolted	large	1.8	4.9
	7	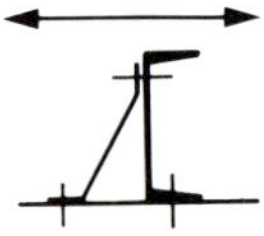	flange bolted	0.13	20.0	>25.0
	8	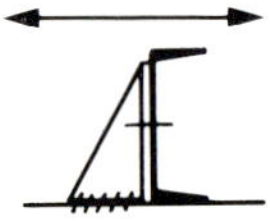	stiffened cleat	0.05	21.8	>25.0
	9	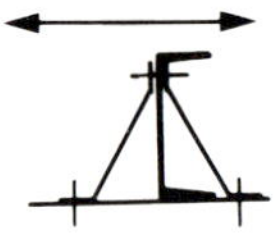	double bent plate	0.04	21.8	>25.0

Purlin type	Connection number	Connection detail	Notes	Worst test results per purlin: Flexibility s_{pr} (mm/kN)	Worst test results per purlin: Elastic load (kN)	Worst test results per purlin: Ultimate load (kN)
254 × 102 × 22 kg/m universal beam	10		2 16 mm bolts	2.6	7.1	11.1
	11		flange unbolted	2.2	4.9	5.8
(152 × 102 × 9.5 angle cleat × 127 mm long)	12		flange bolted	0.86	16.9	>16.9
	13	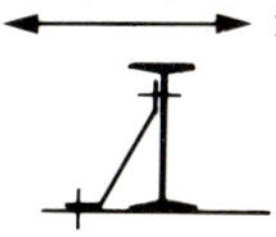	flange unbolted	2.9	3.1	4.0
	14		flange bolted	0.23	16.0	>16.0
	15		double bent plate	0.11	23.1	>23.1
203 × 51 × 2.0 'Z'	16	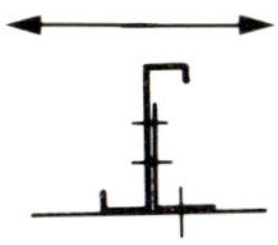	16 mm bolts	1.4	4.0	4.9
(178 × 89 × 9.4 angle cleat × 127 mm long)	17	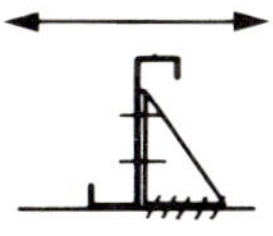	stiffened cleat	0.38	4.0	8.0
	18	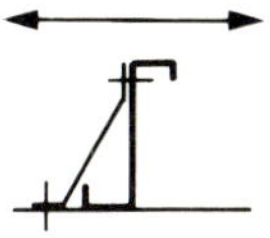	single bent plate	Large	1.8	3.1
	19		double bent plate	0.17	15.1	>15.1

Table 9.13 Reduction factor η for each frame in a building – all frames loaded

*	†	VALUES OF RELATIVE FLEXIBILITY ψ											
		0.01	0.02	0.03	0.04	0.06	0.08	0.10	0.12	0.14	0.16	0.18	0.20
3	2	0.005	0.010	0.015	0.020	0.029	0.038	0.048	0.057	0.065	0.074	0.083	0.091
4	2	0.010	0.020	0.029	0.038	0.057	0.074	0.091	0.107	0.123	0.138	0.153	0.167
5	2	0.015	0.029	0.043	0.056	0.082	0.106	0.129	0.150	0.170	0.190	0.208	0.225
	3	0.020	0.039	0.057	0.075	0.109	0.140	0.170	0.198	0.225	0.250	0.273	0.296
6	2	0.020	0.038	0.056	0.073	0.104	0.134	0.160	0.185	0.208	0.230	0.250	0.268
	3	0.029	0.057	0.083	0.108	0.155	0.198	0.237	0.272	0.305	0.336	0.364	0.390
7	2	0.024	0.047	0.068	0.088	0.124	0.157	0.186	0.213	0.237	0.259	0.280	0.298
	3	0.039	0.074	0.108	0.139	0.196	0.246	0.291	0.331	0.367	0.400	0.429	0.457
	4	0.043	0.084	0.121	0.156	0.219	0.275	0.325	0.369	0.408	0.444	0.476	0.506
8	2	0.029	0.055	0.079	0.101	0.141	0.176	0.207	0.234	0.258	0.280	0.300	0.319
	3	0.048	0.091	0.130	0.167	0.231	0.286	0.334	0.376	0.413	0.446	0.475	0.502
	4	0.057	0.109	0.156	0.199	0.274	0.339	0.394	0.443	0.485	0.522	0.555	0.585
9	2	0.033	0.063	0.089	0.113	0.156	0.191	0.222	0.250	0.274	0.295	0.315	0.333
	3	0.056	0.106	0.151	0.191	0.260	0.318	0.367	0.409	0.446	0.478	0.506	0.532
	4	0.070	0.132	0.187	0.237	0.321	0.390	0.449	0.498	0.540	0.577	0.609	0.637
	5	0.075	0.141	0.199	0.252	0.341	0.414	0.475	0.526	0.570	0.608	0.641	0.670
10	2	0.037	0.070	0.098	0.124	0.168	0.204	0.235	0.261	0.285	0.306	0.325	0.342
	3	0.065	0.121	0.170	0.213	0.285	0.344	0.393	0.434	0.469	0.500	0.528	0.552
	4	0.083	0.154	0.216	0.270	0.360	0.431	0.490	0.539	0.580	0.615	0.645	0.672
	5	0.092	0.171	0.239	0.298	0.396	0.474	0.536	0.588	0.631	0.668	0.700	0.727
11	2	0.041	0.076	0.106	0.133	0.177	0.213	0.244	0.270	0.293	0.313	0.331	0.348
	3	0.073	0.134	0.186	0.231	0.305	0.364	0.412	0.452	0.486	0.516	0.542	0.565
	4	0.095	0.175	0.241	0.299	0.392	0.464	0.521	0.569	0.608	0.641	0.670	0.695
	5	0.109	0.199	0.274	0.338	0.441	0.521	0.583	0.633	0.675	0.709	0.738	0.763
	6	0.113	0.206	0.285	0.351	0.458	0.539	0.603	0.654	0.696	0.731	0.760	0.785
12	2	0.045	0.082	0.114	0.141	0.185	0.221	0.251	0.276	0.298	0.318	0.335	0.351
	3	0.081	0.146	0.201	0.247	0.322	0.380	0.427	0.465	0.498	0.526	0.551	0.573
	4	0.107	0.193	0.264	0.323	0.418	0.489	0.545	0.590	0.628	0.659	0.686	0.709
	5	0.124	0.224	0.305	0.373	0.478	0.557	0.618	0.666	0.705	0.737	0.764	0.787
	6	0.133	0.239	0.325	0.397	0.508	0.590	0.653	0.702	0.741	0.774	0.800	0.823

*No. of frames in building; †frame no. *Note* The number of frames in the building is

Table 9.14 Factors by which η should be divided for central frame only loaded

Value of ψ	Number of frames in building									
	3	4	5	6	7	8	9	10	11	12
0.00	1.00	1.50	2.00	2.50	3.00	3.50	4.00	4.50	5.00	5.50
0.01	1.00	1.50	2.00	2.49	2.98	3.47	3.95	4.43	4.90	5.37
0.02	1.00	1.50	1.99	2.48	2.96	3.43	3.90	4.36	4.81	5.24
0.03	1.00	1.49	1.99	2.46	2.94	3.40	3.86	4.29	4.72	5.12
0.04	1.00	1.49	1.98	2.45	2.92	3.37	3.81	4.23	4.64	5.01
0.06	1.00	1.49	1.97	2.43	2.89	3.31	3.73	4.10	4.48	4.81
0.08	1.00	1.48	1.96	2.41	2.85	3.25	3.65	3.99	4.34	4.63
0.10	1.00	1.48	1.95	2.39	2.82	3.20	3.57	3.89	4.21	4.46
0.12	1.00	1.47	1.94	2.36	2.79	3.14	3.50	3.79	4.08	4.31
0.14	1.00	1.47	1.93	2.34	2.75	3.09	3.43	3.70	3.97	4.18
0.16	1.00	1.46	1.93	2.33	2.72	3.05	3.37	3.62	3.87	4.05
0.18	1.00	1.46	1.92	2.31	2.69	3.00	3.31	3.54	3.77	3.94
0.20	1.00	1.45	1.91	2.29	2.67	2.96	3.25	3.47	3.68	3.83
0.25	1.00	1.44	1.89	2.24	2.60	2.86	3.12	3.30	3.48	3.60
0.30	1.00	1.43	1.87	2.20	2.54	2.77	3.01	3.16	3.31	3.41
0.35	1.00	1.43	1.85	2.17	2.48	2.69	2.90	3.03	3.16	3.24
0.40	1.00	1.42	1.83	2.13	2.43	2.62	2.81	2.92	3.03	3.10
0.45	1.00	1.41	1.82	2.10	2.38	2.55	2.72	2.82	2.92	2.97
0.50	1.00	1.40	1.80	2.07	2.33	2.49	2.65	2.73	2.82	2.86
0.60	1.00	1.38	1.77	2.01	2.25	2.38	2.51	2.58	2.65	2.68
0.70	1.00	1.37	1.74	1.96	2.18	2.29	2.40	2.45	2.50	2.53
0.80	1.00	1.36	1.71	1.91	2.11	2.21	2.30	2.34	2.39	2.40
0.90	1.00	1.34	1.69	1.87	2.05	2.13	2.22	2.25	2.29	2.30
1.00	1.00	1.33	1.67	1.83	2.00	2.07	2.14	2.17	2.20	2.21
1.50	1.00	1.29	1.57	1.69	1.80	1.84	1.88	1.89	1.90	1.91
2.00	1.00	1.25	1.50	1.58	1.67	1.69	1.71	1.72	1.73	1.73

Table 9.13 (*cont.*)

0.25	0.30	0.35	0.40	0.45	0.50	0.60	0.70	0.80	0.90	1.00	1.50	2.00
0.111	0.130	0.149	0.167	0.184	0.200	0.231	0.259	0.286	0.310	0.333	0.429	0.500
0.200	0.231	0.259	0.286	0.310	0.333	0.375	0.412	0.444	0.474	0.500	0.600	0.667
0.265	0.301	0.333	0.362	0.388	0.412	0.454	0.490	0.521	0.548	0.571	0.659	0.714
0.347	0.392	0.432	0.468	0.500	0.529	0.580	0.622	0.658	0.688	0.714	0.805	0.857
0.310	0.347	0.379	0.407	0.432	0.455	0.494	0.526	0.554	0.579	0.600	0.677	0.727
0.448	0.497	0.540	0.576	0.608	0.636	0.684	0.721	0.752	0.778	0.800	0.871	0.909
0.340	0.375	0.406	0.432	0.456	0.477	0.513	0.543	0.569	0.591	0.611	0.683	0.731
0.515	0.563	0.604	0.638	0.667	0.692	0.734	0.767	0.793	0.815	0.833	0.892	0.923
0.569	0.620	0.663	0.698	0.728	0.754	0.795	0.827	0.852	0.873	0.889	0.938	0.962
0.359	0.393	0.421	0.447	0.469	0.488	0.522	0.551	0.575	0.597	0.615	0.685	0.732
0.558	0.603	0.641	0.672	0.698	0.721	0.758	0.787	0.811	0.830	0.846	0.898	0.927
0.646	0.695	0.734	0.765	0.792	0.814	0.849	0.875	0.895	0.911	0.923	0.959	0.976
0.371	0.403	0.430	0.454	0.475	0.494	0.527	0.554	0.578	0.599	0.617	0.686	0.732
0.585	0.627	0.662	0.690	0.715	0.735	0.770	0.796	0.818	0.836	0.851	0.901	0.928
0.695	0.739	0.774	0.802	0.825	0.844	0.874	0.896	0.913	0.926	0.936	0.966	0.979
0.729	0.773	0.808	0.835	0.857	0.875	0.903	0.923	0.938	0.949	0.957	0.981	0.990
0.379	0.409	0.436	0.458	0.479	0.497	0.529	0.556	0.579	0.599	0.618	0.686	0.732
0.602	0.641	0.673	0.700	0.723	0.743	0.775	0.800	0.821	0.838	0.853	0.901	0.928
0.725	0.766	0.797	0.822	0.843	0.860	0.886	0.906	0.920	0.932	0.941	0.968	0.980
0.780	0.820	0.850	0.873	0.891	0.906	0.929	0.944	0.956	0.964	0.971	0.987	0.993
0.383	0.413	0.438	0.461	0.481	0.499	0.530	0.556	0.579	0.600	0.618	0.686	0.732
0.612	0.650	0.680	0.706	0.727	0.746	0.777	0.802	0.822	0.839	0.854	0.901	0.928
0.744	0.781	0.810	0.833	0.852	0.867	0.892	0.910	0.924	0.934	0.943	0.969	0.981
0.812	0.847	0.873	0.893	0.909	0.922	0.941	0.954	0.963	0.970	0.976	0.989	0.994
0.833	0.867	0.892	0.911	0.926	0.938	0.954	0.966	0.974	0.980	0.984	0.994	0.997
0.386	0.415	0.440	0.462	0.482	0.499	0.530	0.557	0.580	0.600	0.618	0.686	0.732
0.618	0.654	0.684	0.709	0.730	0.748	0.779	0.803	0.823	0.840	0.854	0.901	0.928
0.755	0.790	0.817	0.839	0.856	0.871	0.894	0.912	0.925	0.935	0.944	0.969	0.981
0.831	0.863	0.886	0.904	0.918	0.930	0.946	0.958	0.967	0.973	0.978	0.990	0.995
0.865	0.895	0.916	0.932	0.944	0.953	0.967	0.975	0.981	0.986	0.989	0.996	0.998

inclusive of the gable ends. Frame 1 is the end gable, frame 2 the penultimate frame and so on.

Table 9.15 Shallow profile, perpendicular to span, fastened on four sides

DESIGN TABLE - SHEET PERPENDICULAR TO SPAN

SHALLOW PROFILE - FASTENED ON FOUR SIDES

DEPTH(MM)		SPAN-DEPTH RATIO								
		1.00	1.25	1.50	1.75	2.00	2.50	3.00	3.50	4.00
5000.0	QPERM	7.190	5.752	4.794	4.109	3.595	2.876	2.397	2.054	1.798
	K1	2.888	1.887	1.322	0.971	0.739	0.456	0.305	0.214	0.155
	K2	0.849	0.547	0.381	0.280	0.214	0.135	0.093	0.067	0.051
	K3	2.888	1.887	1.322	0.971	0.739	0.456	0.305	0.214	0.155
7500.0	QPERM	7.190	5.752	4.794	4.109	3.595	2.876	2.397	2.054	1.798
	K1	2.409	1.555	1.065	0.768	0.575	0.349	0.227	0.154	0.109
	K2	0.852	0.547	0.378	0.276	0.209	0.131	0.089	0.063	0.047
	K3	2.378	1.535	1.052	0.758	0.568	0.345	0.224	0.153	0.108
10000.0	QPERM	7.190	5.752	4.794	4.109	3.595	2.876	2.397	2.054	1.798
	K1	1.889	1.189	0.813	0.585	0.436	0.262	0.167	0.112	0.078
	K2	0.695	0.442	0.305	0.222	0.169	0.105	0.071	0.050	0.036
	K3	1.843	1.161	0.794	0.571	0.427	0.256	0.164	0.110	0.077
12500.0	QPERM	7.190	5.752	4.794	4.109	3.595	2.876	2.397	2.054	1.798
	K1	1.616	1.021	0.696	0.499	0.370	0.218	0.137	0.090	0.062
	K2	0.631	0.402	0.277	0.202	0.152	0.094	0.063	0.044	0.032
	K3	1.317	0.834	0.571	0.410	0.306	0.183	0.117	0.078	0.054
15000.0	QPERM	7.190	5.752	4.794	4.109	3.595	2.876	2.397	2.054	1.798
	K1	1.427	0.902	0.613	0.436	0.321	0.187	0.116	0.076	0.051
	K2	0.581	0.370	0.255	0.185	0.139	0.085	0.056	0.039	0.028
	K3	0.995	0.631	0.431	0.310	0.231	0.138	0.088	0.059	0.041
20000.0	QPERM	7.190	5.752	4.794	4.109	3.595	2.876	2.397	2.054	1.798
	K1	1.166	0.734	0.494	0.349	0.254	0.145	0.088	0.056	0.038
	K2	0.503	0.319	0.219	0.158	0.118	0.072	0.046	0.032	0.022
	K3	0.706	0.447	0.305	0.218	0.162	0.096	0.061	0.041	0.028
25000.0	QPERM	7.190	5.752	4.794	4.109	3.595	2.876	2.397	2.054	1.798
	K1	0.991	0.620	0.415	0.290	0.210	0.118	0.071	0.045	0.030
	K2	0.444	0.281	0.192	0.138	0.103	0.062	0.040	0.027	0.019
	K3	0.564	0.357	0.242	0.173	0.128	0.075	0.048	0.032	0.022
30000.0	QPERM	7.190	5.752	4.794	4.109	3.595	2.876	2.397	2.054	1.798
	K1	0.864	0.538	0.358	0.249	0.179	0.099	0.059	0.037	0.024
	K2	0.398	0.252	0.171	0.122	0.091	0.054	0.034	0.023	0.016
	K3	0.476	0.300	0.203	0.145	0.107	0.063	0.039	0.026	0.018
35000.0	QPERM	7.190	5.752	4.794	4.109	3.595	2.876	2.397	2.054	1.798
	K1	0.767	0.475	0.315	0.218	0.156	0.086	0.051	0.032	0.021
	K2	0.361	0.228	0.154	0.110	0.081	0.048	0.030	0.020	0.014
	K3	0.414	0.260	0.176	0.125	0.092	0.054	0.034	0.022	0.015
40000.0	QPERM	7.190	5.752	4.794	4.109	3.595	2.876	2.397	2.054	1.798
	K1	0.690	0.426	0.281	0.194	0.138	0.075	0.044	0.027	0.018
	K2	0.330	0.208	0.141	0.100	0.074	0.043	0.027	0.018	0.012
	K3	0.368	0.231	0.156	0.110	0.081	0.047	0.029	0.019	0.013
45000.0	QPERM	7.190	5.752	4.794	4.109	3.595	2.876	2.397	2.054	1.798
	K1	0.627	0.386	0.253	0.174	0.124	0.067	0.039	0.024	0.016
	K2	0.305	0.191	0.129	0.092	0.067	0.039	0.025	0.016	0.011
	K3	0.332	0.208	0.140	0.099	0.073	0.042	0.026	0.017	0.012
50000.0	QPERM	7.190	5.752	4.794	4.109	3.595	2.876	2.397	2.054	1.798
	K1	0.575	0.353	0.231	0.158	0.112	0.061	0.035	0.022	0.014
	K2	0.283	0.177	0.119	0.084	0.062	0.036	0.022	0.015	0.010
	K3	0.302	0.189	0.127	0.090	0.066	0.038	0.024	0.015	0.010

Table 9.16 Shallow profile, parallel to span, fastened on four sides

DESIGN TABLE - SHEET PARALLEL TO SPAN

SHALLOW PROFILE - FASTENED ON FOUR SIDES

DEPTH(MM)		SPAN-DEPTH RATIO								
		1.00	1.25	1.50	1.75	2.00	2.50	3.00	3.50	4.00
5000.0	QPERM	7.190	5.752	4.794	4.109	3.595	2.876	2.397	2.054	1.798
	K1	3.044	2.128	1.555	1.179	0.891	0.543	0.357	0.246	0.177
	K2	0.852	0.655	0.521	0.426	0.330	0.207	0.141	0.101	0.076
	K3	1.445	1.081	0.835	0.664	0.511	0.318	0.213	0.151	0.111
7500.0	QPERM	7.190	5.752	4.794	4.109	3.595	2.876	2.397	2.054	1.798
	K1	2.442	1.628	1.103	0.788	0.585	0.350	0.226	0.154	0.108
	K2	0.793	0.578	0.398	0.289	0.219	0.137	0.095	0.069	0.052
	K3	1.283	0.905	0.620	0.449	0.337	0.207	0.137	0.095	0.069
10000.0	QPERM	7.190	5.752	4.794	4.109	3.595	2.876	2.397	2.054	1.798
	K1	1.954	1.217	0.819	0.580	0.429	0.254	0.161	0.107	0.074
	K2	0.683	0.433	0.297	0.215	0.165	0.106	0.073	0.053	0.040
	K3	1.075	0.678	0.462	0.333	0.249	0.151	0.098	0.068	0.048
12500.0	QPERM	7.190	5.752	4.794	4.109	3.595	2.876	2.397	2.054	1.798
	K1	1.559	0.965	0.646	0.458	0.337	0.196	0.122	0.080	0.054
	K2	0.546	0.345	0.238	0.176	0.135	0.087	0.060	0.043	0.031
	K3	0.859	0.540	0.366	0.262	0.195	0.117	0.075	0.051	0.036
15000.0	QPERM	7.190	5.752	4.794	4.109	3.595	2.876	2.397	2.054	1.798
	K1	1.292	0.796	0.534	0.377	0.275	0.158	0.097	0.061	0.041
	K2	0.454	0.288	0.203	0.150	0.116	0.074	0.051	0.035	0.024
	K3	0.713	0.447	0.302	0.215	0.159	0.094	0.060	0.040	0.028
20000.0	QPERM	7.190	5.752	4.794	4.109	3.595	2.876	2.397	2.054	1.798
	K1	0.960	0.593	0.393	0.274	0.197	0.109	0.064	0.039	0.026
	K2	0.344	0.225	0.159	0.118	0.092	0.056	0.036	0.024	0.016
	K3	0.530	0.330	0.221	0.156	0.115	0.066	0.041	0.027	0.019
25000.0	QPERM	7.190	5.752	4.794	4.109	3.595	2.876	2.397	2.054	1.798
	K1	0.766	0.469	0.308	0.212	0.149	0.079	0.045	0.028	0.018
	K2	0.285	0.188	0.133	0.100	0.074	0.043	0.027	0.018	0.012
	K3	0.420	0.259	0.173	0.121	0.088	0.050	0.031	0.020	0.013
30000.0	QPERM	7.190	5.752	4.794	4.109	3.595	2.876	2.397	2.054	1.798
	K1	0.636	0.386	0.251	0.167	0.116	0.060	0.034	0.020	0.013
	K2	0.246	0.163	0.117	0.082	0.059	0.034	0.021	0.014	0.009
	K3	0.346	0.212	0.140	0.097	0.070	0.039	0.024	0.015	0.010
35000.0	QPERM	7.190	5.752	4.794	4.109	3.595	2.876	2.397	2.054	1.798
	K1	0.543	0.327	0.206	0.136	0.093	0.047	0.026	0.016	0.010
	K2	0.218	0.146	0.098	0.068	0.049	0.028	0.017	0.011	0.007
	K3	0.293	0.179	0.117	0.081	0.058	0.032	0.019	0.012	0.008
40000.0	QPERM	7.190	5.752	4.794	4.109	3.595	2.876	2.397	2.054	1.798
	K1	0.473	0.278	0.173	0.113	0.076	0.038	0.021	0.012	0.008
	K2	0.198	0.127	0.084	0.058	0.042	0.023	0.014	0.009	0.006
	K3	0.253	0.154	0.100	0.069	0.049	0.027	0.016	0.010	0.006
45000.0	QPERM	7.190	5.752	4.794	4.109	3.595	2.876	2.397	2.054	1.798
	K1	0.418	0.239	0.147	0.095	0.064	0.032	0.017	0.010	0.006
	K2	0.183	0.112	0.073	0.050	0.036	0.020	0.012	0.007	0.005
	K3	0.223	0.134	0.087	0.059	0.042	0.022	0.013	0.008	0.005
50000.0	QPERM	7.190	5.752	4.794	4.109	3.595	2.876	2.397	2.054	1.798
	K1	0.368	0.209	0.127	0.082	0.055	0.027	0.014	0.008	0.005
	K2	0.163	0.099	0.064	0.044	0.031	0.017	0.010	0.006	0.004
	K3	0.198	0.119	0.076	0.052	0.036	0.019	0.011	0.007	0.004

Table 9.17 Shallow profile, perpendicular to span, fastened on two sides

DESIGN TABLE - SHEET PERPENDICULAR TO SPAN

SHALLOW PROFILE - FASTENED ON TWO SIDES

DEPTH(MM)		SPAN-DEPTH RATIO								
		1.00	1.25	1.50	1.75	2.00	2.50	3.00	3.50	4.00
5000.0	QPERM	2.984	2.387	1.989	1.705	1.492	1.492	1.492	1.370	1.198
	QPERM2	2.984	2.387	1.989	1.705	1.492	1.193	0.995	0.852	0.746
	K1	1.415	1.002	0.747	0.577	0.458	0.290	0.200	0.146	0.110
	K2	0.650	0.435	0.312	0.234	0.181	0.116	0.080	0.059	0.045
	K3	1.415	1.002	0.747	0.577	0.458	0.290	0.200	0.146	0.110
7500.0	QPERM	2.611	2.089	1.958	1.958	1.958	1.917	1.598	1.370	1.198
	QPERM2	2.611	2.089	1.740	1.492	1.305	1.044	0.870	0.746	0.653
	K1	1.166	0.819	0.580	0.429	0.331	0.213	0.147	0.106	0.078
	K2	0.619	0.415	0.291	0.215	0.165	0.106	0.073	0.053	0.040
	K3	1.159	0.813	0.576	0.426	0.328	0.212	0.146	0.105	0.077
10000.0	QPERM	2.424	2.424	2.424	2.424	2.397	1.917	1.598	1.370	1.198
	QPERM2	2.424	1.939	1.616	1.385	1.212	0.970	0.808	0.693	0.606
	K1	0.968	0.624	0.442	0.331	0.257	0.165	0.113	0.080	0.058
	K2	0.515	0.331	0.232	0.172	0.133	0.085	0.059	0.042	0.031
	K3	0.956	0.616	0.437	0.327	0.253	0.163	0.111	0.079	0.057
12500.0	QPERM	2.890	2.890	2.890	2.739	2.397	1.917	1.598	1.370	1.198
	QPERM2	2.312	1.850	1.542	1.321	1.156	0.925	0.771	0.661	0.578
	K1	0.797	0.527	0.377	0.283	0.219	0.140	0.094	0.066	0.047
	K2	0.450	0.294	0.207	0.154	0.119	0.076	0.052	0.037	0.027
	K3	0.716	0.472	0.337	0.252	0.195	0.125	0.084	0.059	0.043
15000.0	QPERM	3.357	3.357	3.196	2.739	2.397	1.917	1.598	1.370	1.198
	QPERM2	2.238	1.790	1.492	1.279	1.119	0.895	0.746	0.639	0.559
	K1	0.694	0.464	0.333	0.250	0.193	0.122	0.081	0.056	0.040
	K2	0.406	0.267	0.189	0.140	0.108	0.069	0.047	0.033	0.024
	K3	0.573	0.380	0.271	0.203	0.156	0.099	0.067	0.046	0.033
20000.0	QPERM	4.289	3.835	3.196	2.739	2.397	1.917	1.598	1.370	1.198
	QPERM2	2.144	1.716	1.430	1.225	1.072	0.858	0.715	0.613	0.536
	K1	0.570	0.384	0.276	0.206	0.158	0.098	0.064	0.043	0.030
	K2	0.347	0.229	0.162	0.120	0.092	0.058	0.039	0.027	0.019
	K3	0.433	0.288	0.205	0.152	0.117	0.073	0.048	0.033	0.024
25000.0	QPERM	4.794	3.835	3.196	2.739	2.397	1.917	1.598	1.370	1.198
	QPERM2	2.089	1.671	1.392	1.193	1.044	0.835	0.696	0.597	0.522
	K1	0.494	0.333	0.238	0.176	0.134	0.082	0.053	0.035	0.024
	K2	0.306	0.202	0.143	0.105	0.080	0.050	0.033	0.023	0.016
	K3	0.359	0.238	0.169	0.125	0.095	0.059	0.039	0.026	0.019
30000.0	QPERM	4.794	3.835	3.196	2.739	2.397	1.917	1.598	1.370	1.198
	QPERM2	2.051	1.641	1.367	1.172	1.026	0.820	0.684	0.586	0.513
	K1	0.441	0.296	0.210	0.155	0.117	0.071	0.045	0.030	0.020
	K2	0.276	0.182	0.128	0.094	0.072	0.044	0.029	0.020	0.014
	K3	0.311	0.206	0.145	0.107	0.081	0.050	0.032	0.022	0.015
35000.0	QPERM	4.794	3.835	3.196	2.739	2.397	1.917	1.598	1.370	1.198
	QPERM2	2.025	1.620	1.350	1.157	1.012	0.810	0.675	0.578	0.506
	K1	0.400	0.267	0.189	0.138	0.104	0.062	0.039	0.026	0.017
	K2	0.252	0.166	0.116	0.085	0.065	0.040	0.026	0.018	0.012
	K3	0.277	0.183	0.128	0.094	0.071	0.043	0.028	0.019	0.013
40000.0	QPERM	4.794	3.835	3.196	2.739	2.397	1.917	1.598	1.370	1.198
	QPERM2	2.005	1.604	1.336	1.145	1.002	0.802	0.668	0.573	0.501
	K1	0.368	0.244	0.172	0.125	0.094	0.055	0.035	0.022	0.015
	K2	0.233	0.153	0.107	0.078	0.059	0.036	0.023	0.016	0.011
	K3	0.251	0.165	0.115	0.084	0.063	0.038	0.025	0.017	0.012
45000.0	QPERM	4.794	3.835	3.196	2.739	2.397	1.917	1.598	1.370	1.198
	QPERM2	1.989	1.591	1.326	1.137	0.995	0.796	0.663	0.568	0.497
	K1	0.341	0.226	0.158	0.114	0.085	0.050	0.031	0.020	0.013
	K2	0.216	0.141	0.099	0.072	0.054	0.033	0.021	0.014	0.010
	K3	0.230	0.150	0.105	0.076	0.057	0.035	0.022	0.015	0.010
50000.0	QPERM	4.794	3.835	3.196	2.739	2.397	1.917	1.598	1.370	1.198
	QPERM2	1.977	1.581	1.318	1.130	0.988	0.791	0.659	0.565	0.494
	K1	0.318	0.210	0.146	0.105	0.078	0.046	0.028	0.018	0.012
	K2	0.202	0.132	0.092	0.067	0.050	0.030	0.019	0.013	0.009
	K3	0.212	0.138	0.096	0.070	0.052	0.031	0.020	0.013	0.009

Table 9.18 Shallow profile, parallel to span, fastened on two sides

DESIGN TABLE - SHEET PARALLEL TO SPAN

SHALLOW PROFILE - FASTENED ON TWO SIDES

DEPTH(MM)		SPAN-DEPTH RATIO								
		1.00	1.25	1.50	1.75	2.00	2.50	3.00	3.50	4.00
5000.0	QPERM	3.357	2.238	1.865	1.598	1.399	1.119	0.932	0.799	0.699
	K1	1.648	1.016	0.723	0.538	0.410	0.256	0.173	0.123	0.092
	K2	0.689	0.490	0.376	0.298	0.230	0.145	0.099	0.072	0.054
	K3	1.031	0.694	0.516	0.398	0.305	0.192	0.131	0.094	0.070
7500.0	QPERM	2.797	2.238	1.865	1.598	1.399	1.119	0.932	0.799	0.699
	K1	1.305	0.853	0.585	0.424	0.319	0.196	0.131	0.092	0.067
	K2	0.618	0.437	0.301	0.220	0.167	0.105	0.073	0.053	0.040
	K3	0.880	0.602	0.414	0.301	0.228	0.142	0.095	0.067	0.049
10000.0	QPERM	2.797	2.238	1.865	1.598	1.399	1.119	0.932	0.799	0.699
	K1	1.116	0.703	0.479	0.345	0.259	0.158	0.104	0.071	0.051
	K2	0.541	0.343	0.236	0.172	0.132	0.084	0.058	0.042	0.032
	K3	0.761	0.482	0.330	0.239	0.180	0.111	0.073	0.051	0.037
12500.0	QPERM	2.797	2.238	1.865	1.598	1.399	1.119	0.932	0.799	0.699
	K1	0.950	0.596	0.404	0.290	0.217	0.130	0.084	0.057	0.040
	K2	0.446	0.282	0.195	0.144	0.111	0.071	0.049	0.036	0.026
	K3	0.635	0.401	0.274	0.197	0.148	0.090	0.059	0.041	0.029
15000.0	QPERM	2.797	2.238	1.865	1.598	1.399	1.119	0.932	0.799	0.699
	K1	0.824	0.515	0.350	0.250	0.185	0.110	0.070	0.046	0.032
	K2	0.378	0.241	0.169	0.125	0.096	0.062	0.043	0.029	0.021
	K3	0.543	0.342	0.233	0.167	0.125	0.075	0.049	0.033	0.023
20000.0	QPERM	2.797	2.238	1.865	1.598	1.399	1.119	0.932	0.799	0.699
	K1	0.651	0.407	0.274	0.194	0.142	0.081	0.050	0.032	0.021
	K2	0.294	0.192	0.135	0.100	0.078	0.048	0.031	0.021	0.015
	K3	0.420	0.263	0.178	0.126	0.093	0.055	0.035	0.023	0.016
25000.0	QPERM	2.797	2.238	1.865	1.598	1.399	1.119	0.932	0.799	0.699
	K1	0.540	0.335	0.223	0.156	0.112	0.062	0.037	0.023	0.015
	K2	0.246	0.162	0.114	0.085	0.064	0.037	0.024	0.016	0.011
	K3	0.341	0.212	0.142	0.100	0.074	0.043	0.027	0.017	0.012
30000.0	QPERM	2.797	2.238	1.865	1.598	1.399	1.119	0.932	0.799	0.699
	K1	0.460	0.283	0.187	0.128	0.090	0.049	0.029	0.018	0.011
	K2	0.214	0.141	0.101	0.071	0.052	0.030	0.019	0.012	0.008
	K3	0.286	0.177	0.118	0.083	0.060	0.034	0.021	0.014	0.009
35000.0	QPERM	2.797	2.238	1.865	1.598	1.399	1.119	0.932	0.799	0.699
	K1	0.400	0.245	0.158	0.107	0.075	0.040	0.023	0.014	0.009
	K2	0.191	0.127	0.086	0.060	0.044	0.025	0.015	0.010	0.007
	K3	0.246	0.151	0.100	0.070	0.050	0.028	0.017	0.011	0.007
40000.0	QPERM	2.797	2.238	1.865	1.598	1.399	1.119	0.932	0.799	0.699
	K1	0.354	0.212	0.135	0.090	0.063	0.033	0.019	0.011	0.007
	K2	0.174	0.112	0.074	0.052	0.037	0.021	0.013	0.008	0.005
	K3	0.215	0.131	0.086	0.060	0.043	0.024	0.014	0.009	0.006
45000.0	QPERM	2.797	2.238	1.865	1.598	1.399	1.119	0.932	0.799	0.699
	K1	0.317	0.186	0.117	0.078	0.054	0.028	0.015	0.009	0.006
	K2	0.161	0.098	0.065	0.045	0.032	0.018	0.011	0.007	0.005
	K3	0.190	0.116	0.076	0.052	0.037	0.020	0.012	0.007	0.005
50000.0	QPERM	2.797	2.238	1.865	1.598	1.399	1.119	0.932	0.799	0.699
	K1	0.283	0.165	0.103	0.068	0.046	0.024	0.013	0.008	0.005
	K2	0.144	0.088	0.058	0.040	0.028	0.016	0.009	0.006	0.004
	K3	0.170	0.103	0.067	0.046	0.032	0.018	0.010	0.006	0.004

Table 9.19 Deep profile, perpendicular to span, fastened on four sides

DESIGN TABLE - SHEET PERPENDICULAR TO SPAN

DEEP PROFILE - FASTENED ON FOUR SIDES

DEPTH(MM)		SPAN-DEPTH RATIO								
		1.00	1.25	1.50	1.75	2.00	2.50	3.00	3.50	4.00
5000.0	QPERM	7.190	5.752	4.794	4.109	3.595	2.876	2.397	2.054	1.798
	K1	1.998	1.299	0.909	0.668	0.510	0.318	0.215	0.153	0.113
	K2	0.380	0.244	0.170	0.125	0.095	0.061	0.042	0.031	0.023
	K3	1.998	1.299	0.909	0.668	0.510	0.318	0.215	0.153	0.113
7500.0	QPERM	7.190	5.752	4.794	4.109	3.595	2.876	2.397	2.054	1.798
	K1	1.729	1.115	0.766	0.555	0.418	0.257	0.170	0.117	0.084
	K2	0.369	0.236	0.164	0.120	0.092	0.058	0.040	0.029	0.022
	K3	1.729	1.115	0.766	0.555	0.418	0.257	0.170	0.117	0.084
10000.0	QPERM	7.190	5.752	4.794	4.109	3.595	2.876	2.397	2.054	1.798
	K1	1.334	0.842	0.577	0.417	0.312	0.189	0.123	0.083	0.059
	K2	0.279	0.178	0.123	0.090	0.069	0.043	0.030	0.021	0.016
	K3	1.326	0.837	0.573	0.414	0.310	0.188	0.122	0.083	0.058
12500.0	QPERM	7.190	5.752	4.794	4.109	3.595	2.876	2.397	2.054	1.798
	K1	1.171	0.740	0.505	0.363	0.270	0.161	0.102	0.068	0.047
	K2	0.259	0.165	0.114	0.083	0.063	0.040	0.027	0.019	0.014
	K3	0.707	0.449	0.309	0.224	0.168	0.103	0.067	0.046	0.033
15000.0	QPERM	7.190	5.752	4.794	4.109	3.595	2.876	2.397	2.054	1.798
	K1	1.047	0.661	0.449	0.321	0.237	0.139	0.087	0.057	0.039
	K2	0.241	0.154	0.106	0.078	0.059	0.037	0.025	0.018	0.013
	K3	0.502	0.320	0.220	0.159	0.120	0.073	0.048	0.033	0.024
20000.0	QPERM	7.190	5.752	4.794	4.109	3.595	2.876	2.397	2.054	1.798
	K1	0.870	0.546	0.368	0.260	0.189	0.108	0.066	0.043	0.029
	K2	0.213	0.136	0.094	0.068	0.051	0.032	0.021	0.015	0.011
	K3	0.343	0.218	0.149	0.108	0.081	0.049	0.032	0.022	0.016
25000.0	QPERM	7.190	5.752	4.794	4.109	3.595	2.876	2.397	2.054	1.798
	K1	0.749	0.467	0.312	0.218	0.158	0.089	0.053	0.034	0.022
	K2	0.191	0.122	0.084	0.061	0.046	0.028	0.019	0.013	0.009
	K3	0.271	0.172	0.117	0.085	0.063	0.038	0.025	0.017	0.012
30000.0	QPERM	7.190	5.752	4.794	4.109	3.595	2.876	2.397	2.054	1.798
	K1	0.658	0.408	0.271	0.188	0.135	0.075	0.044	0.028	0.018
	K2	0.173	0.110	0.075	0.055	0.041	0.025	0.016	0.011	0.008
	K3	0.227	0.144	0.098	0.071	0.053	0.032	0.021	0.014	0.010
35000.0	QPERM	7.190	5.752	4.794	4.109	3.595	2.876	2.397	2.054	1.798
	K1	0.588	0.362	0.239	0.165	0.118	0.065	0.038	0.024	0.015
	K2	0.159	0.101	0.069	0.050	0.037	0.023	0.015	0.010	0.007
	K3	0.198	0.125	0.085	0.061	0.046	0.027	0.018	0.012	0.008
40000.0	QPERM	7.190	5.752	4.794	4.109	3.595	2.876	2.397	2.054	1.798
	K1	0.532	0.326	0.214	0.147	0.104	0.057	0.033	0.020	0.013
	K2	0.146	0.093	0.063	0.046	0.034	0.021	0.013	0.009	0.006
	K3	0.176	0.111	0.075	0.054	0.040	0.024	0.016	0.010	0.007
45000.0	QPERM	7.190	5.752	4.794	4.109	3.595	2.876	2.397	2.054	1.798
	K1	0.485	0.296	0.193	0.132	0.094	0.051	0.029	0.018	0.012
	K2	0.136	0.086	0.058	0.042	0.031	0.019	0.012	0.008	0.006
	K3	0.158	0.100	0.068	0.049	0.036	0.022	0.014	0.009	0.006
50000.0	QPERM	7.190	5.752	4.794	4.109	3.595	2.876	2.397	2.054	1.798
	K1	0.446	0.272	0.177	0.120	0.085	0.046	0.026	0.016	0.010
	K2	0.127	0.080	0.054	0.039	0.029	0.017	0.011	0.008	0.005
	K3	0.145	0.091	0.062	0.044	0.033	0.020	0.012	0.008	0.006

Table 9.20 Deep profile, parallel to span, fastened on four sides

DESIGN TABLE - SHEET PARALLEL TO SPAN

DEEP PROFILE - FASTENED ON FOUR SIDES

DEPTH(MM)		SPAN-DEPTH RATIO								
		1.00	1.25	1.50	1.75	2.00	2.50	3.00	3.50	4.00
5000.0	QPERM	7.190	5.752	4.794	4.109	3.595	2.876	2.397	2.054	1.798
	K1	2.090	1.519	1.153	0.902	0.689	0.424	0.282	0.197	0.144
	K2	0.381	0.299	0.245	0.206	0.161	0.102	0.070	0.051	0.039
	K3	0.704	0.545	0.439	0.363	0.282	0.178	0.121	0.087	0.065
7500.0	QPERM	7.190	5.752	4.794	4.109	3.595	2.876	2.397	2.054	1.798
	K1	1.792	1.243	0.847	0.609	0.455	0.277	0.183	0.127	0.091
	K2	0.370	0.278	0.192	0.141	0.107	0.068	0.048	0.036	0.028
	K3	0.667	0.493	0.340	0.247	0.188	0.117	0.079	0.056	0.042
10000.0	QPERM	7.190	5.752	4.794	4.109	3.595	2.876	2.397	2.054	1.798
	K1	1.486	0.932	0.631	0.451	0.338	0.206	0.134	0.092	0.065
	K2	0.327	0.208	0.144	0.105	0.081	0.054	0.038	0.029	0.023
	K3	0.582	0.369	0.254	0.185	0.139	0.087	0.058	0.041	0.030
12500.0	QPERM	7.190	5.752	4.794	4.109	3.595	2.876	2.397	2.054	1.798
	K1	1.188	0.741	0.501	0.361	0.270	0.162	0.104	0.070	0.048
	K2	0.262	0.167	0.116	0.087	0.068	0.045	0.033	0.025	0.018
	K3	0.465	0.295	0.202	0.147	0.110	0.068	0.045	0.032	0.023
15000.0	QPERM	7.190	5.752	4.794	4.109	3.595	2.876	2.397	2.054	1.798
	K1	0.986	0.615	0.420	0.301	0.224	0.133	0.084	0.055	0.037
	K2	0.218	0.140	0.100	0.075	0.059	0.040	0.029	0.020	0.015
	K3	0.387	0.245	0.168	0.121	0.091	0.056	0.037	0.025	0.018
20000.0	QPERM	7.190	5.752	4.794	4.109	3.595	2.876	2.397	2.054	1.798
	K1	0.739	0.466	0.316	0.225	0.166	0.094	0.056	0.036	0.023
	K2	0.166	0.111	0.080	0.061	0.049	0.032	0.021	0.014	0.010
	K3	0.289	0.182	0.124	0.089	0.067	0.040	0.026	0.018	0.013
25000.0	QPERM	7.190	5.752	4.794	4.109	3.595	2.876	2.397	2.054	1.798
	K1	0.599	0.376	0.254	0.179	0.128	0.069	0.041	0.025	0.016
	K2	0.139	0.094	0.069	0.054	0.041	0.025	0.016	0.011	0.008
	K3	0.230	0.144	0.098	0.070	0.052	0.031	0.020	0.013	0.009
30000.0	QPERM	7.190	5.752	4.794	4.109	3.595	2.876	2.397	2.054	1.798
	K1	0.504	0.316	0.212	0.143	0.100	0.053	0.031	0.019	0.012
	K2	0.122	0.084	0.062	0.045	0.033	0.020	0.013	0.009	0.006
	K3	0.191	0.119	0.080	0.057	0.042	0.025	0.016	0.011	0.007
35000.0	QPERM	7.190	5.752	4.794	4.109	3.595	2.876	2.397	2.054	1.798
	K1	0.437	0.272	0.175	0.117	0.081	0.043	0.024	0.015	0.009
	K2	0.110	0.077	0.053	0.038	0.028	0.017	0.011	0.007	0.005
	K3	0.162	0.101	0.068	0.048	0.035	0.021	0.013	0.009	0.006
40000.0	QPERM	7.190	5.752	4.794	4.109	3.595	2.876	2.397	2.054	1.798
	K1	0.386	0.233	0.147	0.098	0.067	0.035	0.020	0.012	0.007
	K2	0.102	0.068	0.046	0.033	0.024	0.014	0.009	0.006	0.004
	K3	0.141	0.088	0.059	0.041	0.030	0.017	0.011	0.007	0.005
45000.0	QPERM	7.190	5.752	4.794	4.109	3.595	2.876	2.397	2.054	1.798
	K1	0.347	0.202	0.126	0.083	0.057	0.029	0.016	0.010	0.006
	K2	0.096	0.060	0.040	0.028	0.021	0.012	0.008	0.005	0.003
	K3	0.125	0.077	0.051	0.036	0.026	0.015	0.009	0.006	0.004
50000.0	QPERM	7.190	5.752	4.794	4.109	3.595	2.876	2.397	2.054	1.798
	K1	0.306	0.177	0.110	0.072	0.049	0.025	0.014	0.008	0.005
	K2	0.086	0.053	0.036	0.025	0.019	0.011	0.007	0.004	0.003
	K3	0.111	0.069	0.046	0.032	0.023	0.013	0.008	0.005	0.003

Table 9.21 Deep profile, perpendicular to span, fastened on two sides

DESIGN TABLE - SHEET PERPENDICULAR TO SPAN

DEEP PROFILE - FASTENED ON TWO SIDES

DEPTH(MM)		SPAN-DEPTH RATIO								
		1.00	1.25	1.50	1.75	2.00	2.50	3.00	3.50	4.00
5000.0	QPERM	2.362	1.890	1.575	1.350	1.181	1.181	1.181	1.181	1.181
	QPERM2	2.362	1.890	1.575	1.350	1.181	0.945	0.787	0.675	0.591
	K1	1.040	0.734	0.546	0.421	0.334	0.213	0.148	0.108	0.082
	K2	0.323	0.213	0.151	0.112	0.087	0.055	0.039	0.028	0.022
	K3	1.040	0.734	0.546	0.421	0.334	0.213	0.148	0.108	0.082
7500.0	QPERM	1.989	1.591	1.492	1.492	1.492	1.492	1.492	1.370	1.198
	QPERM2	1.989	1.591	1.326	1.137	0.995	0.796	0.663	0.568	0.497
	K1	0.863	0.607	0.431	0.319	0.247	0.161	0.112	0.081	0.061
	K2	0.304	0.201	0.141	0.104	0.080	0.051	0.036	0.026	0.020
	K3	0.863	0.607	0.431	0.319	0.247	0.161	0.112	0.081	0.061
10000.0	QPERM	1.803	1.803	1.803	1.803	1.803	1.803	1.598	1.370	1.198
	QPERM2	1.803	1.442	1.202	1.030	0.901	0.721	0.601	0.515	0.451
	K1	0.706	0.456	0.323	0.242	0.189	0.122	0.084	0.060	0.044
	K2	0.235	0.151	0.106	0.078	0.060	0.039	0.027	0.019	0.015
	K3	0.703	0.454	0.322	0.242	0.188	0.122	0.084	0.060	0.044
12500.0	QPERM	2.113	2.113	2.113	2.113	2.113	1.917	1.598	1.370	1.198
	QPERM2	1.691	1.353	1.127	0.966	0.845	0.676	0.564	0.483	0.423
	K1	0.584	0.387	0.278	0.209	0.163	0.105	0.071	0.050	0.036
	K2	0.212	0.137	0.096	0.071	0.055	0.035	0.024	0.018	0.013
	K3	0.440	0.289	0.206	0.154	0.119	0.077	0.052	0.037	0.027
15000.0	QPERM	2.424	2.424	2.424	2.424	2.397	1.917	1.598	1.370	1.198
	QPERM2	1.616	1.293	1.077	0.924	0.808	0.646	0.539	0.462	0.404
	K1	0.510	0.342	0.246	0.186	0.144	0.092	0.062	0.043	0.031
	K2	0.194	0.126	0.089	0.066	0.051	0.032	0.022	0.016	0.012
	K3	0.334	0.220	0.157	0.117	0.090	0.058	0.039	0.028	0.020
20000.0	QPERM	3.046	3.046	3.046	2.739	2.397	1.917	1.598	1.370	1.198
	QPERM2	1.523	1.218	1.015	0.870	0.761	0.609	0.508	0.435	0.381
	K1	0.421	0.285	0.205	0.154	0.118	0.074	0.049	0.033	0.023
	K2	0.169	0.111	0.078	0.058	0.044	0.028	0.019	0.014	0.010
	K3	0.241	0.159	0.113	0.084	0.064	0.041	0.027	0.019	0.014
25000.0	QPERM	3.667	3.667	3.196	2.739	2.397	1.917	1.598	1.370	1.198
	QPERM2	1.467	1.174	0.978	0.838	0.733	0.587	0.489	0.419	0.367
	K1	0.367	0.248	0.178	0.132	0.101	0.062	0.040	0.027	0.019
	K2	0.151	0.099	0.070	0.051	0.039	0.025	0.017	0.012	0.009
	K3	0.197	0.130	0.091	0.068	0.052	0.032	0.022	0.015	0.011
30000.0	QPERM	4.289	3.835	3.196	2.739	2.397	1.917	1.598	1.370	1.198
	QPERM2	1.430	1.144	0.953	0.817	0.715	0.572	0.477	0.408	0.357
	K1	0.329	0.222	0.158	0.117	0.089	0.054	0.034	0.023	0.015
	K2	0.137	0.090	0.063	0.046	0.035	0.022	0.015	0.010	0.008
	K3	0.169	0.111	0.078	0.058	0.044	0.027	0.018	0.013	0.009
35000.0	QPERM	4.794	3.835	3.196	2.739	2.397	1.917	1.598	1.370	1.198
	QPERM2	1.403	1.122	0.935	0.802	0.702	0.561	0.468	0.401	0.351
	K1	0.300	0.202	0.143	0.105	0.079	0.047	0.030	0.019	0.013
	K2	0.126	0.082	0.058	0.042	0.032	0.020	0.013	0.009	0.007
	K3	0.149	0.098	0.069	0.050	0.038	0.024	0.016	0.011	0.008
40000.0	QPERM	4.794	3.835	3.196	2.739	2.397	1.917	1.598	1.370	1.198
	QPERM2	1.383	1.106	0.922	0.790	0.692	0.553	0.461	0.395	0.346
	K1	0.277	0.185	0.131	0.095	0.071	0.042	0.026	0.017	0.011
	K2	0.117	0.076	0.053	0.039	0.030	0.018	0.012	0.008	0.006
	K3	0.135	0.088	0.062	0.045	0.034	0.021	0.014	0.009	0.007
45000.0	QPERM	4.794	3.835	3.196	2.739	2.397	1.917	1.598	1.370	1.198
	QPERM2	1.367	1.094	0.912	0.781	0.684	0.547	0.456	0.391	0.342
	K1	0.258	0.172	0.120	0.087	0.065	0.038	0.024	0.015	0.010
	K2	0.109	0.071	0.049	0.036	0.027	0.017	0.011	0.008	0.005
	K3	0.123	0.080	0.056	0.041	0.031	0.019	0.012	0.008	0.006
50000.0	QPERM	4.794	3.835	3.196	2.739	2.397	1.917	1.598	1.370	1.198
	QPERM2	1.355	1.084	0.903	0.774	0.678	0.542	0.452	0.387	0.339
	K1	0.242	0.160	0.112	0.081	0.060	0.035	0.021	0.014	0.009
	K2	0.102	0.066	0.046	0.034	0.025	0.016	0.010	0.007	0.005
	K3	0.113	0.074	0.051	0.037	0.028	0.017	0.011	0.008	0.005

Table 9.22 Deep profile, parallel to span, fastened on two sides

DESIGN TABLE - SHEET PARALLEL TO SPAN

DEEP PROFILE - FASTENED ON TWO SIDES

DEPTH(MM)		SPAN-DEPTH RATIO								
		1.00	1.25	1.50	1.75	2.00	2.50	3.00	3.50	4.00
5000.0	QPERM	3.357	2.148	1.492	1.096	0.932	0.746	0.622	0.533	0.466
	K1	1.321	0.838	0.561	0.392	0.295	0.186	0.126	0.091	0.068
	K2	0.345	0.258	0.200	0.159	0.123	0.078	0.054	0.039	0.030
	K3	0.589	0.422	0.313	0.238	0.182	0.116	0.079	0.057	0.043
7500.0	QPERM	2.238	1.492	1.243	1.066	0.932	0.746	0.622	0.533	0.466
	K1	1.008	0.623	0.429	0.312	0.236	0.147	0.099	0.071	0.052
	K2	0.319	0.227	0.157	0.115	0.088	0.056	0.039	0.029	0.023
	K3	0.517	0.353	0.244	0.178	0.135	0.085	0.058	0.042	0.031
10000.0	QPERM	1.865	1.492	1.243	1.066	0.932	0.746	0.622	0.533	0.466
	K1	0.825	0.522	0.357	0.258	0.195	0.121	0.081	0.057	0.042
	K2	0.278	0.177	0.123	0.090	0.069	0.045	0.032	0.024	0.019
	K3	0.443	0.282	0.194	0.141	0.107	0.067	0.045	0.032	0.024
12500.0	QPERM	1.865	1.492	1.243	1.066	0.932	0.746	0.622	0.533	0.466
	K1	0.710	0.447	0.306	0.222	0.167	0.103	0.068	0.047	0.033
	K2	0.228	0.145	0.101	0.076	0.059	0.039	0.028	0.021	0.016
	K3	0.368	0.234	0.161	0.117	0.088	0.055	0.037	0.026	0.019
15000.0	QPERM	1.865	1.492	1.243	1.066	0.932	0.746	0.622	0.533	0.466
	K1	0.622	0.391	0.269	0.194	0.146	0.089	0.058	0.039	0.027
	K2	0.193	0.124	0.088	0.066	0.052	0.035	0.025	0.018	0.013
	K3	0.315	0.200	0.137	0.099	0.075	0.046	0.031	0.021	0.016
20000.0	QPERM	1.865	1.492	1.243	1.066	0.932	0.746	0.622	0.533	0.466
	K1	0.500	0.317	0.216	0.156	0.116	0.068	0.042	0.028	0.019
	K2	0.150	0.100	0.072	0.055	0.043	0.028	0.019	0.013	0.009
	K3	0.243	0.154	0.105	0.076	0.057	0.035	0.023	0.016	0.011
25000.0	QPERM	1.865	1.492	1.243	1.066	0.932	0.746	0.622	0.533	0.466
	K1	0.421	0.266	0.181	0.129	0.094	0.053	0.032	0.021	0.014
	K2	0.127	0.085	0.062	0.048	0.036	0.022	0.015	0.010	0.007
	K3	0.198	0.125	0.085	0.061	0.045	0.027	0.018	0.012	0.008
30000.0	QPERM	1.865	1.492	1.243	1.066	0.932	0.746	0.622	0.533	0.466
	K1	0.365	0.230	0.155	0.107	0.077	0.043	0.025	0.016	0.011
	K2	0.112	0.076	0.056	0.040	0.030	0.018	0.012	0.008	0.006
	K3	0.166	0.104	0.071	0.050	0.037	0.022	0.014	0.010	0.007
35000.0	QPERM	1.865	1.492	1.243	1.066	0.932	0.746	0.622	0.533	0.466
	K1	0.322	0.202	0.132	0.091	0.064	0.035	0.021	0.013	0.008
	K2	0.101	0.070	0.048	0.034	0.026	0.015	0.010	0.007	0.005
	K3	0.143	0.090	0.060	0.043	0.032	0.019	0.012	0.008	0.005
40000.0	QPERM	1.865	1.492	1.243	1.066	0.932	0.746	0.622	0.533	0.466
	K1	0.289	0.177	0.114	0.078	0.055	0.029	0.017	0.010	0.007
	K2	0.094	0.062	0.042	0.030	0.022	0.013	0.008	0.006	0.004
	K3	0.126	0.078	0.053	0.037	0.027	0.016	0.010	0.007	0.004
45000.0	QPERM	1.865	1.492	1.243	1.066	0.932	0.746	0.622	0.533	0.466
	K1	0.263	0.156	0.100	0.067	0.047	0.025	0.014	0.009	0.006
	K2	0.088	0.055	0.037	0.026	0.019	0.011	0.007	0.005	0.003
	K3	0.112	0.069	0.046	0.033	0.024	0.014	0.009	0.006	0.004
50000.0	QPERM	1.865	1.492	1.243	1.066	0.932	0.746	0.622	0.533	0.466
	K1	0.236	0.139	0.089	0.059	0.041	0.021	0.012	0.007	0.005
	K2	0.079	0.049	0.033	0.023	0.017	0.010	0.006	0.004	0.003
	K3	0.100	0.062	0.041	0.029	0.021	0.012	0.007	0.005	0.003

9.7.5

Before using the expressions given for seam strength, the designer should assure himself that the full strength of the sheet to purlin fasteners included in the design expression will be obtained. See section 2.7.1.

9.7.6

The design expression for strength in the perpendicular member to parallel member (purlin to rafter) connections includes the quantity F_{pr} which is the *design* strength of an individual connection. Representative test results for the strength of a large range of connections are given in table 9.12 (p. 188) and a suitable design value may be estimated from this table.

9.8 Design aids and tables of factors

See tables - pages 174–99.

9.9 Design tables for diaphragms

The following tables may be used for *approximate* design. They apply to the majority of diaphragms where the thickness of the sheeting material is nominally 0.7 mm. The more precise assumptions and limitations are given in chapter 6. Within these limitations, the expressions will usually be found to be amply conservative.

Table 9.15	Shallow profile.	Perpendicular to span.	Fastened on four sides
Table 9.16	Shallow profile.	Parallel to span.	Fastened on four sides
Table 9.17	Shallow profile.	Perpendicular to span.	Fastened on two sides
Table 9.18	Shallow profile.	Parallel to span.	Fastened on two sides
Table 9.19	Deep profile.	Perpendicular to span.	Fastened on four sides
Table 9.20	Deep profile.	Parallel to span.	Fastened on four sides
Table 9.21	Deep profile.	Perpendicular to span.	Fastened on two sides
Table 9.22	Deep profile.	Parallel to span.	Fastened on two sides

Notes

1. Shallow profiles, $h \leqslant 50$ mm; deep profiles, $50 < h \leqslant 85$ mm.
2. Tables give:

   q_{perm} = permissible distributed line load on diaphragm from strength considerations (kN/m)

   k_1 = stiffness of diaphragm (distributed load per mm deflection) with sheet to perpendicular member fasteners in every corrugation at all sheet ends (kN/m/mm)

   k_2 = stiffness with sheet to perpendicular member fasteners in alternate corrugations throughout (kN/m/mm)

   k_3 = stiffness with sheet to perpendicular member fasteners in every corrugation at the extreme edges of the diaphragm but in alternate corrugations elsewhere (kN/m/mm)
3. For diaphragms spanning perpendicular to the span and fastened on two sides only, the values of q_{perm} assume that shear connectors or their equivalent are

provided at the gable. (See fig. 6.2 case 3.) If such connectors are not provided, the values given for $q_{perm\,2}$ must be used.

4. The mid-span deflection is thus given as $\Delta = q/k$.

9.10 Design expressions for an element of a folded plate roof (fig. 9.5)

Note The design expressions are directly analogous to those for diaphragms and identical symbols are used. Thus the subscript p refers to the flange member and the subscript sc refers to the gable. It is convenient to define the strength in terms of the maximum shear V at the gable.

(a) Seam strength

$$\text{At first seam } n_s F_s + \frac{2\,\beta_1}{\beta_3} F_p = \frac{\gamma q L}{2} \frac{(n_{sh} - 2)}{n_{sh}} \quad \text{(see 9.7.4)}$$

$$\therefore V_{ult} = \left(n_s F_s + \frac{2\beta_1}{\beta_3} F_p\right)\left(\frac{n_{sh}}{n_{sh} - 2}\right) = \frac{\gamma q L}{2}$$

(b) Strength in fasteners to gable members

$$V_{ult} = n_{sc} F_{sc} + 2F_p = \frac{\gamma\, q L}{2} \quad \text{(see 9.7.4)}$$

(c) Design shear capacity V^*

V^* is the minimum value of V_{ult} when each of the above strength conditions has been considered.

(d) Requirement for shear buckling

$$\frac{28.8}{b} D_x^{\frac{1}{4}} D_y^{\frac{3}{4}} \geqslant V^*$$

(sheeting fastened to fold-line members in every corrugation trough)

$$\text{or } \frac{14.4}{b} D_x^{\frac{1}{4}} D_y^{\frac{3}{4}} \geqslant V^*$$

(fasteners in alternate troughs)

(e) Requirement for sheet to fold- line member fasteners

$$\frac{0.8bF_p}{p} \geqslant V^*$$

(f) Fold-line members

The fold-line members may be assumed to be fully restrained against lateral buckling by the sheeting and should be designed so that the cross-sectional area A (reduced as necessary for local buckling) is sufficient to carry 1.25 times the design axial thrust, thus in each plate element, $A\sigma_{perm} \geqslant (\gamma\, qL^2)/6.4b$ and the total area required is twice the above value (for both sides).

(g) Calculation of central deflection

By drawing a displacement diagram at a typical fold line, it follows that the maximum vertical deflection in the roof is given by Δ cosec θ where θ is the angle of inclination of the roof planes to the horizontal and Δ is calculated as follows:

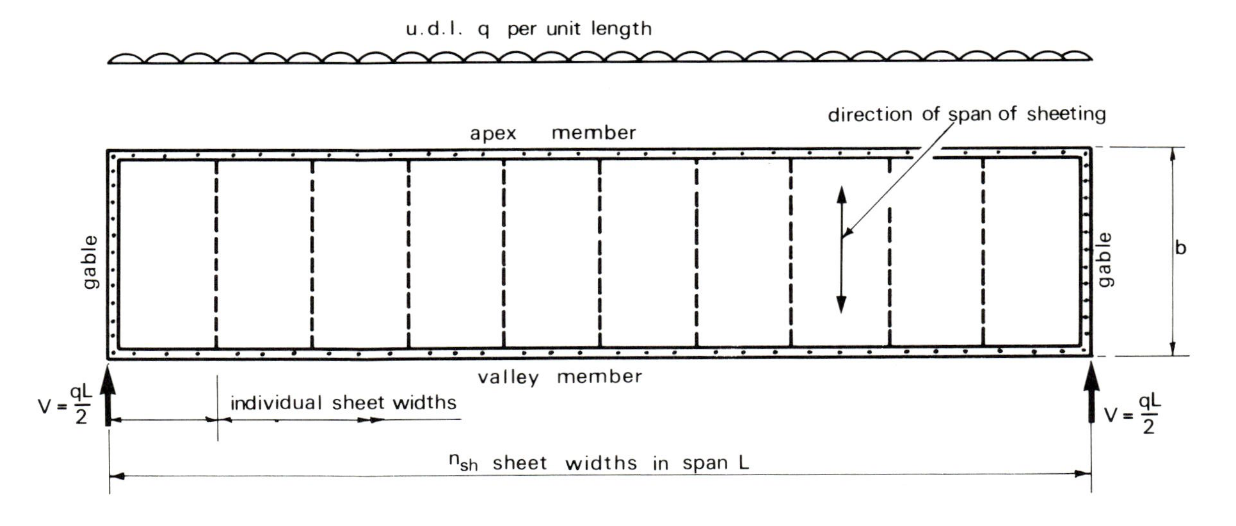

Fig. 9.5 Case considered in section 9.9.

Deflection due to		Expressions	Deflection (mm)
Sheet deformation	sheet distortion	$\Delta_{1.1} = \dfrac{d^{2.5}\,\bar{K}\,qL^2}{8Et^{2.5}\,b^2}$	$\Delta_{1.1} =$
	shear strain	$\Delta_{1.2} = \dfrac{(1+\nu)[1+(2h/d)]\,qL^2}{4Etb}$	$\Delta_{1.2} =$
Flange forces	axial strain in fold line members	$\Delta_{1.3} = \dfrac{qL^4}{38.4\,EAb^2}$	$\Delta_{1.3} =$
Slip at fasteners	sheet to flange fasteners	$\Delta_{2.1} = \dfrac{s_p p q L^2}{4b^2}$	$\Delta_{2.1} =$
	seam fasteners	$\Delta_{2.2} = \dfrac{s_s s_p\,(n_{sh}-2)qL}{8\,(n_s s_p + \beta_1 s_s)}$	$\Delta_{2.2} =$
	fasteners to gable members	$\Delta_{2.3} = \dfrac{s_p s_{sc}\,qL}{2\,(2\beta_1 s_{sc} + n_{sc} s_p)}$	$\Delta_{2.3} =$
Total central deflection in plane of element		$\Delta_{1.1} + \Delta_{1.2} + \Delta_{1.3} + \Delta_{2.1} + \Delta_{2.2} + \Delta_{2.3}$	$\Delta \quad =$

PART TWO

THEORY, TESTS AND ADDITIONAL CONSIDERATIONS

This second part of the book is concerned primarily with the justification of the design expressions given in Part I. The fundamental theory is described together with comparison with test results and comprehensive finite element analyses.

In the later chapters special applications of diaphragm action are discussed such as light gauge steel folded plates and shells and the use of diaphragm action to stabilise rafters.

CHAPTER TEN

Derivation of the design expressions for the basic shear panel

10.1 Introduction

In the U.S.A. empirical and semi-empirical methods of diaphragm design have been available for some years.[1.41, 1.48] These are essentially based on tests on complete diaphragms and involve the extrapolation of test results using empirical factors. The first truly theoretical calculation was derived by Bryan[1.57] who presented a complete design approach based on simple design expressions. This work has provided a sound foundation for later developments. Although the detailed design expressions have changed, in some cases significantly, the basic approach has been shown to be valid. The design expressions which have been accepted for practical usage[1.99, 1.112, 1.114] have been largely derived by Davies.[1.86, 1.110, etc.] Subsequent work by Easley[1.98] and Chockalingum *et al.*[1.107, 1.116] has followed a similar approach.

10.2 Sheet to purlin fastener forces and consequent flexibility

In much of the fundamental work on diaphragm design, attention has been centred on the basic arrangement of an individual panel acting as a cantilever diaphragm with the sheeting running perpendicular to the span as shown in fig. 10.1. This arrangement has the advantage that it is easy to test and it acts in a manner that is in most respects identical to a typical panel of a diaphragm beam carrying the same shear force. The design expressions arise as a result of an assumed internal force distribution in an individual panel. The correct internal force distribution was discovered as a consequence of using the finite element analysis described in Part I, chapter 5 and subsequent analyses continue to justify it as providing a remarkably accurate account of the internal forces. Although diaphragms are in reality statically indeterminate to a high degree, the indeterminacy results in only second-order variations in the force patterns, and the overall behaviour is effectively statically determinate.

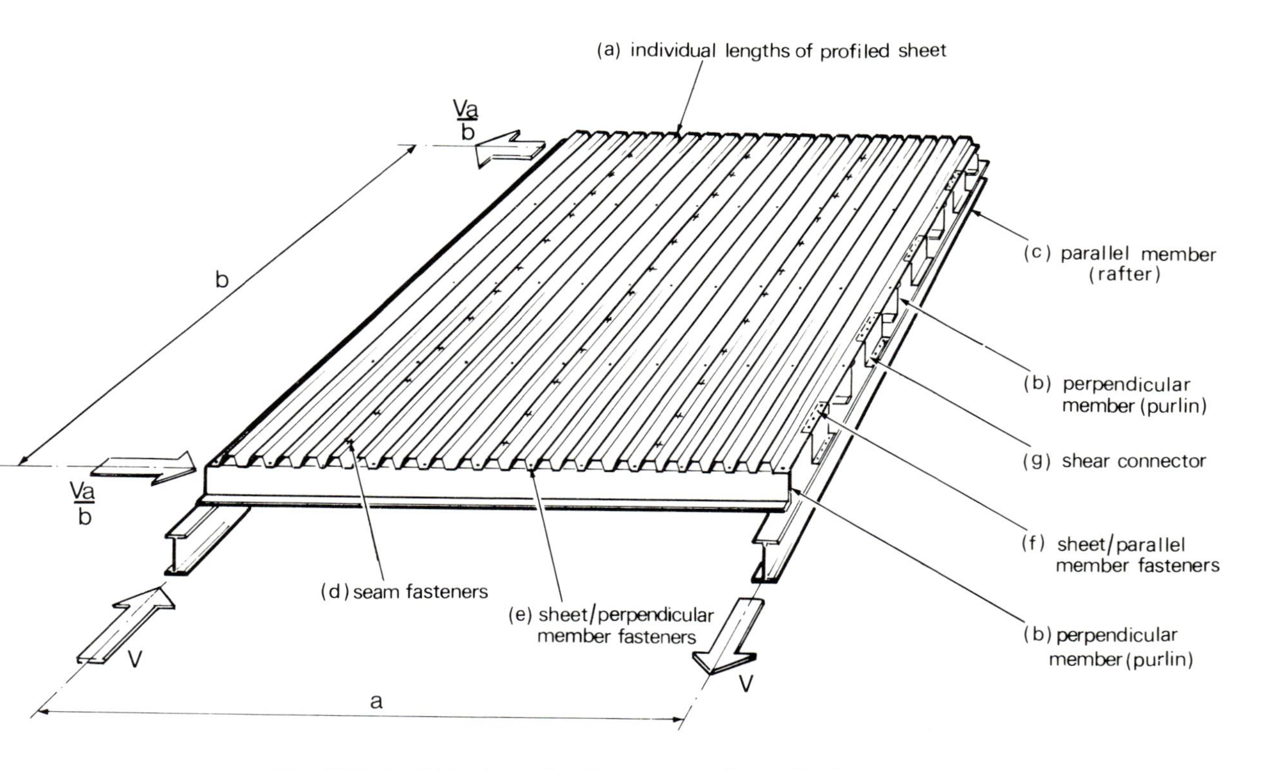

Fig. 10.1 Individual panel acting as a cantilever diaphragm.

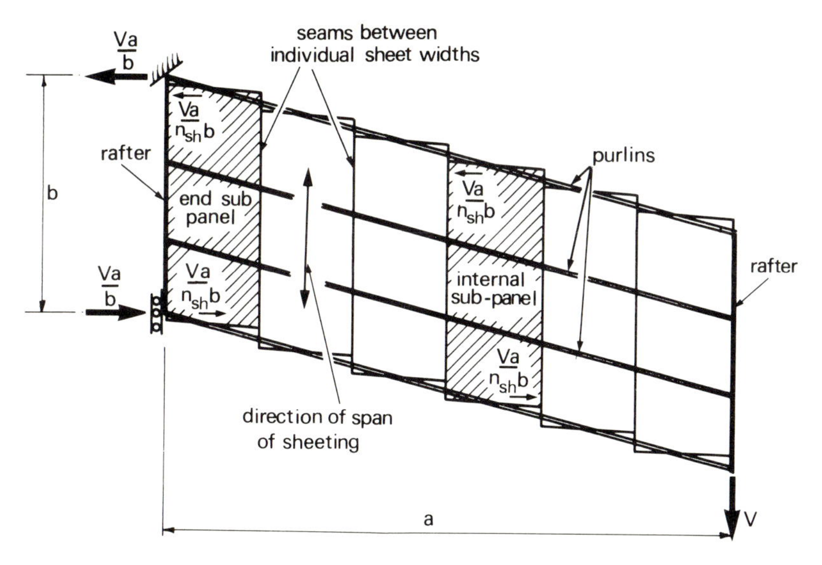

Fig. 10.2 Typical shear panel as an assemblage of n_{sh} sub-panels.

Considering a simple cantilever diaphragm with the sheeting spanning perpendicular to the span of the diaphragm, the externally applied forces are as shown in fig. 10.2. The individual sheet widths within the diaphragm or panel form sub-panels and it is assumed that the total shear force of $(Va)/b$ between the outer purlins and sheeting is equally shared between the sub-panels. The internal force distributions can be developed further by considering the equilibrium of first a typical internal sub-panel and then the special case of the end sub-panel. The 'horizontal'* sheet to purlin forces are transferred by the sheet to purlin fasteners and it is first convenient to consider the implications of these forces as far as the strength and stiffness of the diaphragm are concerned. On examining the results of detailed finite element analysis, it is found that the edge shear of $Va/(n_{sh}b)$ per sub-panel divides itself among the n_f fasteners between the sheet and the purlin in such a way that the two outer fasteners attract only half of the force attracted by each of the internal fasteners. It follows that the force per internal fastener is $Va/[n_{sh}\, b\, (n_f - 1)]$.

The European recommendations for the stressed skin design of steel structures[1.99] (clause 8.32) require that a diaphragm shall fail in a seam or other line of fasteners running parallel to the corrugations and that the strength calculated for any other form of failure, including the failure of the sheet to purlin fasteners in 'horizontal' shear, shall be at least 25% greater than the above calculated design strength, V^*. This leads directly to the general requirement for sheet to perpendicular member (purlin) fasteners given in section 9.3, namely

* In this chapter the terms 'horizontal' and 'vertical' refer to the directions across and up and down fig. 10.2 respectively.

$$\frac{0.8\,(n_f - 1)\,b\,n_{sh}\,F_p}{a} = \frac{0.8bF_p}{p} \geqslant V^* \qquad (10.1)$$

where p = pitch of sheet to purlin fasteners.

There are two reasons for including this mode of failure in the general requirement for a 25% reserve of safety against non-ductile failure modes. The first arises from the observation that the sheet to purlin fasteners are in fact carrying two components of force as they also contribute to the seam strength. However, the maximum forces in the two directions do not arise on the same fastener and test results show that redistribution of force prior to failure tends to minimise the interaction effect. Consequently a formal calculation of the maximum resultant fastener force is not considered necessary or appropriate and the interaction of the force components is embraced within the 25% reserve of safety. Furthermore, as shown in fig. 10.3(a), the shear flow around the sheeting profile includes a tensile force in

(a)

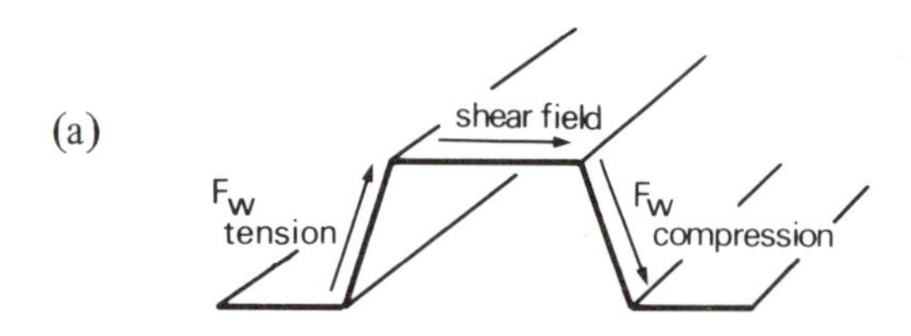

(b)

Fig. 10.3 Secondary effects at sheet to purlin fasteners: (a) local web forces due to shear flow, (b) local distortion resulting in prying action on fasteners.

the web and this results in a prying force on the fastener which can cause a reduction in the carrying capacity. This effect is more significant in deeper profiles and the 25% extra reserve of safety is considered adequate for all practical situations. Figure 10.3(b) shows this prying action in a section of 70 mm depth.

If the flexibility or slip per sheet to purlin fastener is s_p per unit load, it follows that the relative 'horizontal' movement between the sheet and the purlin is $\dfrac{V a s_p}{n_{sh} b(n_f - 1)}$ and the corresponding 'vertical' shear displacement per sub-panel is $\dfrac{2a}{n_{sh} b} \times \dfrac{V a s_p}{n_{sh} b(n_f - 1)}$. Summing this expression over n_{sh} sub-panels and noting that the fastener pitch $p = a/[(n_f - 1)n_{sh})]$ gives the flexibility per unit shear load due to deformation in the sheet to purlin fasteners as

$$c_{2.1} = \frac{2a\, s_p p}{b^2} \qquad (10.2)$$

The above derivations include the implicit assumption that the axial forces due to bending are confined to the two outermost purlins. This is a reasonable assumption for isolated cantilever diaphragms but for diaphragm beams it is more reasonable to assume a linear distribution of bending strain across the section so that some significant axial force is carried by the internal purlins. In the expressions given in section 9.5, the factor α_3 takes account of this. To include α_3 in the expressions for cantilever diaphragms given in section 9.3 would in many cases make unreasonable demands on the minor axis bending stiffness of the fixed rafter and it is simpler to omit it altogether.

10.3 Seam strength and flexibility

Further assumptions are introduced here, namely that the seam slips at all internal seams are equal and denoted by 2Δ and that, as far as relative vertical displacements are concerned, the minor axis bending of the purlins can be neglected compared with deformation at the fasteners. This latter presumption is given further consideration and relaxed somewhat in section 10.5. The equilibrium and compatibility of a typical internal sub-panel may now be considered, as shown in fig. 10.4.

Let n_s = total number of seam fasteners per seam (excluding those which pass through both sheet thicknesses into the purlin below), n_p = number of purlins, s_s = slip (flexibility) per seam fastener per unit load, s_p = slip (flexibility) per sheet to purlin fastener per unit load. Then the total stiffness of a 'vertical' row of seam fasteners is n_s/s_s and the total stiffness of a 'vertical' row of sheet to purlin fasteners is n_p/s_p. Assuming rigid purlins and pure shear of the sheeting 'vertical' fastener forces follow as shown in fig. 10.4. It may be noted that fig. 10.4 incorporates two distinct cases, depending on whether the seam fasteners lie in the troughs or along the crests of the profile. Case 1 will be considered first and in more detail. Case 2

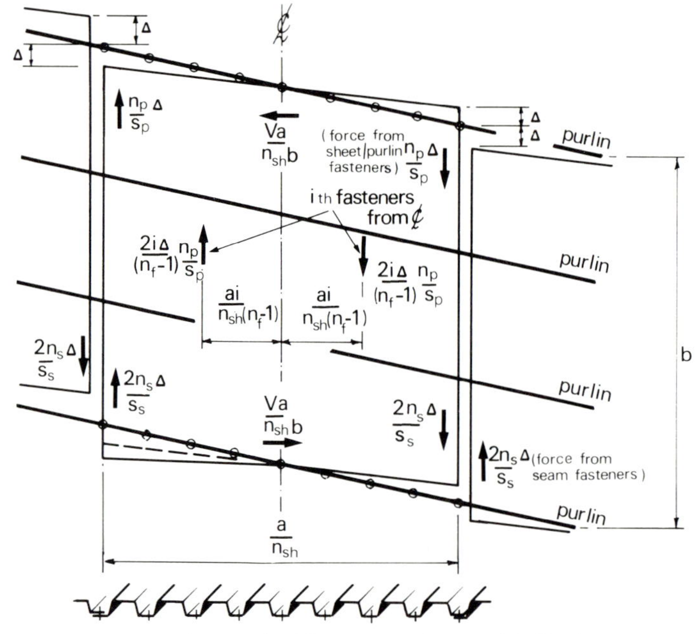

case 1 sheeting fixed with seams in troughs (decking)

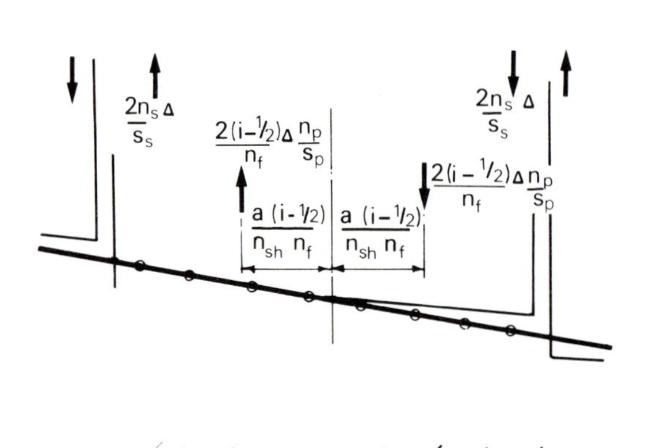

case 2 sheeting fixed with seams at crests

Fig. 10.4 Forces and deformations assumed for typical internal sub-panel.

will be considered much more briefly as the derivation of the governing equations is similar.

For the typical sub-panel, vertical and horizontal equilibrium are ensured by symmetry and it can readily be shown that for moment equilibrium

$$\frac{V}{\Delta} = \frac{2n_s}{s_s} + \frac{\beta_1 \, n_p}{s_p} \tag{10.3}$$

where
$$\beta_1 = \sum_{i=1}^{(n_f-1)/2} \left(\frac{2i}{n_f - 1}\right)^2 \quad (n_f \text{ odd}) \tag{10.4}$$

Figure 10.4 and the above derivation specifically apply to situations in which the total number of sheet to purlin fasteners per member per sheet width, n_f, is an odd number and there is a fastener on the centre line of the sub-panel. If n_f is even it can be readily shown that equation 10.3 still applies but with β_1 replaced by

$$\beta_1 = \sum_{i=1}^{n_f/2} \left(\frac{2_i - 1}{n_f - 1}\right)^2 \quad (n_f \text{ even}) \tag{10.5}$$

When consideration is given to case 2, where the seam fasteners lie along the crests of the corrugations and do not therefore coincide with a line of sheet to purlin fasteners, the basic approach remains the same and the expressions change only slightly. The equation of moment equilibrium retains the same form but the expressions for β_1 become

$$\beta_1 = \sum_{i=1}^{(n_f-1)/2} \left(\frac{2i}{n_f}\right)^2 \quad (n_f \text{ odd}) \tag{10.6}$$

and
$$\beta_1 = \sum_{i=1}^{n_f/2} \left(\frac{2i - 1}{n_f}\right)^2 \quad (n_f \text{ even}) \tag{10.7}$$

The above four expressions for β_1 are tabulated in table 10.1.

It now follows that the seam slip per unit load $c_{2.2}$ can be obtained by summing $2\Delta/V$ over the $(n_{sh} - 1)$ internal seams giving

$$c_{2.2} = \frac{2\, s_s\, s_p\, (n_{sh} - 1)}{2n_s\, s_p + \beta_1 n_p s_s} \tag{10.8}$$

In deriving the expression for seam strength, it is assumed that the seam fasteners have yielded with the load per fastener equal to the design strength F_s and that failure takes place when the sheet to purlin fasteners adjacent to the seam reach their design strength F_p. This results in an expression which is slightly different from that derived in reference[1.86] and which is used in the European recommendations.[1.99] The new expression has a simpler and more universally applicable form. In the great majority of situations the difference in calculated seam strength will be small but the new expression has been found to give better results for one particular case, namely with the sheeting fixed with seams in the crests and with weak seam fasteners but relatively strong sheet to purlin fasteners.

The justification for the new expressions is that in most fixing systems the seam fasteners yield first, often at a load close to that causing yield in the adjacent sheet to purlin fasteners. If there is any significant imbalance in the fastener strengths or if the sheet to purlin fasteners are not on the line of the seam, the seam fasteners are likely to yield even earlier but redistribution of internal forces will quickly bring about the assumed design situation. The situation at failure is therefore as shown in

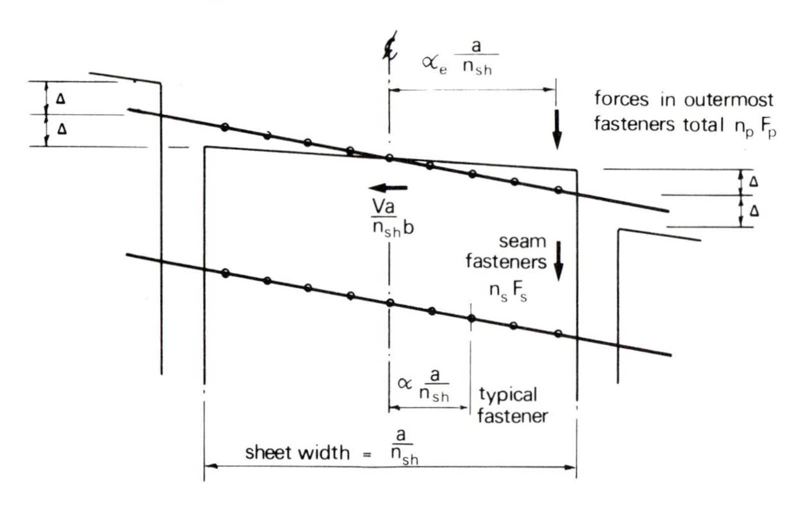

Fig. 10.5 Typical internal sub-panel at failure.

fig. 10.5. Let $\alpha a/n_{sh}$ = distance from centre line to a typical fastener and α_e = value of α for outermost fastener(s). Then, horizontal and vertical equilibrium are again ensured by symmetry and for moment equilibrium

$$\frac{Va}{n_{sh}} = \frac{a}{n_{sh}} n_s F_s + \sum \left(\frac{\alpha a}{n_{sh}}\right)^2 \left(\frac{2n_{sh}}{a}\right)\left(\frac{n_p}{s_p}\right)\Delta \tag{10.9}$$

i.e.

$$\frac{V - n_s F_s}{\Delta} = 2\left(\frac{n_p}{s_p}\right)\sum \alpha^2 \tag{10.10}$$

But $2\Sigma\, \alpha^2 = \beta_1$ for each of the four arrangements of sheet to purlin fasteners considered previously so that it follows that

$$\Delta = \frac{V - n_s F_s}{\beta_1\ (n_p/s_p)} \tag{10.11}$$

The total force in the outermost 'vertical' line of sheet to purlin fasteners can now be evaluated and equating this to the total characteristic strength gives the following expression for the design shear strength V_{ult}.

$$\left[\frac{V_{\text{ult}} - n_s F_s}{\beta_1\ (n_p/s_p)}\right](2\alpha_e)\left(\frac{n_p}{s_p}\right) = n_p F_p \tag{10.12}$$

i.e.

$$V_{\text{ult}} = n_s F_s + \frac{\beta_1}{\beta_3} n_p F_p \tag{10.13}$$

where, for consistency of symbols in the design expressions, $\beta_3 = 2\alpha_e$. It may be noted that, in contrast with the expression given in the European recommendations, this expression is good for both the sheeting and decking cases (seam fasteners in crests or troughs). Furthermore, β_3 = (distance between outermost fasteners) ÷ (sheet width), = 1.0 for decking where sheet to purlin fasteners lie on the seam, $= (n_f - 1)/n_f$ for sheeting with seam fasteners in the crests.

10.4 Strength and flexibility in end sub-panels

If the diaphragm is connected to the supporting structure on four sides it is conservative to assume that all of the shear force passes through the shear connectors or equivalent members which provide a direct connection between the sheeting and the rafter. In this case the design shear strength V_{ult} is simply the product of the number of shear connectors n_{sc} and their characteristic shear strength F_{sc},

i.e.
$$V_{ult} = n_{sc} F_{sc} \tag{10.14}$$

Similarly, the resulting flexibility at each rafter is simply the flexibility s_{sc} of an individual connector divided by the number of connectors and, as a cantilever diaphragm includes connections to two rafters, the flexibility component $c_{2.3}$ due to connections to the rafters is simply

$$c_{2.3} = \frac{2s_{sc}}{n_{sc}} \tag{10.15}$$

If only two sides are fastened, the total shear force in each rafter must be transferred into the diaphragm through the purlin to rafter connections and the sheet to purlin fasteners. Figure 10.6 shows the assumed situation in the end sub-panel. There is a difficulty here in that if the slip in the first seam is assumed to be 2Δ, as it must be if all the internal sub-panels are to behave identically, and if the displace-

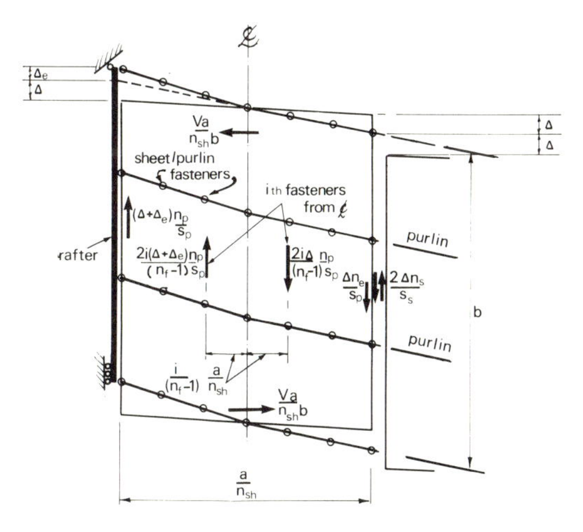

Fig. 10.6 Forces and deformations assumed for end sub-panel.

ment pattern is to have the assumed linear form, there is only one variable Δ_e to satisfy two requirements for equilibrium, namely equilibrium of vertical forces and moments. It is found to be adequate to accept this situation and to satisfy only equilibrium of vertical forces while accepting a slight imbalance of moments. The potential violation of moment equilibrium proves to be of no consequence and the alternative of choosing a displacement pattern with an additional variable would excessively complicate the design expressions.

Comparing figs. 10.5 and 10.6, the requirement for vertical equilibrium can be simply expressed as

$$\Delta_e = \frac{2\,n_s s_p}{\beta_2 s_s n_p}\Delta \tag{10.16}$$

where $$\beta_2 = \sum_{i=1}^{(n_f-1)/2} \frac{2i}{n_f-1} = \frac{n_f+1}{4} \quad \text{(for } n_f \text{ odd as drawn)} \tag{10.17}$$

or $$\beta_2 = \sum_{i=1}^{n_f/2} \frac{2i-1}{n_f-1} = \frac{n_f^{\,2}}{4(n_f-1)} \quad \text{(for } n_f \text{ even)} \tag{10.18}$$

The total slip between the sheet and the end of the purlin is therefore

$$\Delta + \Delta_e = \frac{(2n_s s_p + \beta_2 s_s n_p)}{\beta_2 s_s n_p}\Delta \tag{10.19}$$

and using the relationship between the shear force V and the half seam slip Δ obtained previously for a typical internal sub-panel (equation 10.3) it follows that

$$\frac{\Delta + \Delta_e}{V} = \frac{(2n_s s_p + \beta_2 s_s n_p)}{\beta_2 s_s n_p} \times \frac{s_s s_p}{(2n_s s_p + \beta_1 s_s n_p)} \tag{10.20}$$

Now the total force in the line of sheet to purlin fasteners adjacent to the rafter is given by $n_p\,(\Delta + \Delta_e)/s_p$ and equating this to the design capacity of these fasteners gives

$$V_{\text{ult}} = \beta_2 n_p F p\left(\frac{2n_s s_p + \beta_1 n_p s_s}{2n_s s_p + \beta_2 n_p s_s}\right) \tag{10.21}$$

The expression in brackets will always be quite close to unity. It is therefore simpler to omit this term and to take as the design expression for strength

$$V_{\text{ult}} = \beta_2 n_p F_p \tag{10.22}$$

The total relative movement between the sheeting and the rafters at each gable is found by adding to the expression for $\Delta + \Delta_e$ above an allowance for flexibility in the purlin to rafter connections. If the flexibility in these connections is s_{pr} and if the same approximation as above is used, namely

$$\frac{2n_s s_p + \beta_1 n_p s_s}{2n_s s_p + \beta_2 n_p s_s} \simeq 1 \qquad (10.23)$$

then the following expression is obtained for the flexibility in the connections to the rafters when only two sides of the diaphragm are fastened:

$$c_{2.3} = \frac{2}{n_p}\left(s_{pr} + \frac{s_p}{\beta_2}\right) \qquad (10.24)$$

10.5 The factors β_1 and β_2

The factors β_1 and β_2 included in the expressions for strength and flexibility discussed above reflect the distribution of sheet to purlin fastener force in a direction parallel to the corrugations. In the above derivations a linear distribution of force was assumed giving rise to the values of β_1 and β_2 in table 10.1 which is in accordance with the European recommendations.[1.99] The theoretical derivations can readily accommodate other distributions of fastener force and in the original research[1.61,1.86] a more conservative parabolic distribution of force was also considered. Alternative assumptions of this nature do not affect the basic equations, they are merely reflected in alternative values of the factors β_1 and β_2.

Table 10.1 Values of β_1 and β_2 with linear variation of fastener force

Total number of fasteners per sheet width n_f	Factor β_1		Factor β_2
	Case 1 – sheeting	Case 2 – decking	
2	0.25	1.0	1.0
3	0.44	1.0	1.0
4	0.63	1.11	1.33
5	0.80	1.25	1.50
6	0.97	1.40	1.80
7	1.14	1.56	2.00
8	1.31	1.71	2.29
9	1.48	1.88	2.50
10	1.65	2.04	2.78

The strictly correct values of β_1 and β_2 are influenced by such factors as the minor axis bending stiffness of the purlins and the use of a single set of figures is of course a compromise. As variations in the values of β_1 and β_2 have, in most cases, only a secondary influence on the design strengths and stiffnesses and as the linear variation values appeared to give results in reasonable agreement with comparable finite element and test results these values were adopted for the European recommendations. However, it is possible to present rational arguments for the more conservative values based on a parabolic variation of fastener force and these alternative values are given in table 10.2. A more precise theory, whereby it is

Table 10.2 Alternative values of β_1 and β_2 with parabolic variation of fastener force

Total number of fasteners per sheet width n_f	Factor β_1		Factor β_2
	Case 1 – sheeting	Case 2 – decking	
?	0.13	1.0	1.0
3	0.30	1.0	1.0
4	0.44	1.04	1.11
5	0.53	1.13	1.25
6	0.71	1.22	1.40
7	0.84	1.33	1.56
8	0.97	1.45	1.71
9	1.10	1.56	1.88
10	1.23	1.68	2.04

possible to calculate whether to use the linear or quadratic distribution of fasteners force in evaluating β_1 and β_2, has been given for light gauge steel folded plate elements.[3.19] This is directly applicable to diaphragms as follows. Let $\rho = [(a/n_{sh})^3 G_{eff}b]/(EI)$ where a/n_{sh} is the width of an individual sheet, b is the depth of the diaphragm, EI is the minor axis flexural rigidity of the purlins and G_{eff} is the effective shear modulus of the sheeting (see section 5.2.1). Then for $\rho < 8000$ use linear variation (table 10.1), for $8000 \leqslant \rho \leqslant 400\,000$ use parabolic variation (table 10.2) and for $\rho > 400\,000$ use parabolic variation based on reduced sheet width $(a/n_{sh})_{eff} = \sqrt[3]{(400\,000\, EI/G_{eff}\, b)}$.

Since the writing of the European recommendations, the authors have given further consideration to the correct values to be used for β_1 and β_2. They are now of the opinion that it is better to recommend for general use the more cautious approach given by the assumption of a parabolic variation of force and therefore to use the factors given in table 10.2 in preference to those given in table 10.1 unless the use of the latter is justified by the more detailed analysis given above. For this reason, table 9.5 in the summarised design expressions is a repeat of table 10.2 and is therefore not the same as the corresponding table in the European recommendations.

10.6 Flexibility due to profile distortion

When profiled metal sheeting is loaded in shear, the profile distorts as shown in figs. 2.17 and 2.18. The first practical design expression for the displacement due to this effect was prepared by Bryan[1.57] and had the form

$$c_{1.1} = \frac{0.144ad^4K}{Et^3b^3} \tag{10.25}$$

where a = width of diaphragm measured normal to the corrugations
b = depth of diaphragm measured parallel to the corrugations

d = pitch of the corrugations
E = Young's modulus
t = net thickness of the sheeting
K = a constant for a given profile

The value of K depends on the way the sheeting is fastened to the supporting structure and values for all trapezoidal profiles in common use in Britain were tabulated[1.57] for discrete fasteners in every trough, alternate troughs and every third trough of the corrugations. The basic deficiency of the above equation was that it was based on an analysis in which the fold-line members were assumed to remain straight as shown in fig. 10.7(a). It is now known that the fold-line members curve as the profile distorts as shown in fig. 10.7(b). As the corrugation length b increases, much of the distortion becomes concentrated near the ends and the assumption that the fold lines remain straight becomes increasingly inaccurate.

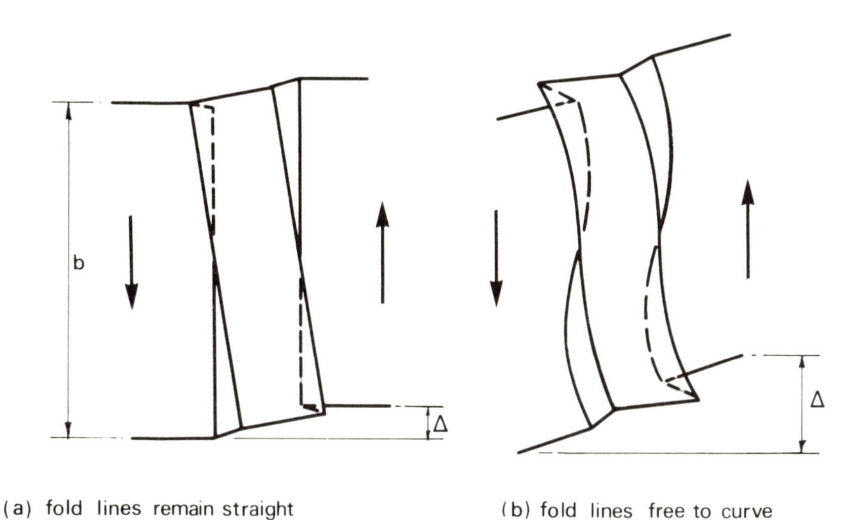

Fig. 10.7 Distortion of corrugation in plan.

An improvement to this analysis was made by Horne and Raslan[1.35] whereby a single sinusoidal plate movement was superimposed on the linear movement shown in fig. 10.7(a) and incorporated in an energy analysis to give a better solution though one that was significantly less flexible than the reality. Much significant work was also carried out by Libove and his associates, e.g. reference 1.62, though the results were not presented in a form that was readily usable for stressed skin design. The design expressions used in the European recommendations and repeated herein arise out of the work of Davies and Lawson[1.78, 1.110] and take the form

$$c_{1.1} = \frac{ad^{2.5}\bar{K}}{Et^{2.5}b^2} \qquad (10.26)$$

Where $\bar{K}$ is an alternative sheeting constant which is tabulated in tables 9.6 and 9.7 for trapezoidal profiles and table 9.8 for arc and tangent profiles.

Davies and Lawson extended the work of Horne and Raslan by including many more non-linear displacement terms in their analysis. In their analysis, it is assumed that a typical cross-section of a corrugation can distort freely with the total displacement being expressed in terms of the individual plate displacements U_T, U_S and U_B defined in figure 10.8. The individual plate displacements due to bending in

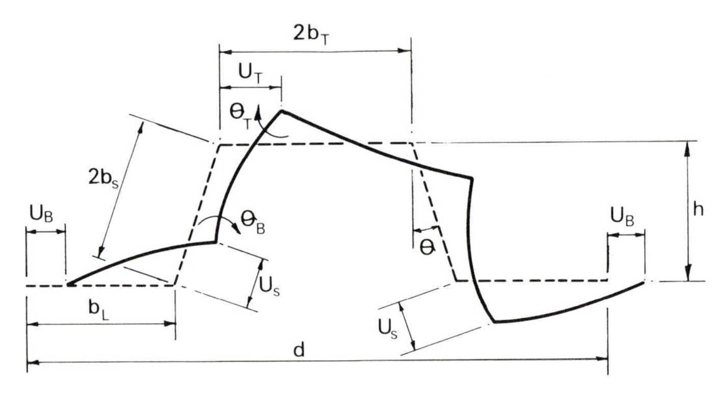

Fig. 10.8 Profile dimensions and displacements. Fasteners in every trough.

the plane of the plates are expressed as Fourier series superimposed in the case of U_T and U_S on linear plate movements. Thus:

$$\left.\begin{aligned} U_T &= a_1 y + \sum_{n=1}^{5} a_{n+1} \frac{b}{2n\pi} \sin \frac{2\pi n y}{b} \\ U_S &= a_7 y + \sum_{n=1}^{5} a_{n+7} \frac{b}{2n\pi} \sin \frac{2\pi n y}{b} \\ U_B &= \sum_{n=1}^{5} a_{n+12} \frac{b}{2n\pi} \sin \frac{2\pi n y}{b} \end{aligned}\right\} \quad (10.27)$$

where b is the length of the corrugation and y is the distance along the corrugation measured from its centre line. The in-plane shear strain γ in the plates is expressed by the relationships:

$$\left.\begin{aligned} \gamma_T &= \gamma_1 + \gamma_2 \cos \frac{2\pi y}{b} \\ \gamma_S &= \gamma_3 + \gamma_4 \cos \frac{2\pi y}{b} \\ \gamma_B &= \gamma_5 + \gamma_6 \cos \frac{2\pi y}{b} \end{aligned}\right\} \quad (10.28)$$

The total deformation of the single corrugation is therefore expressed in terms of a set of functions with 23 variable coefficients which form a coefficient vector **V** where

$$\mathbf{V} = a_1, a_2, \ldots, a_{17}, \gamma_1, \gamma_2, \ldots, \gamma_6 \qquad (10.29)$$

The solution procedure involves first modifying the displacement functions in order that they satisfy the boundary conditions and expressing the total strain energy in terms of the displacement coefficients. The total strain energy in a deformed corrugation is expressed as the sum of the energies due to: bending of the cross section, longitudinal bending of the plate elements, longitudinal axial strains in the plate elements, shear strain in the plate elements and torsion of the plate elements. The minimum potential energy condition is then found by minimising the total energy with respect to variations in each of the displacement coefficients. When the minimum potential energy condition is substituted back into the expressions for the total energy E_{tot}, the total shear flexibility $c_{1.1} + c_{1.2}$ of the corrugation is obtained as

$$c_{1.1} + c_{1.2} = \frac{\Delta^2}{2E_{tot}} \qquad (10.30)$$

and the distortional flexibility $c_{1.1}$ is obtained when the pure shear flexibility $c_{1.2}$ is subtracted where

$$c_{1.2} = \frac{2(b_L + 2b_s + b_T)}{tbG} \qquad (10.31)$$

The full derivation of $c_{1.1}$ has not been given as it is extremely involved and can be found in reference 1.110. However, a number of additional factors need to be considered if the analysis is to be used in practical situations and these are discussed below.

10.6.1 Influence of the number of terms in the displacement functions

If, in the analysis described above, only a_1 and a_{17} are retained and the remaining variable coefficients a_2, a_3, . . ., etc. removed from the analysis, Bryan's original analysis is obtained. Figure 10.9 shows how, in a typical analysis an increase in the number of sine terms results in an increase in the distortional flexibility and hence in the apparent value of the sheeting constant K. As the length of the corrugation increases more terms are required to reproduce the displacement pattern accurately. Physically, as the length increases, the non-linear part of the total distortion becomes more concentrated near the ends of the corrugation and more terms are required to reproduce this behaviour. It is clear that the displacement functions are sufficiently comprehensive to achieve convergence to an accurate solution within the practical range of lengths.

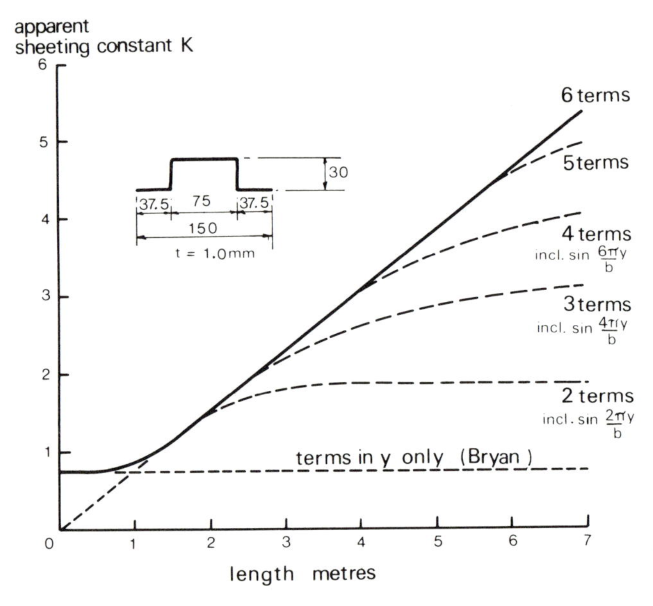

Fig. 10.9 Illustrating the effect of increasing the number of terms in the displacement functions.

10.6.2 The influence of attachments to intermediate purlins

The most important single factor in the increase of K with length appears to be the horizontal displacement U_B of the bottom plate. If $a_{13}, a_{14}, \ldots, a_{17}$ are removed from the analysis a large reduction in K is obtained, in many cases reducing K almost to its value based on linear displacements (Bryan's theory). It is apparent that in a real situation, where the sheeting may be fastened to intermediate purlins as well as at its ends, horizontal movement of the bottom plate will be restrained and a significant reduction of K may be expected. Analytically, this can be treated by preventing bottom plate movement at the points of attachment to the purlins though it is appreciated that this could imply more restraint than may be realised in a practical situation. The additional constraints were incorporated in the analysis and from the results the values of the factor α_1 given in table 9.3 were deduced.

10.6.3 The influence of members supporting the sheeting from below

The above derivations all assumed that complete freedom of vertical movement existed at the bottom of the side plates over the whole length of the corrugation whereas in practice, as illustrated in fig. 10.10, vertical downward movement is prevented whenever the sheeting passes over a supporting member. Corrugation distortion is a maximum at the ends of the corrugations and the supporting members at the ends can have a significant influence on the flexibility of the sheeting. Vertical support from intermediate members is much less significant.

In an energy analysis such as that described above, it is difficult to include this

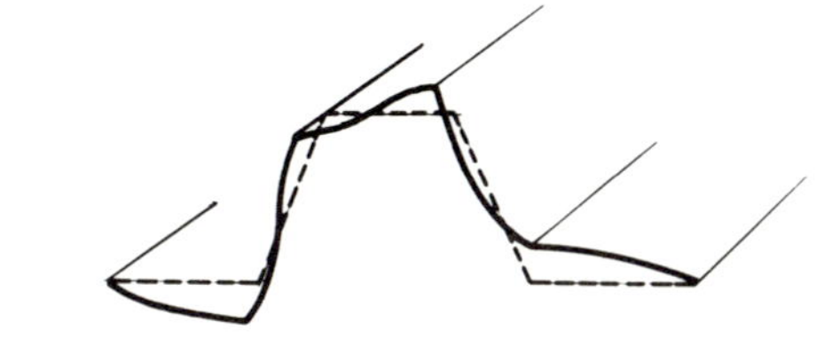

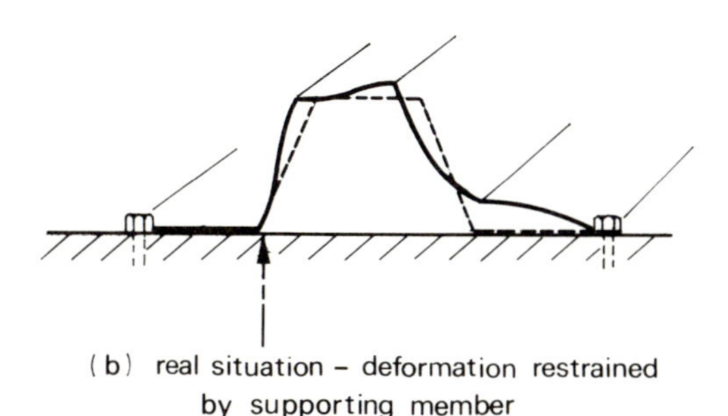

Fig. 10.10 Deformations at the sheet ends: (a) deformation assumed in energy analysis, (b) real situation – deformation restrained by supporting member.

effect in a precise manner but readily possible to allow for it in an approximate way. If the flexibility is considered to be modified by a reduction factor r when the propping influence of supporting members is considered it was found that r is very nearly constant as the length of the corrugation varies although the flexibility itself is not. Consequently it is adequate to calculate reduction factors on the basis of linear plate movements (Bryan's method) and to apply these to the more rigorous results calculated on the basis of a much more comprehensive analysis. The adequacy of this procedure will be illustrated later with reference to both finite analysis and experimental results.

10.6.4 Finite element analysis of individual corrugations

The success of energy methods of analysis depends on the ability of the displacement functions to follow the actual deformations of the prototype and this cannot always be predicted. Consequently it is necessary to have some yardstick whereby the accuracy of the energy analysis may be evaluated. Such a yardstick is provided by the finite element method which is capable of giving reliable solutions of particular problems though at a greatly increased cost in time of computation. A suitable finite element model is shown in fig. 10.11. Davies and Lawson used simple 24 degree-of-freedom folded plate elements having 6 degrees of freedom at each corner node and found acceptable convergence provided that the element aspect ratio did not become excessive. An important feature of fig. 10.11 is the provision of edge members of high axial stiffness and zero bending stiffness. These members coincide with the neutral axis of bending of the bottom plate and ensure com-

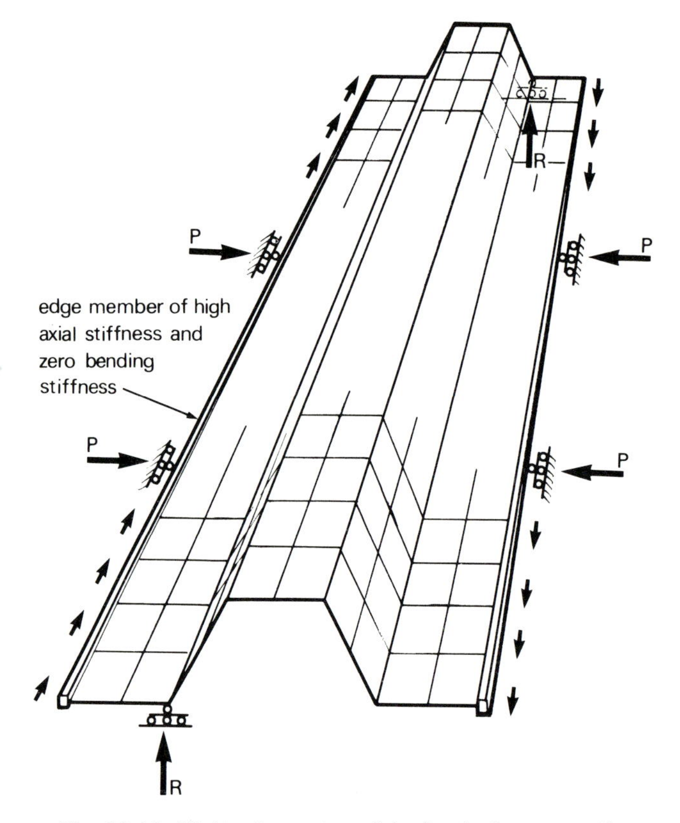

Fig. 10.11 Finite element model of a single corrugation.

patibility of deformation between adjacent corrugations. The supports P and R are optional and allow the influence of supporting members to be investigated.

10.6.5 Measurement of flexibility by testing

The testing of actual panels of profiled metal sheeting presents an apparently attractive means of obtaining reliable data by which to judge the merits of the different analytical techniques. A suitable apparatus for this purpose is shown in figs. 10.12 and 10.13 and some test results are quoted later. However, testing presents some major difficulties for reasons which follow, and the comparison of theory and experiment has to be made with judgement and caution.

A fundamental difficulty in all of this work is the definition of the boundary conditions. If the individual corrugations are considered it is clear that the longitudinal edge condition is different at the sides of the panel, where there is a tendency for the edge to be held straight by the framing members, from the condition internally, where there is a compatibility requirement with adjacent corrugations. Because of this situation, it is not possible to test a single corrugation. Instead a whole field of

Fig. 10.12 Apparatus to determine the distortional flexibility $c_{1.1}$ shown without sheeting.

corrugations must be tested and it must be borne in mind that there will be corrugations at the edge of the field with non-typical boundary conditions. Furthermore, experiments cannot be set up to measure $c_{1.1}$ in such a way that all of the other components of diaphragm flexibility are eliminated. Nevertheless, testing provides a potentially reliable method of evaluating the distortional flexibility provided that the test set-up is arranged in such a way that the other flexibility components are first minimised and then deducted analytically. It should be appreciated that the accuracy of this approach diminishes with increasing length as the magnitude of the distortional flexibility diminishes relative to the other components.

10.6.6 Comparison of results for fasteners in every trough

A typical overall pattern of results for a sheeting profile is shown in fig. 10.14 which shows the variation of flexibility with length of corrugation and with various conditions of support. Other similar comparisons are given in reference 1.110 covering both sheeting and decking profiles. For illustrative purposes it is convenient to plot the flexibility in terms of the profile property K defined in equation 10.25 realising that K is nearly constant if the outer edges of the bottom plate are held straight and that K increases linearly with length according to equation 10.26. The

Fig. 10.13 Apparatus clad with a decking profile.

curves make a full comparison between energy methods and finite element methods. Experimental results for no intermediate purlins are also included.

From fig. 10.14 and other similar figures, the following observations can be made.

(a) For the basic case with no consideration of the effect of supporting members and no intermediate restraints (curves 0 and $1u$) the level of agreement between the energy method and the finite element analysis is good. The energy method is consistently slightly more flexible (higher value of K) and clearly gives accurate results.
(b) The propping effect of member support at the ends is also adequately treated by the proposed approximate method (curves 0 and $1p$). In particular the finite element results confirm that the reduction in flexibility is given by a factor which is constant with length and that this factor can be obtained with reasonable accuracy using an energy method based on linear plate movements.
(c) Over the practical range of interest, K increases linearly with length and equation 10.26 is a considerable improvement over equation 10.25. Suitable values of $\bar{K}$ can be accurately evaluated by the energy method outlined above including the propping effect of supporting members at the sheet ends and it is these values that are tabulated in table 9.6 for the entire range of interest.

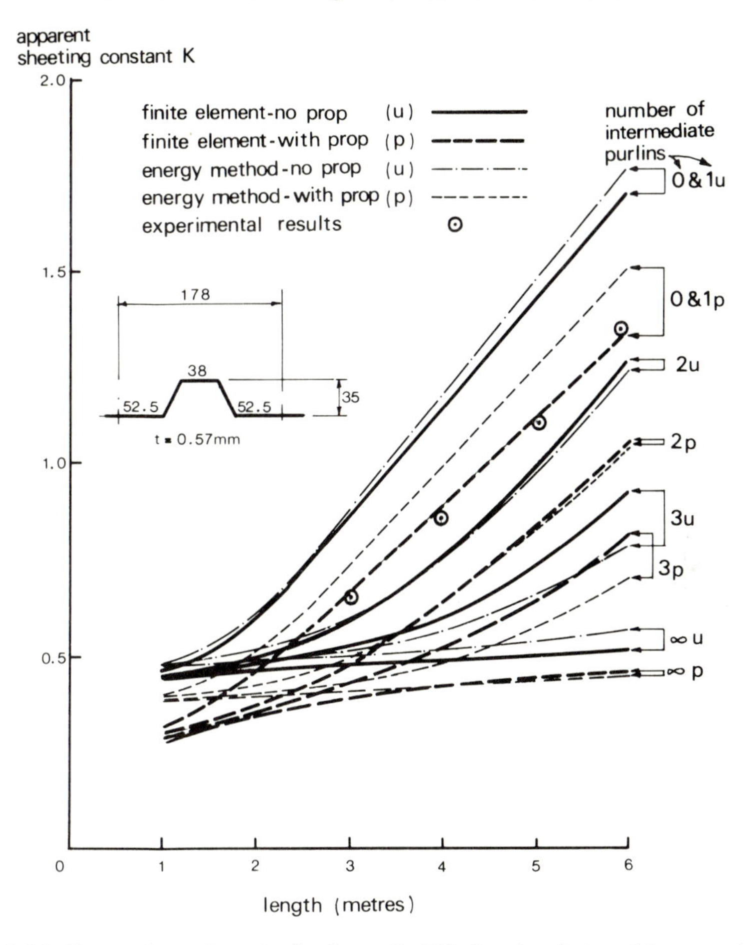

Fig. 10.14 Comparison of results for Longrib 700 sheeting fastened in every trough.

(d) Bearing in mind the problems described in section 10.6.5 the proposed treatment gives a good agreement with the experimental results. The experimental results tend to be lower than the theoretical with slightly greater differences for the longer lengths. The reasons for this are the non-typical corrugations near the edges of the tested sheets as explained previously.

(e) Two or more intermediate purlins cause a significant reduction in flexibility. Four intermediate purlins may be sufficient to reduce the flexibility almost to the value obtained when the edges are held straight (curves ∞u and ∞p). The energy method has only limited success in following this behaviour. Two intermediate purlins can be adequately dealt with (curves $2u$ and $2p$) but with three or more purlins the flexibility can be seriously underestimated. This is clearly a consequence of the inability of the displacement functions to follow the more complex displacement patterns required. For these cases the finite element results are clearly more reliable.

10.6.7 Approximate treatment for intermediate purlins

In the course of their investigation, Davies and Lawson carried out some 80 finite element analyses of single corrugations fastened in every trough with 2, 3, 4 or 5 intermediate purlins and with a wide range of spans and profile types. As a result of these analyses it became apparent that the effect of intermediate purlins could be conservatively covered by a simple reduction factor which is independent of the profile or the span. Thus

$$c_{1.1} = \frac{a\, d^{2.5}\, \alpha_1\, \bar{K}}{E\, t^{2.5}\, b^2} \tag{10.32}$$

where α_1 is given in table 9.3. It may be noted that α_1 replaces the corresponding factor f_1 included in Bryan's earlier treatment of the problem[1.57] and which was obtained on a completely different basis.

10.7 Flexibility with fasteners in alternate troughs

Fastening in alternate troughs results in flexibilities that are much greater than those obtained when the sheeting is fastened in every trough. The reason for this is the concertina-like deformation mode illustrated in fig. 10.15 in which the unfastened bottom plate in the middle of a pair of corrugations rotates about a vertical axis as the adjacent corrugations open and close.

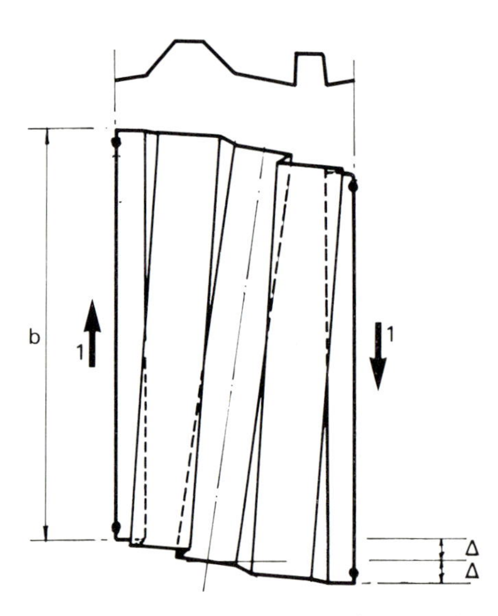

Fig. 10.15 Concertina-like deformation with fasteners in alternate troughs.

In order to deal with this behaviour analytically it is convenient to assume that the total shear flexibility of a pair of corrugations arises as the sum of two quite separate modes of distortion as illustrated in fig. 10.16. The two modes are: flexi-

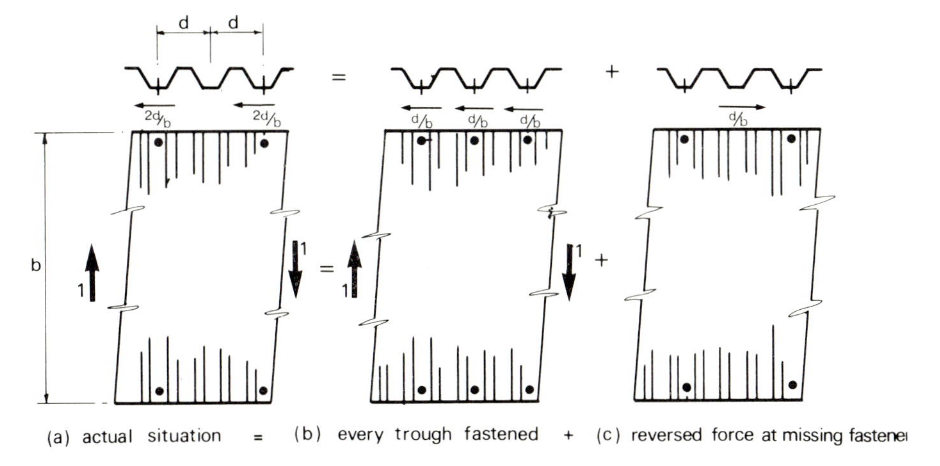

Fig. 10.16 Analytical procedure for fasteners in alternate troughs.

bility due to every trough fastened as shown in fig. 10.16(b) and as already considered; flexibility due to the concertina-like deformation obtained when the force in the missing fasteners is reversed as shown in fig. 10.16(c). It is thus necessary to consider only the flexibility due to the second of these modes and to add to this the flexibility already obtained for every trough fastened. Thus

$$\bar{K} = \bar{K}_e + \bar{K}_a \tag{10.33}$$

where the subscripts e and a refer to every trough fastened (fig. 10.16(b)) and alternate troughs fastened (fig. 10.16(c)) respectively.

In order to determine $\bar{K}_a$, it is necessary to proceed as before using a minimum potential energy method with assumed displacement functions. The total deformation is expressed in terms of the bottom plate movements U_{B1} and U_{B2} defined in fig. 10.17 and the corresponding displacement functions are:

$$\left.\begin{aligned} U_{B1} &= a_1 y + a_2 \frac{b}{2\pi} \sin \frac{2\pi y}{b} + a_3 \frac{b}{4\pi} \sin \frac{4\pi y}{b} + a_4 \frac{b}{6\pi} \sin \frac{6\pi y}{b} \\ U_{B2} &= a_5 \frac{b}{2\pi} \sin \frac{2\pi y}{b} + a_6 \frac{b}{4\pi} \sin \frac{4\pi y}{b} + a_7 \frac{b}{6\pi} \sin \frac{6\pi y}{b} \end{aligned}\right\} \tag{10.34}$$

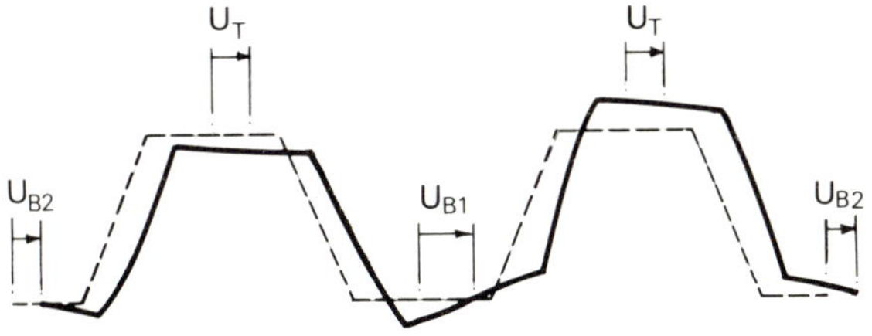

Fig. 10.17 Profile displacements, fasteners in alternate troughs.

As a consequence of the antisymmetry of the deformation pattern, the top plate movement U_T is given by

$$U_T = \tfrac{1}{2}(U_{B1} + U_{B2}) \tag{10.35}$$

As before, the analysis proceeds by expressing the total potential energy in terms of the seven coefficients in the displacement functions and minimising this with respect to variations in these coefficients. As the energy due to shear strain in the plate elements has already been included in $\bar{K}_e$ it does not arise again here and the components of the total energy are energy due to bending of the cross-section, energy due to longitudinal bending of the plate elements, energy due to axial strains in the side plates and energy due to torsion of the plate elements. Details of the evaluation of these components are given in reference 1.110. The minimum potential energy condition may now be obtained by minimising the energy with respect to variations in the variables $a_2 \ldots a_7$ and the shear displacement Δ calculated as before. The total shear flexibility is then obtained by adding to this value the corresponding flexibility obtained for the case of every trough fastened as illustrated in figure 10.16.

10.7.1 The influence of attachments to intermediate purlins

As before, the influence of intermediate purlins may be introduced into the analysis by equating U_{B2} to zero at the appropriate points and using the equations so obtained to eliminate displacement coefficients from the minimisation process.

10.7.2 The influence of members supporting the sheeting from below

As for the case of sheeting fastened in every trough, the presence of members supporting the sheeting from below prevents free movement of the corrugations and reduces the flexibility. As this effect also distorts the antisymmetry of the deformations it is extremely difficult to include an accurate allowance for it in the above energy derivations. It is sufficient, and much simpler to allow for it approximately as before. Therefore a reduction factor is calculated based on linear plate movements and applied without modification to longer sheet lengths where the plate displacements may be far from linear. This procedure again proved successful when the results from the energy method were compared with those obtained using finite elements.

10.7.3 Comparison of results for sheeting fastened in alternate troughs

The effect of varying the number of terms in the displacement functions was investigated for the case of fasteners in alternate troughs. The pattern was very similar to that shown in figure 10.9 for fasteners in every trough although here convergence was slightly more rapid. The seven terms shown in equations 10.34 were sufficient to achieve full convergence for spans of up to about 7 m. Because of the considerably increased size of the finite element problem, the range of comparisons is somewhat more restricted for the case of fasteners in every trough. However full comparisons

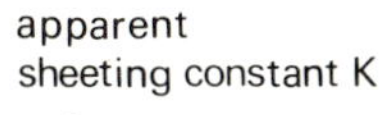

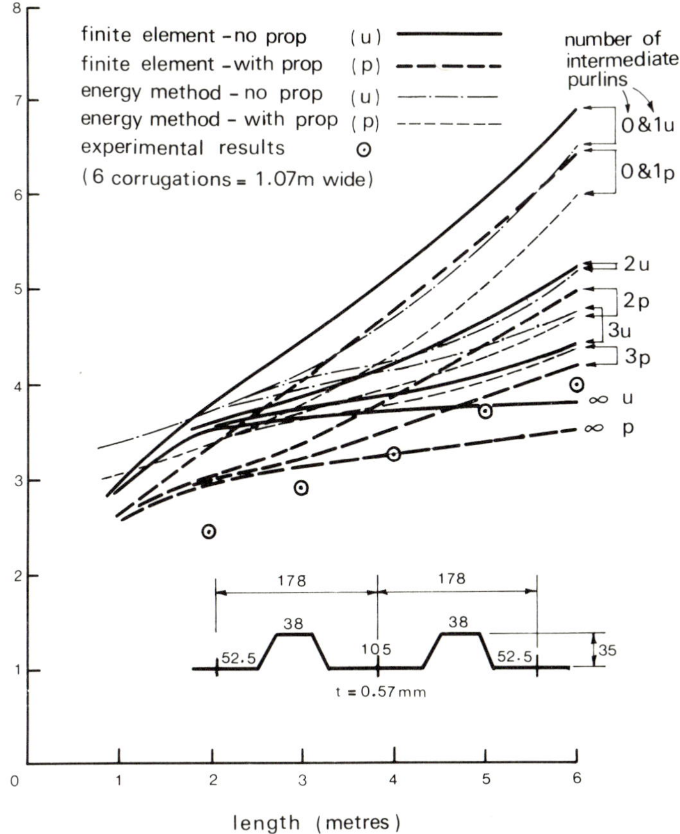

Fig. 10.18 Comparison of results for Longrib 700 sheeting fastened in alternate troughs.

for a typical sheeting profile are given in fig. 10.18. Similar comparisons for a decking profile are given in reference 1.110.

The following observations may be noted:

(a) There is again reasonable agreement between the finite element and energy analyses over the practical range of sheet lengths though here the energy method does not necessarily predict higher flexibilities.

(b) The propping effect of the supporting members can be adequately dealt with in the same approximate manner as for fasteners in every trough.

(c) The shape of the curves of K versus sheet length is somewhat different from those obtained with fasteners in every trough. In particular K does not become linear with sheet length at an early stage although it does become very nearly so for longer sheet lengths. There is a clear tendency for K to increase with sheet length so that Bryan's expression (equation 10.25) is not adequate.

(d) The experimental results shown are much less flexible than would be suggested by either finite element or energy analysis. However, this is not surprising as the width of the sheet under test was hardly sufficient for free distortion of the profile to take place without interference from the edge members. It is interesting to note that a similar difference is found consistently in tests on complete diaphragms that are within the size limits that can be conveniently installed in a laboratory. The theory is evidently conservative for relatively small diaphragms but there is no reason to believe that it will be so for diaphragms of practical proportions.
(e) The considerations regarding intermediate purlins are the same as before.

10.7.4 Practical treatment for fasteners in alternate troughs

As the increase in K with length is nearly linear for sheets of practical length it is clear that equation 10.26 again provides a practical design expression whereby the flexibility due to profile distortion $c_{1.1}$ may be estimated. Furthermore, the energy method described above provides a reasonable basis for calculating suitable values for the profile constant $\bar{K}$ and values calculated on this basis are given in table 9.7. Some 36 finite element analyses were carried out on pairs of corrugations fastened in alternative troughs and with 2, 3 or 4 intermediate purlins. These showed that the values of the factor α_1 given in table 9.3 are also applicable to the case of sheeting or decking fastened in alternate troughs.

10.8 Profile distortion in arc and tangent sheeting

With corrugated sheeting having an arc-and-tangent profile, shear flexibility due to distortion of the profile can arise in much the same way that it does with a trapezoidal profile. The continuously curved profile results in greater stiffness than in an equivalent trapezoidal profile but this consideration may be offset by the fact that arc and tangent sheeting frequently has a corrugation pitch as small as 75 mm so that fastenings to the supporting structure may only be made through every third or even fourth trough.

Mathematically, the problem is also rather different. The first analysis was carried out by McKenzie.[1.3] For the purpose of his analysis the corrugations were assumed to be made up of a series of circular arcs fastened to the supporting members in every trough. Furthermore, his analysis corresponded directly with that of Bryan for trapezoidal profiles in that he also assumed that shear warping was the result of linear movements of all points of the corrugation along the length. As before the solution process involved the minimisation of the total potential energy of the deformed corrugation.

Wu and Libove[1.37] extended this work to include lateral movement of the generator lines thus introducing longitudinal as well as cross-sectional bending energy. They assumed that the corrugation shape had a sine wave rather than a circular arc form, claiming that this was a closer approximation to cross-section of commercially available sheeting. The results obtained by Wu and Libove were significantly more flexible than those of McKenzie as a consequence of the greater freedom of movement permitted by their displacement model. However they did not attempt to verify their solution by comparison with test results and as they only considered fastening through every trough, which is relatively rare in practice, their results are of limited practical importance.

A much more comprehensive investigation was undertaken by Lawson.[1.90] He also approximated the cross-sectional shape by a sine wave and used an energy minimisation process to obtain the shear flexibility. Figure 10.19 shows the basic parameters of the problem for the analysis of a single corrugation for which the displacement functions used were:

$$\left.\begin{aligned} U_T &= a_1 y - \sum_{n=1}^{5} a_{n+1} \frac{b}{2n\pi} \sin \frac{2n\pi y}{b} \\ U_B &= \sum_{n=1}^{5} a_{n+1} \frac{b}{2n\pi} \sin \frac{2n\pi y}{b} \end{aligned}\right\} \quad (10.36)$$

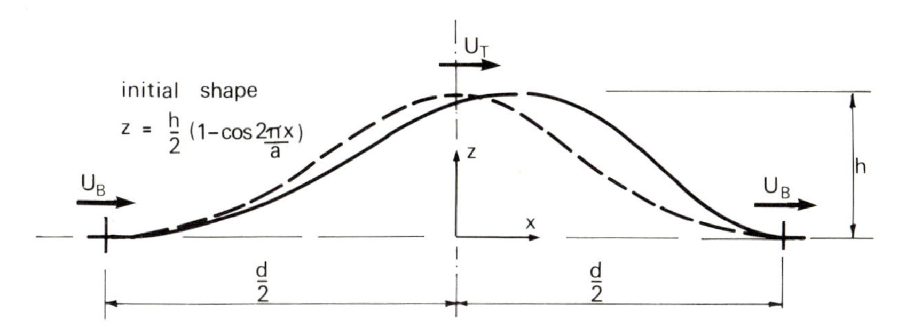

Fig. 10.19 Geometry and displacement functions for arc and tangent sheeting.

By expressing total potential energy in terms of these displacement functions and by minimising with respect to each of the displacement coefficients a_i in turn the value of the distortional flexibility was obtained.

10.8.1 Influence of attachments to intermediate purlins

As before, attachment to intermediate purlins can be considered by preventing the bottom plate movement at the points of attachment. This was done for both two and three intermediate purlins resulting in significant reductions in the flexibility.

10.8.2 Results of analysis and comparison with test results, etc.

For consistency of presentation, it is convenient to express the results in terms of Bryan's sheeting constant K which appears in equation 10.25. Figure 10.20 sum-

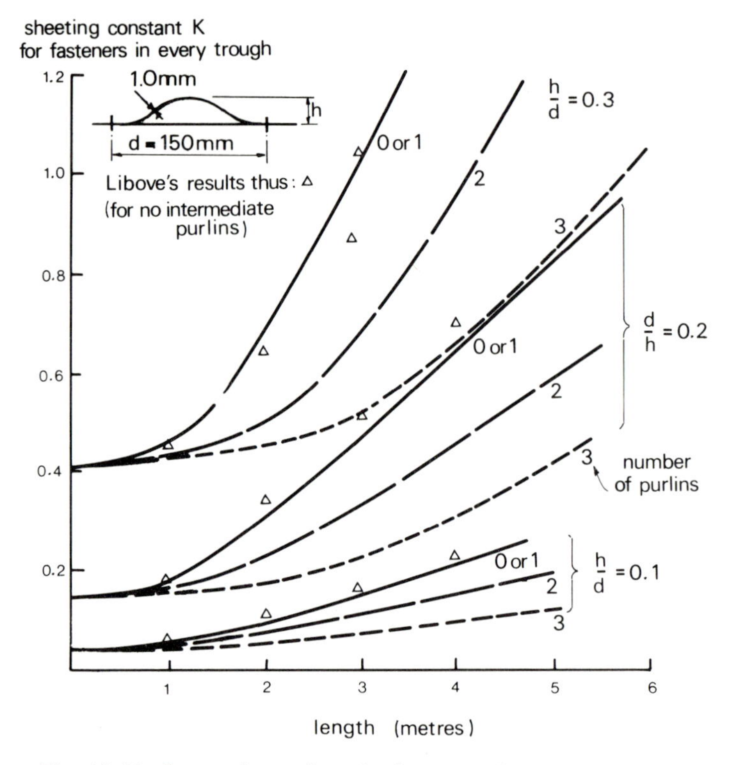

Fig. 10.20 Comparison of results for arc and tangent sheeting.

marises the results and offers some comparisons with the work of Libove. It is immediately clear that for practical sheet lengths, K is approximately proportional to the sheet length b and it is appropriate to use equation 10.26 for arc-and-tangent sheeting as well as trapezoidal sheeting. On this basis, the appropriate sheeting constant for practical use is $\bar{K}$ and values of $\bar{K}$ obtained by Lawson are tabulated in table 9.8. It is interesting to note that, for no intermediate purlins, Lawson's results agree well with those of Libove. However, the influence of intermediate purlins is significant, resulting in greater reductions in flexibility than were obtained for trapezoidal profiles. For this reason the values of the reduction factor α_1 are not appropriate here and instead the values of the net value of $\bar{K}$ including the influence of intermediate purlins are tabulated in table 9.8. Lawson carried out a single test in order to check the validity of his theory and obtained acceptable comparison between theory and experiment though it is difficult to draw any meaningful conclusions from a single result.

10.8.3 Solution for alternate trough attachments

With alternate trough fastenings the mechanism of concertina deformation accounts for a considerable increase in the shear flexibility. The essential considerations discussed in section 10.7 and illustrated by figs. 10.15 and 10.16 still apply so that it is necessary to consider the additional deformation caused by the reversal of the forces in the missing fasteners and to add this to the flexibility already obtained for the case of every corrugation fastened. Thus, the bottom plate movements in adjacent troughs are governed by the functions

$$\left.\begin{aligned} U_{B1} &= a_1 y - a_2 \frac{b}{2\pi} \sin \frac{2\pi y}{b} - a_3 \frac{b}{4\pi} \sin \frac{4\pi y}{b} \\ U_{B2} &= a_2 \frac{b}{2\pi} \sin \frac{2\pi y}{b} + a_3 \frac{b}{4\pi} \sin \frac{4\pi y}{b} \end{aligned}\right\} \tag{10.37}$$

and the analysis proceeds as before. The results are expressed in terms of $\bar{K}$ and tabulated for practical usage in table 9.8. Once again, a single experimental result gave an acceptable comparison between theory and experiment.

10.8.4 Multiple trough fixings with arc-and-tangent profiles

In practice, the relatively small pitch of the corrugations means that for strength purposes, the fixings may be placed through every third or even every fourth corrugation trough. Lawson shows that, based on a theory which assumes that the generator lines remain straight, attachment in every third trough results in a flexibility 2.67 times greater than with alternate trough attachment and if the fastening is only in every fourth trough the multiplying factor increases to 5.0. In the absence of any better theory for a problem of great complexity it is proposed that these multiplying factors should be applied to the results for the analysis with generator lines permitted to curve and it is considered that this procedure will give rise to safe results. The above multiplying factors are repeated in table 9.8. It should be noted that the standard 3 in (75 mm) arc and tangent profile is a profile of shallow depth and is therefore more likely to be subject to global buckling than the trapezoidal profiles in common use. For this reason a check on the buckling load is particularly important (see section 10.13). The authors are of the opinion that if buckling is at all critical in diaphragms constructed in this profile the sheet to purlin fasteners should not be spaced in more than alternate corrugations.

10.8.5 General comment regarding the results for arc and tangent profiles

It will have been observed from the foregoing comments that the results presented in table 9.8 have significantly less sound basis than those given in tables 9.6 and 9.7 for trapezoidal profiles. As Lawson himself observed, they are only valid to the extent that his very simple displacement functions are able to follow the possibly more complex behaviour of the real profiles and this is a matter for conjecture. Furthermore, an independent check by finite element methods is much more difficult as modelling by a series of flat plates is not possible in this instance. As the number of elements around the profile is increased, only very slow convergence is obtained due to the sensitivity of the problem and an impracticably large number of elements would be required for a reliable solution by this method. Consequently an alternative solution using curved shell elements or some alternative independent technique must be sought and no results are so far available. The results obtained by Libove for single corrugations are not considered to be a valid independent check as it appears that his analysis implies a similar displacement of a given cross-section to that assumed by Lawson. The results given in table 9.8 are therefore offered as being the best available to date.

10.9 Influence of sheet end laps and alternative fastening arrangements on profile distortion

Practical diaphragms often have depths which are considerably in excess of the readily available lengths of sheeting so that individual sheets must be overlapped at intermediate purlins. Such end laps in the sheeting permit a certain amount of relative movement between the sheets and result in an increase in flexibility. Figure 10.21 illustrates the problem. When the effect of end laps is considered in conjunction with the alternative fastener arrangements that are possible at the sheet ends and where the sheets pass over purlins, it becomes clear that there are a number of alternative arrangements that have practical significance. The most important of these are shown in table 9.1, together with suitable modifications to the flexibility component $c_{1.1}$ in the form of factors α_1 and α_4. In table 9.1,

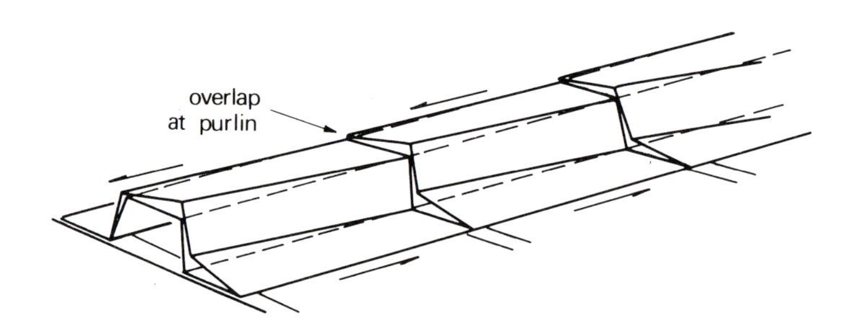

(a) overall view of deformation

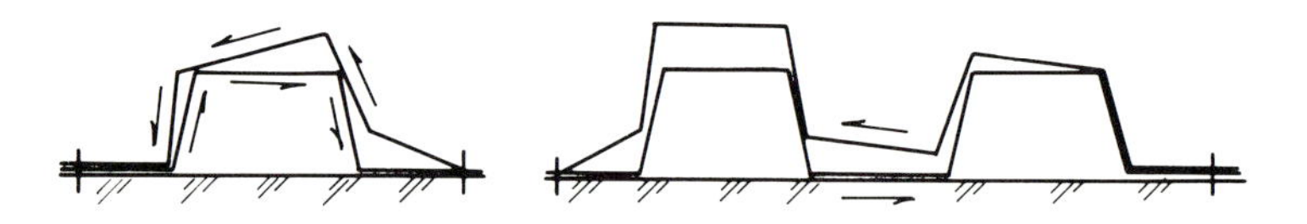

(b) alternative sections at lap – every or alternate corrugation fastened

Fig. 10.21 Relative deformation between sheets at end laps: (a) overall view of deformation, (b) alternative sections at lap – every or alternate corrugation fastened.

arrangements (1) to (3) arise out of the work already considered in sections 10.5 to 10.7. The treatment of arrangement (4) is logical and has been justified by comparison with the results (unpublished) of finite element analysis. Arrangements (5) to (8) have been considered in some detail both theoretically and experimentally by Lawson[1.90] and the design expressions given are rational simplifications of much more complex equations.

10.10 Influence of bonded insulation

When profiled metal cladding is used as decking, a frequently encountered practice is to bond insulation in the form of fibreboard or polyurethene foam to the decking with an adhesive such as hot bitumen and then to bond several layers of roofing felt in a similar manner to the upper surface of the insulation. Such a roofing system may be expected to restrict the free deformation of the decking profile and to improve the performance of the roof when acting as a diaphragm. The influence of bonded insulation has been studied in some detail by Lapin[1.66] and his conclusions may be summarised as follows:

(a) Any increase in strength gained by bonded insulation is small and unreliable and should not be considered in design.
(b) Bonded insulation has a small but tangible influence on the stiffness of decking fastened to the supporting structure through every corrugation trough but the influence on the flexibility of the complete diaphragm is not sufficient to warrant taking this into account in design.
(c) Bonded insulation is particularly effective in resisting the concertina-like movement associated with the distortion of profiles fastened to the supporting structure through alternate troughs. A conservative practical treatment for this case is to multiply $c_{1.1}$ by the following factor - for profile height $h \leqslant 50$ mm: 0.7; for profile height $50 < h < 80$ mm: 0.5.
(d) There are no serviceability problems with diaphragms incorporating built-up insulation. Hot bitumen adhesive was found to be capable of maintaining the bond between the decking and insulation at all stages of loading.

The above considerations give rise to the provisions of note 9.7.1 which suggests that the decrease in flexibility when the decking is fastened to the supporting structure through alternate troughs may be taken into account in the design calculations.

10.11 Flexibility due to shear strain in the sheeting

Figure 10.8 shows a typical corrugation which has a perimeter length of $2(b_L + 2b_s + b_T)$. If the thickness is t and the length b, the shear stress arising from unit shear force is $1/bt$ and the shear strain in each face of the profile is therefore given by

$$\gamma = \frac{1}{btG} = \frac{2(1+\nu)}{btE} \tag{10.38}$$

It follows that the flexibility due to shear strain in a single corrugation of width d is

$$c_{1.2} = \frac{4(1+\nu)(b_L + 2b_s + b_T)}{btE} \quad (10.39)$$

and in a complete panel of width a is

$$c_{1.2} = \frac{4(1+\nu)(b_L + 2b_s + b_T)a}{b\,d\,t\,E} \quad (10.40)$$

However, $c_{1.2}$ is a relatively insignificant component of the total flexibility c in the majority of diaphragms and it is usual to approximate the perimeter to that of the equivalent rectangular profile, namely $d[1 + (2h/d)]$ and to take for cantilever diaphragms (section 9.3)

$$c_{1.2} = \frac{2a(1+\nu)[1 + (2h/d)]}{b\,t\,E} \quad (10.41)$$

For diaphragm beams (section 9.5) a further factor α_2, which is tabulated in table 9.3, is introduced to take account of the variation in shear strain across the depth of the diaphragm due to the effect of intermediate pullins.

10.12 Flexibility due to axial strain in the edge members

In most calculations of diaphragm stiffness or flexibility, it is convenient to treat the flexibility due to axial strain in the edge members as an equivalent shear flexibility while recognising that, strictly speaking, it is a bending effect. For the cantilever diaphragm shown in fig. 10.1, if the cross-sectional area of the edge members is A, their effective second moment of area is $Ab^2/2$ and the bending deflection under unit load gives the equivalent shear flexibility as

$$c_3 = \frac{2a^3}{3EAb^2} \quad (10.42)$$

10.13 Shear buckling of diaphragms

Shear buckling in diaphragms can take one of two forms. The first possibility is local buckling of the flat plate elements forming the profile as shown in fig. 10.22.

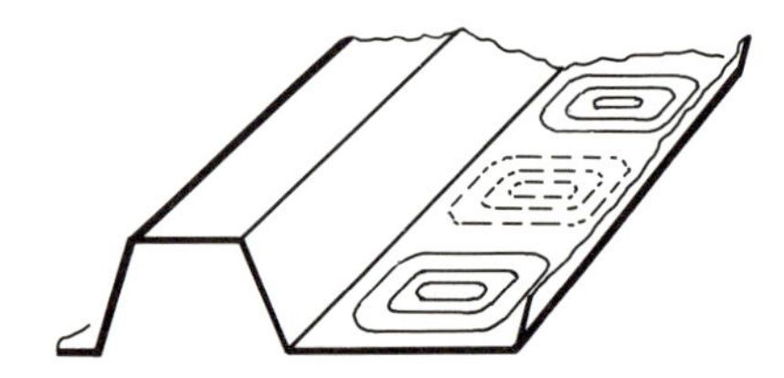

Fig. 10.22 Local shear buckling of trapezoidal sheeting.

This mode is not considered to be important as it has only once been observed in extensive testing of diaphragms and then in thin sheeting with unusually large flat areas between the raised portions of the corrugations. If a diaphragm using a profile with plate elements having an unusually large breadth to thickness ratio is to be used, the shear stress to cause local buckling in shear can be checked against the classical buckling equation, namely

$$\tau_{cr} = \frac{k\pi^2 E}{12(1-\nu^2)(h/t)^2} \tag{10.43}$$

where k = buckling coefficient which may be conservatively taken as 5.35
E = Young's modulus
ν = Poisson's ratio
h/t = breadth to thickness ratio of the plate element.

A more important possibility is that the sheeting may suffer overall shear buckling whereby one or more buckling waves may form passing through the corrugations across the whole width of the panel as shown in fig. 10.23. The usual way of approaching this problem analytically is to treat the profiled sheeting as an orthotropic plate thereby neglecting any interaction effects as the buckling wave tends to distort the profile. Comparison with experimental results tends to support the view

Fig. 10.23 Overall shear buckling of trapezoidal sheeting.

that this treatment is valid though there remain some reservations regarding the boundary conditions.

The first investigation of practical significance was carried out by Hlavacek[1.23] who studied the shear instability of orthotropic panels using an energy approach based on an assumed shape of the buckling wave. This was later refined by Easley and McFarland[1.24] and Easley[1.71], resulting in a buckling formula that is both simple and easy to use. It is Easley's formula that is the basis of the design expressions given in chapter 9. Finally, Lawson[1.90] examined Easley's formula in the light of practical boundary conditions and concluded that it could err significantly on the unsafe side if the sheeting was fixed to the supporting structure through alternate corrugation troughs though it proved quite satisfactory for every trough fixing. The theory assumes that the sheet at the edges of the diaphragm and at internal purlins behaves as though simply supported. With alternate corrugations fastened, there is the possibility that a significant buckling wave may pass between adjacent fasteners.

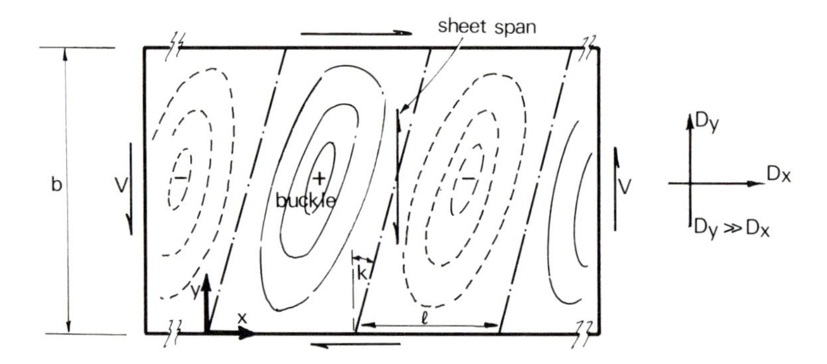

Fig. 10.24 Geometry of buckling waves in an orthotropic plate.

Figure 10.24 illustrates the assumed buckling configuration in a region of pure shear. The buckled wave is defined by the equation

$$w = A \sin \frac{\pi}{l}(x - ky) \sin \frac{\pi y}{b} \tag{10.44}$$

where k is the inclination of the buckled wave to major bending direction, l is the wave pitch and x and y are orthogonal co-ordinates. The solution for the buckling load follows by establishing the total potential energy of the buckled plate in terms of the two variables, namely the wave pitch and inclination. By differentiating the total energy expression with respect to the variables in turn, minimum energy expressions are obtained which may be used to develop an equation for the shear buckling load V_{ult} which takes the form

$$V_{ult} = D_y \frac{\pi^2}{b}\left(\frac{l^2}{2kb^2} + 3k + \frac{k^3 b^2}{2l^2}\right) + D_x \frac{\pi^2}{2kl^2} \tag{10.45}$$

where k is the smallest root of

$$8D_y{}^2k^8 + \frac{27}{4}D_yD_{xy}\,k^6 + \left(11D_xD_y - \frac{11}{4}D_{xy}{}^2\right)k^4$$

$$+\left(\frac{D_{xy}{}^3}{4D_y} - 3D_xD_{xy}\right)k^2 + \left(\frac{D_{xy}{}^2D_x}{4D_y} - D_x{}^2\right) = 0 \qquad (10.46)$$

and where D_x and D_y = orthogonal bending stiffness and D_{xy} = torsional stiffness. Now profiled metal sheeting gives rise to stiffnesses that are several orders of magnitude different in the two orthogonal directions so that it is not unreasonable to neglect D_x and D_{xy} when compared with D_y and this results in a considerable simplification of equations 10.45 and 10.46 to give

$$V_{\text{ult}} = \frac{36}{b}D_x{}^{\frac{1}{4}}\,D_y{}^{\frac{3}{4}} \qquad (10.47)$$

Lawson[1.90] showed that it is reasonable to apply this expression to each of the $(n_p - 1)$ regions of a diaphragm between adjacent purlins each of depth $b/(n_p - 1)$ provided that the fastenings were sufficiently close together to confine the buckling waves to these regions. Thus, for a diaphragm having a total of n_p equally spaced purlins, the buckling load given by orthotropic plate theory is

$$V_{\text{ult}} = \frac{36}{b}D_x{}^{\frac{1}{4}}\,D_y{}^{\frac{3}{4}}\,(n_p - 1)^2 \qquad (10.48)$$

Lawson carried out extensive experimental and theoretical investigations of shear panels with intermediate purlins and sparse fixings to both the perimeter and intermediate members. Naturally such considerations cause a considerable increase in the complexity of the theoretical expressions. He concluded his investigation by stating that, for the special case of single span panels fastened to the supporting structure through every trough, Easley's formula 10.47 may be used with confidence. For all other situations, the true buckling load is likely to fall below that given by equations 10.47 or 10.48 as appropriate. However, a reasonably safe design expression can be obtained by taking 50% of the value given by equation 10.48 and the results will in most cases be amply conservative. This is the basis of the expressions given in chapter 9.

Finally, it should be observed that overall buckling is generally a non-ductile failure mode and a well-designed diaphragm should fail in a mode which causes tearing of the sheet material at the fasteners. Modes such as buckling should have an additional 25% reserve of safety. For this reason, in the expressions given in chapter 9, equations 10.47 and 10.48 are multiplied by a further factor of 0.8 to give the general requirement for shear buckling in the form

$$\frac{14.4}{b}D_x{}^{\frac{1}{4}}\,D_y{}^{\frac{3}{4}}\,(n_p - 1)^2 \geqslant V^* \qquad (10.49)$$

10.14 Comparisons with finite element and test results

The finite element analysis of diaphragms was described in section 5.2. In sections 7.1 and 7.2 design calculations and brief comparison with finite element results were given for three diaphragms which had been tested. In this section, such comparisons are considered in more detail.

The first diaphragm considered in section 7.1 was tested for demonstration purposes at the University of Salford on a number of occasions with remarkably consistent results. It is designated A_2 and a finite element representation is shown in fig. 10.25. A similar diaphragm designated A_1 with sheet to purlin fasteners in every corrugation trough was also tested but not to failure. Naturally, finite element analysis gives a wealth of information regarding the internal force distribution, not all of which is amenable to comparison with test results. In particular, detailed distributions of fastener forces are given which can be compared with those assumed in the theory but there is no way of measuring these in a test. The only information relevant to fastener forces that is given by a test is the failure load and this may be influenced by inelastic redistribution of internal force prior to failure. For this reason, comparison of the distribution of fastener forces assumed in the theory with those predicted by finite element analysis has a particular importance and much of the justification of the theory rests on this basis.

Only two results of significance can be obtained from a typical test namely the flexibility and ultimate strength of the complete diaphragm. It is also important that the theory should be able to predict those quantities with adequate accuracy. Examination of typical finite element results shows that along a given seam there is very little variation of fastener force and it is adequate simply to consider average values. Similarly, for sheet to purlin fastener forces acting in a direction parallel to

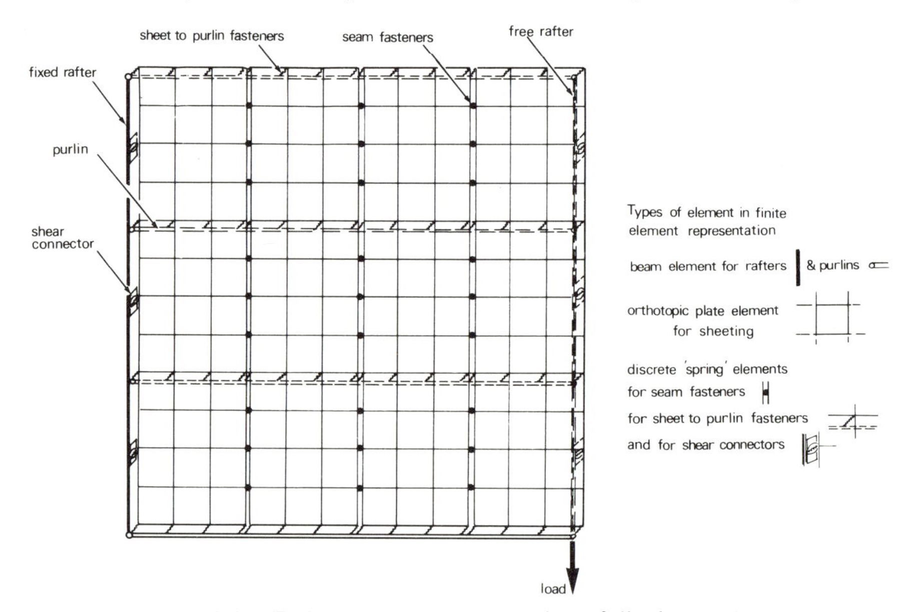

Fig. 10.25 Finite element representation of diaphragm A_2.

the seam there is very little variation between purlins and it is again adequate to take average values. Finally, for sheet to purlin fastener forces acting normal to the seam, the only significant forces are those in the outermost purlins and these invariably follow exactly the distribution described in section 10.2. Consequently, for panels A_1 and A_2 the important comparisons are those shown in fig. 10.26. In

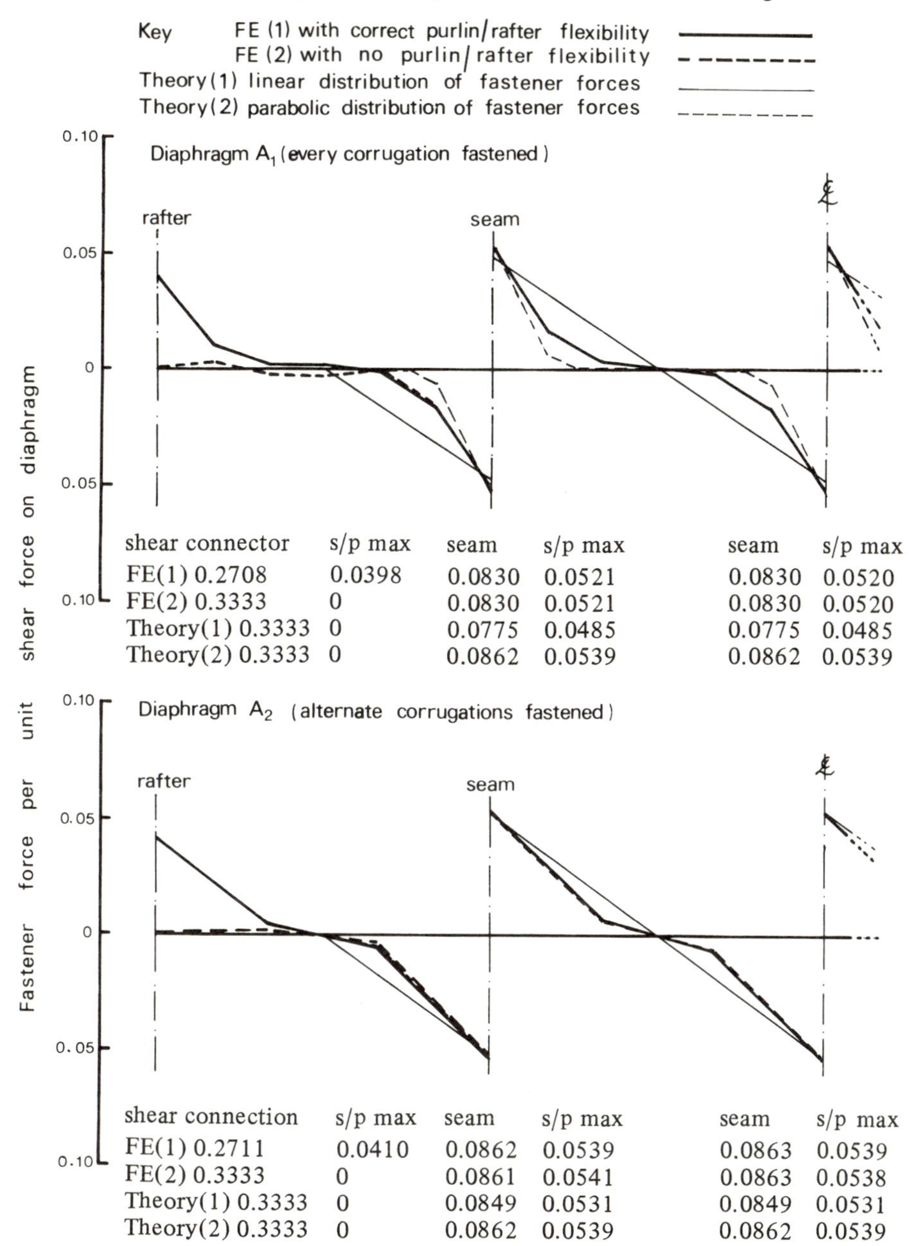

Fig. 10.26 Theoretical fastener forces for diaphragms A_1 and A_2.

interprèting the forces shown in fig. 10.26 it is important to note that the values of the relative stiffness parameter ρ described in section 10.5 are 4 312 000 for diaphragm A_1 and 409 000 for diaphragm A_2. These values are very much at the higher end of the range and are such that the parabolic distribution of fastener force (values of β_1 given in table 10.2) is much more appropriate than the linear distribution (values of β_1 given in table 10.1). It may therefore be expected that the European recommendations could be unconservative unless the values of β_1 are reduced in accordance with section 10.5. Consideration of fig. 10.26 shows that this is so but only to a relatively minor extent. The critical fastener forces at the seams are sufficiently accurate for all practical purposes. The forces in the sheet to shear connector fasteners will always be conservative because of the neglect of the contribution of the sheet to purlin fasteners adjacent to the rafters.

The comparison between the fundamental quantities of strength and flexibility obtained from tests and the alternative analyses is given in table 10.3. The design strengths of the diaphragms are lower than the test results because they are based on the design strength of the fasteners, which are lower than the ultimate values but the alternative analyses are directly comparable with each other. It is unfortunate that there is no test result available for the failure load of diaphragm A_1 but it would have clearly been above 34.0 kN and would probably have reflected some significant redistribution of internal force when compared with the finite element analysis. Some more recent test results relevant to this case are given in chapter 14 as part of a test series concerned with diaphragms with openings. The general conclusion regarding the predicted failure loads is that the assumption of a linear distribution of sheet to purlin fastener force tends to be unconservative when compared with the finite element analysis for these particular diaphragms but this has already been anticipated above because of the high value of the relative flexibility factor ρ. As the finite element analysis is by nature a linear elastic analysis and as fastener response is non-linear from an early stage, there will always be a significant favourable redistribution of force prior to failure and the slightly low strength values revealed by finite element analysis are not necessarily a cause for concern. Indeed, the design expression for seam failure assumes some such redistribution by considering both the seam fasteners and adjacent sheet to purlin fasteners to have reached their ultimate load simultaneously. Nevertheless, these results provide a pointer to the desirability of adopting the more cautious approach based on the parabolic distribution of sheet to purlin fastener force as discussed earlier. The predictions of flexibility require no comment except to note that the measured flexibility of diaphragm A_2 is lower than the theoretical prediction. This seems to be typically the case for the relative small diaphragms tested in the laboratory when fastened to the supporting structure through alternate corrugation troughs. The discrepancy is evidently in the calculation of the flexibility $c_{1.1}$ due to profile distortion and is probably because the relatively rigid rafters ensure that the free distortion of the outermost flutes is restrained.

If the shear connectors are omitted from diaphragms A_1 and A_2 we have diaphragms B_1 and B_2 respectively which are fastened on two sides only. For these diaphragms the important comparisons of fastener forces are shown in fig. 10.27.

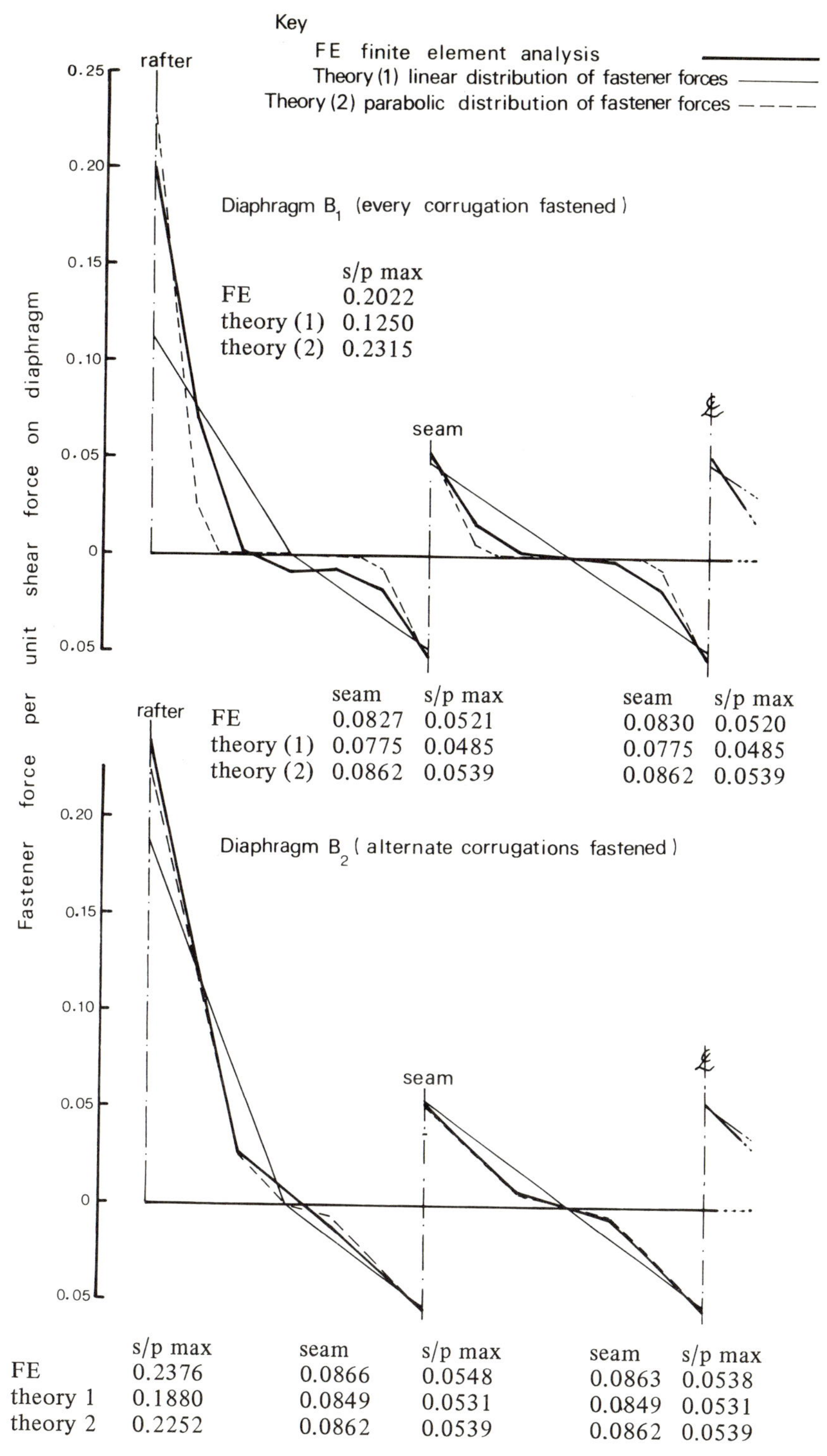

Fig. 10.27 Theoretical fastener forces for diaphragms B_1 and B_2.

Table 10. 3 Calculated and observed behaviour of tested diaphragms

		Strength (kN) and failure mode	Flexibility (mm/kN)
Diaphragm A_1	calculated design values linear	32.6 (shear connectors)	0.253
	quadratic	27.1 (seam)	0.260
	finite element analysis	27.7 (seam)	0.260
	test results	–	0.256
Diaphragm A_2	calculated design values linear	28.1 (seam)	1.34
	quadratic	27.1 (seam)	1.35
	finite element analysis	26.7 (seam)	1.34
	test results	34 (seam)	0.93
Diaphragm B_1	calculated design values linear	29.0 (end s/p)	0.409
	quadratic	15.7 (end s/p)	0.454
	finite element analysis	17.9 (end s/p)	0.456
	test results	30 (end s/p)	0.69
Diaphragm B_2	calculated design values linear	19.3 (end s/p)	1.526
	quadratic	16.0 (end s/p)	1.542
	finite element analysis	15.3 (end s/p)	1.555
	test results	19 (end s/p)	1.15

The significance of the forces in the sheet to purlin fasteners adjacent to the rafter is immediately obvious. These forces are far larger than any others and they dominate the design when a diaphragm is fastened on two sides only. This situation is often termed indirect shear transfer because the applied shear force in the rafter can only be transferred into the sheeting through the purlin to rafter connections and the sheet to purlin fasteners. Large fastener forces are induced near the rafters though there is some tendency for these forces to spread into the panel and this is taken into account by the factor β_2. It can be seen that the theory based on a parabolic distribution of sheet to purlin fastener force is again quite successful in following this behaviour though the linear theory is unconservative. The distinction is reflected in the test results so that for failure in the end sheet to purlin fasteners it may be important to recognise that the linear theory can be unconservative with relatively flexible purlins and to calculate accordingly. However, the consequences of using the values of β_2 given in table 10.1 for all structures, as suggested by the European recommendations, may not be serious because it has been found that the performance of complete structure is quite robust with respect to failure of the end sheet purlin fasteners (see section 12.7).

With both diaphragms B_1 and B_2 it is interesting to note that the forces at all internal seams are identical to those for diaphragms A_1 and A_2 respectively. Clearly the conditions at the rafter have negligible influence on the conditions internally, a result which justifies one of the major assumptions made earlier. Both panels B_1 and B_2 were tested to failure so that for these two panels the comparisons given in table 10.3 are complete. The general conclusion regarding the value of β_2 is further borne out by the comparison of the experimental and theoretical results for failure load. The design values based on the linear theory are very similar to the test results despite the fact that the former incorporate the material factor and the statistical reduction of fastener strength. For these particular diaphragms it is clearly necessary either to use the lower values of β_1 and β_2 or to recognise the significance of the relative flexibility factor ρ and to calculate accordingly. More importantly, the basic theory is clearly sound when the correct values of β_1 and β_2 are used and if any modification to the European recommendations is required it is merely to follow the approach adopted in this book and to use less optimistic values of β_1 and β_2, particularly when the purlins are flexible relative to the shear stiffness of the sheeting.

It will be appreciated that a large number of diaphragm tests have been carried out by the authors and by other workers in the field and it is not possible to quote all of these in detail. The results that have been quoted are believed to be typical of the agreement that is obtained when test results are compared with the theories expounded in this book. Further comparison between theory and experiment can be found in various other parts of the book, notably in sections 7.1 and 7.2 where calculations for two tested diaphragms are given in full and in chapter 14 where the test results for six diaphragms containing openings and two without openings are considered in some detail. Further extensive testing of closely related structures is considered in chapter 15.

CHAPTER ELEVEN

Design expressions for panel assemblies

11.1 Introduction

It was shown in chapter 3 that a complete roof may be considered to be an assembly of individual panels and that the extension of the design expressions derived in chapter 10 to the typical problem shown in fig. 11.1 follows very simple principles. If the roof consists of a total of n individual panels each of flexibility c, the strength of the complete roof depends on the strength of the critical end panel which carries the maximum shear force of

$$V = \left(\frac{n-1}{2}\right) P \tag{11.1}$$

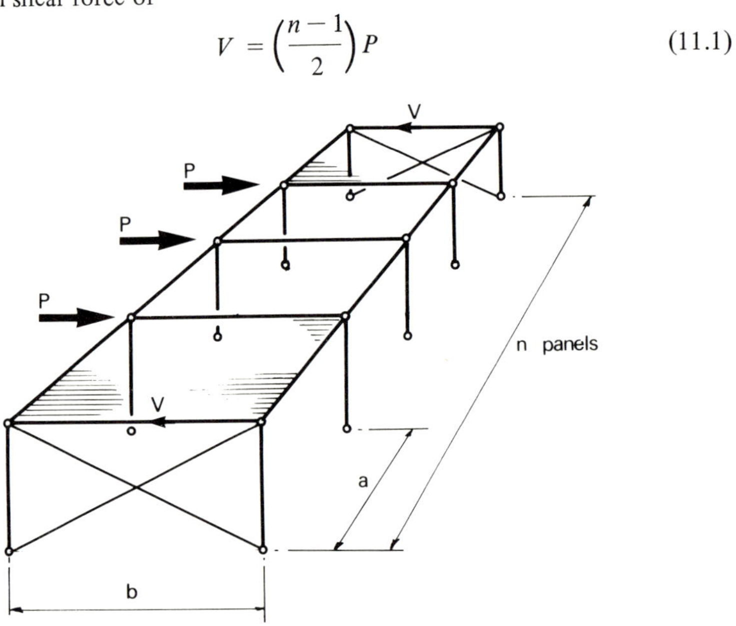

Fig. 11.1 Diaphragm action in flat roofed construction.

Furthermore, the deflection at any point can be obtained by starting at a gable and summing the individual panel deflections so that the maximum deflection at mid-span is given by

$$\Delta_{max} = \frac{cn^2 P}{8} \tag{11.2}$$

This reasoning means that many of the design expressions given in chapters 3 and 9 follow without further explanation. In this chapter only those whose derivations are not obvious are considered in more detail.

11.2 Flexibility due to movement at the gables and intermediate rafters

If each individual panel is fastened to the supporting structure on four sides, the considerations leading to the *design* of the shear connectors are shown in fig. 11.2.

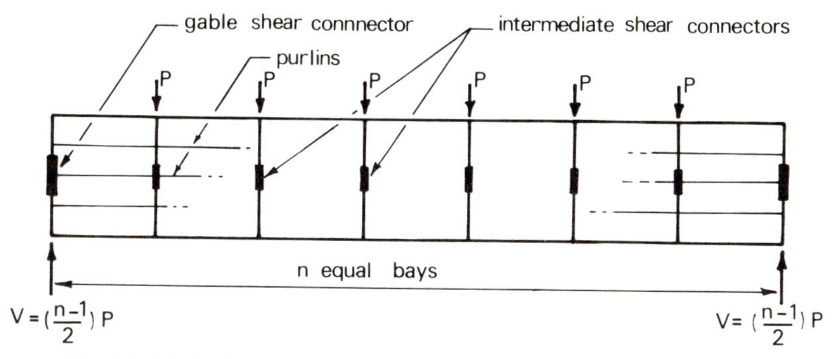

Fig. 11.2 Diaphragm beam with each panel fastened on four sides.

The intermediate shear connectors serve to transfer the individual point loads P from the frames to the sheeting whereas the gable point loads must transfer the entire accumulated shear force $V = [(n-1)/2]\,P$ to the gable steelwork and thence to the ground. It follows that normally the intermediate shear connectors will have a number of fasteners n'_{sc} sufficient to carry the smaller load P whereas the gable shear connectors will incorporate $n_{sc} = [(n-1)/2]\,n'_{sc}$ fasteners sufficient to carry the much larger shear force V. If this is the case, the movement in each group of shear connectors will be the same

i.e.

$$\frac{s_{sc}}{n'_{sc}} = \left(\frac{n-1}{2}\right)\frac{s_{sc}}{n_{sc}} \tag{11.3}$$

where s_{sc} = slip (flexibility) per shear connector fastener per unit load. The total deflection at the centre of the roof due to this cause will be

$$\Delta_{2.3} = \frac{(n+1)}{2}\frac{s_{sc}}{n'_{sc}}P = c_{2.3}\frac{n^2 P}{8} \tag{11.4}$$

where $c_{2.3}$ = the required flexibility component averaged over the complete diaphragm,

so that
$$c_{2.3} = \frac{4(n+1)}{n^2}\frac{s_{sc}}{n'_{sc}} \qquad (11.5)$$

If the intermediate shear connectors are omitted in fig. 11.2, the internal panels are fastened to the supporting structure on two sides only and the forces P must pass into the sheeting through the purlin to rafter connections and the sheet to purlin fasteners. In this case, it will usually be reasonable to assume that movement at the end rafter is relatively small and can be ignored and that all significant movement takes place internally. Then, the movement at each internal rafter is $[s_{pr} + (s_p/\beta_2)]\ (P/n_p)$ where s_p = slip (flexibility) per sheet to purlin fastener per unit load, s_{pr} = movement of purlin to rafter connection per unit load, β_2 = factor given in table 9.5 which arises in the manner described in section 10.4 and the total movement is

$$\left(\frac{n-1}{2}\right)\left(s_{pr} + \frac{s_p}{\beta_2}\right)\frac{P}{n_p} = c_{2.3}\frac{n^2 P}{8} \qquad (11.6)$$

Thus,
$$c_{2.3} = \frac{4(n-1)}{n^2 n_p}\left(s_{pr} + \frac{s_p}{\beta_2}\right) \qquad (11.7)$$

where $c_{2.3}$ = the required flexibility component averaged over the complete diaphragm as before. If the movement at the gable is considered in the above derivation, the correct expression for the total movement becomes

$$\frac{(n-1)\,s_{sc}P}{2n_{sc}} + \left(\frac{n-1}{2}\right)\left(s_{pr} + \frac{s_p}{\beta_2}\right)\frac{P}{n_p} = c_{2.3}\frac{n^2 P}{8} \qquad (11.8)$$

i.e.
$$c_{2.3} = \frac{4(n-1)}{n^2}\left[\frac{s_{sc}}{n_{sc}} + \frac{1}{n_p}\left(s_{pr} + \frac{s_p}{\beta_2}\right)\right] \qquad (11.9)$$

Alternatively, the end panel can be considered as a special case with a flexibility given by

$$c_{2.3} = \frac{s_{sc}}{n_{sc}} + \frac{4(n-1)}{n^2 n_p}\left(s_{pr} + \frac{s_p}{\beta_2}\right) \qquad (11.10)$$

and with the flexibility of the remaining panels unchanged from equation 11.7.

Finally, if no shear connectors are provided at either the gables or the intermediate frames, the gable shear force V must also pass through the purlin to rafter connections and the sheet to purlin fasteners giving, for the total movement at mid-span,

$$2\left(\frac{n-1}{2}\right)\left(s_{pr} + \frac{s_p}{\beta_2}\right)\frac{P}{n_p} = c_{2.3}\frac{n^2 P}{8} \qquad (11.11)$$

i.e.

$$c_{2.3} = 8\,\frac{(n-1)}{n^2 n_p}\left(s_{pr} + \frac{s_p}{\beta_2}\right) \tag{11.12}$$

Again there is the alternative more exact treatment whereby the internal panels have a flexibility given by equation 11.7 and the end panels have a flexibility given by

$$c_{2.3} = \left[\frac{1}{n_p} + \frac{4(n-1)}{n^2 n_p}\right]\left(s_{pr} + \frac{s_p}{\beta_2}\right) \tag{11.13}$$

11.3 Flexibility due to axial strain in the edge members

The technique of replacing the flexibility due to axial strain in the edge members, which is strictly a bending phenomenon, by an equivalent shear flexibility is a convenient though not essential part of the design process described in this book. For the case of diaphragms acting independently of the frames to carry the total in-plane load there is no difficulty in treating the axial strain effect correctly as a bending displacement and indeed this is advocated in current American practice[1.15] and has been used in Britain in the construction of design tables.[1.126] When diaphragms act in conjunction with rigid-jointed frames there are considerable advantages in treating the bending displacement of the diaphragm by an equivalent shear flexibility and it is to some extent with this in mind that the present theory has developed.

If the bending resistance of the diaphragm is provided entirely by the two edge members of cross-sectional area A acting as a beam of second moment of area $Ab^2/2$, and if the point loads P shown in fig. 11.1 are replaced by an equivalent uniformly distributed load $q = P/a$ per unit length, equating the bending deflection to the equivalent shear deflection gives:

$$\frac{10\,q\,n^4 a^4}{384\,E\,A\,b^2} = \frac{c_3\,n^2\,(aq)}{8} \tag{11.14}$$

where c_3 is the equivalent shear flexibility

i.e.

$$c_3 = \frac{n^2 a^3}{4.8\,E\,A\,b^2} \tag{11.15}$$

If the bending resistance of the diaphragm is calculated assuming that all of the members running in the direction of span contribute according to the usual assumption of a linear distribution of bending strain across the diaphragm, the second moment of area may be calculated as

$$I = 2A \sum_{i=1}^{(n_p-1)/2} \left(\frac{i\,b}{n_p - 1}\right)^2 \quad \text{(for odd values of } n_p\text{)} \tag{11.16}$$

or
$$I = 2A \sum_{i=1}^{n_p/2} \left(\frac{(i-\frac{1}{2})b}{n_p - 1}\right)^2 \quad \text{(for even values of } n_p\text{)}$$

i.e.
$$I = \frac{1}{\alpha_3} \frac{Ab^2}{2} \tag{11.17}$$

where α_3 is a reduction factor for bending deflection given by

$$\left.\begin{aligned} \alpha_3 &= \frac{1}{4 \sum_{i=1}^{(n_p-1)/2} \left(\frac{i}{n_p - 1}\right)^2} \quad (n_p \text{ odd}) \\ \text{or} \quad \alpha_3 &= \frac{1}{4 \sum_{i=1}^{n_p/2} \left(\frac{i-\frac{1}{2}}{n_p - 1}\right)^2} \quad (n_p \text{ even}) \end{aligned}\right\} \tag{11.18}$$

α_3 is tabulated in table 9.3 and it may be noted that the reduction factor applicable to axial force in the edge purlin takes the same form. The expression for the equivalent shear flexibility now takes the form given in Part I, namely

$$c_3 = \frac{n^2 a^3 \alpha_3}{4.8\, E\, A\, b^2} \tag{11.19}$$

It is interesting to note that Bryan[1.76] has shown that on the basis of the theory of the deflected shape of a simply supported beam carrying a uniformly distributed load, the equivalent shear flexibility varies between $n^2a^3\alpha_3/(6EAb^2)$ at the gable and $n^2a^3\alpha_3/(4EAb^2)$ at the centre. Bearing in mind that c_3 is only one of six components of the total shear flexibility c and often not a dominant one, equation 11.19 is considered to be a perfectly adequate approximation to the true behaviour for all practical purposes.

11.4 Profile distortion with the sheeting spanning parallel to the span of the diaphragm

The situation to be considered when the sheeting spans parallel to the span of the diaphragm is shown in fig. 11.3. In simple terms this situation has been considered in sections 2.9 and 3.4. The design for strength is based on the design of the end panel as a special case of the basic shear panel. The deflection calculation is based on the shear flexibility of the individual panels in the usual way. The relevant design expressions are given in chapter 9. These design expressions include an empirical factor α_5 which takes account of an important aspect of the behaviour of practical diaphragms in which the sheeting spans parallel to the span of the diaphragm.

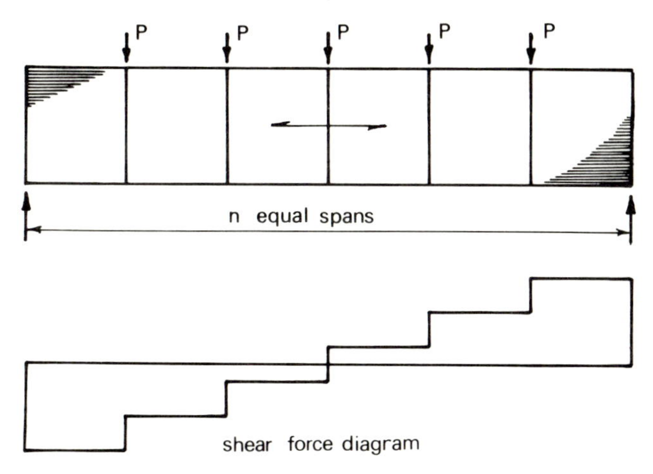

Fig. 11.3 Sheeting spanning parallel to span of diaphragm.

As is shown in fig. 11.3, the sheeting runs continuously through the full length of the diaphragm and the shear force changes from positive to negative within the sheet length. The situation is further complicated by end laps in the sheeting which may occur on some but not necessarily all supporting members. It is not immediately clear what form the profile distortion term $c_{1.1}$ should take in these circumstances. This problem has been studied both theoretically and experimentally in some depth by Lawson[1.90] who derived some complex formulae to deal with this situation. A rational simplification of these formulae is included in table 9.2.

CHAPTER TWELVE

Interaction of panels and stiff frames

12.1 Introduction

The methods of analysis available for rigid jointed steel frames interacting with roof and gable diaphragms have been described in some detail in chapter 4. The alternative methods may be summarised as: manual elastic analysis, computer elastic analysis, manual plastic analysis and computer plastic analysis. Manual elastic analysis depends on tables of reduction factors which are tabulated as tables 9.13 and 9.14 in chapter 9. In this chapter it is shown how these tables were derived. Originally such tables were manually derived by considering each possible number of frames as a separate case and obtaining a series of explicit expressions for the reduction factor[2.2] The general solution of the problem has not been given previously and is therefore treated in some detail in sections 12.2 and 12.3.

During the development of the methods of stressed skin design, no less than four full size or semi-full size structures have been instrumented and tested. In three cases the tests were continued to failure. These tests will be described in sections 12.5 to 12.8, the results compared with the theory, and appropriate conclusions drawn. It should be noted that since these tests were originally reported significant improvements have been made to the design expressions and techniques of analysis. For this reason, the comparison between experiment and theory is now much better than that given in the original publications. These comparisons are given in some detail because they provide an important justification of the theory and also because, in their present form, they are not available elsewhere.

12.2 Reduction factors for frame moments

A simple example of the calculation of the reduction factors given in table 9.13 has already been given in section 4.2. In generalising this calculation it is convenient for illustrative purposes to express the problem in terms of a sheeted rectangular portal frame while realising that the resulting factors are of more general application. The general problem is shown in fig. 12.1 where the complete structure comprises two rigid gable frames, a number of identical intermediate frames of flexibility k (see fig. 4.4(a)) each carrying a horizontal load P and a number of identical shear panels of flexibility c (see fig. 4.4(b)). In order to preserve a more sensible subscript notation for this particular problem, and in contrast to the notation used elsewhere, the gable frames are not numbered so that the subscripts refer only to the intermediate frames.

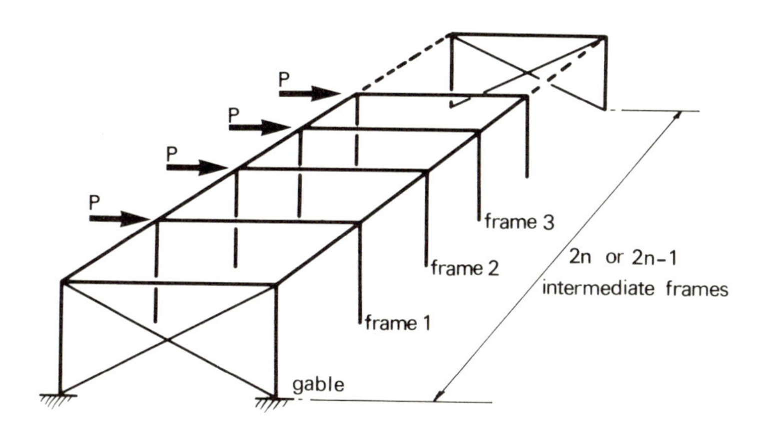

Fig. 12.1 Sheeted rectangular portal frame structure.

There are two cases to consider depending whether there are an even number ($2n$) or an odd number ($2n - 1$) of intermediate frames. Considering first the case of an even number of frames, at a typical frame i let the applied force P divide itself between the frame and the diaphragm so that R_i is carried by the frame and $P - R_i$ by the diaphragm. The forces R_i are therefore redundants in the problem which must be determined by considering compatability of deflections between the frames and the completed diaphragm as shown in plan in fig. 12.2. As the problem is symmetrical about the centre frame, fig. 12.2 shows only one half of the structure. Noting that frame n is on the centre line of the structure, the shear force V_i in panel i (above frame i in fig. 12.2) is

$$V_i = (n - i + \tfrac{1}{2})P - \sum_{j=i}^{n} R_j + \tfrac{1}{2}R_n \tag{12.1}$$

but this shear force is responsible for the change in deflection between frames $i - 1$ and i so that

$$\Delta_i - \Delta_{i-1} = c\,V_i \tag{12.2}$$

Furthermore, for a typical frame,

$$\Delta_i = k\,R_i \tag{12.3}$$

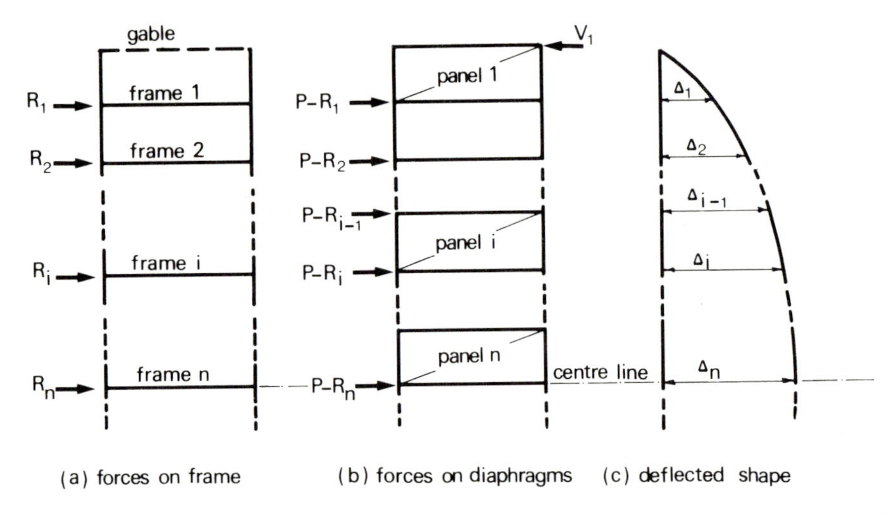

Fig. 12.2 Forces and displacements in frames and diaphragms (odd number of frames): (a) forces on frames, (b) forces on diaphragms, (c) deflected shape.

Combining equations 12.2 and 12.3, and substituting for the ratio c/k the relative flexibility ψ we have

$$R_i - R_{i-1} = \psi V_i \tag{12.4}$$

Finally, substituting for V_i using equation 12.1 and re-arranging gives the generalised compatability condition

$$-R_{i-1} + (\psi + 1) R_i + \psi \sum_{j=i+1}^{n} R_j - \tfrac{1}{2}\psi R_n = (n - i + \tfrac{1}{2}) \psi P \tag{12.5}$$

This equation is valid at all frames provided that at the first frame the first term is omitted and at the last frame the summation is omitted. Thus equations of the form of 12.5 provide n equations to solve for the n unknowns $R_1, \ldots, R_i, \ldots, R_n$. For solution, the problem is most conveniently set up in matrix form, thus

$$\begin{array}{c} \\ (1) \\ (2) \\ \vdots \\ (i-1) \\ (i) \\ \vdots \\ (n-1) \\ (n) \end{array}
\begin{array}{c} \begin{array}{cccccccc} (1) & (2) & \ldots & (i-1) & (i) & \ldots & (n-1) & (n) \end{array} \\
\begin{bmatrix}
\psi+1 & \psi & \ldots & \psi & \psi & \ldots & \psi & \psi/2 \\
-1 & \psi+1 & \ldots & \psi & \psi & & \psi & \psi/2 \\
\vdots & \vdots & & \vdots & \vdots & & \vdots & \vdots \\
0 & 0 & \ldots & \psi+1 & \psi & \ldots & \psi & \psi/2 \\
0 & 0 & \ldots & -1 & \psi+1 & \ldots & \psi & \psi/2 \\
\vdots & \vdots & & \vdots & \vdots & & \vdots & \vdots \\
0 & 0 & \ldots & 0 & 0 & \ldots & \psi+1 & \psi/2 \\
0 & 0 & \ldots & 0 & 0 & \ldots & -1 & \psi/2+1
\end{bmatrix} \end{array}
\begin{bmatrix} R_1 \\ R_2 \\ \vdots \\ R_{i-1} \\ R_i \\ \vdots \\ R_{n-1} \\ R_n \end{bmatrix}
=
\begin{bmatrix} (n-\frac{1}{2})\psi \\ (n-1\frac{1}{2})\psi \\ \vdots \\ (n-i+1\frac{1}{2})\psi \\ (n-i+\frac{1}{2})\psi \\ \vdots \\ 1\frac{1}{2}\psi \\ \frac{1}{2}\psi \end{bmatrix} P \tag{12.6}$$

Solving these equations gives the values of the redundant force R_i.

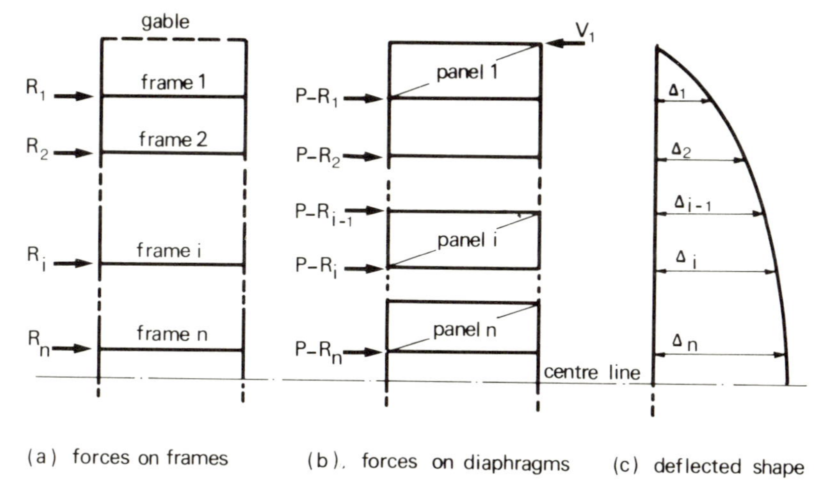

Fig. 12.3 Forces and displacements in frames and diaphragms (even number of frames): (a) forces on frames, (b) forces on diaphragms, (c) deflected shape.

If there is an even number of intermediate frames in the structure, the problem is again symmetrical and the interaction of forces between the frames and the diaphragm over half of the structure is as shown in fig. 12.3. In this case, frame n lies one half a bay away from the centre line of the structure and the centre shear panel is unstressed. The shear force V_i in panel i (above frame i in fig. 12.3) is now given by

$$V_i = (n - i + 1)P - \sum_{j=i}^{n} R_j \tag{12.7}$$

Equations 12.2, 12.3, and 12.4 still hold good so that the generalised compatability condition becomes

$$-R_{i-1} + (\psi + 1)R_i + \psi \sum_{j=i+1}^{n} R_j = (n - i + 1)\,\psi P \tag{12.8}$$

As before this equation is valid for all values of i provided that for $i = 1$ the first term is omitted and for $i = n$ the summation is omitted. The problem set up in matrix form for solution is therefore

$$\begin{array}{c} \\ (1) \\ (2) \\ \cdot \\ \cdot \\ \cdot \\ (i-1) \\ (i) \\ \cdot \\ \cdot \\ \cdot \\ (n-1) \\ (n) \end{array}
\begin{array}{c} \begin{array}{cccccccccc} (1) & (2) & \ldots & \ldots & (i-1) & (i) & \ldots & \ldots & (n-1) & (n) \end{array} \\
\left[\begin{array}{cccccccccc}
\psi+1 & \psi & \ldots & \ldots & \psi & \psi & \ldots & \ldots & \psi & \psi \\
-1 & \psi+1 & \ldots & \ldots & \psi & \psi & \ldots & \ldots & \psi & \psi \\
\cdot & \cdot & & & \cdot & \cdot & & & \cdot & \cdot \\
\cdot & \cdot & & & \cdot & \cdot & & & \cdot & \cdot \\
\cdot & \cdot & & & \cdot & \cdot & & & \cdot & \cdot \\
0 & 0 & \ldots & \ldots & \psi+1 & \psi & \ldots & \ldots & \psi & \psi \\
0 & 0 & \ldots & \ldots & -1 & \psi+1 & \ldots & \ldots & \psi & \psi \\
\cdot & \cdot & & & \cdot & \cdot & & & \cdot & \cdot \\
\cdot & \cdot & & & \cdot & \cdot & & & \cdot & \cdot \\
\cdot & \cdot & & & \cdot & \cdot & & & \cdot & \cdot \\
0 & 0 & \ldots & \ldots & 0 & 0 & \ldots & \ldots & \psi+1 & \psi \\
0 & 0 & \ldots & \ldots & 0 & 0 & \ldots & \ldots & -1 & \psi+1
\end{array}\right] \end{array}
\left[\begin{array}{c} R_1 \\ R_2 \\ \cdot \\ \cdot \\ \cdot \\ R_{i-1} \\ R_i \\ \cdot \\ \cdot \\ \cdot \\ R_{n-1} \\ R_n \end{array}\right]
=
\left[\begin{array}{c} n\psi \\ (n-1)\psi \\ \cdot \\ \cdot \\ \cdot \\ (n-i+2)\psi \\ (n-i+1)\psi \\ \cdot \\ \cdot \\ \cdot \\ 2\psi \\ \psi \end{array}\right] P \tag{12.9}$$

Equations 12.6 and 12.9 are, of course, readily programmable for computer solution as the assembly of the individual rows of the matrix is repetitive using equations 12.5 and 12.8. A computer program was written to assemble and solve these equations and the values given in table 9.13 were obtained in this way. For unit values of P, the values of R_i given by the above equations are identical to the required reduction factors for frame forces η_i.

12.3 Reduction factors for one frame only loaded

If, in fig. 12.1, only one frame is loaded, diaphragm action is much more effective as the cladding not only carries a proportion of the load back to the stiffened gables, it also serves to distribute the load between the frames. Obviously, the critical case is when the loaded frame is in the centre of the structure as diaphragm action is of least benefit and the frame forces and deflections are a maximum. For an odd number of frames, the problem is still symmetrical and the forces and deflections in the frames and the diaphragm are as shown in fig. 12.4 for one half of the structure. In fig. 12.4, as the loaded frame is at the centre of the structure, the shear force in the ith panel is given by

$$V_i = \tfrac{1}{2}P - \sum_{j=i}^{n} R_j + \tfrac{1}{2}R_n \qquad (12.10)$$

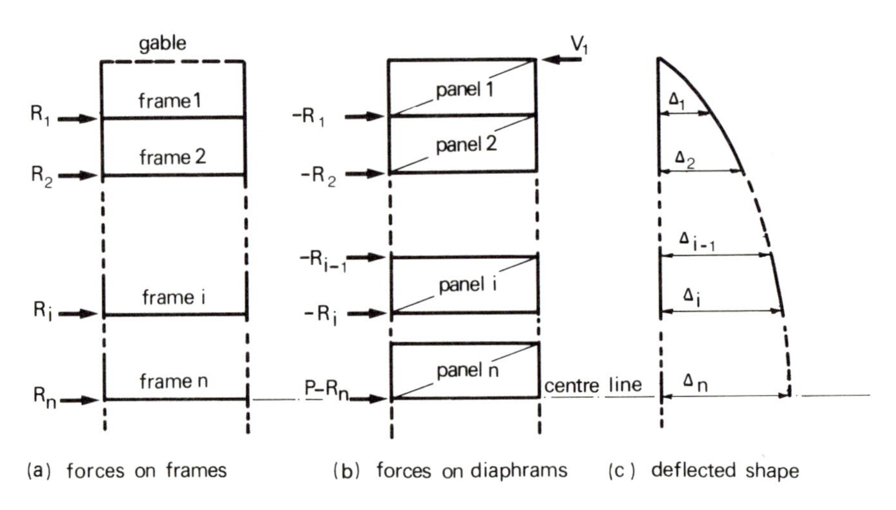

Fig. 12.4 Forces and displacements (odd number of frames, centre frame only loaded): (a) forces on frames, (b) forces on diaphragms, (c) deflected shape.

and, proceeding as before, the generalised compatibility condition becomes

$$-R_{i-1} + (\psi + 1)R_i + \psi \sum_{j=i+1}^{n} R_j - \frac{\psi}{2}R_n = \frac{\psi}{2}P \qquad (12.11)$$

It follows that the matrix representation of the problem has the same form as equation 12.6 with the exception that the right hand side vector consists of n identical terms all equal to $\frac{1}{2}\psi P$. Computationally it is convenient to treat the two cases together and to set up equations 12.6 with two right hand sides, one for all frames loaded and the other for the centre frame only loaded. Although the solution obtained for the single load case includes the full pattern of frame forces it is not usually necessary to know this and the factors tabulated in table 9.14 are solely concerned with the reduction in the force in the central frame. They take the form of an additional factor by which the value of η for the centre frame with all frames loaded should be divided to give the corresponding figure for that frame only loaded.

Finally, if there is an even number of frames, and only one frame is loaded, the critical case is when one of the two frames adjacent to the centre line is loaded and this is not a symmetrical problem. As the procedure for this case shows how the general problem of any combination of frame loads may be tackled, it is useful to consider it in a little detail. It is necessary to consider the complete structure containing n intermediate frames and for the most general load case, the forces and deflections in the frames and the diaphragms are as shown in fig. 12.5. Taking moments about the lower gable,

$$V_1 = \left(\frac{1}{n+1}\right)\sum_{j=1}^{n} (P_j - R_j)(n - j + 1) \tag{12.12}$$

Hence the shear force in typical panel i (above frame i in Fig. 12.5) is given by

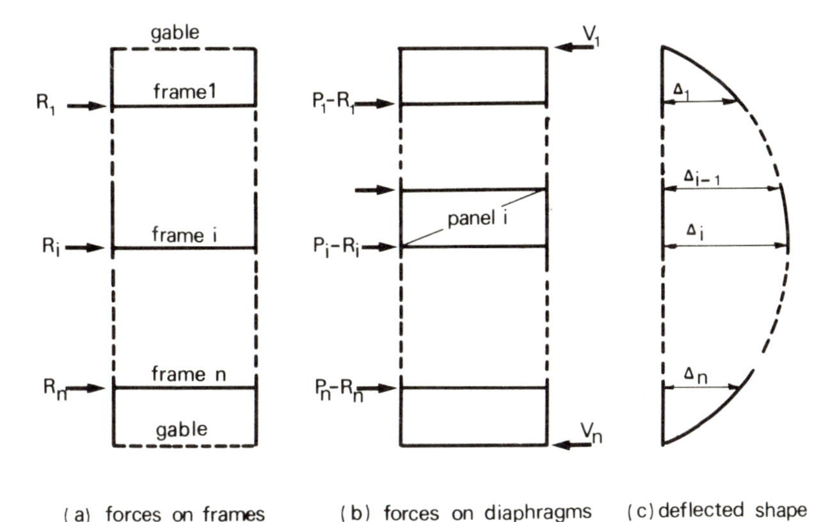

Fig. 12.5 Forces and displacements in frames and diaphragms (general case): (a) forces on frames, (b) forces on diaphragms, (c) deflected shape.

$$V_i = V_1 - \sum_{j=1}^{i-1} (P_j - R_j) \tag{12.13}$$

$$= \frac{1}{n+1}\left[\sum_{j=1}^{i-1} (P_j - R_j)(-j) + \sum_{j=i}^{n} (P_j - R_j)(n - j + 1)\right] \tag{12.14}$$

Equations 12.2, 12.3 and 12.4 again hold good so that substituting equation 12.14 into equation 12.4 gives the generalised compatibility condition as

$$\begin{aligned} R_i - R_{i-1} + \frac{\psi}{n+1}\left[\sum_{j=1}^{i-1} -jR_j + \sum_{j=1}^{n} (n-j+1)R_j\right] \\ = \frac{\psi}{n+1}\left[\sum_{j=1}^{i-1} -j\,P_j + \sum_{j=1}^{n} (n-j+1)P_j\right] \end{aligned} \tag{12.15}$$

For the particular case of interest, n is an even number and a single load appears on frame $n/2$ so that the right hand side reduces to

$$\left.\begin{aligned} &\frac{\psi}{n+1}\left(-\frac{n}{2}P\right) \quad (\text{for } i < n/2) \\ \text{or} \quad &\frac{\psi}{n+1}\left[\left(\frac{n}{2}+1\right) P\right] \quad (\text{for } i \geqslant n/2) \end{aligned}\right\} \tag{12.16}$$

The matrix equations for this latter case are therefore

$$\begin{bmatrix} \frac{n\,\psi}{n+1}+1 & \frac{(n+1)\psi}{n+1} & \frac{(n-i)\psi}{n+1} & \frac{(n-i+1)\psi}{n+1} & \frac{2\psi}{n+1} & \frac{\psi}{n+1} \\ \frac{-\psi}{n+1}-1 & \frac{(n-1)\psi}{n+1}+1 & \frac{(n-i)\psi}{n+1} & \frac{(n-i+1)\psi}{n+1} & \frac{2\psi}{n+1} & \frac{\psi}{n+1} \\ \frac{-\psi}{n+1} & \frac{-2\,\psi}{n+1} & \frac{(n-i)\psi}{n+1}+1 & \frac{(n-i+1)\psi}{n+1} & \frac{2\psi}{n+1} & \frac{\psi}{n+1} \\ \frac{-\psi}{n+1} & \frac{-2\,\psi}{n+1} & \frac{-(i-1)\,\psi}{n+1}-1 & \frac{(n-i+1)\psi}{n+1}+1 & \frac{2\psi}{n+1} & \frac{\psi}{n+1} \\ \frac{-\psi}{n+1} & \frac{-2\,\psi}{n+1} & \frac{-(i-1)\,\psi}{n+1} & \frac{-i\,\psi}{n+1} & \frac{2\psi}{n+1}+1 & \frac{\psi}{n+1} \\ \frac{-\psi}{n+1} & \frac{-2\,\psi}{n+1} & \frac{-(i-1)\,\psi}{n+1} & \frac{-i\,\psi}{n+1} & \frac{-(n-1)\psi}{n+1}-1 & \frac{\psi}{n+1}+1 \end{bmatrix} \begin{bmatrix} R_1 \\ R_2 \\ R_{i-1} \\ R_i \\ R_{n-1} \\ R_n \end{bmatrix} = \begin{bmatrix} \frac{-n\,\psi}{2(n+1)} \\ \frac{-n\,\psi}{2(n+1)} \\ \frac{-n\,\psi}{2(n+1)}^{*} \\ \frac{-n\,\psi}{2(n+1)}^{*} \\ \frac{(n+2)\psi}{2(n+1)} \\ \frac{(n+2)\psi}{2(n+1)} \end{bmatrix} P \tag{12.17}$$

Note Terms marked with an asterisk are $\frac{(n+2)\psi}{2(n+1)}$ if $i \geqslant n/2$.

Equations 12.15 and 12.17 represent elementary computational problems which can be easily programmed for a desk-top computer if solutions to problems outside the scope of the design tables are required. The results given in table 9.14 for even number of frames were obtained using the above formulation.

12.4 An alternative general solution for reduction factors

Horne has shown[1.7] that an approximation to the reduction factors η_i, sufficiently accurate for all practical purposes, can be obtained explicitly by performing an analysis which replaces the discrete resistance to sway of the individual frames by a uniformly distributed resistance. The diaphragm itself continues to act as a shear field so that the problem reduces to that of a shear field contained within an elastic medium. By solving the governing differential equation, Horne showed that if there were n intermediate frames, the reduction factor η_s for a typical frame would be approximated by

$$\eta_s = 1 - \frac{\cosh s\sqrt{\psi}}{\cosh \frac{1}{2}(n+1)\sqrt{\psi}} \tag{12.18}$$

where s is the frame number counted from the centre of the structure. For an odd number of frames $s = 0, 1, 2, \ldots, (n-1)/2$ and for an even number of frames $s = \frac{1}{2}, \frac{3}{2}, \frac{5}{2}, \ldots, (n-1)/2$. A somewhat more complex expression was also obtained for the case of a single frame loaded, namely

$$\eta_s = \frac{2(1 - e^{-\sqrt{(\psi/2)}})}{\coth\left(\frac{n+1}{2} + s\right)\sqrt{\psi} + \coth\left(\frac{n+1}{2} - s\right)\sqrt{\psi}} \tag{12.19}$$

Equations 12.18 and 12.19 may be used whenever tables 9.13 and 9.14 are inapplicable.

12.5 Tests on a semi-full-size pitched roof portal frame structure

In the 1960s when stressed skin theory was being developed, interest was concentrated on the influence of the cladding in reducing the stresses and deflections in conventional construction. Consequently a number of large-scale tests on complete clad structures were undertaken in order to evaluate this effect. The first of these was carried out at the University of Manchester and reported by Bryan and El-Dakhakhni in 1964.[2.2] The general arrangement of this test in shown in fig. 12.6. Figure 12.7 shows the structure set up in the laboratory ready for testing.

Figure 12.8(a) shows details of the individual frames which were fabricated from 76 mm × 76 mm × 12.6 kg/m R.S.J. The stanchion bases could be either fixed or pinned as shown in fig. 12.8(b) so that the effect of the cladding on frames of two different stiffnesses could be investigated. The sheeting was 26 gauge standard 76 mm arc and tangent profile which was fastened to 38 mm × 38 mm × 6.2 mm angle purlins with self-tapping screws at 229 mm centres (i.e. through every third corrugation trough). Though not stated in the original paper, the seams were fastened through their crests with 6 mm nuts and bolts at 457 mm centres. No attempt was made to promote additional stressed skin action by the addition

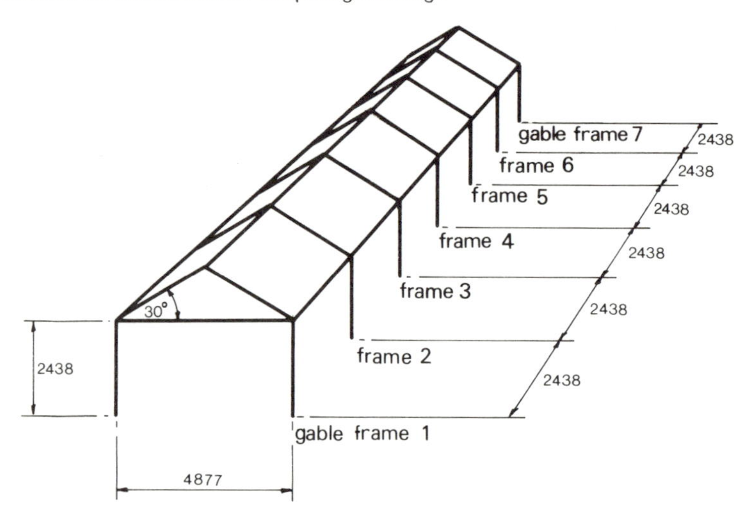

Fig. 12.6 General arrangement of structure.

Fig. 12.7 Structure ready to test.

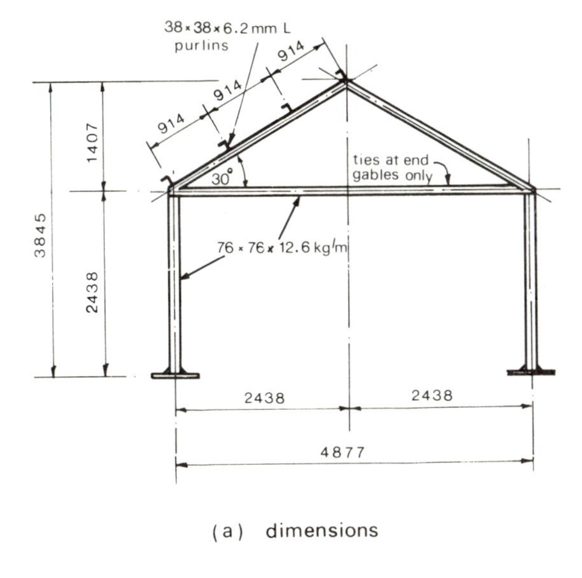

(a) dimensions

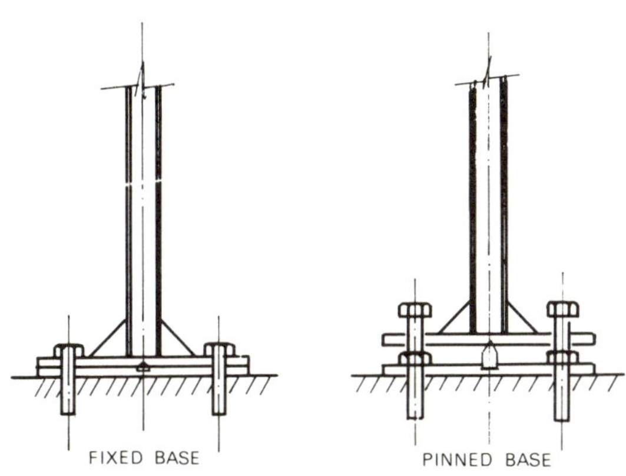

(b) alternative base details

Fig. 12.8 Dimensions and details of frames: (a) dimensions, (b) alternative base details.

of shear connectors or the like so that the sheeting was fastened to the supporting structure on two sides only.

12.5.1 Strength and stiffness of cladding panels

After completion of the testing of the complete building, two central panels from one roof slope were detached from the remainder of the shed and tested horizontally as a two bay diaphragm beam subject to a single central point load. The general

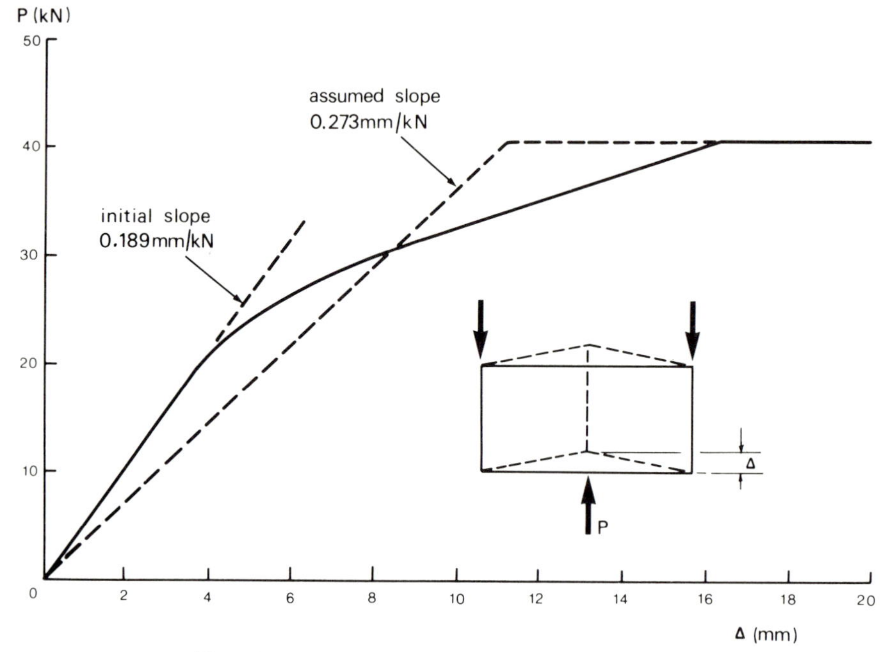

Fig. 12.9 Load–deflection curve for roof panel.

arrangement is shown in fig. 12.9 together with the load–deflection curve obtained. The shear flexibilities used in the subsequent calculations, namely 0.377 mm/kN in the elastic range and 0.546 mm/kN for the elastic–plastic calculations up to failure are also shown. It will be appreciated that at the time of this test, no comprehensive theory for the analysis of the test results was available. Moreover, not all of the parameters necessary for current calculation procedures were measured so that subsequent interpretation of the test results is difficult. However, it would appear that the design expressions given in section 9.3 give a calculated flexibility of approximately 0.66 mm/kN which accords with recent experience in which small diaphragms fastened to the supporting structure through alternate or every third corrugation appear to be stiffer than the theory would predict.

Failure of the diaphragm was by buckling at a load of 20.5 kN. The calculated buckling strength according to section 9.3, however, was 34.1 kN which means that in the test the sheeting buckled prematurely. A photograph of the buckled roof panel (taken at failure of the complete structure) is shown in fig. 12.10. The buckling wave has passed between the fasteners connecting the sheeting to the intermediate purlins and it is clear that these fasteners were not sufficiently close together to confine the buckle to the region between two purlins as assumed by the theory. This is a somewhat unusual diaphragm incorporating very thin sheeting of shallow depth and for such cases it is strongly recommended that if buckling is at all critical the sheet to purlin fasteners should not be spaced in more than alternate corrugations.

Fig. 12.10 End roof panel at failure of structure.

12.5.2 Response of the complete structure in the elastic range

The shed was tested by applying large point loads to the apexes of the frames. Each frame was loaded with 12.5 kN which produced a maximum stress in the pinned base frames of 162N/mm^2 and which was approximately equivalent to a uniformly distributed load of 2.01 kN/m^2. Deflection readings were taken during loading and, in addition, the frames were fully instrumented with electrical resistance strain gauges and Maihak accoustic gauges so that the bending moment diagrams could be drawn. Full details of the results are given in references 2.1 and 2.2. The spread stiffness of the frame was calculated to be k_{sp} = 1.60 mm/kN with a pinned base and k_{sp} = 1.09 mm/kN with a fixed base and the equivalent horizontal shear flexibility of the roof panels was c_h = 0.377 sec^2 30° = 0.502 mm/kN (see section 4.2.2). The relative flexibility $\psi_{sp} = c_h/k_{sp}$ was therefore equal to 0.315 for the pinned based frame and 0.462 for the fixed base frame and the reduction factors η for the frame forces follow directly from table 9.13. Agreement between the theoretical predictions and the experimental results was in all respects excellent and the results can be summarised by the comparison between the theoretical and experimental reduction factors η given in table 12.1.

12.5.3 Behaviour up to failure

After the completion of comprehensive testing in the elastic range the structure was finally loaded to failure. The structure was also analysed by computer as described

Table 12.1 Comparison of reduction factors for pitched roof portal frame structure

		All frames loaded		One frame loaded	
		Theory	Test	Theory	Test
Pinned base	frame 2	0.384	0.40	0.633 / 2.52	0.66 / 2.41
	frame 3	0.575	0.60		
	frame 4	0.633	0.66		
Fixed base	frame 2	0.463	0.48		
	frame 3	0.675	0.70		
	frame 4	0.736	0.76		

in sections 4.3 and 4.5. Experimental and theoretical load-deflection curves are shown in fig. 12.11. Corresponding curves for the unclad structure are also shown for the purposes of comparison. Bearing in mind the approximate nature of the bi-linear representation of shear panel behaviour as well as the neglect of such second order effects as strain hardening and frame instability, the agreement between the experimental and theoretical curves is remarkably good. The theoretical ultimate load is 35.9 kN. The maximum load appearing on the experimental curves is 37.4 kN although the maximum load carried[2.2] was 40.3 kN, at a greatly increased

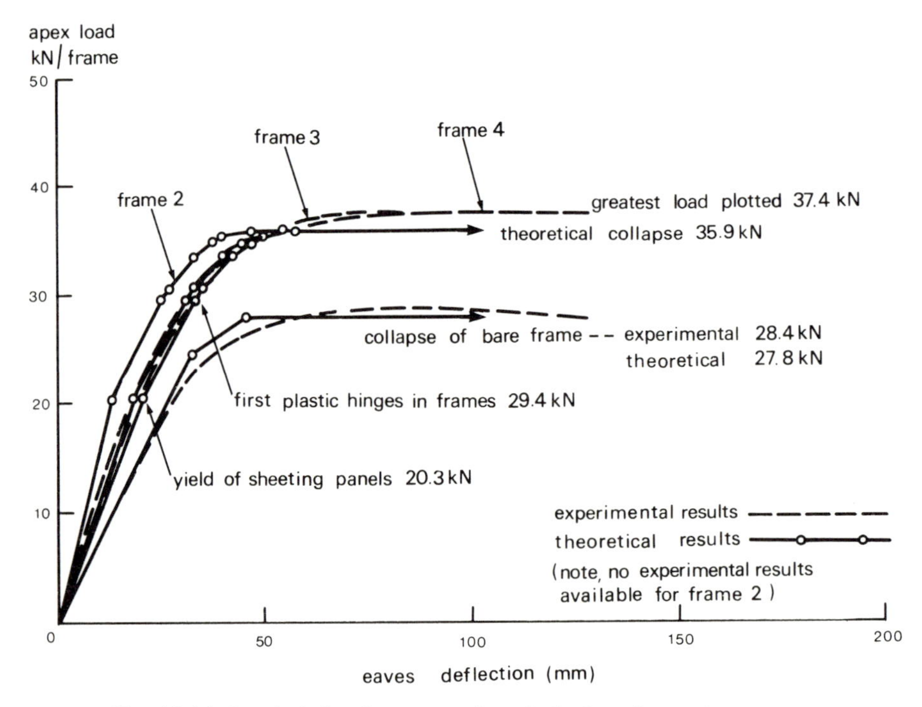

Fig. 12.11 Load–deflection curves for pitched roof portal structure.

deflection. Photographs show pronounced buckling of the sheeting panels and gross deformations. The theoretical analysis shows that the end panels of sheeting failed at a load of 20.3 kN before the first plastic hinges formed in the central frame at a load of 29.4 kN. The theoretical order of formation of plastic hinges in the frames is shown in fig. 12.12 illustrating the way in which plasticity spread progressively towards the outer frames. Clearly the experimental structure failed in a complete, three-dimensional plastic collapse mechanism.

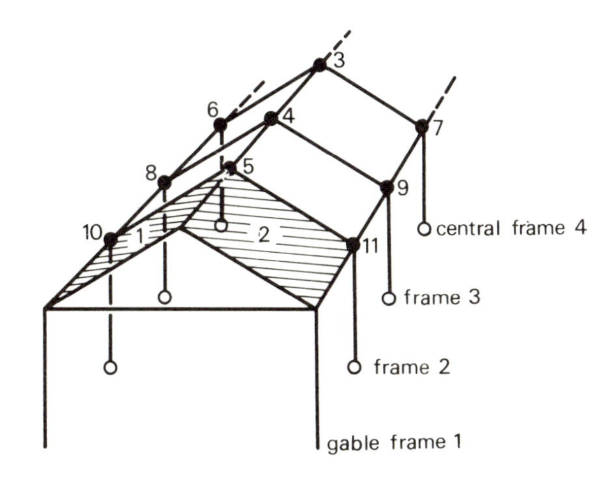

Fig. 12.12 Order of formation of plastic hinges at collapse.

12.6 Full-scale tests on an actual structure[2.5]

At a similar time to the laboratory test reported in section 12.5 it became possible to carry out on-site tests on a structure of 150 ft (45.7 m) span which was under construction at Garstang in Lancashire. The structure is shown in fig. 12.13 and was 335 ft 0 in. (102 m) long, having two rigid gable frames and nine intermediate frames. The main frames were spaced at 33 ft 6 in. (10.2 m) centres and details of an individual frame are shown in fig. 12.14. The frames were designed as having pinned bases but once the concrete floor slab had been cast during construction they behaved as though partially fixed, a factor which made interpretation of the test results rather difficult.

The roof cladding consisted of 20 gauge trapezoidally profiled aluminium decking with a depth of 2.53 in. (64.3 mm), insulated with a 1 inch (25 mm) layer of cork and covered with mineral felt. In each roof slope there were two stretches of patent glazing extending practically the full length of the building. The roof construction was quite conventional, no attempt being made to produce a design showing a high degree of stressed skin action. Indeed, the use of a relatively deep profile in aluminium fastened on two sides only resulted in a particularly flexible roof deck. As a late change in the design specification resulted in a frame with a load factor of 2.24 against collapse, the frame was extremely stiff and this, combined

Fig. 12.13 Steel framework under construction.

with particularly flexible roof sheeting, resulted in a structure that was unusually insensitive to stressed skin action.

The frames were loaded by means of a 10 ton (100 kN) load which could be hung from the apex of each frame as shown in fig. 12.15. Provision was made for up to 3 of the 9 intermediate frames to be loaded simultaneously. Results for the case of all frames loaded simultaneously were obtained using the principle of superposition. During loading, deflections were measured and frame bending moments could also be determined from electrical resistance strain gauges mounted on the frames prior to construction. Typical results are shown in figs. 12.16 and 12.17. Because of the practical factors referred to above it is not possible to give full theoretical comparisons but it is clear that even with the high relative flexibility of the sheeting there is a significant reduction in the bare frame moments. For frames loaded individually the measured deflections were about 0.4 of the bare frame values and for all frames loaded together they were about 0.5 of the bare frame values.

12.7 Tests on a rectangular portal frame building[2.10]

The test on a rectangular portal frame building was conducted on an outdoor site at Barton, near Manchester. The structure was conceived as a scaled down representation of a typical rectangular portal frame building with no attempt being made to modify details in order to promote stressed skin action. As a consequence, the

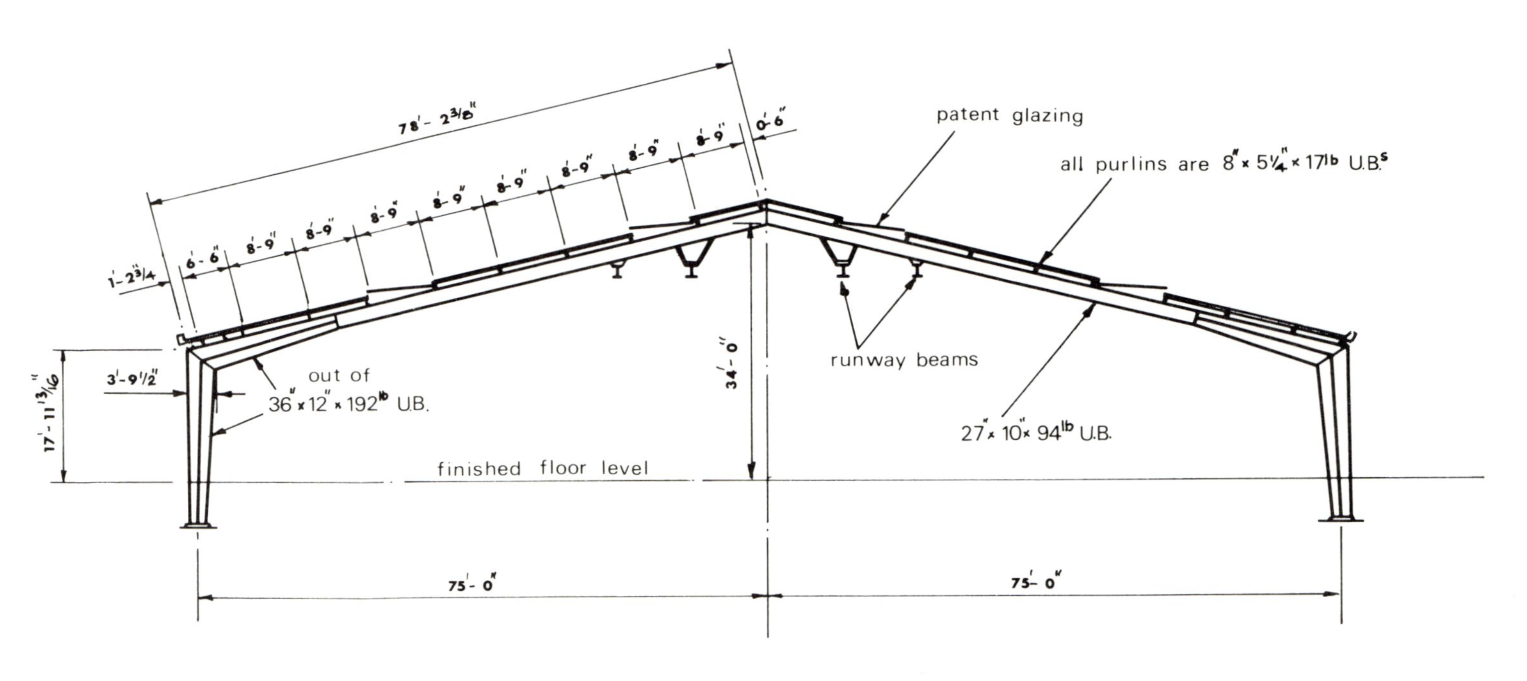

Fig. 12.14 Typical steel frame.

Fig. 12.15 Apex point load.

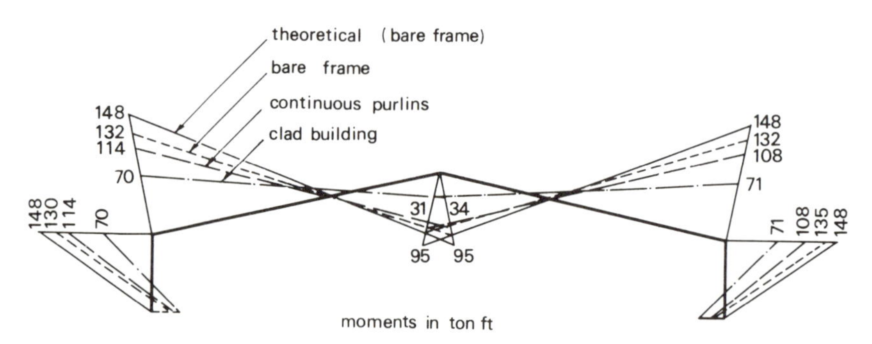

Fig. 12.16 Bending moment diagram due to a 10 ton load on frame 7.

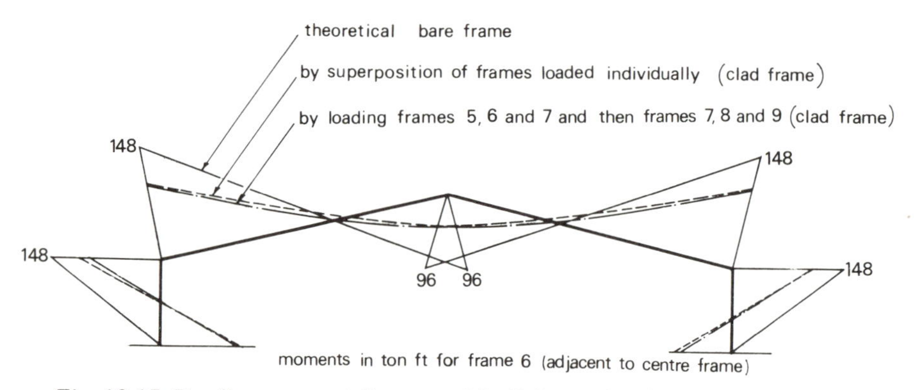

Fig. 12.17 Bending moment diagram with all frames loaded simultaneously.

sheeting panels again contributed to the behaviour by indirect shear transfer. During the series of tests on this building, interest centred on the contribution of the cladding in resisting side load simulated by point loads at the level of the eaves. The general arrangement of the building is shown in fig. 12.18 and a photograph of the complete structure ready to test is shown in fig. 12.19. The frames were fabricated from 203 mm X 133 mm X 25 kg/m U.B. sections with an average full plastic

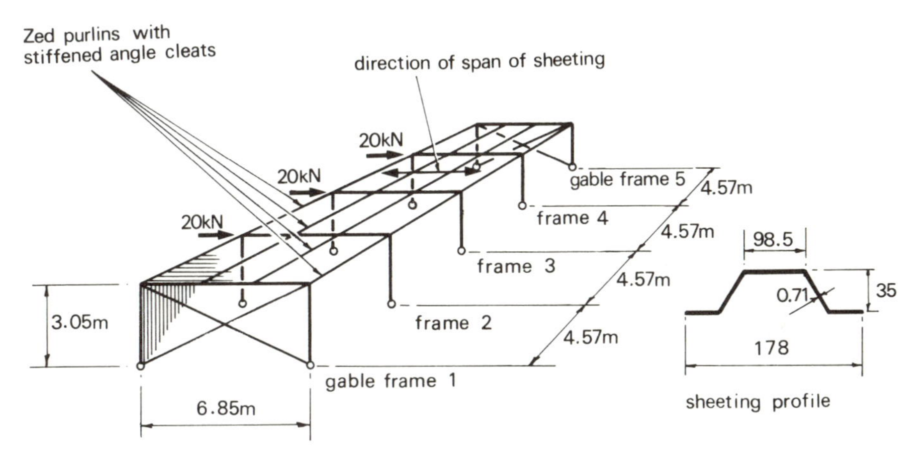

Fig. 12.18 General arrangement of rectangular framed building.

Fig. 12.19 Sheeted building ready to test.

moment of resistance obtained experimentally as 78.3 kNm. The diagonal bracing shown in the end gables was removable so that the gable shear could be carried by either the braced frame or the frame and gable sheeting acting as a shear panel. The properties of the panels of sheeting were calculated, and no attempt was made to test complete panels in this instance.

Two separate collapse tests were carried out on this building in order to investigate different aspects of its behaviour. In each test, equal side loads at the level of the eaves were applied to the three intermediate frames and increased in steps until failure of the structure occurred. For the first test, the diagonal bracing was removed from the gable ends so that the end frames were stiffened by sheeting panels consisting of metal coated steel sheeting 0.71 mm thick in widths of 686 mm fixed to angle sheeting rails by 6.1 mm o.d. self-tapping screws in alternate corrugations. The pitch of the corrugations was 172 mm, the depth 35 mm and the seams of the sheets were fastened by 4.8 mm aluminium blind rivets at 457 mm centres. This construction resulted in a gable panel with a calculated flexibility of 0.800 mm/kN and ultimate shear strength of 18.9 kN corresponding to failure at the sheet to sheeting rail fasteners at the sheet ends.

The roof sheeting was similar to the gable sheeting in both cross-section and fixing details and was carried on four Z-purlins. Each panel had a calculated flexibility of 0.676 mm/kN and an ultimate shear strength of 16.8 kN again corresponding to failure in the sheet to purlin fasteners at the sheet ends. The calculated flexibilities and ultimate strengths have been amended since previous publications of the results of this test.[2.10,2.25] This reflects improvements in the design expressions in recent years. In particular the importance of the failure mode involving the sheet to supporting member fasteners at the sheet ends in diaphragms subject to indirect shear transfer has only recently been recognised and this results in a reduction in the calculated design strength of these panels. For some of the tests, a superimposed load of 0.718 N/m^2 was applied by means of sandbags as shown in fig. 12.20. This allowed some consideration of the interaction effects of combined vertical and side loading.

As the reduction factors described in section 12.2 are not applicable to structures which have flexible (sheeted) gables, the analysis was carried out by computer using the plane frame simulation described in sections 4.3 and 4.5. The mathematical model for the half structure, utilising symmetry, is shown in fig. 12.21. For this analysis, the roof panels are yielding ties having a cross-sectional area given by $A = L/(c\ E) = 6850/(0.676 \times 207) = 49.0$ mm^2 and a yield strength of 16.8 kN. The gable panel was likewise represented by a tie having an area of 41.3 mm^2 and a yield strength of 18.9 kN. During the test, strain gauge readings allowed the frame bending moment to be measured and readings of sway deflection were also taken. As a consequence a full comparison between theory and experiment in the elastic range is available and this is summarised in table 12.2. The calculations clearly fall within the expected range of accuracy of such an experiment. Furthermore, the effect of the superimposed load is small but beneficial. As expected, the applied vertical load restricted free distortion of the sheeting profile with a consequent reduction in deflections. Theoretical load-deflection curves to failure, together with

Fig. 12.20 Superload of 718 N/m^2 on roof.

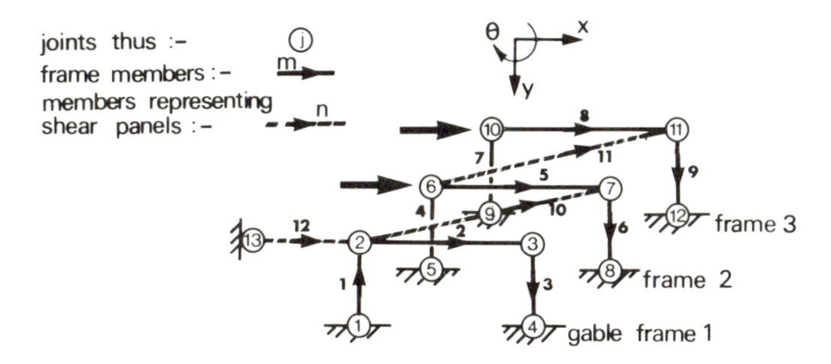

Fig. 12.21 Computer analysis of rectangular building with flexible gables.

the corresponding experimental results are shown in fig. 12.22. In view of the nature of the test results, a second theoretical analysis was also carried out in which the ultimate strength of the roof panels was increased to that for seam failure, namely 42.4 kN. It can be seen that in the range between first fastener yield and failure, the experimental curves lie between the alternative theoretical curves.

Two factors emerge from a consideration of these curves. The first is that although the end sheet to purlin fasteners did yield during the test and some tearing of the sheeting at these fasteners was observed, this caused only a slight non-linearity in the load-deflection curve. The structure continued to accept load without significant distress while the critical fasteners redistributed load to those adjacent

Table 12.2 Calculated and measured frame response under a side load of 20 kN per frame

		Horizontal deflection (mm)			Eaves bending moment (kNm)	
		Gable frames 1 and 5	Frames 2 and 4	Frame 3	Frames 2 and 4	Frame 3
Bare frame	calculated	–	41.3	41.3	30.5	30.5
	measured	–	40.5	40.5	28.9	28.9
Complete building	calculated	8.8	19.2	22.4	14.2	16.5
	measured (no superload)	9.0	22.9	25.2	15.3	16.5
	measured (with superload)	9.3	20.2	22.3	15.2	15.6

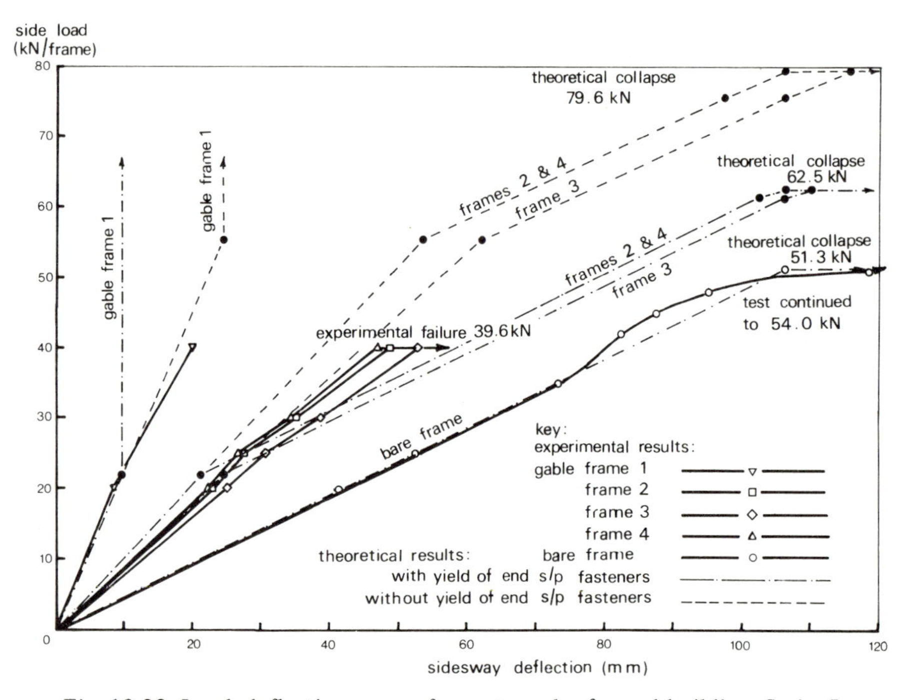

Fig. 12.22 Load–deflection curves for rectangular framed building, Series I.

to them. This test therefore suggests that stressed skin structures are particularly robust with respect to this failure mode although it is not suggested that it should receive different treatment from the more ductile seam failure modes. Secondly, as a consequence of the redistribution of load during yielding of the end sheet to purlin fasteners, the forces at the seams in the end panels increased and failure of the structure took place when, at a load of 39.6 kN per frame, the blind rivets in the side seams of the end panel of roof sheeting sheared, accompanied by tearing of the sheeting in the sheet to purlin fasteners. Most of the load carried by shear of the sheeting panels was immediately shed to the frames with a sudden increase of deflection and some secondary damage, and the test was terminated.

Failure of the structure occurred due to non-ductile fracture of the seam fasteners at a comparatively early stage of loading. The yield load of the bare frame was approximately 44.6 kN and so the roof sheeting panels did not possess sufficient ductility for the yield load of the bare frame to be reached without the panels suffering severe damage. This undesirable state of affairs could have been avoided by the use of monel metal instead of aluminium blind rivets.

For the second test at Barton, the Z-purlins were replaced by angles and the spacing of the sheet to purlin and seam fasteners was halved. This resulted in a reduction of the shear flexibility of the roof sheeting panels to 0.249 mm/kN and an increase in the ultimate shear strength of the end panels to 21.0 kN for failure in the end fasteners and 70.6 kN for seam failure. The gables were diagonally braced, making them effectively rigid in their own planes. In the elastic range of loading, the full comparison between theory and experiment is summarised in table 12.3. The calculations again fall within the expected range of accuracy of such an experiment. The effect of the superimposed load is again small.

Table 12.3 Calculated and measured frame response under a side load of 20 kN per frame (Test Series II)

		Horizontal deflection (mm)			Eaves bending moment (kNm)	
		Gable frames 1 and 5	Frames 2 and 4	Frame 3	Frames 2 and 4	Frame 3
Complete building	calculated	0	6.3	8.4	4.6	6.2
	measured (no superload)	1.8	5.9	7.6	4.9	5.3
	measured (with superload)	2.5	6.6	6.6	5.1	5.7

Experimental and theoretical load-deflection curves to failure are shown in fig. 12.23. As before, two sets of theoretical curves are given and the experimental results fall between them. It must be concluded from this that the structure is again very robust with respect to failure in the end sheet to purlin fasteners and significant non-linearity in the load-deflection curve does not occur until a load of approximately twice the theoretical load for yield at these fasteners. It is immediately obvious from the load-deflection curves that, despite the continued use of aluminium blind rivets as seam fasteners, the sheeting panels possessed considerable and adequate ductility. The failure load of the test frame was 85.1 kN which is considerably higher than the theoretical value of 65.3 kN and in fact closer to the

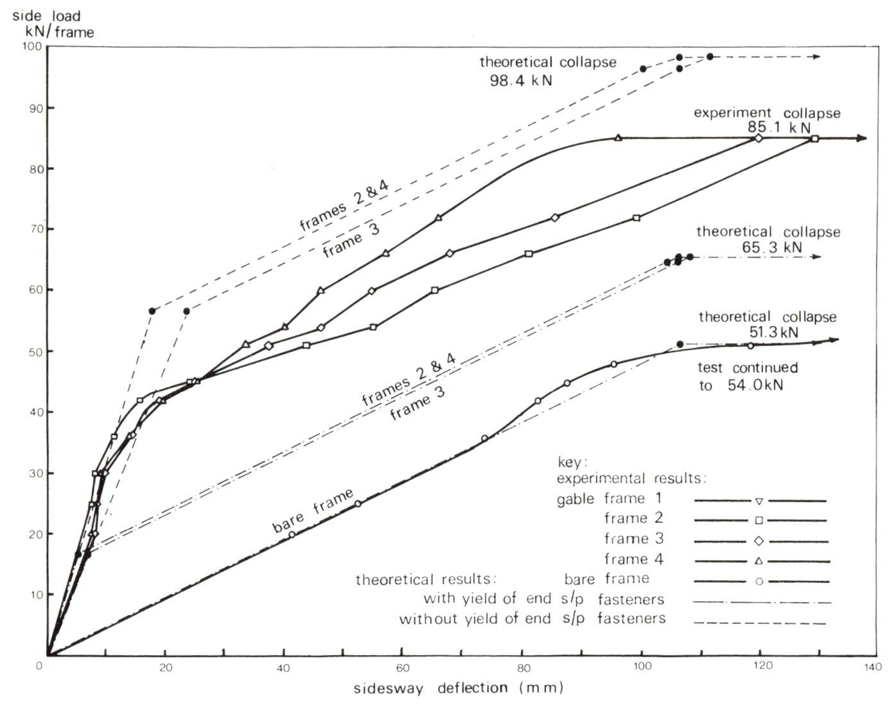

Fig. 12.23 Load-deflection curves for rectangular framed building, Series II.

alternative theoretical value of 98.4 kN which neglects the calculated panel failure mode in the end sheet to purlin fasteners. During the test it was noticed that the foot of the leeward stanchion of frame 2 was tending to lift and efforts to restrain this tendency were not completely successful. It is for this reason that frame 2 shows a higher deflection than frames 3 and 4 and the test results must have been influenced to some extent by the redistribution of diaphragm action caused by this mishap. Notwithstanding this eventuality, the sheeting panels in the end bays sustained plastic shear deformations of the order of 75–100 mm which reflects a considerable amount of ductility in the panels.

12.8 Full-scale laboratory tests on a pitched roof portal building[2.19]

Despite the considerable size of this structure, this test was carried out indoors in the Fitton Structures Laboratory of the University of Salford. Figure 12.24 shows the general arrangement of the structure and loading. The structure differed from the previous two in a number of significant respects. First it was conceived as a stressed skin design and designed accordingly. The columns were from 178 mm × 102 mm R.S.J., the rafters were from 152 mm × 89 mm R.S.J. and the purlins were 140 mm × 45 mm × 2 mm cold rolled Z-sections. These sections represent a saving in weight of about 25% in the main frames when compared with the most economic conventional design. Because of the stressed skin concept, shear connectors were

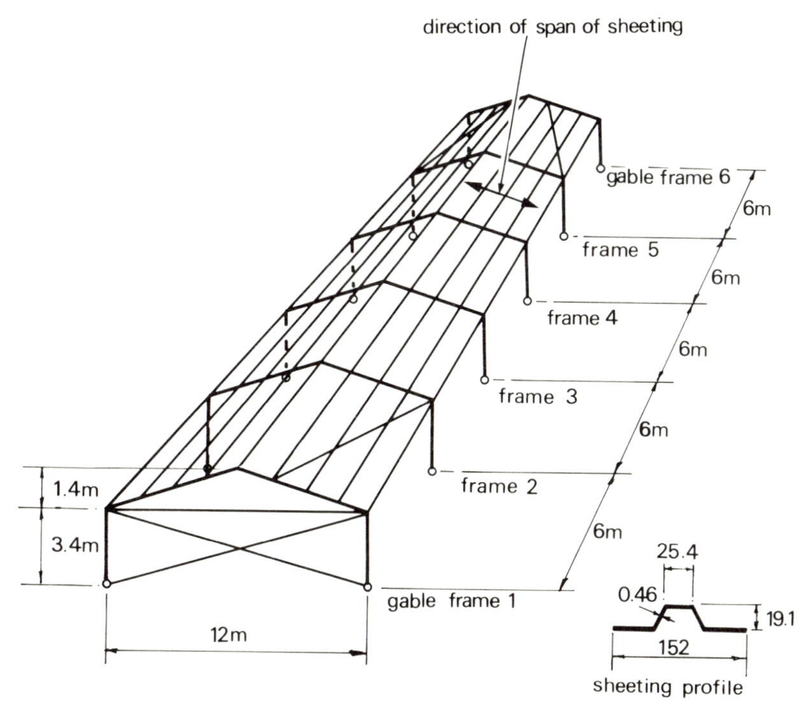

Fig. 12.24 General arrangement of pitched roof portal structure.

used to connect the sheeting panels to the frames so that the panels acted by direct shear transfer. An additional new feature was that translucent plastic sheet roof lights were introduced amounting to $12\frac{1}{2}\%$ of the roof area. Diagonal bracing was incorporated in the end bays in the plane of the sheeting so that the complete end bay sheeting panels were considerably stronger and stiffer than the others. The steel roof sheeting was 0.46 mm thick Everclad L5 and was fastened to the purlins by 6.1 mm self-tapping screws in every corrugation. The seam fasteners were 4.8 mm aluminium blind rivets at 250 mm centres and there were sixteen 6.1 mm self-tapping screws per rafter fastening the sheets to the shear connectors.

The structure was designed for agricultural loading, the total load on each frame at the working load being 42.5 kN split up into a series of point loads at the purlins as shown in fig. 12.25. During the tests, the vertical load was applied through the roof sheeting by timber and steel grillages and hydraulic jacks. The structure was also investigated for stiffness under two side loads of 2.5 kN acting in the same direction at each eave. These side loads were applied by means of wire ropes which passed over pulleys and which were loaded with dead weights.

A general view of the building prepared for testing is shown in fig. 12.26. The frame in the foreground was not part of the complete structure but was an individual unclad frame which was tested for comparison purposes. It was connected to the clad structure by loosely bolted purlins in order to ensure adequate lateral stability. The structure was instrumented with strain gauges and provision was made for the

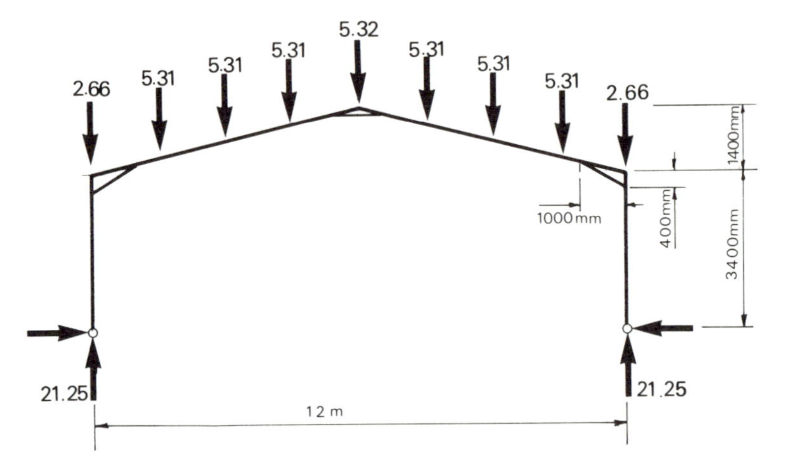

Fig. 12.25 Design loads per frame.

measurement of deflections so that a complete record of the behaviour in the elastic range was obtained. The structure was finally loaded to collapse and fig. 12.27 shows the building at the completion of testing. The plastic hinges in the frames are clearly visible.

12.8.1 Strength and flexibility of roof sheeting

As the calculation of the strength and flexibility of the panels of roof sheeting in this case is influenced by the presence of both the roof lights and the bracing in the

Fig. 12.26 General view of test building.

Fig. 12.27 Building after final test to collapse.

end bays it is important to review it in some detail. The arrangement of an internal panel with roof lights is shown in fig. 12.28. The roof lights were simply panels of translucent plastic sheeting which had the same profile as the remainder of the roof cladding and which were lapped into the lengths of roof sheeting in the usual way. Such translucent panels are much more flexible than the sheeting they replace and, for design purposes, a suitable safe procedure is to neglect their stiffness and strength and to treat them as unframed openings. The design procedure is given in section 5.5.1 and requires that the strength and flexibility be first calculated for the panel in the absence of openings, according to section 9.5 and then these quantities are modified in accordance with the pattern of roof lights.

The parameters in the design expressions are as follows:

a = frame spacing = 6000 mm
A = cross-sectional area of purlin = 494 mm^2
b = rafter length = 6160 mm
d = pitch of corrugations = 152 mm
E = modulus of elasticity = 207 kN/mm^2
F_p = ultimate strength of sheet to purlin fasteners = 2.76 kN
F_s = ultimate strength of seam fasteners = 1.6 kN
F_{sc} = ultimate strength of shear connector fasteners = 2.76 kN
h = height of profile = 19.1 mm
$\bar{K}_1$ = sheeting constant (every trough fastened) = 0.048
n = number of panels in length of building = 5
n_b = number of sheet lengths within depth = 2
n_f = number of sheet to purlin fasteners per sheet width = 6

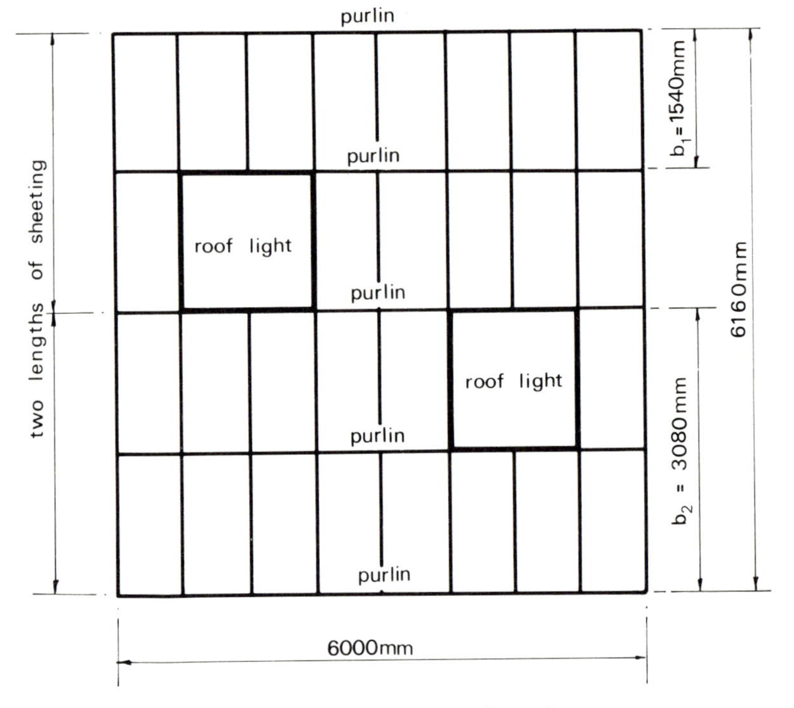

Fig. 12.28 Typical roof panel.

n_p = total number of purlins = 5
n_s = number of seam fasteners per side lap = 25
n_{sc} = number of sheet to shear connector fasteners per rafter = 16
n_{sh} = number of sheet widths per panel = 8
p = pitch of sheet to purlin fasteners = 152 mm
s_p = slip per sheet to purlin fastener per unit load = 0.35 mm/kN
s_s = slip per seam fastener per unit load = 0.35 mm/kN
s_{sc} = slip per shear connector fastener per unit load = 0.35 mm/kN
t = sheet thickness = 0.46 mm
α_1 = 1.00
α_2 = 0.67
α_3 = 0.80
} correction factors, see tables 9.1 and 9.3
Note α_1 is based on the number of purlins per sheet length = 3
α_4 = $(1 + 0.3\, n_b) = 1.6$
β_3 = $(n_f - 1)/n_f = 5/6 = 0.833$
β_1 = 0.71, see table 9.5
ν = Poisson's ratio = 0.25

∴ Calculation of seam strength:

$$V_{\text{ult}} = n_s F_s + \frac{\beta_1}{\beta_3} n_p F_p = (25 \times 1.6) + \left(\frac{0.71}{0.833} \times 5 \times 2.76\right) = 51.76 \text{ kN}$$

Note F_s and F_p are *ultimate* values of fastener strength and V_{ult} is therefore the ultimate value of the seam strength for legitimate comparison with the test results. Calculation of strength at shear connectors: $V_{ult} = n_{sc} F_{sc} = 16 \times 2.76 = 44.16$ kN. $\therefore$ Design shear capacity is $V^* = 44.16$ kN. The strength in shear buckling is not critical and the requirement for sheet to purlin fasteners is $0.8\ b\ F_p/(p\ \alpha_3) \geqslant V^*$ and $0.8\ b\ F_p/(p\ \alpha_3) = 0.8 \times 6160 \times 2.76/(152 \times 0.80) = 111.9$ kN so that the requirement is satisfied.

Calculation of flexibility components:

$$c_{1.1} = \frac{a\,d^{2.5}\,\alpha_1\,\alpha_4\,\bar{K}_1}{Et^{2.5}\,b^2} = \frac{6000 \times 152^{2.5} \times 1.0 \times 1.6 \times 0.048}{207 \times 0.46^{2.5} \times 6160^2} = 0.1164$$

$$c_{1.2} = \frac{2a\,\alpha_2\,(1+\nu)\,[1+(2h/d)]}{E\,t\,b}$$

$$= \frac{2 \times 6000 \times 0.67 \times 1.25 \times [1 + (2 \times 19.1/152)]}{6160 \times 207 \times 0.46} = 0.0214$$

$$c_{2.1} = \frac{2a\,s_p\,p\,\alpha_3}{b^2} = \frac{2 \times 6000 \times 0.35 \times 152 \times 0.80}{6160^2} = 0.0135$$

$$c_{2.2} = \frac{2\,s_s\,s_p\,(n_{sh}-1)}{2\,n_s s_p + \beta_1\,n_p s_s} = \frac{2 \times 0.35 \times 0.35 \times 7}{(2 \times 25 \times 0.35) + (0.71 \times 5 \times 0.35)}$$

$$= 0.0915$$

$$c_{2.3} = \frac{8\,s_{sc}\,(n-1)}{n_{sc}\,n^2} = \frac{8 \times 0.35 \times 4}{16 \times 5^2} = 0.0280$$

$$c_3 = \frac{n^2 a^3 \alpha_3}{4.8\,EAb^2} = \frac{5^2 \times 6000^3 \times 0.8}{4.8 \times 207 \times 494 \times 6160^2} = 0.2319$$

$$\text{Total flexibility} = 0.5027 \text{ mm/kN}$$

Note The expression for $c_{2.3}$ differs from that in section 9.5 since it assumes the same number of sheet/shear connector fasteners at both the gables and intermediate frames.

12.8.2 Modification for effect of openings on strength and stiffness according to section 5.5.1

Each opening cuts a seam and divides the panel into two sections whose depths are $b_1 = 1540$ mm and $b_2 = 3080$ mm. $\therefore \Sigma b_i^2 = 1540^2 + 3080^2 = 11\,858\,000$ mm^2. Noting that all fastenings at sheet ends, including those to the translucent panels at the openings, pass through every corrugation, $\bar{K}$ is constant and if the total shear force in the panel is $V^* = 44.16$ kN, the force in the region of depth 1540 mm is $V_1 = 44.16 \times 1540^2/11\,858\,000 = 8.832$ kN. The strength of this region is $(\beta_1/\beta_3)\,n_{p1}F_p + n_{s1}F_s = [(0.71/0.833) \times 2 \times 2.76] + (6 \times 1.6) = 14.3$ kN. As the strength is greater than the load, there is no reduction in carrying capacity in this region.

Similarly, the shear force in the region of depth 3080 mm is $V_2 = 44.16 \times 3080^2/11\,858\,000 = 35.33$ kN and the strength of this region is $(\beta_1/\beta_3)\,n_{p2}F_p + n_{s2}F_s = [(0.71/0.833) \times 3 \times 2.76] + (13 \times 1.6) = 27.9$ kN. This is less than the load attracted so that the calculated diaphragm strength in the absence of the openings must be reduced in proportion to give $V^* = 44.16 \times 27.9/35.33 = 34.8$ kN.

However, in the test on the complete building, failure took place in the shear connector fasteners and it may be concluded that, possibly with the benefit of some redistribution of load, the translucent panels did not weaken the structure nearly as much as the above calculation predicts. The method of analysis for diaphragms with openings is itself conservative and the inclusion of a plastic panel is not as weakening as the provision of a roof light arrangement with no strength in the plane of the roof. Consequently, for the analysis of the complete building, in order to obtain more reasonable comparison between theory and experiment, the ultimate strength of the panels was taken to be the value for failure at the shear connectors, namely 44.16 kN. The factor of α_h for the increase in the flexibility component $c_{1.1}$ is given by

$$\alpha_h = \frac{1}{a}\sum_j a_{sj} + \frac{1}{a}\sum_k a_{hk}\frac{b^2}{\sum_i b_i^2}$$

$$= \frac{3000}{6000} + \left(\frac{3000}{6000} \times \frac{6160^2}{11\,858\,000}\right) = 2.100$$

Consequently, in the panel with openings $c_{1.1} = 0.1164 \times 2.100 = 0.2444$ mm/kN and the total flexibility becomes $c = 0.6307$ mm/kN.

12.8.3 Strength and stiffness of end panels including bracing

As the end bays of the roof incorporated erection bracing, it is necessary to take this into account in order to obtain a true evaluation of the stiffening effect of the roof panels. Furthermore, it is helpful to give some thought to the most effective way to include such bracing in a stressed skin structure. Since the sheeting acts as a shear panel, the top purlin of fig. 12.28 will be in compression. If the end roof panels are braced, and the bracing taken to the apex of the gable frame, then the top purlins will be in compression from this cause also. For this reason, the bracing is taken to the second purlin point as shown in fig. 12.29.

Due to the bracing alone, the shear flexibility is given by:

$$c_{\text{bracing}} = \frac{\delta U}{\delta P} = \sum \frac{FL}{AE} \cdot \frac{\delta F}{\delta P}$$

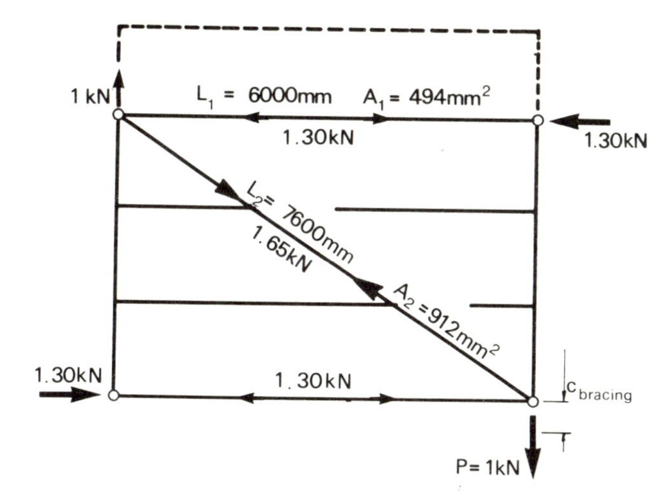

Fig. 12.29 Arrangement of bracing in end roof panel.

$$= \frac{2 \times 1.30 \times 6000 \times 1.30}{494 \times 207} + \frac{1.65 \times 7600 \times 1.65}{912 \times 207}$$

$$= 0.20 + 0.11 = 0.31 \text{ mm/kN}$$

If an increase of 50% of this flexibility is allowed due to slip at the bolted connections, then $c_{\text{bracing}} = 0.46$ mm/kN. The stiffness of the end roof panel is the combined stiffness of the bracing and sheeting. It follows that in the end panel (between frames 1 and 2 in fig. 12.24) omitting for the moment the bending flexibility c_3, a shear deflection of 1 mm induces a shear resistance in the sheeting of $1/c_{\text{sheeting}} = 1/0.399 = 2.51$ kN, and a shear resistance in the bracing of $1/c_{\text{bracing}} = 1/0.46 = 2.17$ kN. The total shear resistance of panel 1-2 is therefore 4.68 kN, and the shear flexibility $c_{1\text{-}2} = 1/4.68 = 0.214$ mm/kN. This may be expressed as

$$\frac{1}{c_{1\text{-}2}} = \frac{1}{c_{\text{sheeting}}} + \frac{1}{c_{\text{bracing}}}$$

To this must be added the 'bending' flexibility c_3 giving the total equivalent flexibility in the end panels of $c_{1\text{-}2} = 0.214 + 0.232 = 0.446$ mm/kN.

The shear strength of the end panel is the combined ultimate strength of the sheeting, as calculated above, and the bracing system shown in fig. 12.29. The ultimate strength of the bracing system will be due to either the tensile strength of the diagonal tie or the compressive strength of a purlin.

(a) Diagonal tie. For shear load V, force in tie $= 1.65\,V$. Yield load of tie (discounting bolt hole and half outstanding leg) $= 536 \times 247$ N $= 132$ kN. Hence $1.65\,V = 132$ or $V = 80$ kN.

(b) Compression of purlin. For shear load V, force in purlin $= 1.30\,V$. Since the purlin is fastened to the sheeting, it can only buckle about the xx axis. For the purlin in question $r_{xx} = \sqrt{(I_{xx}/A)} = \sqrt{(146 \times 10^4/494)} = 55$ mm. If the purlin is assumed to be fixed at one end and pinned at the other, the slenderness ratio $l/r_{xx} = 0.85 \times 6000/55 = 93$ and table 17a of B.S. 449: Part 2: 1969 permits an allowable stress of 87 N/mm^2 or a buckling stress (using a load factor of 1.7) of 148 N/mm^2. Hence $1.3\ V = 494 \times 148$ N or $V = 56.3$ kN. The lowest shear load of the bracing system is thus 56.3 kN, so that the total shear strength of the end panel is therefore $V^* = 44.2 + 56.3 = 100.5$ kN.

12.8.4 Analysis of structure and comparison with test results

For the analysis of the complete structure, it is again convenient to use the computer techniques described in sections 4.3 and 4.5 whereby the structure is reduced to an equivalent plane frame. The structure has two axes of symmetry so that it is sufficient to analyse one quarter of the complete building as shown in fig. 12.30.

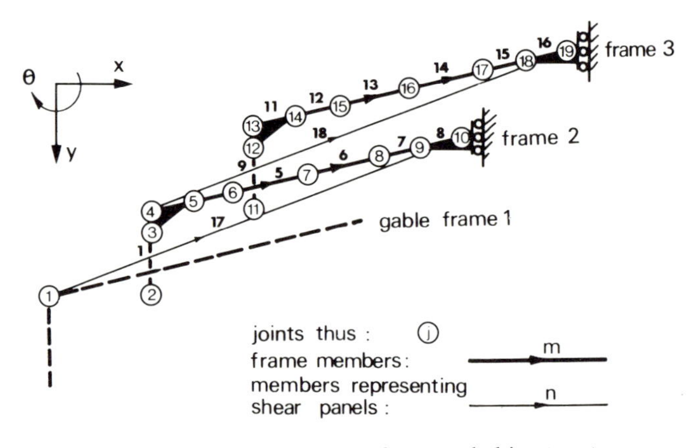

Fig. 12.30 Computer analysis of stressed skin structure.

In the elastic range of loading, comparison between theory and experiment was excellent and is summarised for deflections in table 12.4. A similar comparison was also obtained between theoretical and experimental bending moments. The very large reduction in the deflection under side load should be specially noted. Experimental and theoretical load-deflection curves to failure are shown in fig. 12.31. As a consequence of the lower pitch of the roof and the extra strength of the end panels, this structure did not exhibit the tendency shown in the two previously described tests where the roof panels yielded significantly before onset of plasticity in the frames. Here the theoretical analysis shows that the plastic hinges in the frames form first and final failure is brought about by yield of the sheeting panels after the two centre frames have become mechanisms.

If the complete structure is analysed, the computed failure mode is shown in fig. 12.32. This mode is unsymmetrical and involves the two centre frames only. However, a similar but symmetrical failure mode is also possible at the same load level and as the unsymmetrical mode involves some bending of the sheeting panels which is ignored in the analysis, the symmetrical mode occurs preferentially in practice.

Table 12.4 Calculated and observed behaviour of pitched roof portal building

		Calculated value	Observed value
Unclad frame	Eaves deflection under design superimposed load	16.6 mm	20.1 mm (test 1) 18.2 mm (test 2)
	Eaves deflection under side loads of 2.5 kN	33.3 mm	34.0 mm (test 1) 31.7 mm (test 2)
Clad structure	Maximum eaves deflection under design loads	14.6 mm	16.3 mm (test 1) 14.3 mm (test 2)
	Maximum eaves deflection under side loads of 2.5 kN (all frames loaded)	3.6 mm	3.3 mm (test 1) 3.1 mm (test 2)

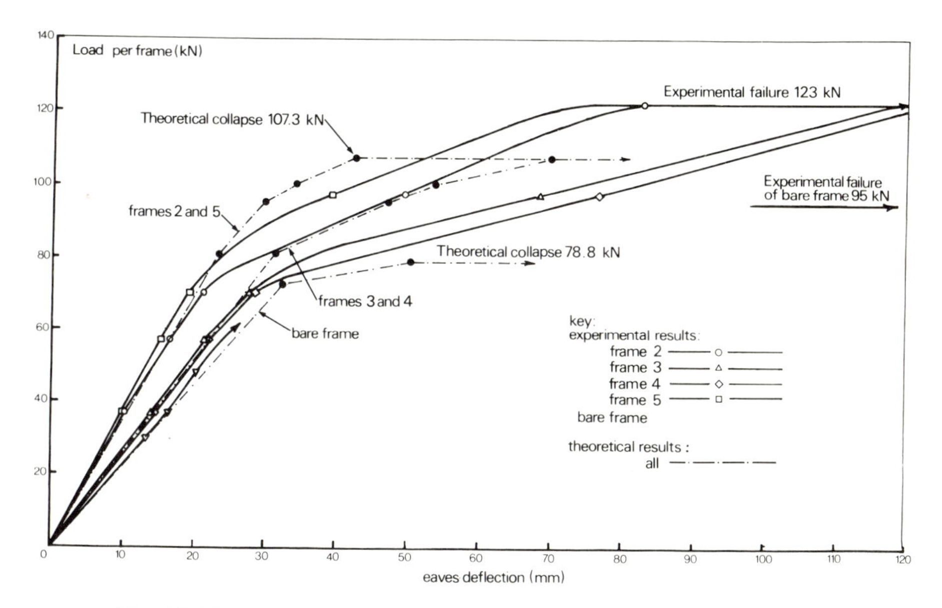

Fig. 12.31 Load–deflection curves for pitched roof portal structure.

Analysis of the part structure shown in fig. 12.30 automatically results in the symmetrical mode. At a total vertical load per frame of 80.6 kN, plastic hinges were predicted at the eaves of the centre frames followed by similar plastic hinges in the two outer frames at a load of 95.2 kN. The centre frames were predicted to become mechanisms by the formation of rafter hinges at a load of 100.0 kN. Theoretical failure finally occurred at a load of 107.3 kN by yield of the penultimate (shaded) sheeting panels.

The good agreement between theory and experiment in the elastic range has already been noted. The shape of the experimental load–deflection curves indi-

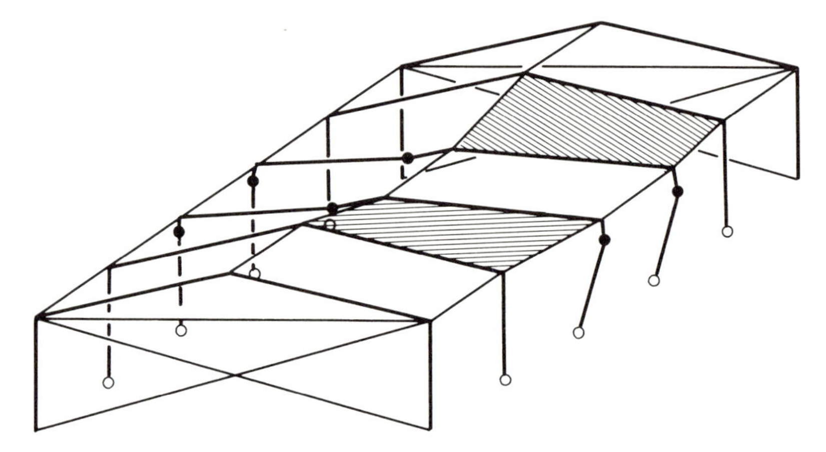

Fig. 12.32 Computed unsymmetrical failure mode of pitched roof structure.

cates, as expected, that in the elastic-plastic range, the structure is more flexible than predicted due to the non-linearity of the behaviour of the shear panels. However, the final strength of the structure is more than expected and experimental failure was obtained at a load of 122 kN. The large deflections and ductile failure indicate the robustness of this type of structure. The shape of the load-deflection curves and the failure loads suggest that the full plastic moment of the members of the frames may have been larger than the values used in the theoretical analysis and in this connection it is interesting to note that the percentage increase in failure load due to the cladding was 28% experimentally and 36% theoretically. Bearing in mind the very light cladding this demonstrates a useful increase in strength.

12.9 Conclusions from large-scale testing

The four tests described in sections 12.5 to 12.8 are remarkable for their size and the comprehensive manner in which they cover all of the major aspects of the interaction between shear panels and rigid jointed frames. They demonstrate quite conclusively that clad buildings are robust and that their behaviour can be predicted in both the elastic range and the post-elastic range up to plastic collapse. Thus the methods of stressed skin design can be applied with confidence in all situations where cladding interacts with rigid jointed steel frames.

The above general statement requires one major qualification. In the first of the two tests reported in section 12.7 the seam fasteners were aluminium blind rivets and premature seam failure occurred as a consequence of the brittle nature of these fasteners which failed by breakage of the fastener rather than by tearing of the sheeting. It is a general requirement of stressed skin design that fastener failure should be ductile and this demands that failure at an individual fastener should be by elongation of its hole followed by tearing of the sheeting around the fastener. Most fasteners in common use are satisfactory in this respect, some aluminium blind rivets being the major exception.

The tests reported in section 12.7 are also notable because shear panel yield took place at a very early stage of loading; in this instance at a load which was a fraction of the yield load of a bare frame. This possibility should not be overlooked. It has two practical consequences. In the first place it means that, in conventionally designed sway frames, satisfactory design of the frames alone does not ensure satisfactory performance of the cladding. This point is emphasised in more detail in section 4.6. Secondly, it follows that in the plastic design of clad structures it is essential to carry out an elastic analysis at the working loads. It is an obvious serviceability requirement that yield at the fasteners should not take place at the working loads. This is discussed further in section 4.4.

CHAPTER THIRTEEN

Fasteners for stressed skin structures

13.1 Introduction

The fasteners that are of particular interest to the designers of a stressed skin structure are those connecting the sheeting to the supporting structure (sheet to purlin and sheet to shear connector fasteners) which may be termed 'thin to thick' fasteners because they connect the relatively thin sheeting to the thicker members below and those connecting side laps between adjacent sheets (seam fasteners) which may be termed 'thin to thin' fasteners. The forces on these fasteners caused by stressed skin action are essentially shear forces and it is the shear strength and shear flexibility of these fasteners that are important in stressed skin design. However, the sheet to purlin fasteners and, to a much lesser extent, the sheet to shear connector fasteners are also subject to tensile forces from wind suction and at the edges of a roof these uplift forces may well be very significant.

Evidently the sheet to purlin fasteners may be subject to combined shear and tensile loading, a subject which will be considered later. At this stage it is sufficient to note that in a stressed skin design according to the principles described in this book the critical fasteners will usually be the seam fasteners or the sheet to shear connector fasteners and in these fasteners combined loading is not significant. Furthermore, the tensile loading condition of sheet to purlin fasteners is an important topic in its own right and, as the designers of stressed skin roofs should be aware of the considerations, some detailed attention is given to this topic. In establishing design values for fastener strength and stiffness, testing plays an important role and in recent years much attention has been devoted to establishing rational test procedures. Notable work on this subject has been reported from Sweden,[6.3] U.S.A.,[6.9] and Germany[6.10] and this formed the basis of discussions within the European Convention for Constructional Steelwork with a view to defining unified European recommendations for fastener tests. This work was co-ordinated by Berry in England[6.14, 6.15] who carried out further testing in order to evaluate the relative merits of the alternative procedures and in order to consider in more detail the important question of shear flexibility. The European work culminated in the publication of 'European recommendations for the testing of connections in profiled sheeting and other light gauge steel components'[6.18] and, using the procedures described therein, Grimshaw[6.26] evaluated the characteristic shear strengths and flexibilities of many of the fastener types in common use in the U.K. It is these values that are tabulated in tables 9.9 and 9.10. Much of the Swedish effort[6.1,6.3] has been devoted to the derivation of design expressions for the strength of fasteners and these are discussed later. The problem is that there are so many variables that any attempt at conservative design expressions is likely to err excessively on the safe side. As testing is reasonably quick and cheap there is much to be said for relying on test results for fastener properties.

The work discussed above has been concerned mainly with mechanical fasteners such as self-drilling, self-tapping screws, blind rivets and fired pins. It has also considered to a lesser extent spot welding. Interest in the electric arc welding of sheet steel has been concentrated in the U.S.A. and has resulted in the description of suitable procedures in order to ensure satisfactory welds[6.19] and valid design expressions.[6.23,6.24] It will be appreciated that in the case of welded joints the problems of varying fastener types do not arise and it is much more appropriate to rely on design expressions so that the need for subsequent testing is greatly diminished. The design expressions given in table 9.11 are based on American work and provide all the information necessary to determine weld strength. As the flexibility of welded connections is relatively small it will usually be adequate to neglect it or to adopt a small nominal value.

Another important topic which is quite independent of those discussed above is the performance of purlin to rafter connections. This has only been considered by Bryan and El-Dakhakhni[1.20,1.57] who tested a large number of typical connections and tabulated values of strength and flexibility. It is these values that are reproduced without further comment in table 9.12.

13.2 Fasteners in shear-test procedures and failure modes

There are a large number of fastener types and sizes which may be used to produce acceptable connections in stressed skin structures. Some of the principal types are shown in fig. 13.1. In considering the performance of these fasteners, the important considerations are the strength, flexibility and ductility of the connections that they make and these can only be established by testing.

The standard shear test is known as the 'single lap joint shear test' in which a two fastener lap joint of standard dimensions is placed in a tensile testing machine and loaded to failure. The standard dimensions are defined in fig. 13.2 and table 13.1. Fig. 13.3 shows a typical test in progress. The standard shear test incorporates two fasteners and the results obtained are an average for the two fasteners concerned. In general a test incorporating a single fastener lap joint will give almost identical results for fastener strength but a considerable reduction in flexibility as a result of the jamming effect of distortions due to eccentricities within the joint. The

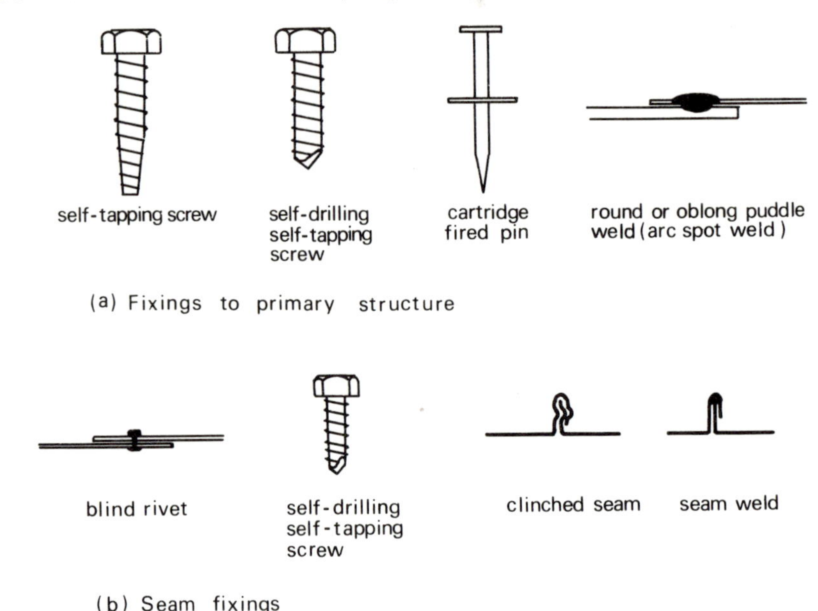

Fig. 13.1 Some suitable fasteners for stressed skin structures.

European recommendations allow a single fastener test to be used where it is considered that such a test is more representative of the conditions in the actual structure than a double fastener test. It is recommended that for stressed skin structures the double fastener test should always be used as giving safe results though there are good arguments that the single fastener test is more representative in the case of sheet to purlin fasteners. Figure 13.4 shows a single fastener lap joint after testing in which the fastener is a 6.3 mm dia. self-drilling self tapping screw. The deformation due to joint eccentricity is very apparent.

Before discussing the results obtained from typical fastener tests it is convenient to consider the typical failure modes and to review these in the light of the important requirement of ductility. It may be recalled that in order to ensure an adequate capability for redistribution of internal forces within a diaphragm it is considered essential to avoid a brittle failure at the fastener and therefore acceptable failure modes usually involve tearing of the sheeting in the vicinity of the fastener.

Table 13.1 Dimensions for standard shear test

Fastener diam. d (mm)	Specimen dimensions (mm) w	L_1	e_1	s_1	l
$\leqslant 6.5$	60	260	30	60	150
> 6.5	$10d$	$200 + 10d$	$5d$	$10d$	$20d + 30$
tolerance	±2	±5	±1	±1	±5

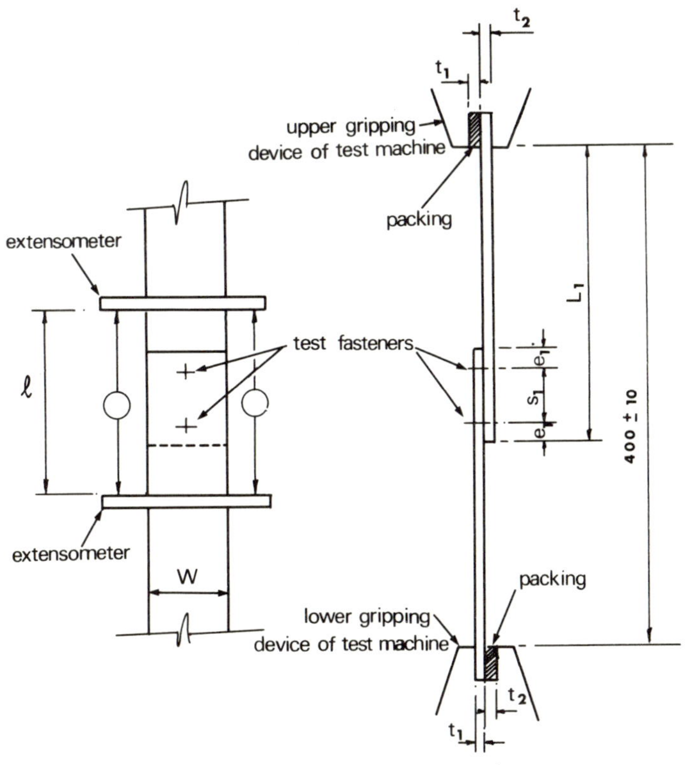

Fig. 13.2 Standard shear test specimen.

(a) *Shear failure of the fastener itself* A typical failure of this type is shown in fig. 13.5 in which two 5.5 mm dia. self-drilling, self-tapping screws were connecting together two steel straps of 3.25 mm thickness. This mode of failure will normally only occur in a stressed skin situation when the sheeting is unusually thick. The exception to this rule is the aluminium blind rivet which tends to fracture before yield of the sheeting for sheet thicknesses greater than about 0.8 mm. This mode of failure is of course brittle and should be avoided in stressed skin structures.

(b) *Failure by bearing and tearing in the thinner sheet* This type of failure is usual in thin to thick connections and is extremely ductile. A typical example is shown in fig. 13.6. The results obtained for self-drilling self-tapping screws failing in this mode are considerably influenced by the presence or otherwise of a neoprene washer. Such a washer may cause a 10–20% decrease in strength and a very considerable increase in flexibility. Typical load–deflection curves illustrating this point are shown in fig. 13.7. The results are also influenced by the thickness of the thicker strap. With the 3.25 mm strap shown in fig. 13.6, there is very little tilting of the fastener but with the thinner straps used to simulate the lighter end of the range of cold formed purlins (say 1.6 mm to 2.0 mm thick) there is a tendency for the fastener to tilt and this has an adverse effect on both the strength and the stiffness of the connection.

Fig. 13.3 Standard shear test in progress.

(c) *Fastener inclination followed by elongation of the hole and stripping of the formed thread in the lower sheet* This is the common form of failure when self-tapping screws are used to form thin to thin connections. A typical example is shown in fig. 13.8. This form of failure will be sufficiently ductile provided that the lower sheet has an adequate thickness and the thread cutting operation causes an adequate burr. For this reason the lower sheet should have a thickness of not less than 0.65 mm and self-drilling, self-tapping screws are preferable to screws that require pre-drilling of the lower sheet.

Fig. 13.4 Lap joint with single 6.3 mm dia. self-drilling, self-tapping screw.

(d) *Crushing of fastener in combination with tilting and bearing* This is the usual mode of failure of hollow blind rivets regardless of whether or not the mandrel remains within the body of the rivet. Fig. 13.9 shows a typical example. This form of failure is usually sufficiently ductile.

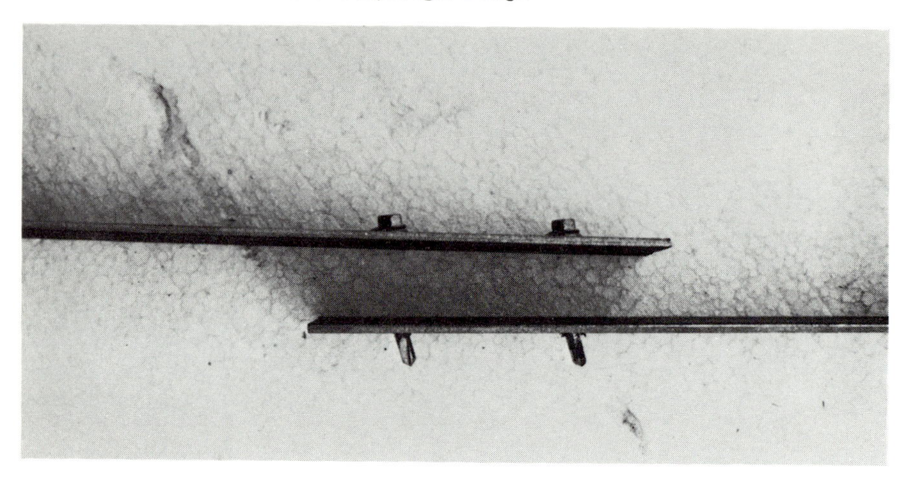

Fig. 13.5 5.5 mm dia. self-drilling, self-tapping screws; straps 2 × 3.25 mm.

Fig. 13.6 6.3 mm self-drilling, self-tapping screws; straps 0.76/3.25 mm.

(e) *Edge failure in the sheeting* This mode of failure only occurs when the fastener is placed too close to the edge of the sheeting and is illustrated in fig. 13.10. The dimensions of the standard shear test are designed to avoid this mode of failure which should not occur in practice if the minimum edge distances specified in section 2.5 are adhered to. There is also a related end failure if the fastener is placed

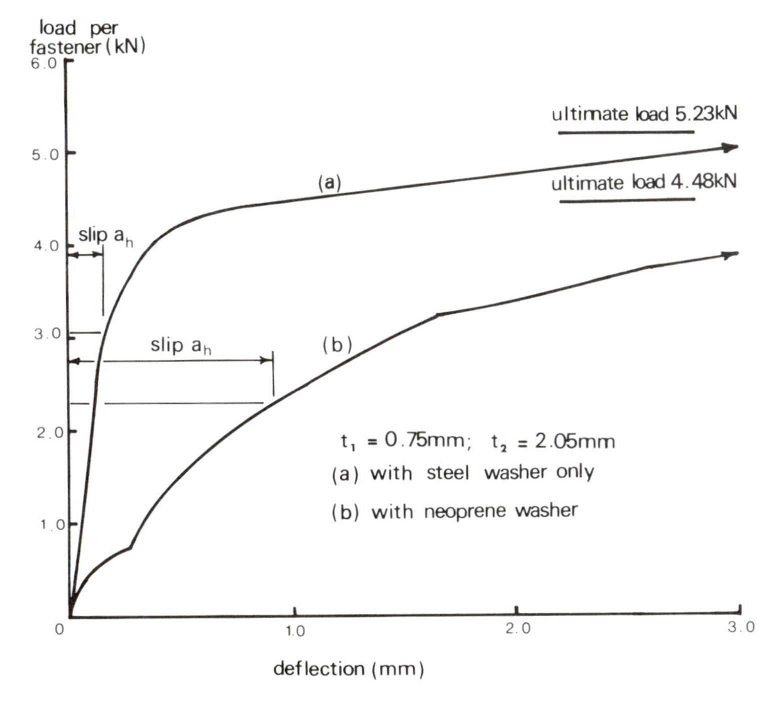

Fig. 13.7 Load–deflection curves for thin to thick connections with 6.3 mm dia. self-drilling, self-tapping screws.

Fig. 13.8 5.5 mm self-drilling, self-tapping screws; straps 2 X 0.76 mm.

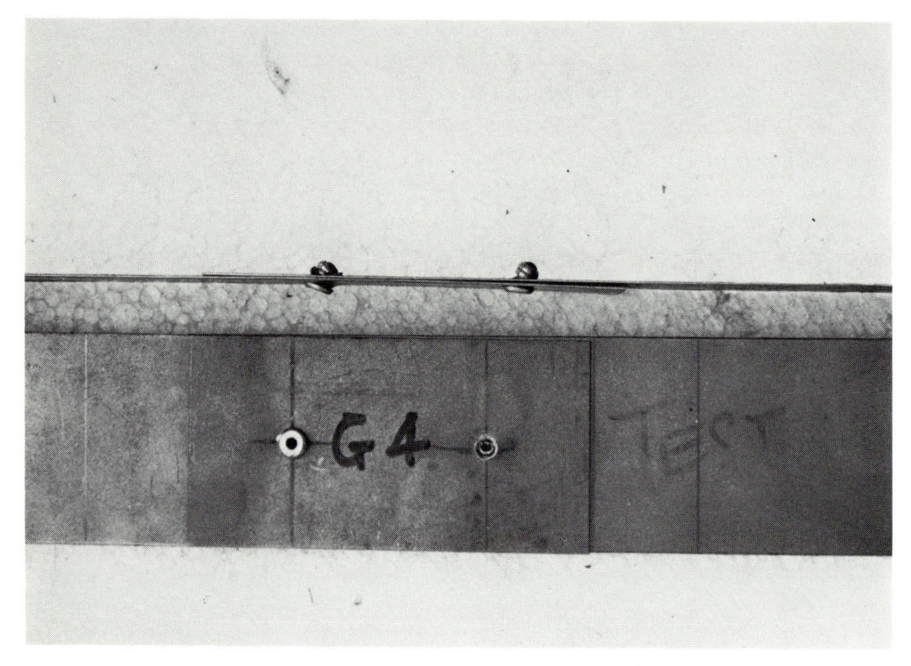

Fig. 13.9 4.8 mm aluminium rivets; straps 2 × 0.76 mm.

too near the end of the sheet. For convenience the minimum distances of the centres of fasteners from the edge of the sheet are repeated here as follows (where d is the diameter of the shaft of the fastener): seam and shear connector fasteners: edge distance $> 1.5d$ and 8 mm; all other fasteners: edge distance $> 1.5d$ and 10 mm; all fasteners: end distance $> 3.0d$ and 20 mm.

13.2.1. Test procedure and interpretation of results

It will be appreciated that fastener characteristics are somewhat variable quantities and are influenced by such factors as workmanship and speed of testing. For this reason it is necessary to pay careful attention to the test procedure and then to interpret the results cautiously and on a sound statistical basis. Attention here is concentrated on the case where values are required for a given fastener acting in conjunction with a single specified sheet thickness. Comprehensive procedures for dealing with a range of sheet thicknesses will be found in the European recommendations.[6.18]

When making up the test specimen it is important to follow as closely as possible the procedures that are likely to be adopted on site. Particular attention should be paid to the following factors: diameter of predrilled holes, tightening torque or depth setting control for threaded fasteners, type of tool and cartridge for cartridge fired pins and strength and thickness of the sheeting and (where applicable) the supporting member. Because of the variable nature of the results, particularly the slip or flexibility values, it is necessary to carry out at least five tests on each particular combination of fastener and sheet thickness. The statistical procedures advocated to interpret these results are such that it is usually advantageous to carry out more than the minimum number of tests. Furthermore, the European recommendations require that, if the minimum five tests include one in which the ultimate load differs from the mean of the series by more than 10%, at least three further tests should be carried out, thus increasing the minimum number of tests to eight. If the test is carried out too quickly the strength and stiffness of the connection may be over-estimated. For this reason it is necessary to restrict the speed of testing to reasonable limits. The limits specified in the European recommendations are: rate of loading (initial stages of testing) 1 kN/min; rate of straining (later stages of testing) 1 mm/min. During testing, deformation readings should be taken at intervals of about one tenth of the expected ultimate load of the connection and loading should be continued until the applied load cannot be maintained. For an individual test, the ultimate load is defined as the maximum load recorded during the test or the load at which the first significant drop occurs in the load–deflection diagram. With double fastener connections the ultimate load per fastener is taken as one half of the ultimate load of the connection.

The characteristic strength of the fastener P_k is calculated as follows. Let n

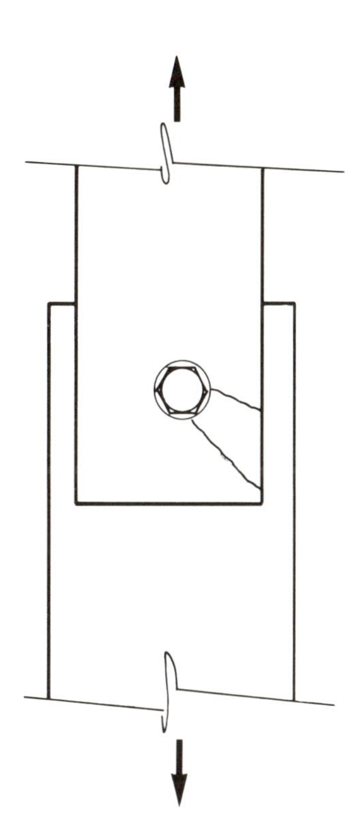

Fig. 13.10 Edge failure in the sheeting.

be the number of tests carried out and P_u the observed ultimate load per fastener from an individual test. Then $P_m = \Sigma P_u/n$ = mean ultimate load per fastener, and

$$\left.\begin{aligned} s &= \sqrt{\left(\frac{\Sigma(P_u - P_m)^2}{n-1}\right)} \\ \text{or} \quad s &= \sqrt{\left(\frac{\Sigma P_u{}^2 - n\Sigma P_m{}^2}{n-1}\right)} \\ \text{or} \quad s &= \sqrt{\left(\frac{n\Sigma P_u{}^2 - (\Sigma P_u)^2}{n(n-1)}\right)} \end{aligned}\right\} = \text{standard deviation of the ultimate load per fastener,} \qquad (13.1)$$

and $P_k = P_m - cs$ where c is a statistical coefficient taken from table 13.2 which is derived from the 'students t distribution' based on a lower one sided tolerance limit of 95% and a 50% confidence limit. The design strength (F_p, F_s or F_{sc} as appropriate) is obtained from the characteristic strength by dividing by the appropriate material factor γ_m, which, in the European recommendations is taken as 1.11. Thus

$$\begin{bmatrix} F_p \\ F_s \\ F_{sc} \end{bmatrix} = P_k/1.11 = 0.9\,P_k = 0.9\,[P_m - cs] \qquad (13.2)$$

For double fastener connections, the load-deformation curve for an individual fastener is taken to be the load-deformation curve for the connection with the load values divided by two.

Table 13.2 Statistical coefficient c for evaluation of fastener characteristic strength

Number of tests in test series	5	8	10	13	16	21	25	30	50	∞
c	2.13	1.89	1.83	1.78	1.75	1.72	1.71	1.70	1.67	1.64

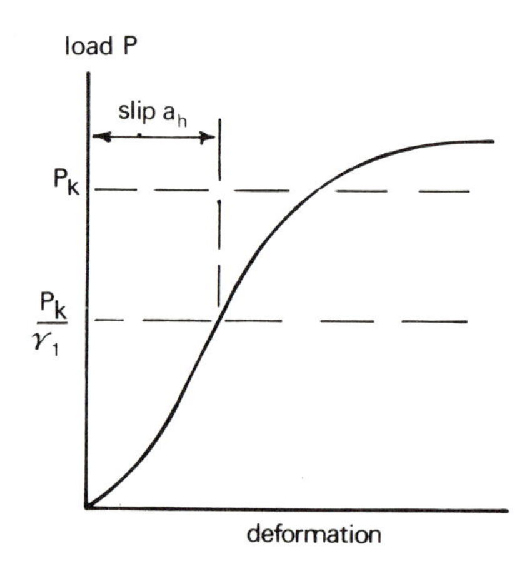

Fig. 13.11 Evaluation of slip.

The slip or flexibility of an individual fastener is taken as the value of deformation read off the load–deformation curve at the maximum working load as shown in fig. 13.11. For the values appropriate to the European recommendations, γ = partial load factor for wind = 1.5, γ_m = material factor = 1.11 and $\gamma_1 = \gamma\gamma_m$ = 1/0.6. The design shear flexibility (s_p, s_s, s_{sc}) per unit load is obtained from the average slip values for individual fasteners as

$$\begin{bmatrix} s_p \\ s_s \\ s_{sc} \end{bmatrix} = \frac{1}{P_k/\gamma_1} \times \frac{\Sigma a_h}{n} \tag{13.3}$$

A typical family of load-deflection curves showing the variability and non-linearity of slip values is shown in fig. 13.12. Fortunately, fastener slip is only one of the components of diaphragm flexibility and is often overshadowed by profile deformation and/or axial strain in the edge members so that the use of average values at conservative load levels for these quantities usually results in an adequate prediction of diaphragm flexibility. Figure 13.12 also shows some corresponding results from an alternative test which will be described in section 13.2.3. The ultimate loads obtained from the two alternative tests are very similar.

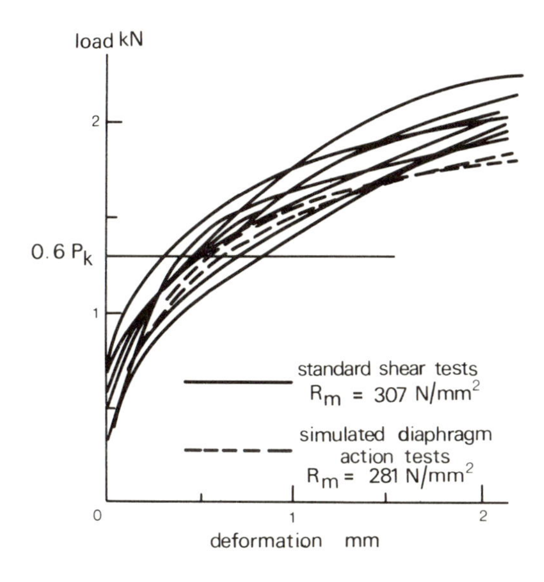

Fig. 13.12 Load deformation curves: 5.5 mm self-drilling, self-tapping screws; straps 2 × 0.76 mm.

13.2.2 Typical test results

Since the publication of the European recommendations for the testing of connections[6.18] in 1978 a comprehensive test programme incorporating many of the fasteners in common use in the U.K. has been carried out at the University of

Salford.[6.26] This programme has adhered carefully to the provisions of the European recommendations and the results are summarised in tables 9.9 and 9.10. These tables therefore supersede results obtained prior to 1978. The results given in tables 9.9 and 9.10 may be used with confidence for the purpose of design. For situations not covered by the tables the appropriate testing may be carried out or it may be possible to obtain a satisfactory estimate of the relevant properties using the design expressions discussed in section 13.3. On examining the design expressions in section 13.3 it will be observed that the strength of a mechanically fastened connection failing in a ductile mode which involves tearing of the sheeting is considered to be proportional to the ultimate strength of the sheeting. If the sheeting strength quoted for a relevant test in tables 9.9 and 9.10 is not representative of a particular application, the fastener strengths should be adjusted on the basis of proportionality to the ultimate strength of the sheeting to be used.

13.2.3 Alternative shear test

Certain types of connection, notably the upstanding seams shown in fig. 13.1 are not amenable to testing by means of the single lap joint shear test and must be subject to a test procedure which more exactly simulates the shear condition in an actual seam. A suitable apparatus, which was initially developed at Cornell University in the U.S.A.[6.9] is shown diagrammatically in fig. 13.13 and pictorially in fig. 13.14. This alternative shear test should be used whenever the standard shear test is unsuitable for testing the connection or property under consideration. It also has obvious research applications and was used at the University of Salford to determine the limiting fastener edge distance values given in section 13.2(e). The standardised dimensions of the test specimens for this test are given in fig. 13.15 and table 13.3.

Table 13.3 Specimen dimensions for alternative shear test

Fastener diameter	Specimen dimensions (mm)		
d (mm)	w	e_2	s_1
$\leqslant 6.5$	92.5	10	60
> 6.5	$82.5 + e_2$	$1.5d$	$10d$

The test procedures and the evaluation of results for the alternative shear test are identical for those for the standard test as described in section 13.2.1.

13.3 Design expressions for fasteners in shear

Design expressions for the strength of fasteners in shear have been given by Baehre and Berggren.[6.3] These are lower bound values based on many hundreds of tests and may therefore be applied with confidence to most applications. However, no expressions for flexibility are given so that if these expressions are used instead of tests in diaphragm calculations the necessary flexibilities must be estimated. Furthermore, no consideration appears to have been given to such important matters as

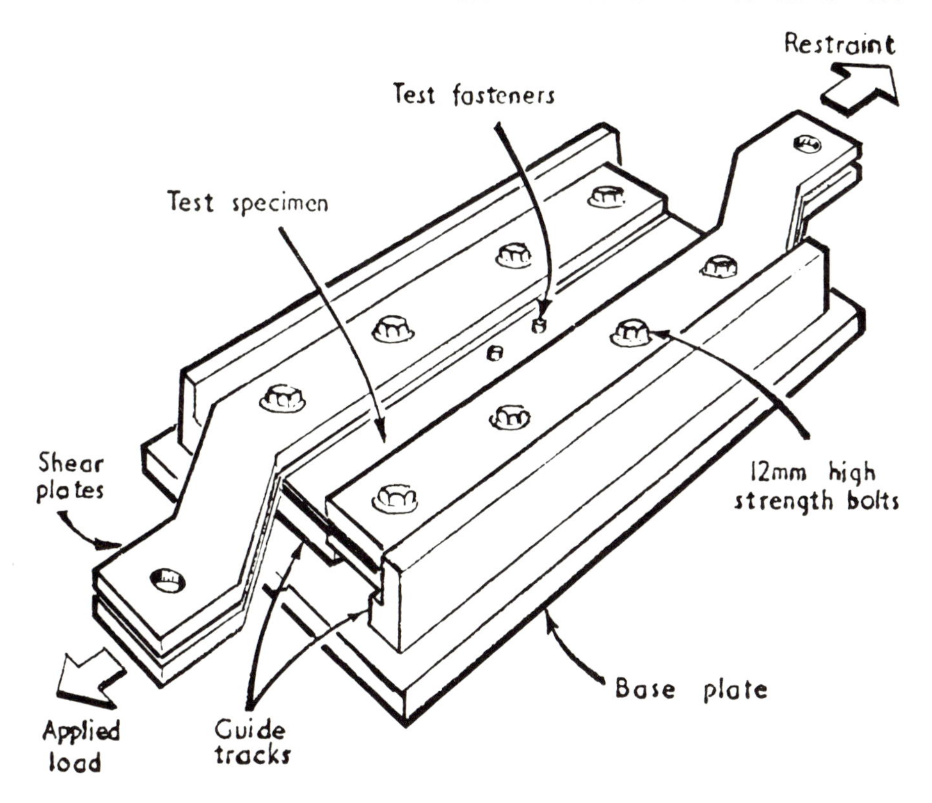

Fig. 13.13 Apparatus for alternative shear test.

the distinction between self-drilling, self-tapping screws and plain self-tapping screws or the influence of flexible neoprene washers. Consequently, the expressions are in general very conservative when compared with recent test results, as shown in tables 9.9 and 9.10. Indeed, they are 100% or more conservative in certain cases which implies a significant loss in economy. Furthermore, the general trend of the theoretical results, particularly with regard to variations in sheet thickness, does not always agree with the test results. This is particularly noticeable for rivets passing through thicker sheets when the design expressions may even be found to be unsafe. The design expressions include for all possible modes of failure including failure of the fastener itself and tensile or edge failure of the parent metal. In view of the particular applications under consideration and in particular that only thin sheeting is likely to be used and edge and end failures are prevented by the provision of adequate edge distances, only the directly relevant failure modes are considered here. For full information it is necessary to consult the original paper.

It will be noted that the design expressions of Baehre and Berggren include the ultimate strength of the thinner sheet σ_{ult}. In their work for the European Coal and Steel Community,[6.13] Stark and Toma have accepted the equations of Baehre and Berggren except that σ_{ult} is replaced by the yield stress σ_y thereby making the

Fig. 13.14 Apparatus for alternative shear test.

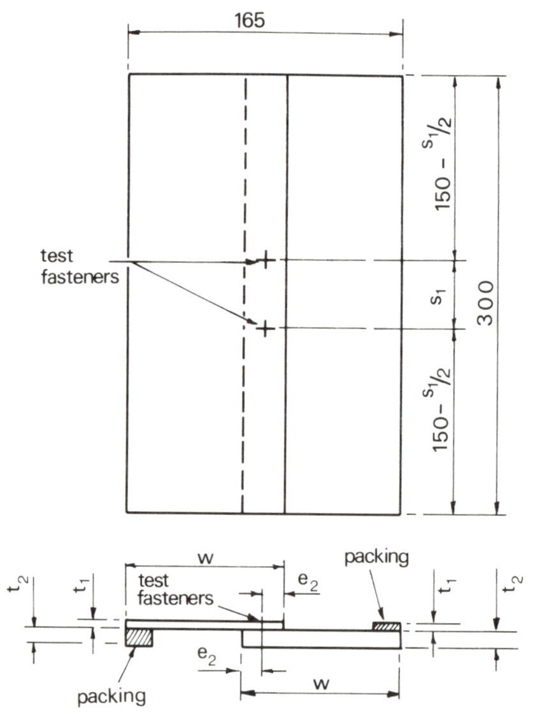

Fig. 13.15 Specimen for alternative shear test.

equations even more conservative. They have also included an expression for another failure mode, namely 'hole bearing'. This is, however, only found to be critical for rare combinations of fastener and sheet thickness and even then gives values only slightly lower than Baehre and Berggren. It is not easy to decide whether the calculation of fastener strength should be based on σ_{ult} or σ_y and it is probably not important provided that the resulting formula is safe when compared with test results. As the Baehre and Berggren formulae appear to be adequate in this respect these are included in the paragraphs which follow. More conservative results will of course be obtained if σ_{ult} is replaced by σ_y.

In his work on screwed fasteners, Strnad[6.25] has derived a more complex series of expressions for both strength and flexibility. These appear to give slightly better values for fastener strength than those of Baehre and Berggren and therefore are included below. Once again these expressions apply to both self-tapping and self-drilling screws and do not take into account the effect of the sealing washer, if any, though they appear to be adequately conservative when compared with available test results as shown in tables 9.9 and 9.10. This omission to give due consideration to the influence of the washer makes the calculation of flexibility unreliable and so the expressions are not taken further.

13.3.1 Screwed connections

For failure due to screw inclination and yield in bearing the design procedure is as follows.

Let d = shaft diameter of the screw (mm)
F = ultimate strength of the connection in shear (N)
t_1 = thickness of the thinner sheet being joined (mm)
t_2 = thickness of the thicker sheet being joined (mm)
σ_{ult} = ultimate tensile strength of the thinner sheet (N/mm²)

$$\text{then } \left.\begin{aligned} K_1 &= 0.156\,[(t_2/t_1) - 1]^2 + 0.35 \quad \text{for } t_2/t_1 < 2.5 \\ K_1 &= 0.70 \quad \text{for } t_2/t_1 \geqslant 2.5 \end{aligned}\right\} \tag{13.4}$$

$$\text{and } F = K_1(d + 10)(t_1{}^2 + 0.22)\,\sigma_{ult} \tag{13.5}$$

The above expression applies to both self-tapping and self-drilling, self-tapping screws and to all washer arrangements. The additional expression for 'hole bearing' given by Stark and Toma[6.13] is

$$F = 2.1\,d\,t\,\sigma_{ult} \tag{13.6}$$

As mentioned above, this is only critical on rare occasions though it may be found to influence the design strength of small diameter screws.

The alternative expressions given by Strnad[6.25] are as follows:

Let σ_{y1} = design stress of thinner sheet being joined (N/mm²)
σ_{y2} = design stress of thicker sheet being joined (N/mm²)

Note: according to the European recommendations, the design stress is equal to the yield stress. The remaining symbols are as above.

Then if $$x = \frac{t_2\ \sigma_{ult2}}{t_1\ \sigma_{ult1}} \quad (x \not> 3) \qquad (13.7)$$

$$K = 0.80 + 0.35\,(x - 1) \qquad (13.8)$$

$$t' = 0.5\,[t_1\,(x - 1) + t_2\,(3 - x)] \text{ (effective thickness)} \qquad (13.9)$$

$$\sigma_y' = 0.5\,[\sigma_{y1}\,(x - 1) + \sigma_{y2}\,(3 - x)] \text{ (effective yield stress)} \qquad (13.10)$$

The ultimate strength of the connection in shear is

$$F = Kt'\sigma_y'\ (\mathrm{d} + 5) \qquad (13.11)$$

13.3.2 Blind rivets

In the case of blind rivets, it is known that, particularly for aluminium rivets, failure of the rivet itself is an important possibility. However, Baehre and Berggren do not give a design expression for this case, stating that the manufacturer's guaranteed value for shear strength should be used. For failure due to rivet inclination and yield in bearing they give the following design procedure: Using the symbols defined in 13.3.1 above,

$$\left.\begin{aligned} K_1 &= 0.111\,[(t_2/t_1) - 1]^2 + 0.65 && \text{for } t_2/t_1 < 2.5 \\ K_1 &= 0.90 && \text{for } t_2/t_1 \geqslant 2.5 \end{aligned}\right\} \qquad (13.12)$$

Note: it is assumed that the head of the rivet is placed against the thinner sheet. If this is not the case, K_1 is always 0.65.

$$F = K_1\,(d + 5)\,({t_1}^2 + 0.22)\,\sigma_{ult} \qquad (13.13)$$

13.3.3 Resistance spot welded connections

For all the significant modes of failure, namely shear failure or yield in bearing and tearing of the parent metal, Baehre and Berggren give two families of design curves which are reproduced below as figs. 13.16(a) and 13.16(b). The ultimate strength of a single overlap connection between as-rolled or hot-dip galvanised sheets is given as:

$$F = K_1\bar{F} \qquad (13.14)$$

where $\bar{F}$ is read off the appropriate fig. 13.16 and K_1 is a correction factor which may be made equal to unity when the weld parameters and corresponding strengths are under stringent control.

The above procedures apply specifically to material with an ultimate strength of 363 N/mm^2. For other values σ_{ult} of the ultimate strength, a modification factor of ($\sigma_{ult}/363$) should be applied. Finally, as noted on fig. 13.16, the above procedure applies to sheet thicknesses within the range $t_1 \leqslant t_2 < 2.5t_1$. Where $t_1 \geqslant 2.5t_2$, the above procedure may still be used provided that the resulting value of F is also less than the following two expressions:

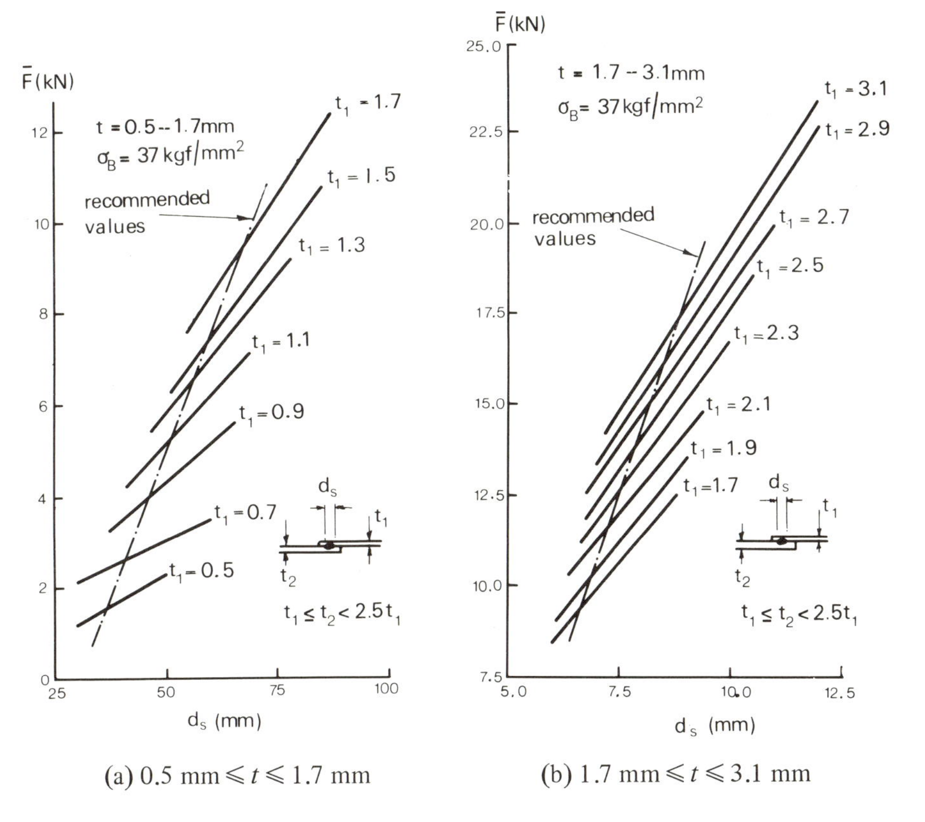

(a) 0.5 mm $\leqslant t \leqslant$ 1.7 mm (b) 1.7 mm $\leqslant t \leqslant$ 3.1 mm

Fig. 13.16 Diagrams for determining the permissible load in resistance spot- welded connections.

$$F = (\pi d_s^2/4)\,\sigma_{\text{ult}} \tag{13.15}$$

$$F = 3.5 t_1 d_s \sigma_{\text{ult}} \tag{13.16}$$

13.3.4 Arc welded connections

The main types of arc welded connection that are likely to be used in diaphragm construction are shown in fig. 13.17. Gas-shielded welding is often advantageous when welding the thin material usually associated with sheeting and extremely fast welding speeds may be obtained. The making of such welds demands skill on the part of the welder and it is essential to use correct techniques, as it is possible to make a weld of sound appearance which has little strength. Welded diaphragms have been extensively used in the U.S.A. and largely as a consequence of interest in this particular application, there is a well-established technology for the electric arc welding of thin sheet steel.[6.19, 6.23, 6.24] Some general guidance regarding the making of these welds is given in section 2.10 but, for a full treatment, reference 6.19 should be consulted. It is good practice to require that the deposited weld material should have a tensile strength at least equal to that of the members being joined and when this is the case the failure modes, though complicated and difficult to categorise, usually involve tearing of the plate adjacent to the weld. Failure is usually accompanied by significant out of plane distortion. Shear of the weld itself rarely occurs in well-made welds.

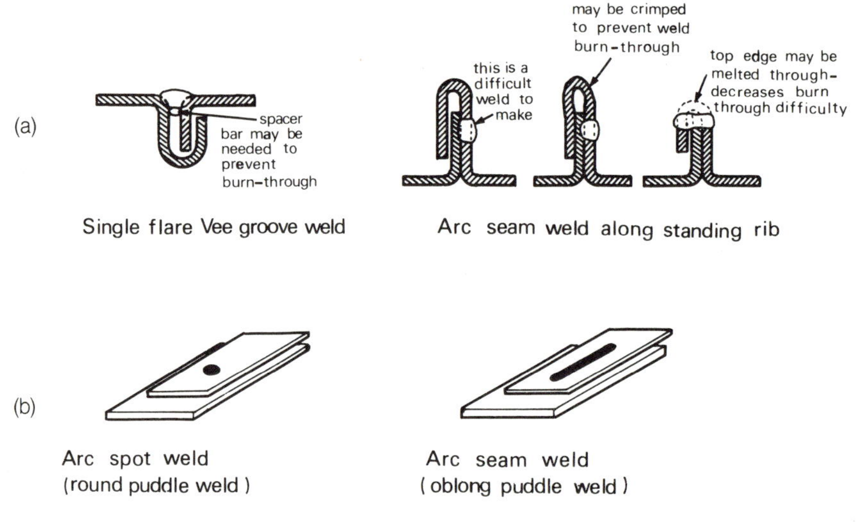

Fig. 13.17 Weld types for welded diaphragms.

As a result of tests on several hundred welded connections, expressions for the ultimate loads of single welds were developed by Pekoz and McGuire at Cornell University.[6.24] The expressions given in table 9.11 have been derived by the authors by modifying the given expressions according to the statistical treatment described in section 13.2.1. They are therefore true characteristic strengths and may be used as such in design calculations.

13.3.5 Conclusions regarding the design expressions

The design expressions discussed in the above sections cover both welded connections and certain types of mechanical fasteners. In the case of welds the parameters are clearly defined and there is no difficulty in deriving expressions for strength that are of universal validity. Furthermore, flexibility, for which no design expressions are available, is of greatly reduced importance. It follows that for welded connections the design expressions have no serious deficiencies and should normally be used when calculating diaphragm strength. When calculating diaphragm flexibility, movement in the welds may be neglected or a small nominal flexibility used.

Conversely, for mechanical fasteners, there are a large number of proprietary components available, each having different characteristics, so that it is very difficult to include all of the relevant parameters in design expressions. For this reason, the available expressions may prove to be excessively conservative in some instances and may even be unsafe in others. Furthermore, there are no design expressions for fastener flexibility which may be a significant component of the total flexibility of the diaphragm. It follows that, for all types of mechanical fasteners, the properties should normally be determined by testing and the design expressions should only be used when no relevant test results are available and when minimising the number of fasteners is not crucial to the economy of the design.

13.4 Fasteners in tension: test procedures and failure modes

The European recommendations for the testing of connections[6.18] recognise no less than four alternative procedures for testing sheet to supporting member fasteners in tension. In general these alternative tests give similar results for the tensile failure load though not for the deformations prior to failure which may be considerable. The alternative procedures reflect to some extent the practice in different countries but more significantly the fact that the performance of the connection is influenced not only by the fastener itself and the thickness and strength of the sheeting through which it passes but also by the geometry of the sheeting profile. The profile geometry and the test apparatus used always influence the deformations prior to failure so that it is meaningless to quote deflection values unless one of the more complicated alternative tests is used ('large-scale tension test' or 'alternative tension test 2' in the European recommendations). Strength values may also be influenced in a similar way if the fastener passes through a flange in a sheeting profile of high width to thickness ratio or if the distortion of the connected flange is likely to be significantly influenced by the webs. For such cases one of the two alternative tests quoted above should always be used.

The standard tension test fixture is the simplest of all the alternatives and is shown in fig. 13.18 and the standard test specimen for use in this apparatus is shown in fig. 13.19. This figure allows very easy clamping of the specimen, but, the fixed dimensions together with the rigid clamping of the webs means that it serves only as a model of real profiled sheeting. However, it has been found that this model gives satisfactory results for many sheeting profiles particularly those fixed as decking where the fastener passes through the narrower flange. The failure modes which are likely to occur during such a tension test are as follows. It should be appreciated that they may also occur in combination:

(a) *Tensile failure of the fastener itself* (see fig. 13.20) This failure mode is only likely to occur when the sheeting is excessively thick for the fastener or when an unsuitable or faulty fastener is used.
(b) *Pull out of the fastener* (see fig. 13.21) This failure mode may occur when the support member is insufficiently thick or when there is insufficient thread engagement.
(c) *Pull over of the sheeting* (see fig. 13.22) In this mode, the sheeting tears around the fastener head or washer.
(d) *Pull through of the sheeting* (fig. 13.23) Here, the sheeting distorts sufficiently to pull through from under the head of the fastener and its washer. This is the most

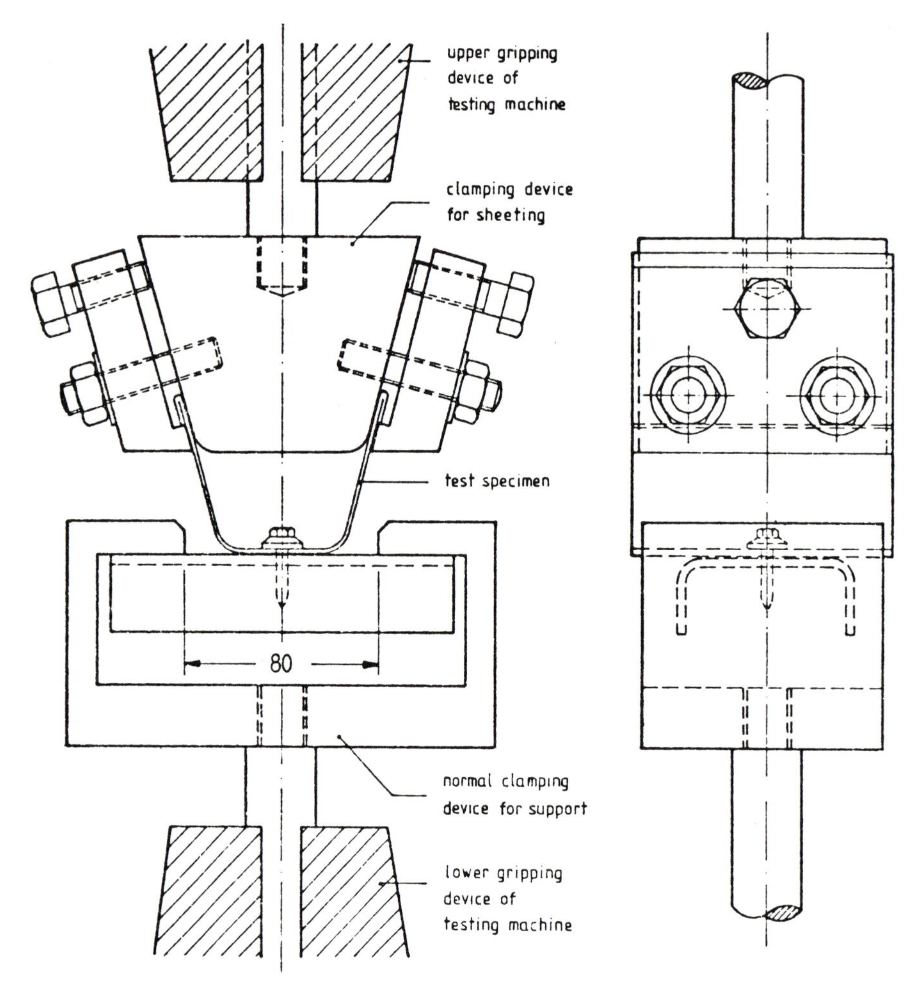

Fig. 13.18 Standard tension test fixture.

frequent mode of failure and is always accompanied by a significant amount of sheet distortion and possibly also distortion of the washer. It is with this and the next mode of failure that the profile geometry starts to become important.

(e) *Gross distortion of the sheeting* (see fig. 13.24) This mode of failure is shown diagrammatically in fig. 13.24. It is clear that it is almost entirely a function of the profile geometry rather than the fastener and that, to some extent at least, this mode is present in almost all tests on fasteners in tension. It is not at all clear how to define a serviceability or failure limit for this case and this must be left to the discretion of the person carrying out the tests. The European recommendations include simply the statement 'Permanent profile distortion which reduces the safe load carrying capacity of the sheeting constitutes failure'.

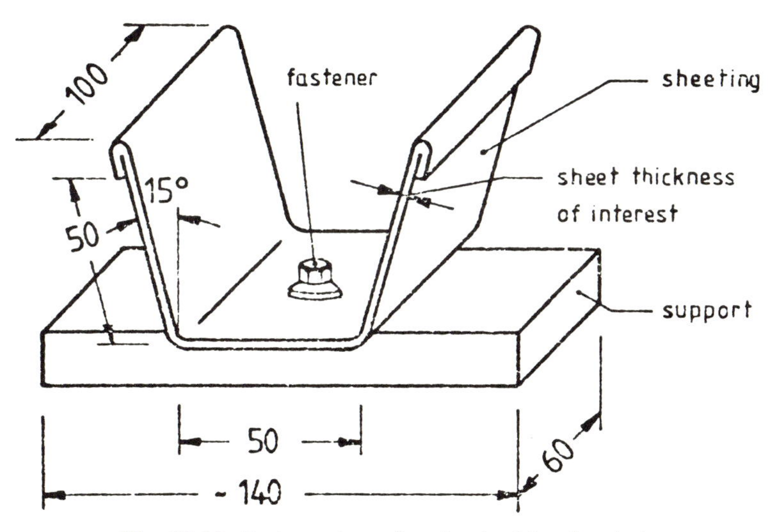

Fig. 13.19 Test specimen for standard tension test.

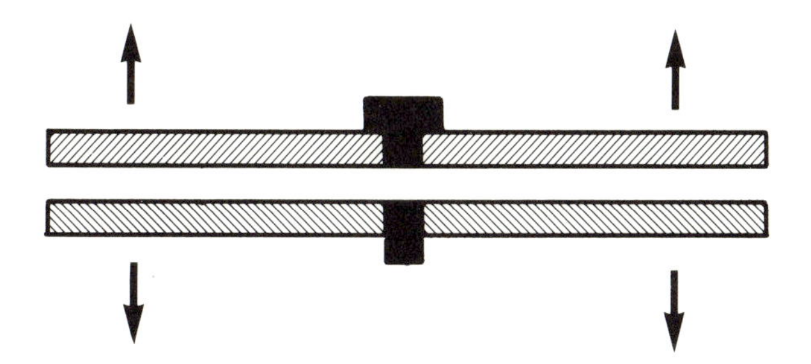

Fig. 13.20 Tensile failure of fastener.

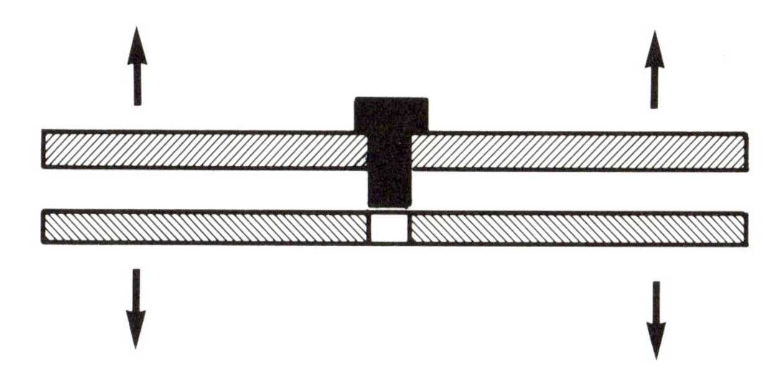

Fig. 13.21 Pull out of the fastener.

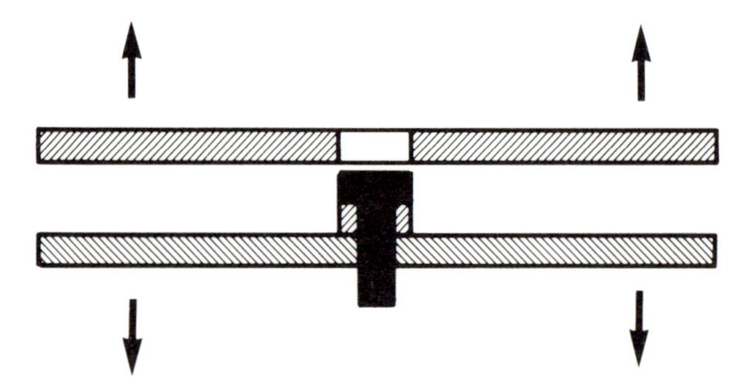

Fig. 13.22 Pull over of the sheeting.

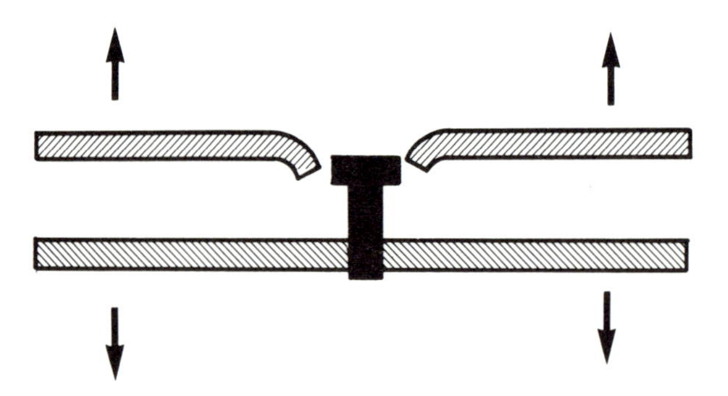

Fig. 13.23 Pull through of the sheeting.

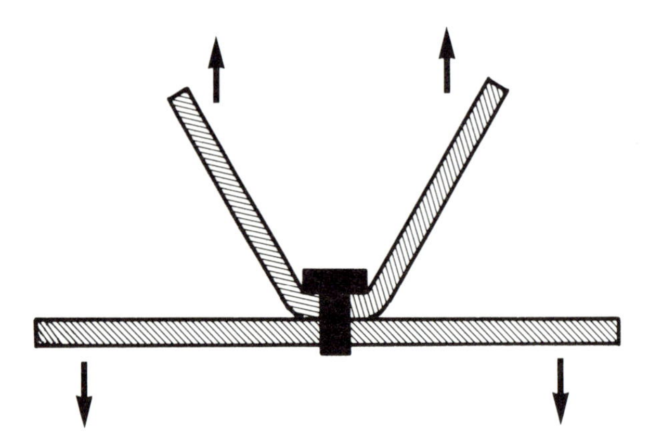

Fig. 13.24 Gross distortion of the sheeting.

13.4.1 Influence of flexible support members

The pull out or pull through strength of a fastener in tension may be significantly reduced if the fastener becomes inclined as a consequence of asymmetrical deformation of a light gauge steel support member. This effect can be included in the standard tension test by incorporating a support member with the required amount of flexibility, as shown in fig. 13.25. This arrangement has been found to give satisfactory results for most channel, angle or Z sections likely to be used in practice.

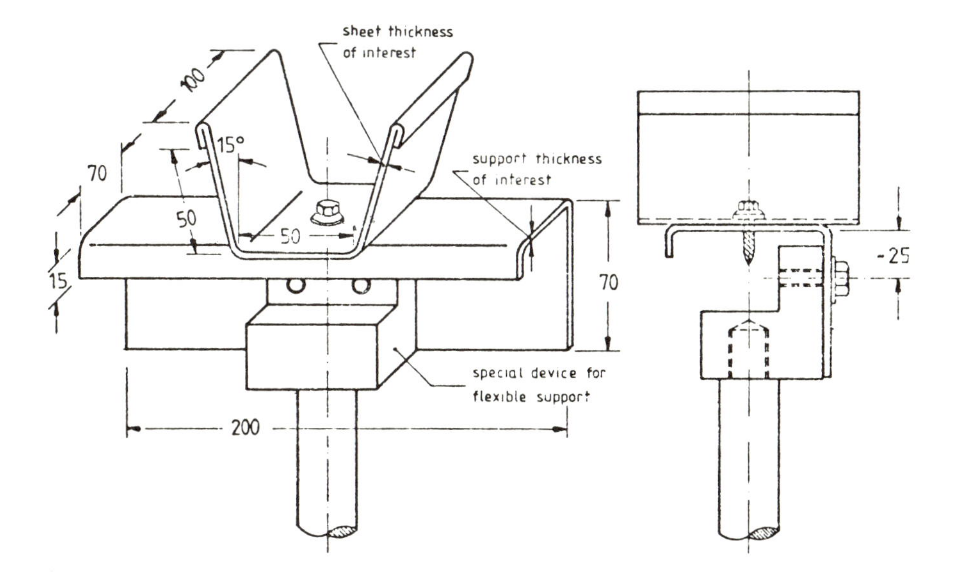

Fig. 13.25 Tensile test specimen with flexible support member.

13.4.2 Alternative tension test procedures

The standard tension test has been described in some detail. The alternatives will be mentioned only briefly as full details can be found in the European recommendations for the testing of connections.[6.18]

(a) *Alternative tension test 1* This test is similar in many respects to the standard test but uses a short (200 mm) length of the actual sheeting profile and a fastening arrangement to accommodate this. The short length of the test specimen and the possible necessity of supporting angles at the ends of the specimen mean that deformations around the fasteners are not necessarily those that would occur in practice.

(b) *Alternative tension test 2* Recognising the deficiencies of the first two alternatives, this test incorporates a much larger piece of sheeting of length equal to 12 times the width of the fastened flange and either two or three corrugations wide. A much more comprehensive test fixture is therefore required but realistic deformations are obtained and the European recommendations detail a procedure whereby these may be measured.

(c) *Large-scale tension test* This test is a full-scale prototype test of a panel containing at least three purlins and two widths of sheeting as shown in fig. 13.26. It recognises that, for two-span sheeting, failure will occur in the connections to the centre support and conditions at this support are reproduced as precisely as possible. Naturally this is an extremely expensive procedure and is only used when unique features or special materials are involved.

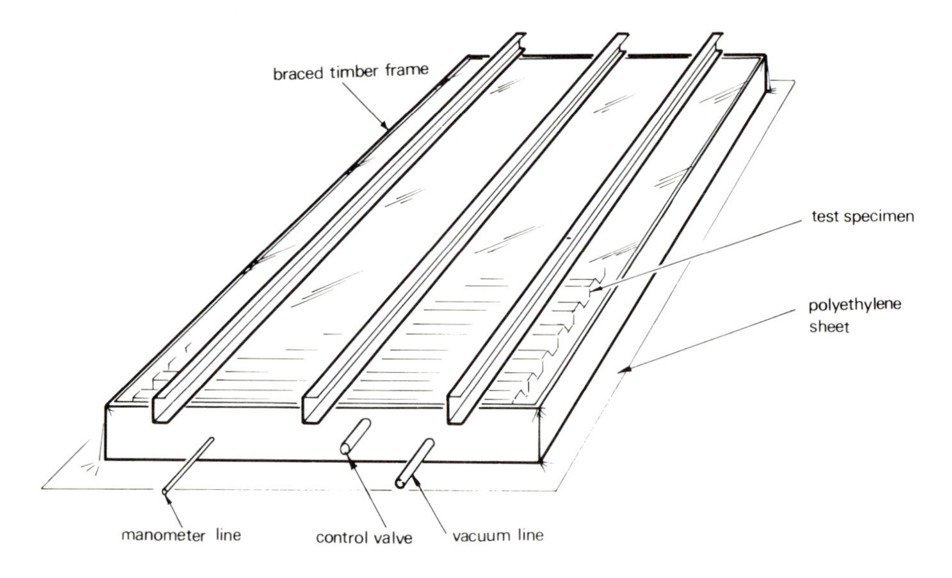

Fig. 13.26 Large-scale tension test apparatus.

13.4.3 Typical test results

Because of the many variables involved, there has been no systematic attempt to obtain representative values for fastener tensile strengths. However, a number of tests on 6.3 mm diameter self-drilling, self-tapping screws have been reported and some of these are summarised in table 13.4. Some further test results highlighting the difficulties inherent in this subject will be found in reference 6.11.

13.5 Influence of repeated loading on fastener performance

In section 3.5.5, tests on complete diaphragms[1.46] and a complete building[2.44] were quoted as demonstrating that repeated loading need not be considered in determining the design strength of a diaphragm. As the failure modes of the majority of diaphragms involve shear failure of fasteners, there has been a certain amount of interest in determining the fatigue life of fasteners in shear though not all of this work has been reported in English. However, some typical results for rivets have been reported by Baehre[6.11] and as these are typical of other types of mechanical fastener they are reproduced in fig. 13.27. As a result of these and other similar tests it appears that shear connections are rarely affected by less than 10 000 cycles of loading.[6.16, 6.18] Similarly, Strnad[6.25] has recently reported an investigation of

Table 13.4 Results of tensile tests on 6.3 mm self-drilling self-tapping screws

sheeting					
profile	thickness (mm)	ultimate strength (N/mm²)	ultimate load (kN)	test fixture	failure mode
flat sheet	0.53	314	3.20	alternative 1	
	0.76	314	5.01	”	
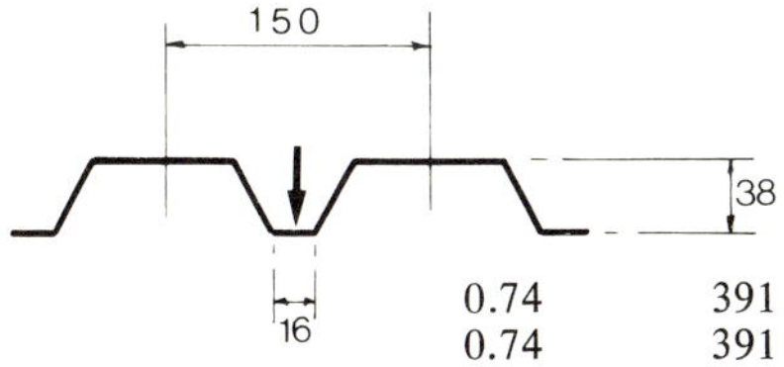	0.74	391	6.59	alternative 1	
	0.74	391	7.45	large scale	
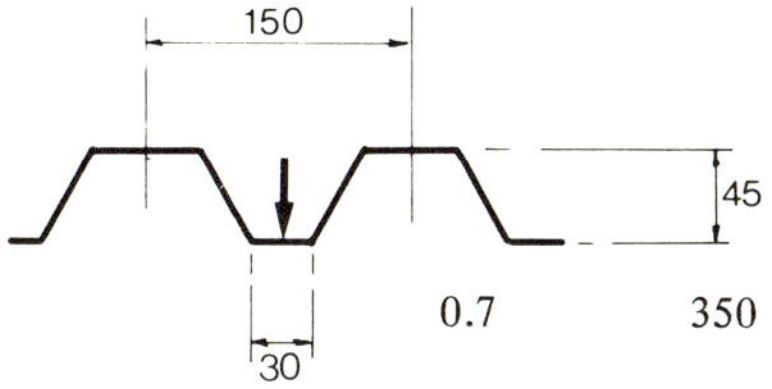	0.7	350	5.3	alternative 2	
			7.2	”	
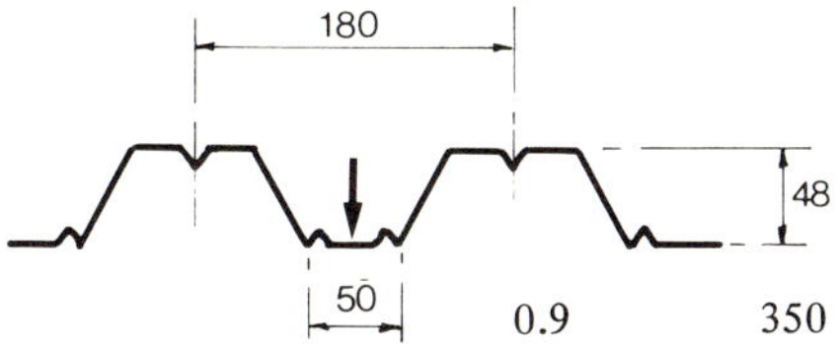	0.9	350	8.6	alternative 2	
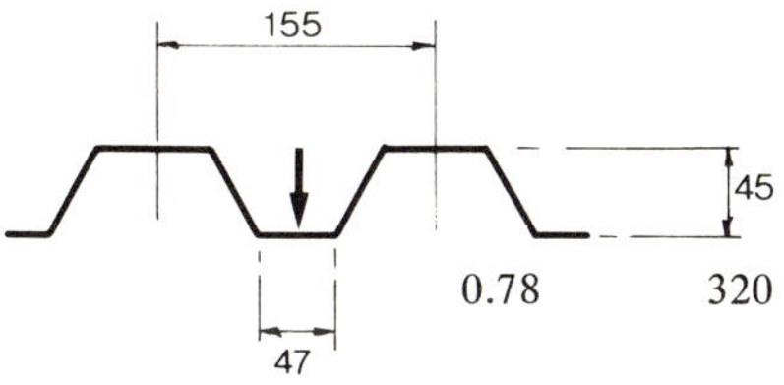	0.78	320	6.50	alternative 1	pull through
			6.00	”	pull over
			5.75	alternative 2	pull out
			6.00	”	pull through
as above but fastener had metal/neoprene bonded washer	0.78	320	7.20	alternative 1	pull through
			6.50	”	pull through
			6.75	”	pull through
			7.25	alternative 2	pull through
			6.75	”	pull through
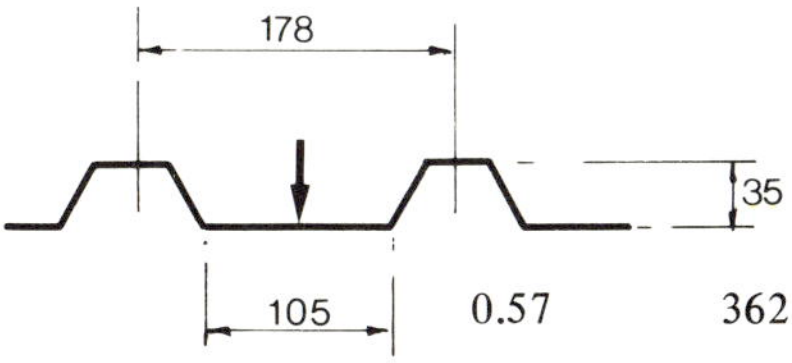	0.57	362	4.50	alternative 1	pull through
			3.60	”	pull through
			4.00	alternative 2	pull through
			4.00	”	pull through

(*Note* Position of fastener shown by arrow.)

(*cont.*)

Table 13.4 (*cont.*)

profile	sheeting: thickness (mm)	ultimate strength (N/mm²)	ultimate load (kN)	test fixture	failure mode
as above but fastener had metal/neoprene bonded washer.	0.57	362	4.30	alternative 1	pull through
			5.00	”	pull through
			4.00	”	pull through
			4.50	”	gross distortion
			4.25	”	gross distortion

screwed connections subject to both uni-directional and reversed repeated loading. His results for strength are in accordance with those of Baehre. In addition, he showed that under repeated reversed loading the hysteresis loop is not stable and deflections tend to grow slowly. As reversals of peak shear load in diaphragms are rare it is not thought that this effect causes any serviceability problems.

Test series	$R=\frac{P_{min}}{P_{max}}$	Freq. (Hz)	Test material: t_k[mm]	Fy[N/mm²]	Qual.	Fastener: rivets (USM): ϕ[mm]	Material	Type
B	0.1	25	0.77	433	Sub 350	4.8	Steel	SD 630 BS
C	0.1	25	0.72	474	Sub 350	4.8	Monel	LD 630 BS
D	0.1	25	0.74	467	Sub 350	4.8	Aluminium	AD 66 BSLF
E	0.25	25	0.80	405	Sub 350	4.8	Steel	SD 630 BS
F	0.50	25	0.77	436	Sub 350	4.8	Steel	SD 630 BS

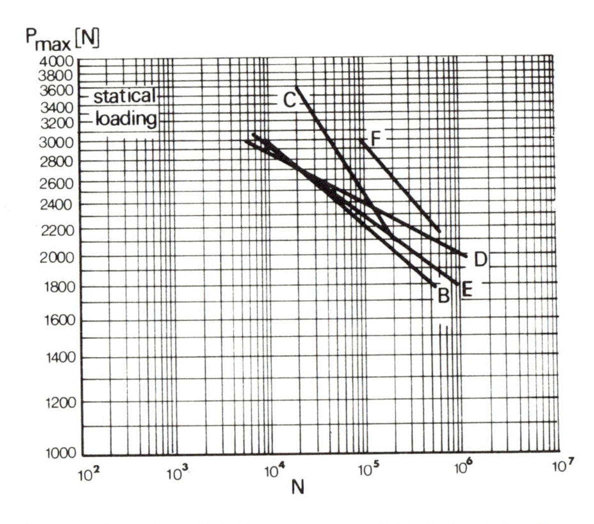

Fig. 13.27 Typical results of fatigue tests on blind rivets in shear. (Baehre)

Conversely it has been shown that tension connections may become unserviceable, or fail, at loads considerably below their ultimate static strength after less than 1000 cycles of loading. Although this factor is not directly relevant to stressed skin design it is certainly relevant to the design of fastening systems for light gauge steel roofs as it is clear that repeated loading made a significant contribution to the damage caused in Darwin by cyclone 'Tracy'[6.7, 6.8] in December 1974.

13.6 Combined loading of fasteners

In general, when a stressed skin diaphragm is subject to wind load at least some of the sheet to purlin fasteners will be subject to both shear and tension loading. For this reason, the European recommendations for stressed skin design[1.99] include an interaction formula whereby the influence on design of the combined forces may be investigated. The relevant formula is

$$(F_t/F_t^*)^2 + (F_v/F_v^*)^2 \leqslant 1 \qquad (13.17)$$

where F_v = design shear load in fastener,
F_t = design tensile load in fastener,
F_v^* = design shear strength of fastener,
F_t^* = design tensile strength of fastener.

As this formula involves second powers of the ratios of load to strength the degree of interaction is not large unless the fastener is near to failure in both shear and tension.

Now, in diaphragm design, except for the special case of diaphragms fastened on two sides only, forces in the sheet to purlin fasteners rarely govern the design. They are also subject to the rule that failure modes other than those involving a seam or other line of fasteners in a line parallel to a seam should be subject to an additional factor of safety of 1.25. It follows that, in the majority of diaphragms, the interaction will not influence the design. However, designers should be aware of the fact that sheet to purlin fasteners are subject to combined loading and be prepared to use the above formula when necessary. This could be particularly important in diaphragms fastened on two sides only.

13.7 Corrosion of fasteners

Questions are frequently asked regarding the influence of corrosion on the performance of stressed skin structures. The first part of the answer is relatively easy. The stress levels in the sheeting due to stressed skin action are so low that if corrosion takes place, the sheeting will fail in bending due to primary loading long before it fails in shear due to stressed skin action. There is therefore no problem unless there is a danger of a *much higher rate* of corrosion in the vicinity of the fasteners. The answer as to whether there is any danger of this nature lies with the manufacturers of the fasteners but the authors are not aware of any evidence to suggest that there is a problem. The only relevant test results known to the authors are the unpublished results of a small number of simple accelerated weathering tests carried out at the University of Salford on some joints made with self-drilling, self-tapping screws with neoprene sealing washers and plastic-coated sheets. The tests were terminated when some discolouration was evident due to corrosion of the sheeting. On unfastening the joints, the swarf trapped below the washer was still bright and there was no sign whatsoever of corrosion around the fastener. These tests do not answer all the questions that might be asked but they do indicate that, in general, there will not be any problem. It is much more likely that, if there is any corrosion in or around the fastener, it will have considerably more effect on the sheet under wind suction than on diaphragm action.

13.8 Material factors for fasteners

In the tests summarised in tables 9.9 and 9.10, in 38 of the 43 combinations of fastener and strap thickness tested, all of the test values of ultimate load fell within ±15% of the mean. Taking all of the tests the maximum deviation from the mean was 23%. This accords with the results of other researchers who have found that fastener shear strengths are remarkably consistent. It follows that, provided that the degree of site supervision is sufficient to detect consistent malpractice, the material factors for fasteners need not be excessive.

In the European recommendations, this consistency of performance is recognised and the material factor γ_m for fasteners is taken as 1.11 so that the design strength is taken as 0.9 times the characteristic strength. Bearing in mind that the characteristic strength of fasteners is the average of several test results minus approximately two standard deviations and that, in comparison, the material factor for steel members is 1.0, this procedure appears to the authors to be adequately conservative. Nevertheless, some national standards imply rather higher material factors for fasteners than the value recommended above, for instance the value given in the recently released British 'draft for public comment'[1.113] is 1.2 and rather higher values than this are implied in the safety factors suggested in a Swedish report[6.3] though these are admitted to be conservative.

CHAPTER FOURTEEN

Diaphragms with openings

14.1 Introduction

Openings are often necessary in light gauge steel diaphragms to accommodate roof lights or large flues, etc. and in practice a great many diaphragms contain significant openings. Despite this, until recently, very little effort has been devoted to the design of diaphragms with openings. Bryan[1.46] tested two such diaphragms and drew some limited conclusions. The main work on the subject is by Davies and Lawson[1.108] and this chapter is largely taken from their paper.

The European recommendations[1.99] incorporate two statements regarding openings in diaphragms, namely: (clause 8.27) 'openings for roof lights or other purposes shall not exceed 15% of the area of each portion of a diaphragm between adjacent main frames or lines of support unless such openings are suitably stiffened'; (clause 8.3(d)) the basic design expressions given in chapter 9 of this book may be used without modification provided that 'there shall be no openings other than randomly arranged openings totalling no more than 3% of the area between adjacent main frames or lines of support'. These statements were written prior to the work described in reference 1.108 and were based on limited experience. Nevertheless, they reflect good practice and the authors see no reason to amend them provided that they are interpreted with sound engineering judgement and caution. In particular the second statement applies only to relatively small openings. A single opening of 3% of the area of a diaphragm could be a large opening and positioned unfavourably it could cause a significant weakening of the diaphragm. It is for this reason that the Metal Roof Deck Association[1.126] has adopted a more cautious stance and specifically limited the use of its basic design tables to no more than 2% of *small* randomly arranged openings. A systematic investigation of the effects of various arrangements of openings on the strength and stiffness of diaphragms has also been undertaken[1.112, 1.117] and the conclusions from this will be discussed later.

The influence of openings on the design procedure has been introduced in chapter 5, particularly in section 5.5. The main considerations may be summarised as follows:

(a) Openings which cut a seam cause a reduction in seam strength partly due to the removal of material but also because the seam is divided into regions which will share load in proportion to their stiffnesses which are not in general in proportion to their strengths.
(b) Openings cause a sudden discontinuity in the shear deflection profile which in turn may cause local high values of purlin minor axis bending moment and sheet to purlin fastener force.
(c) There is also a consequent increase in the shear flexibility of the panel as a whole.
(d) In general, large openings should be provided with framing or trimming members on all four sides and these members should be carried through to the adjacent purlins or other supporting members. A minimum requirement is that framing members should be provided at the cut ends of the sheeting and the sheeting fastened to these members or other provision made to prevent the excessive profile distortion which would otherwise result.

In discussing the design of diaphragms containing openings, two computer methods of analysis were described whereby the importance of the above considerations might be evaluated, namely a finite element analysis and the plane truss analogy. A manual analysis suitable for design office use was also described. In this chapter a series of tests on diaphragms containing openings is described and the results are discussed in the light of the above considerations. The design procedure given in section 5.5 is thus shown to be conservative.

14.2 Tests on diaphragms containing openings

In establishing design methods for diaphragms containing openings, testing and careful observation must play an important part because certain aspects of behaviour (e.g. local deformation of the sheeting at the corner of the opening or twisting of the purlin due to local forces in the sheet to purlin fasteners) are difficult to quantify and can best be examined experimentally. For this reason a series of eight tests were carried out in order to establish the modes of failure and to provide experimental values of strength and stiffness whereby the alternative analytical approaches could be evaluated. The test arrangement was the conventional cantilever diaphragm shown with a single opening in fig. 14.1. An alternative arrangement with two openings is shown in fig. 14.2. In addition to the data shown in fig. 14.1, the following applied to all of the tested diaphragms:

Purlins and side trimmers : Z1720 $I_{yy} = 34.53\ \text{cm}^4$
Upper and lower trimmers : Z1420 $I_{yy} = 20.04\ \text{cm}^4$
Fasteners to purlins and trimmers: 1/4-14 self-drilling, self-tapping screws with neoprene washers.

Flexibility : $s = 0.18$ mm/kN
Average ultimate strength : $F_p = 3.77$ kN

Seam fasteners : steel blind rivets
Flexibility : $s_s = 0.15$ mm/kN
Average ultimate strength : $F_s = 1.95$ kN

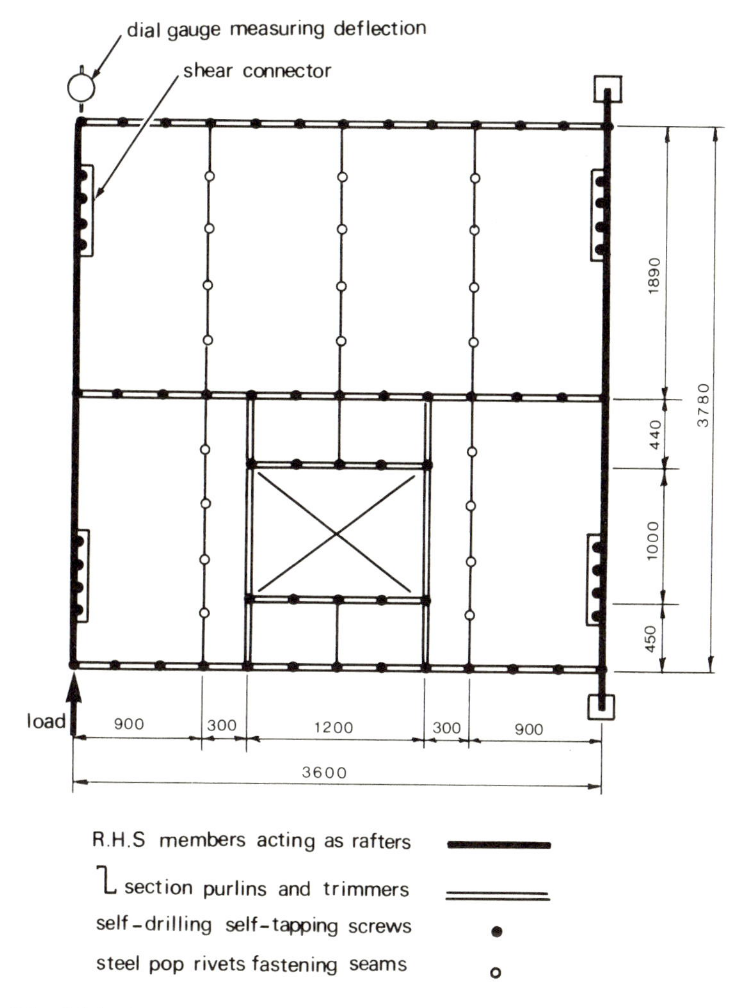

Fig. 14.1 General arrangement of test diaphragm (single opening).

The following options were available:

(a) The number of openings could be varied. Tests were conducted with 0, 1 and 2 openings, the sizes and positions being as shown in figs. 14.1 and 14.2.
(b) The shear connectors (s/c) could be retained (direct shear transfer designated D) or omitted (indirect shear transfer designated I).
(c) The sheet to purlin (s/p) fasteners could be in every trough of the corrugations (designated E) or alternate troughs (designated A).

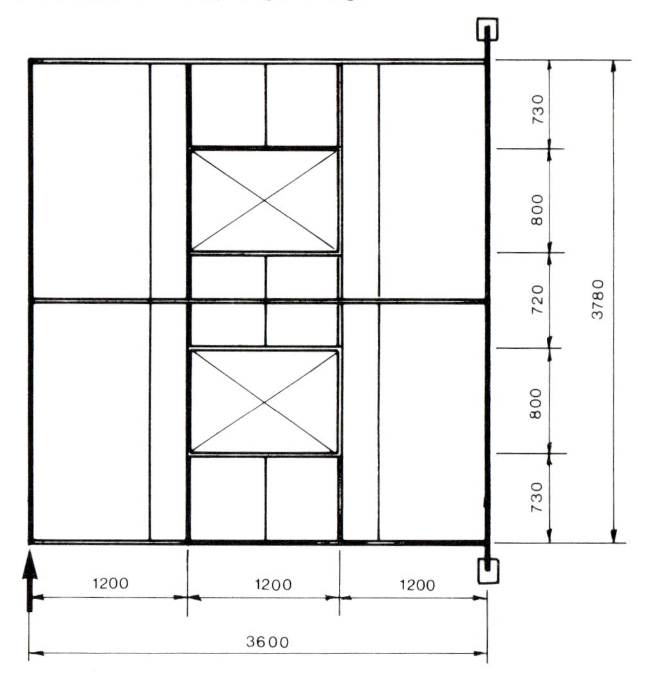

Fig. 14.2 Positions of openings (tests 2 and 7).

(d) The openings could be fully trimmed as shown (designated F) or trimmed at the top and bottom of the openings only (designated T & B). It may be noted that the latter trimmers are essential in order to restrain the shear distortion of the profiled sheeting.

The arrangement of seam fasteners for plain seams and a seam cut by a single opening is shown in fig. 14.1. A similar arrangement was used for the panels with two openings. The self-drilling, self-tapping screws fastening the sheet to the trimmers passed through both sheet thicknesses in the central seam so that the total strength of this seam was very nearly the same as that of a plain seam.

In addition to various combinations of the above options, tests were carried out using the two different available profiles shown in fig. 14.3 and designated ST35 and R15 respectively. A view of the apparatus as set up for test no. 1 is shown in fig. 14.4. Details and results for the complete test series are summarised in table 14.1, the notation being as defined above. Load deflection curves are given later in fig. 14.9. In table 14.1, the simple flexibility calculation is according to section 5.5 using the values of $\bar{K}$ tabulated in chapter 9. However, as discussed in section 10.7, the expression for the calculation of the flexibility due to profile distortion using $\bar{K}$ is not very accurate for the short sheet lengths between openings particularly when the fasteners to the purlins and framing members pass through alternate troughs only. For this reason a second column of calculated flexibilities is included based on similar reasoning but using accurate values of the effective shear modulus

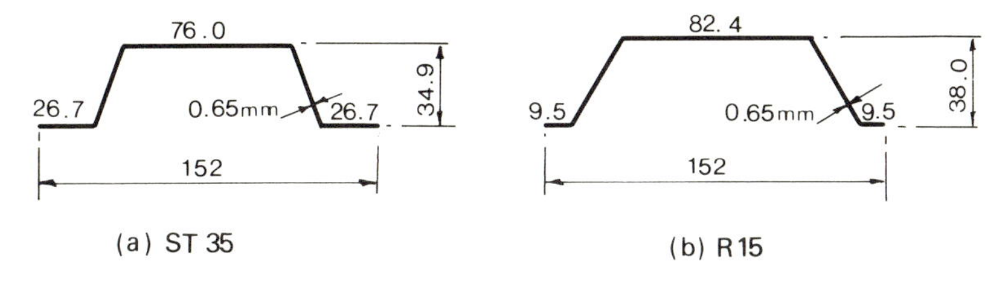

Fig. 14.3 Decking profiles used in the tests.

obtained by finite element analysis as described in section 10.6.4. It may be observed that in diaphragms 2 and 8, which have two openings, the total depth of openings is 1600 mm which is considerably more than one third of the depth of the diaphragm. They therefore violate the conditions given in section 5.5.1 as representing good practice.

The most important conclusions from the observations of the tests themselves are as follows:

(a) As anticipated, it is clear that the presence of an opening cutting a seam may weaken that seam even though there is no reduction in the total strength of the fasteners in that seam. This is because the relative flexibilities of the regions of the diaphragm may be so different that there is very little force carried by the more flexible region or regions.
(b) In several tests, damage to the sheet to purlin fasteners was apparent at load

Fig. 14.4 Diaphragm set up for test no. 1.

Table 14.1 Details and experimental results for the complete test series

test no.	sheet type	no. of openings	trimmers	sheet to purlin fasteners	shear transfer	failure load (kN)	flexibility (mm/kN)	failure mode	secondary damage	simple flexibility calculation (mm/kN)	flexibility calculation using accurate G_{eff} (mm/kN)
1	ST35	1	T & B	A	D	22.0	2.0	central seam above hole	s/p and sheet/ trimmer fasteners in line with hole	1.77	2.01
2	ST35	2	T & B	A	D	15.5	4.3	s/p fasteners in line with holes	sheet distortion at corners of hole. Bending of purlins	4.07	7.56
3	ST35	1	T & B	E	D	31.0	0.40	mainly in central seam above hole	side seams	0.37	0.36
4	ST35	1	F	A	D	24.5	1.8	mainly in central seam above hole	s/p and sheet/ trimmer fasteners in line with hole	1.77	2.01
5	ST35	0	–	A	D	31.6	1.0	central seam	s/c fasteners	1.22	1.22
6	R15	0	–	A	D	32.0	1.4	side seam		1.49	1.49
7	R15	1	F	A	I	13.6	2.4	end s/p fasteners	distortion of purlins at ends	2.22	2.52
8	R15	2	F	A	D	24.0	3.4	side and central seams		5.07	9.43

levels below those at which damage would normally have been expected in the absence of the openings. Although significant bending of the purlins was only observed in one test, purlin bending moments were evidently increased and must also be examined.

(c) The simple flexibility calculation given in section 5.5 is adequate for the cases of a single opening but not for two openings. It is shown later that in tests 2 and 8 much of the shear in the vicinity of the openings was carried by vierendeel action in the purlins and this resulted in unacceptably high minor axis bending moments. Consequently these two tests represent impractical arrangements.

(d) Significant local distortion of the sheeting was only observed in test 2 for which the situation at failure is shown in fig. 14.5. This test represents the worst possible combination of parameters (two openings without side trimmers and with sheet to purlin fasteners in alternate troughs only) and may be justifiably considered to represent bad practice. Local distortion of the sheeting is, in general, not a design factor because the sheeting is able to accept quite large movements without distress and if fastener forces and purlin bending moments are controlled there is unlikely to be any problem with the sheeting.

Fig. 14.5 Diaphragm of test no. 2 at failure.

(e) It is clear that the internal forces in the region of an opening are complex and that the simplified design procedures described in section 5.5 must be justified by comprehensive analyses that demonstrate the nature of these forces as well as by test results.

14.3 Finite element analysis

The finite element analysis of diaphragms incorporating openings has been described in chapter 5 and is a well established technique suitable for research and development. It also provides a useful design aid provided that the data can be generated automatically. Unfortunately, it does not appear feasible to develop a data generator for the general case of a diaphragm with one or more openings so that this method does not provide a practicable design office approach for this type of problem. Nevertheless, it is an accurate and reliable method of analysing diaphragms and provides a yardstick whereby other techniques may be assessed.

A finite element simulation appropriate to the tested diaphragms with one opening and sheet to purlin fasteners in alternate corrugations is shown somewhat diagrammatically in fig. 14.6. The particular trimmer and fastener details shown are appropriate to test 4 but other details can be substituted with only minor modifications to the data. The arrangement of trimmers for test 4 is shown in fig. 14.7. The data for this arrangement allowed meaningful investigations to be made concerning tests 2, 4 and 7. Tests 5 and 6, which fell within the scope of the available data generator, were also analysed. As an alternative simpler analysis was also available, it was not thought necessary to undertake the preparation of data appropriate to tests 2, 3 and 8. Finite element analyses provide an enormous amount of data and it is only possible to present a limited amount of information here. An appropriate comparison of results will be given in section 14.5 after an alternative analysis has been described.

14.4 Approximate analysis of diaphragms with openings

The approximate analysis of irregular diaphragms by simulating them as plane frames has also been described in chapter 5. Using this technique diaphragms incorporating openings can be analysed using readily available computer programs for the analysis of plane frames. Furthermore, the problems of data preparation are considerably simplified. A suitable plane frame analogy for a diaphragm containing a single opening is shown diagrammatically in fig. 14.8. By suitable manipulation of the member stiffnesses the same arrangement can also be used to analyse a diaphragm with two openings. The following points may be noted in connection with fig. 14.8.

(a) The joints are permitted to have freedom in the y direction but are partially restrained so that movement in the x direction is prevented. An alternative procedure is to complete the trusses using suitable members of large cross-sectional area.

(b) In the x direction, dimensions are in accordance with the prototype and sheet to purlin fasteners are represented individually.

(c) In the y direction, the dimensions are arbitrary and purlins and sheet to purlin fasteners that are subject to similar conditions of internal force and displacement are grouped together.

(d) The purlins have appropriate minor axis bending stiffness and the remaining members have axial stiffness only. The members shown by heavy lines are sufficiently

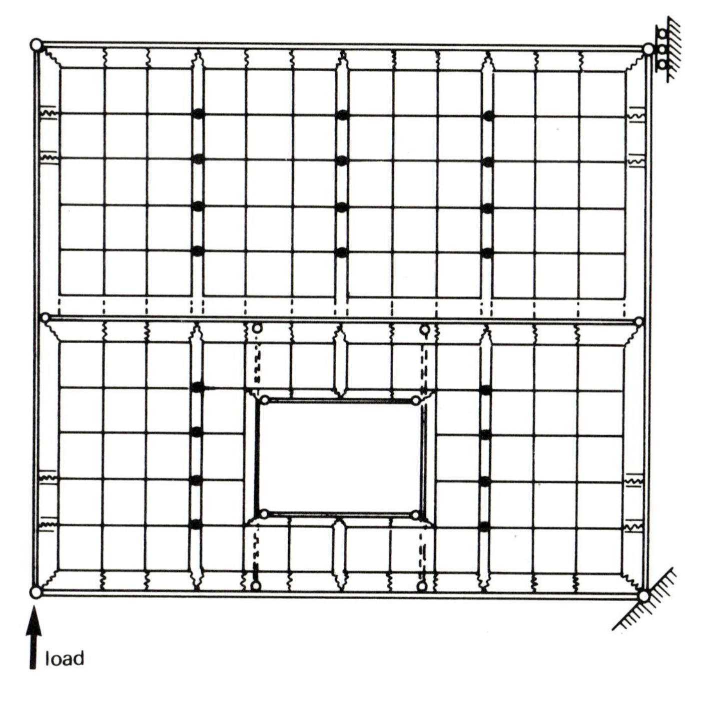

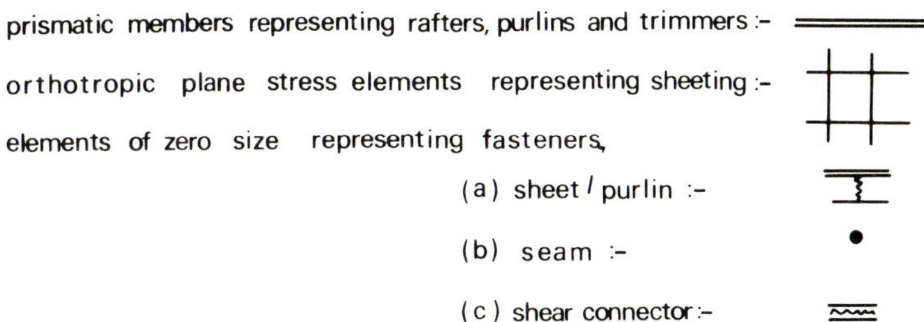

Fig. 14.6 Finite element representation of test no. 4.

stiff for their axial strains to be neglected.
(e) The diagonal members represent the flexibility of profiled steel sheeting and are given an appropriate cross-sectional area as described in section 5.3.
(f) As a suitable program was available, the opportunity was taken to investigate the elastic-plastic behaviour of the diaphragms. Thus the elements representing fasteners were allowed to yield at an appropriate axial load and the purlins were allowed to develop plastic hinges. This possibility of investigating the elastic-plastic behaviour proved to be of great importance as the redistribution of internal forces is much more significant in diaphragms containing openings than in plain diaphragms. However, the use of a simple bi-linear fastener characteristic underestimates the deflections in the elastic-plastic range as fastener load-deflection curves are highly non-linear.

Fig. 14.7 Arrangement of main framing and trimmers for test no. 4.

As was shown in chapter 5, this simulation appears to give perfectly adequate agreement with finite element analysis for detailed internal forces. Here it is also interesting to compare experimental and theoretical load–deflection curves.

14.5 Comparision of theoretical and experimental results

A comprehensive comparison of the significant experimental and theoretical results is given in table 14.2. Experimental and theoretical (elastic-plastic) load-deflection curves are compared in fig. 14.9. In these comparisons two sets of theoretical results are given. The upper line of results in table 14.2 was obtained using the full minor axis stiffness of the purlins (I_{yy} = 34.53 cm^4). The lower line of results used a reduced stiffness (I_{yy} = 14.20 cm^4) which gives approximate consideration to the tendency of the purlins to twist. For tests 5 and 6 which had no openings, only one set of results is given as the results were virtually identical. The test results will be discussed with reference to the theoretical results for purlins of reduced stiffness which are considered to be more realistic. The alternative results for purlins of full stiffness are not greatly different and when these are compared with the test results the conclusions are similar.

Taking the tests one at a time, the following points are worthy of note:

14.5.1 Test 1

The theoretical analysis showed that yield of the two outer seams at a load of 22.5 kN would be quickly followed by yield of the part of the central seam above the opening at a load of 22.8 kN. This latter eventuality caused a considerable loss of stiffness though the diaphragm was in theory able to accept further load with successive yielding of sheet to purlin fasteners. The initial flexibility was adequately predicted but the test results showed flexibility greater than the theoretical in the later stages of loading. This is typical of most of the results and is an obvious consequence of using a simple bi-linear representation of the highly non-linear fastener load-deflection characteristic. The experimental failure of the upper part of the central seam at a load of 22.0 kN is in reasonable agreement with the

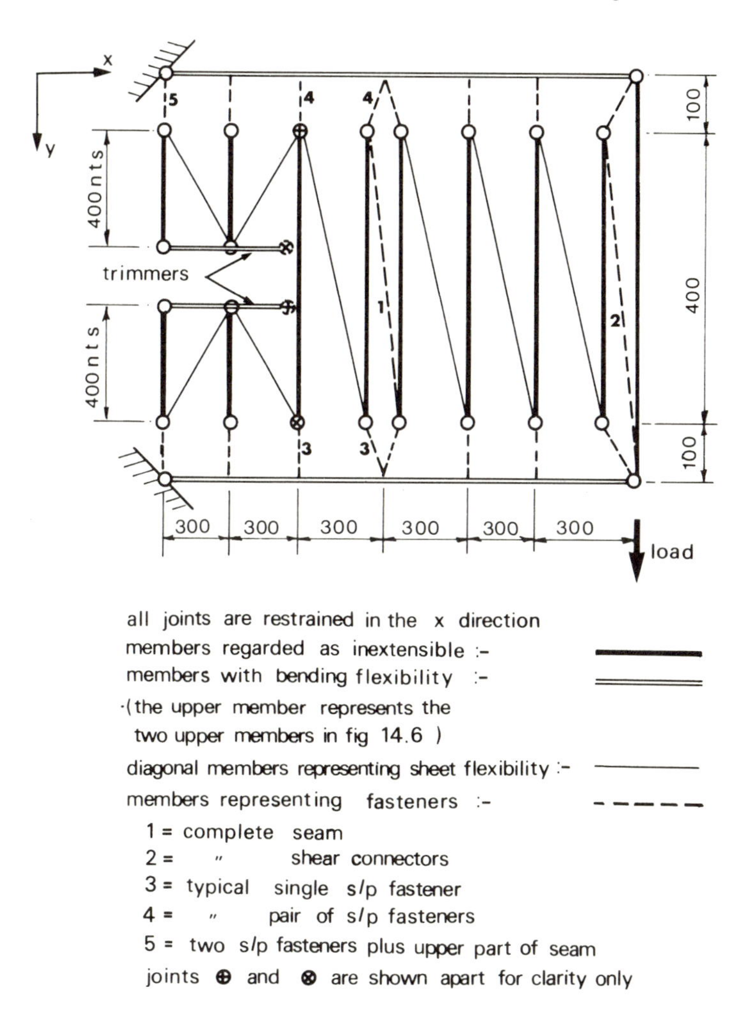

Fig. 14.8 Simulation of a diaphragm with an opening.

Table 14.2 Comparison of experimental and theoretical results

experiment			finite element analysis				approximate (truss analogy) analysis					
test no.	flexibility (mm/kN)	failure load (kN)	flexibility (mm/kN)	failure load (kN)	s/p fastener force (kN)	max purlin B.M (kNmm)	flexibility (mm/kN)	failure load elastic (kN)	failure load elastic–plastic (kN)	s/p fastener force (kN)	max purlin B.M (kNmm)	failure mode and subsequent behaviour
1	2.0	22.0	1.99 2.10	21.0 21.3	.192 .165	59.2 39.8	1.82 1.89	21.9 22.2	22.3 22.5	.154 .126	47.5 30.8	Side seam. Upper part of centre seam failed at 24.7/22.8 kN.
2	4.3	15.5					3.03 3.80	7.9 7.8	7.9 7.8	.475 .484	143.2 119.1	Sheet to purlin fastener yield. Side seams failed at 16.4/17.5 kN and outer parts of centre seam at 30.7/30.5 kN.
3	0.40	31.0					0.358 0.361	21.9 21.0	21.8 21.0	.0187 .0166	7.3 3.5	Upper part of centre seam. Side seam failed at 28.6/28.2 kN.
4	1.8	24.5	1.89 2.01	20.7 21.0	.194 .165	56.1 38.8	1.81 1.88	20.6 21.3	21.1 21.6	.200 .161	52.5 34.4	Side seam. Upper part of centre seam failed at 24.6/22.7 kN.
5	1.0	31.6	1.22	27.1	.010	1.0	1.21	27.1	27.0	.010	1.0	Seam failure.
6	1.4	32.0	1.49	27.1	.009	1.0	1.49	27.1	27.0	.010	1.0	Seam failure.
7	2.4	13.6	2.36 2.49	12.3 12.3	.213 .183	61.4 43.8	2.27 2.36	12.2 12.2	12.2 12.2	.224 .184	58.4 39.7	End sheet to purlin fastener (typical of indirect shear transfer).
8	3.4	24.0					3.32 4.14	14.4 13.5	14.6 13.5	.597 .632	154.3 133.8	Side seam. Outer parts of centre seam failed at 29.5/28.6 kN but only after s/p fastener yields.

Note s/p fastener force in above table refers to the average sheet/purlin fastener force per purlin in line with the edge of the hole.

theoretical predictions though it is significant that no distress to the side seams was observed.

14.5.2 Test 2

This test represents an extremely severe case in which the theoretical analysis predicted yield of the highly stressed sheet to purlin fasteners at the sides of the openings at a load of 7.8 kN followed by yield of the two outer seams at a load of 17.5 kN. The elastic-plastic analysis showed a progressive increase of flexibility as successive fasteners yielded but no clearly defined failure. In an alternative analysis allowing plastic hinge action in the purlins, the purlins yielded at a load of 8.7 kN and this caused a further sudden increase in flexibility as shown by the broken line in fig. 14.9. The initial flexibility of the test diaphragm was adequately predicted but the test diaphragm deteriorated rapidly after the yield of the critical sheet to purlin fasteners and failed at a load of 15.5 kN due to severe deformation around the opening (fig. 14.5). Though interesting from the theoretical point of view, this diaphragm must be considered to be unsatisfactory from the practical point of view.

14.5.3 Test 3

This test was the only test on a diaphragm in which the sheeting was fastened to the purlins through every trough of the corrugations. As fastening in every corrugation reduces the shear flexibility of the sheeting, and hence the discontinuity of shear deflection at the edge of the hole, by an order of magnitude it must improve the performance of the diaphragm by a considerable amount. This improvement is reflected in both the experimental and theoretical load-deflection curves. The upper part of the central seam was predicted to yield at a load of 21.0 kN but at this stage the region of sheeting below the opening was almost unstressed. There was no appreciable increase in flexibility until the outer seams also yielded at a load of 28.2 kN. Thereafter the diaphragm was capable of accepting further load but with significantly increased flexibility. The test results showed a failure load of 31.0 kN with failure taking place in the upper part of the central seam but with the outer seams close to failure. The theoretical ultimate load of the corresponding panel without any opening was 28.7 kN.

14.5.4 Test 4

This test was a repeat of test 1 but with the opening trimmed on all four sides. Apart from a small decrease in flexibility the theoretical load-deflection curve was almost identical to that of the first test. The test results confirmed the small reduction in flexibility and also showed an increase in failure load from 22.0 kN to 24.5 kN. The experimental failure load could have been enhanced by some bending moments passing through the trimmer joints. These were assumed to be pinned for the purposes of analysis.

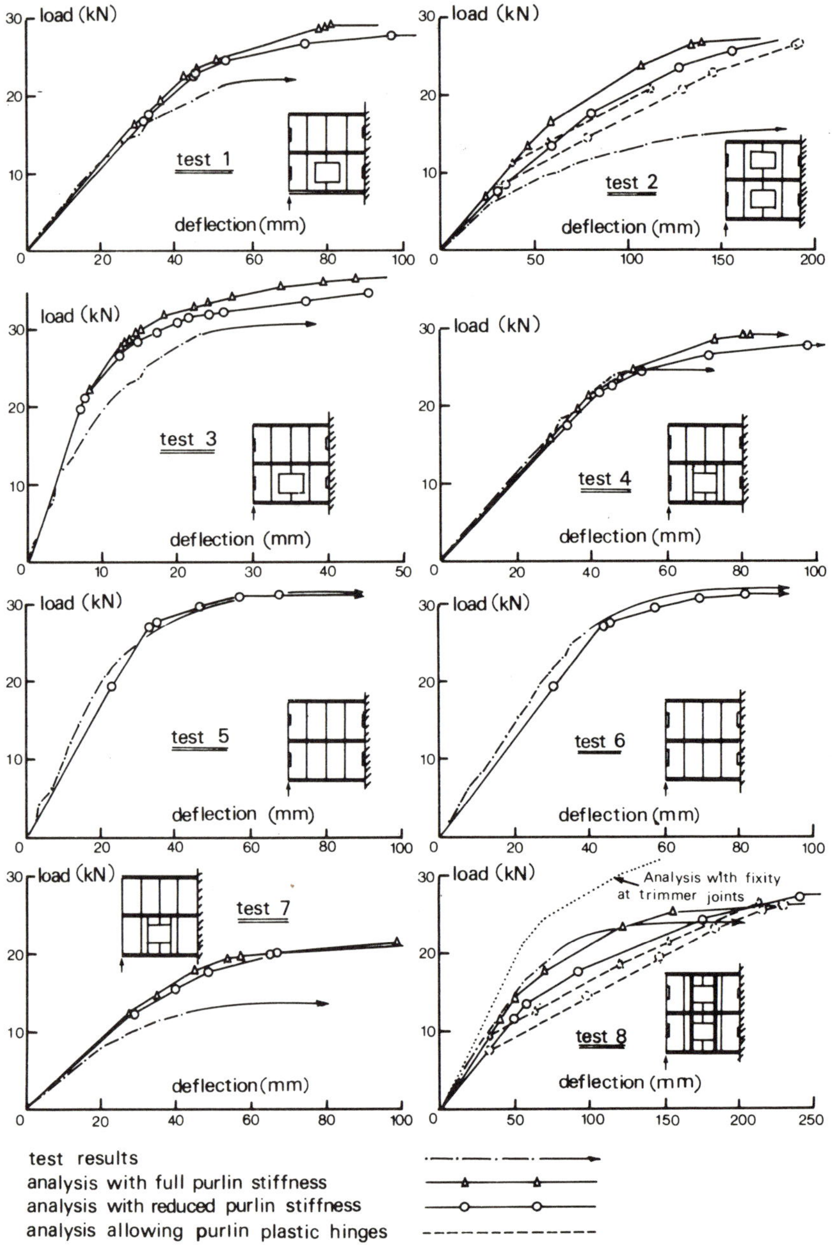

Fig. 14.9 Load–deflection curves for tests.

14.5.5 Tests 5 and 6

These tests were carried out for comparison purposes on panels without openings. The theoretical failure loads, calculated using the expressions given in chapter 9 but using average ultimate values of fastener strength rather than design values, were both 27.5 kN and this value compares well with the alternative theoretical values given in table 14.2. The theoretical elastic-plastic load deflection curves show significant redistribution of load before failure in a collapse 'mechanism' at a load of 31.2 kN. The observed failure loads of 31.6 kN and 32.0 kN respectively suggest that this redistribution may have taken place.

14.5.6 Test 7

This test differed from the other seven tests in that the shear connectors were omitted and therefore the applied shear force passed from the rafters into the decking through the purlin to rafter connections and sheet to purlin fasteners. Although the test panel contained an opening the results are dominated by the high forces in the outermost sheet to purlin fasteners. Failure of the test panel took place at a load of 13.6 kN when the sheet material tore at these fasteners accompanied by twisting of the ends of the purlins. This failure mode was discussed in some detail in section 10.14. The theoretical failure load, calculated according to chapter 9, is 12.8 kN which is in reasonable agreement with both the alternative theoretical values given in table 14.2 and the observed failure load. Detailed analysis confirms that the critical end sheet to purlin fastener forces are unaffected by the opening in the diaphragm.

14.5.7 Test 8

For this test, the panel incorporated two fully trimmed openings and the test results were evidently strongly influenced by the stiffness of the trimmer system. This is the only test in which the experimental load-deflection curve lay above the theoretical in the non-linear region and this result could only be attributable to the stiffness of the joints between the trimmer members. Accordingly, a further analysis was performed in which the trimmer joints were prevented from rotating. The results are shown as the dotted line in fig. 14.9. The initial flexibility was reduced from 4.14 mm/kN to 2.42 mm/kN and equally large reductions of flexibility were found at later stages of loading. As the test result lay roughly between the two alternative theoretical analyses, the above supposition appears proven. The analysis with rigid trimmer joints revealed outer seam yield at 21.0 kN followed by yield of part of the central seam at 24.9 kN. These figures are in reasonable agreement with the experimentally observed failure of the side and central seams at a load of 24.0 kN.

This test utilised a very similar arrangement to that of test 2 though with the addition of the side trimmers. Although these trimmers reduce the local high fastener forces they do not reduce the purlin minor axis bending moments and an alternative analysis allowing purlin plastic hinges, again showed purlin yield with an accompanying increase in flexibility at the low load of 7.4 kN. Even though the complete trimmer system helps to contain the high fastener forces and increased the failure load from 15.5 kN in test 2 to 24.0 kN in test 8, bending in the purlins means that this still represents an unsatisfactory arrangement.

14.6 Conclusions from test results and analysis

(a) In comparison with finite element analysis, the approximate truss analogy gives a perfectly adequate representation of the elastic response of the diaphragms and the added complications of a full finite element analysis are unnecessary.
(b) Redistribution of internal forces due to fastener yield can be significant. In particular, initial high forces at the seams adjacent to the openings dissipate quickly and it is unnecessary to consider these in detailed design.
(c) High forces may occur in the sheet to purlin fasteners adjacent to the sides of openings and these can be large enough to cause premature failure. However, if all four sides of the openings are trimmed and if fasteners between the side trimmers and the sheets are incorporated, these fastener forces are much reduced. The avoidance of unduly high local sheet to purlin fastener forces must be considered to be essential.
(d) Excessive bending of the purlins about their minor axes does not appear to cause any reduction in the strength of the diaphragm and early purlin yield may indeed be beneficial in reducing local fastener forces. However, severe minor axis bending of the purlins is likely to be accompanied by excessive twisting and should be avoided.
(e) The tests described above were severe cases in which it was expected that the openings would cause a significant reduction in both the strength and stiffness of the diaphragms. Tests 2 and 8 considered a situation which made the region of the openings so flexible that in the initial elastic phase most of the shear was carried by the purlins. Nevertheless in test 8 the failure load was only reduced by 13% below the theoretical failure load of the same diaphragm without openings (27.5 kN). A similar result was obtained for test 4 although, conversely, the corresponding tests without side trimmers (tests 2 and 1 respectively) performed less satisfactorily. It follows that diaphragms with large fully trimmed openings are robust and even with sheet to purlin fasteners in alternate corrugations are only subject to small decreases in failure load. When, as will usually be the case, the fasteners are in every corrugation the situation is even more favourable (test 3). Because of this robust nature, it appears possible to rely on a relatively simple analysis provided that an adequate estimate can be made of the following properties: (increased) flexibility, (reduced) ultimate load, local high sheet to purlin fastener force and local high purlin minor axis bending moment. A simplified analysis for the two latter properties will now be described.

14.7 Design expressions for local forces near openings

Notwithstanding the success of the approximate (truss analogy) method of analysis which brings the problem within the capability of the average design office it remains desirable to provide a more readily usable approximate approach for practical arrangements of openings. In this approximate analysis the fasteners are treated as a continuum and it is assumed that all of the purlins behave identically. The differential equations which govern the behaviour of the purlins and fasteners in the vicinity of the openings can then be determined and solved for the appropriate boundary conditions. This approach is considered to be valid provided that the following conditions are satisfied:

(a) Openings occur singly or in bands running parallel to the corrugations.
(b) The opening or band of openings has a total depth which is less than one third of the depth of the diaphragm.
(c) Openings are spaced so that in a direction normal to the corrugations the clear distance between openings or bands of openings is at least equal to the width of the largest adjacent opening.

The above conditions may be considered to represent good practice and may be considered to be necessary even if it is proposed to carry out a more detailed analysis. It should be observed that of the cases tested, tests 2 and 8 with two openings violate the second condition.

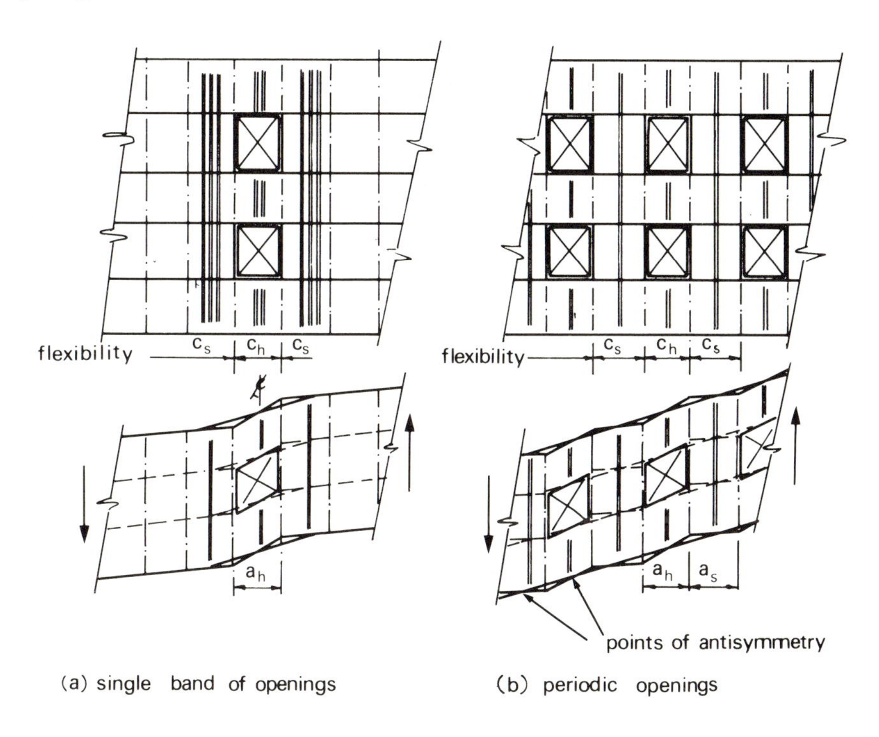

Fig. 14.10 Cases for approximate analysis.

In deriving the design expressions which follow, two different cases were considered as shown in fig. 14.10. In the first case (a) a single section of high flexibility c_h caused by an opening or band of openings occurs within an infinite length of

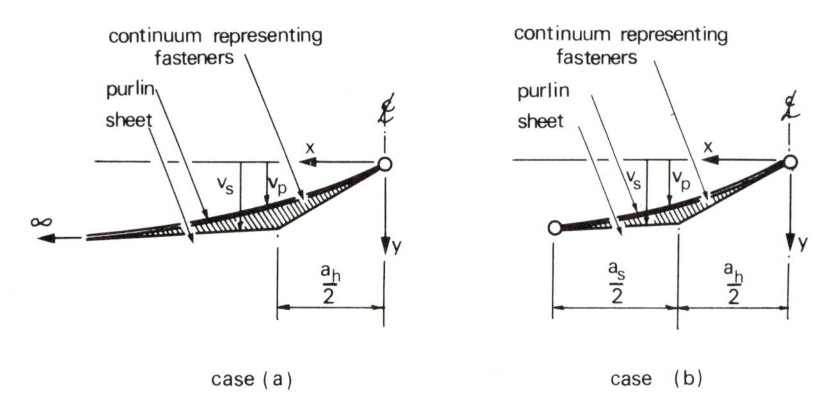

Fig. 14.11 Displacement components.

flexibility c_s. In the second case (b), flexible sections occur periodically at regular intervals. For both cases, the differential equations governing the behaviour of the assembly are identical though the boundary conditions differ. The two situations are shown in fig. 14.11 and, using the notation defined in that figure, the behaviour of the three constituent elements is governed by the following equations:

purlin
$$\frac{EId^4 v_p}{dx^4} = q \tag{14.1}$$

fastener
$$(1/sp)\,(v_s - v_p) = q \tag{14.2}$$

sheet
$$\frac{1}{c}\frac{d^2 v_s}{dx^2} = n_p q \tag{14.3}$$

where EI = flexural rigidity of a single purlin about its minor axis,
n_p = number of purlins,
s = flexibility of an individual fastener,
p = pitch of fasteners,
q = equivalent fastener force per unit length,
v_s, v_p = displacements of sheeting and purlin respectively in y direction.

It follows then that the required differential equation for purlin behaviour is:

$$sp\frac{d^6 v_p}{dx^6} - c\,n_p\frac{d^4 v_p}{dx^4} + \frac{1}{EI}\frac{d^2 v_p}{dx^2} = 0 \tag{14.4}$$

This equation applies to both sections of purlin provided that the appropriate c_s or c_h is substituted for c. The simultaneous solution of this equation for the two sheet flexibilities with the appropriate boundary conditions is not trivial and an appropriate numerical procedure is given in reference 1.90. However, it is found that when realistic values are substituted into this solution the results for the two cases are similar and the required values *per unit shear force* can reasonably be approximated by the following equations:

$$M_{max} = 0.007\,(c_h - c_s)I^{\frac{3}{4}} \text{ kNmm/kN} \quad (14.5)$$

$$F_a = 0.015\,(c_h - c_s)I^{\frac{1}{4}} \text{ kN/kN (alternate trough fastening)} \quad (14.6)$$

$$F_e = 0.010\,(c_h - c_s)I^{\frac{1}{4}} \text{ kN/kN (every trough fastening)} \quad (14.7)$$

where I is the second moment of area of the purlin about its minor axis and c_h and c_s are the sheet flexibilities as defined in fig. 14.10 in units of mm/kN/m length.

These formulae have the safe property of giving reasonably accurate values in the practical range of flexibility difference ($c_h - c_s < 0.5$ mm/kN/m) but over-estimating the forces and moments with more flexible arrangements. They have been checked by comparison with suitable finite element analyses. The design procedure detailed in section 5.5 may therefore be considered justified.

14.8 Application of the design procedure to the tested diaphragms

The application of the design procedure of section 5.5 to the tested diaphragms is given in table 14.3. The following points may be noted.

(a) The calculations have been carried out strictly in accordance with the design expressions although the accuracy of these reduces for the unrealistically short sheet lengths and alternate trough fastenings used in the test diaphragms. The results given in table 14.3 cannot therefore be strictly compared with the corresponding values in table 14.2 which were obtained using accurate values for the effective shear modulus G_{eff}. Nevertheless, the results given are considered accurate enough for all practical purposes and this objection would not apply to diaphragms of more realistic depth used in practical situations.
(b) The diaphragms used in tests 2 and 8 are clearly ruled out on the basis of the high purlin bending moments. In fact, the purlins are carrying most of the shear in the region of the openings and the flexibility calculation given above is not valid.
(c) The diaphragms used in tests 3 and 4 are completely satisfactory as far as the design procedure is concerned and the design strengths could be raised to those of the corresponding diaphragms without openings simply by strengthening the seam above the opening.
(d) For the diaphragm used in test 1 the design procedure also reveals a low strength with respect to the sheet to purlin fasteners in line with the edge of the opening.

14.9 Systematic investigation of diaphragms with openings

The full design expressions, including the modifications for the effect of openings are simple in nature and readily amenable to programming for computer solution. This has been done by the first author in a way that allowed a systematic investigation to be made of the effect on strength and stiffness of various arrangements of openings. The main parameters used for this investigation were those used for the design tables described in chapter 6.[1.126] The sizes of diaphragm investigated covered the complete range of the design tables and openings were typically one metre square at various spacings. As a large number of small openings have a more

Table 14.3 Application of the design procedure to the tested diaphragms

	Test results		Design calculations							
test no.	flexibility (mm/kN)	failure (kN)	basic V_{ult} (kN)	basic c (mm/kN)	modified c (mm/kN) (using α_h)	reduced V_{ult} (kN)	$c_h - c_s$ (mm/kN/m)	M_{max} (kN mm/kN)	F_e or F_a (kN/kN)	design load (kN)
1	2.0	22.0	27.5	1.22	1.77	19.5	0.4553	45.4 23.3	0.166 0.133	19.5
2	4.3	15.5	27.5	1.22	4.07	22.8	2.375	236.8 121.6	0.864 0.692	4.4 5.5
3	0.40	31.0	29.7	0.28	0.37	19.6	0.0597	6.0 3.1	0.0145 0.0116	19.6
4	1.8	24.5	27.5	1.22	1.77	19.5	0.4553	45.4 23.3	0.166 0.133	19.5
8	3.4	24.0	27.5	1.50	5.07	22.8	2.983	297.4 152.7	1.085 0.868	3.5 4.3

Note the upper figures are for full purlin stiffness and the lower figures for reduced stiffness

severe effect than the same area of larger openings, the results are conservative for larger sized openings. For the purposes of this investigation, it was assumed that at each opening the ends of the corrugation flutes were fastened to trimming members in every trough. This represents good practice and can mean that, in certain cases of diaphragms otherwise fastened to the supporting structure through alternate troughs, openings may have no adverse effect on either stiffness or strength.

For strength, no consistent pattern of results emerged. A single opening, strategically placed, covering a very small percentage area of the diaphragm could have the same effect on the strength as a number of openings totalling a substantial percentage of the total area. It was not therefore found to be possible to establish any simple reduction factor for diaphragm strength based on percentage area and, if the effect of openings is likely to be significant, the strength calculations must always be carried out more precisely. The converse is true, however, for diaphragm stiffness. Typical results for diaphragms with a profile height of 50 mm and fasteners to the supporting structure in every corrugations are shown in fig. 14.12. Similar results were obtained for profile heights of 85 mm and for fasteners in alternate corrugations. In each case a clearly defined linear lower bound to the stiffness of the diaphragm was obtained giving rise to a simple reduction factor. The stiffness reduction factors for each of the four cases investigated were as shown in table 14.4. These factors are repeated in section 6.7.2 where they are applied specifically to design tables for metal roof decks. They may well be found useful as providing general guidance in other situations.

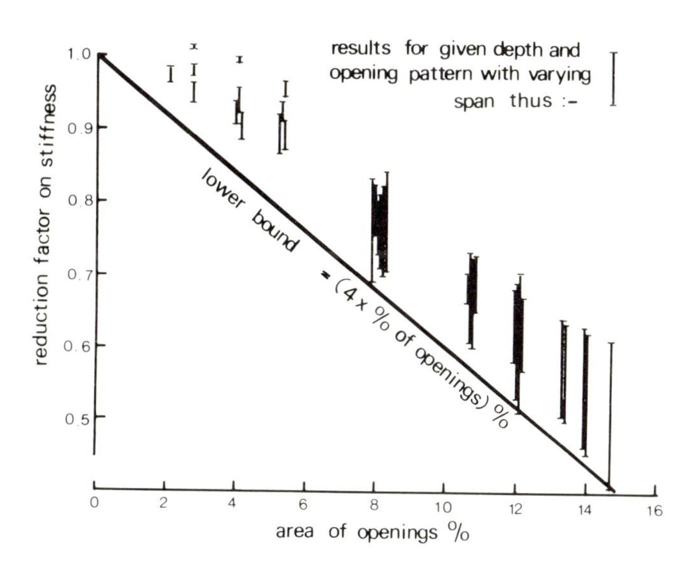

Fig. 14.12 Effect of openings on diaphragm stiffness.

Table 14.4 Reduction factors for diaphragm stiffness

Profile height (mm)	Fastenings to supporting structure	Reduction factor on stiffness expressed as a multiplier on the percentage area of openings
50	every corrugation	4
50	alternate corrugations	2½
85	every corrugation	5
85	alternate corrugations	2

14.10 Practical considerations

It is often found that additional openings through stressed skin diaphragms are required at a late stage of construction or even after a building has been in use for some time. It is important that large openings should not be cut through diaphragms without giving due consideration to the implications for the stability of the structure. This is largely a matter of educating contractors, architects and building owners to appreciate that profiled steel cladding is no longer an external addition to a steel frame which is stable in isolation. For this reason both the European recommendations[1.99] and the draft British Standard[1.113] both require buildings which rely for their stability on the stressed skin action of the roof sheeting to carry notices identifying them as such. If such notices are necessary it is hoped that the necessity is only temporary until those responsible for the construction and maintenance of buildings become more familiar with stressed skin principles.

It follows that, in general, when an additional large opening is required, the engineer responsible for the design will be consulted so that he may investigate the implications. There are usually two possibilities: in many cases he will be able to show by calculation that the necessary opening will not reduce the design strength of the structure below the design load nor cause unacceptable deflections, or he may find that additional fasteners in the vicinity of the opening are required or that the opening requires special framing.

Finally, it is useful to recall that diaphragms containing openings are robust and the considerations of this chapter are not intended to give cause for undue concern. Holes for small diameter pipes or flues will not cause any noticeable loss of strength or stiffness and may be inserted without the need for additional calculations.

CHAPTER FIFTEEN

Light gauge steel folded plate roofs

15.1 Introduction

New developments in stressed skin design will undoubtedly be concentrated towards applications involving the replacement of conventional framing members by light gauge steel diaphragms or shells. The first and most logical development is the light gauge steel folded plate roof. The basic concept is shown in fig. 15.1. The complete roof structure has only two primary elements, the longitudinal fold line members and the sheeting spanning between them. The individual roof planes are long relatively narrow diaphragms acting rather like inclined deep plate girders which gain mutual lateral stability from each other. The fold-line members at ridge and valley are cold formed from flat steel strip and carry axial forces; the sheeting acts as a web and contributes the shear stength. The proportions are such that the behaviour under shear is usually more significant than that under bending.

The concept of the light guage steel roof originated in the U.S.A. as a result of research carried out at Cornell University in the early 1960s. Typical American practice has been to use two-skin construction in which a flat steel soffit plate stiffened by spot welded 'hat' sections is connected to longitudinal fold line members by intermittent seam welding. This all-welded construction is immensely stiff and strong but also relatively expensive. It reflects the fact that the site welding of light gauge steelwork is widely used in the U.S.A. though virtually unknown in the rest of the world.

American practice has developed following a single test on a folded plate structure of 42 ft 6 in. (13.0 m) span carried out by Nilson[3.3] at Cornell University and shown in fig. 15.2. As a result of this test and the associated analytical work, Nilson demonstrated a number of fundamental principles applicable to the design of light gauge steel folded plates, namely:

(a) Panels of profiled steel sheeting span between fold-line members so that uniformly distributed loads on the roof appear as line loads at the fold lines as far

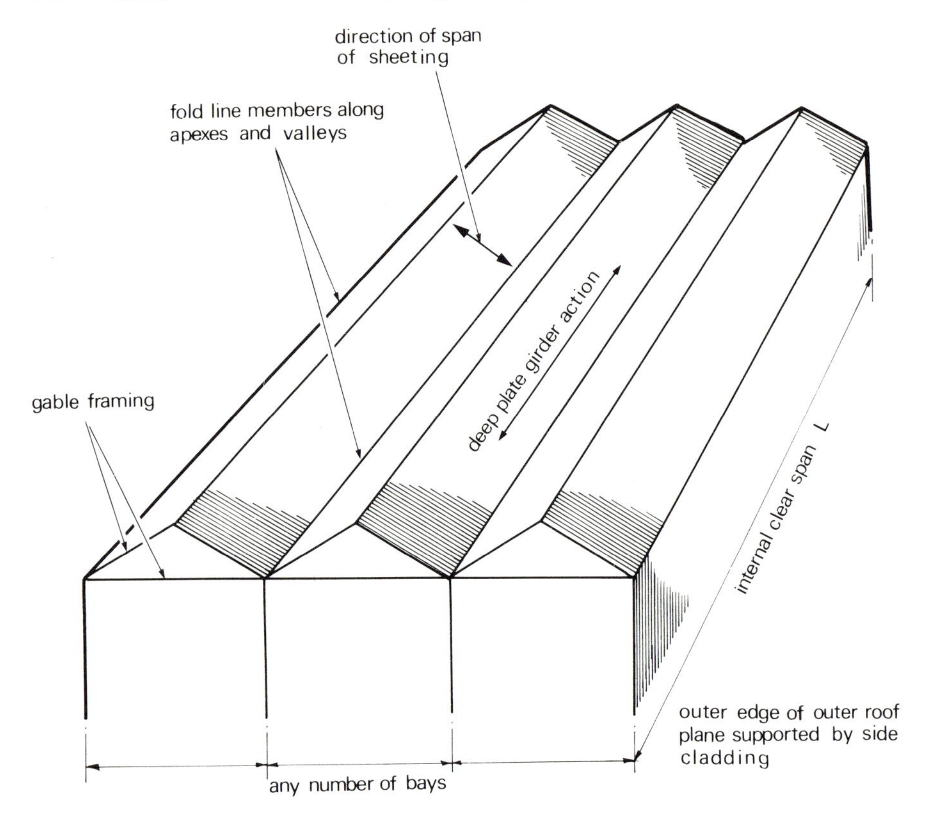

Fig. 15.1 General arrangement of typical light gauge steel folded plate roof

as overall behaviour is concerned. The almost complete lack of bending rigidity transverse to the corrugations means that the sheets span one way only; there is no redistribution of load along the panel.

(b) Line loads on the fold lines resolve themselves into in-plane loads on the two plate elements which meet at a given fold line. Out-of-plane bending stiffness of complete plate elements can be neglected when compared with the considerable in-plane stiffness so that it is merely necessary to resolve the line load into two components in the planes of the plates. A necessary consequence of the lack of out-of-plane stiffness is that both edges of each individual plate elements must be stiffened either by another plate element meeting at an appreciable angle or by some other means such as an edge beam or vertical cladding.

(c) It follows that the force system acting on an individual plate element is statically determinate and consists solely of an in-plane distributed load. Thus the basic design problem is as shown in fig. 15.3 and it is necessary to predict the strength and stiffness of such typical plate elements.

(d) Provided that the deflection of the individual plate elements can be estimated, the deflection of the complete roof can be derived by considering simple displacement diagrams at the fold lines.

Fig. 15.2 Test on an all-welded folded plate structure.

Light gauge steel roofs can have a variety of cross sections such as those shown in fig. 15.4. The simple saw-tooth arrangement (a) is the most efficient but many others are possible provided that there is an appreciable angle between adjacent roof planes in order to ensure the out-of-plane stability of individual planes. The outer edge of the outermost plane requires similar provision in the form of the side cladding of the building or short cantilever edge planes as shown in figs. 15.1 and 15.4.

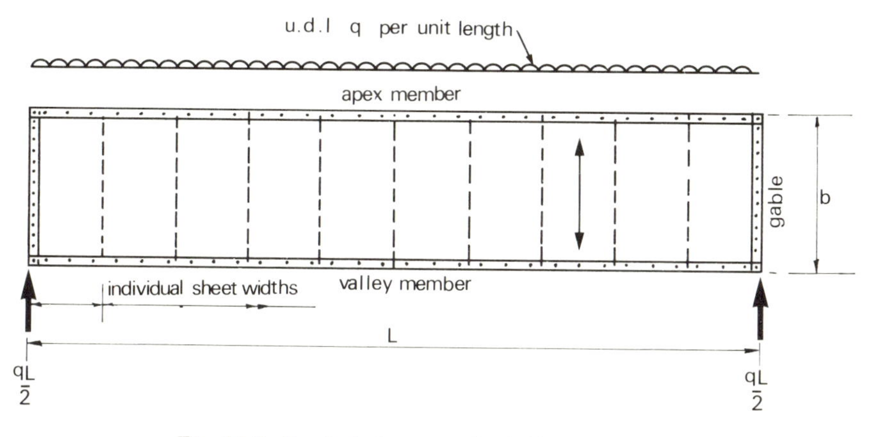

Fig. 15.3 Typical element of a folded plate roof.

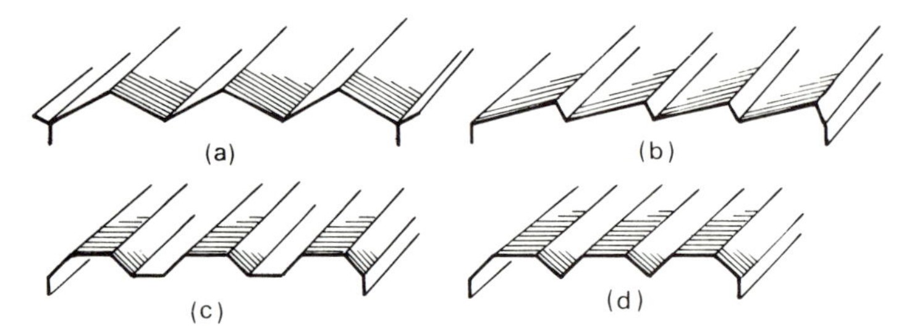

Fig. 15.4 Some alternative cross-sections for folded plate roofs.

As a result of Nilson's work, about 100 light gauge steel folded plate structures are known to have been built in the U.S.A. with spans ranging from 6 m to 34 m. Fig. 15.5 shows a typical example. Other examples are described in references 3.4, 3.5, etc. Recent development work in the U.K. has concentrated on extending folded plate theory to include roofs constructed of a single skin of profiled steel sheeting fastened with conventional fasteners such as self-drilling, self-tapping screws or blind rivets. The resulting structure is significantly less expensive than its all-welded predecessor but it is also less stiff and strong. However, the stiffness and strength of the structure can be reliably predicted and are found to be adequate for spans in excess of 20 m without the need for excessive numbers of fasteners or unusually thick sheeting.

15.2 Design of folded plate roofs

The usual criterion of design will be either strength or deflection under a uniformly distributed vertical load. In order to design the individual roof elements it is first necessary to resolve this vertical load into the plane of the elements as shown in fig. 15.6. Thus, if w is the load per unit area in plan, the line load q per unit length on a typical roof element is given by

$$q = wb \cot \theta \tag{15.1}$$

An important decision that must be taken at an early stage concerns the choice of the roof sheeting profile. The first essential is that the sheeting should be capable of spanning simply supported between the fold-line members. For this, manufacturers' safe load tables will usually suffice. However, the possibly conflicting requirements for buckling strength and deflection must also be borne in mind and it should be appreciated that for long spans many fasteners will be required and their design strength is proportional to the net thickness of the sheeting. The design then centres around the problem of predicting the strength and stiffness of a typical roof plane subject to a uniformly distributed load as shown in Fig. 15.3. This has been shown to be[3.19] a special case of a light gauge steel diaphragm and can be analysed on the same basis. Thus, by considering assumed internal force distributions, simple expressions can be derived for the strength in each of the possible failure modes and the plate elements can be designed using these. Similarly,

Fig. 15.5 Light gauge steel folded plate roof in the U.S.A.

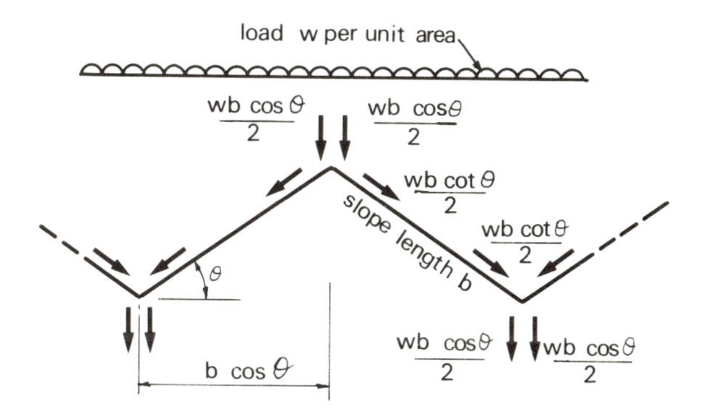

Fig. 15.6 Loads on a typical roof element per unit length.

expressions can be derived for the various components of the total deflection so that the deflection Δ at mid-span of the plate element arises as the sum of the following components:

$\Delta_{1.1}$ distortion of the corrugation profile of the sheeting
$\Delta_{1.2}$ shear strain in the sheeting
$\Delta_{1.3}$ bending action causing axial strains in the flanges

$\Delta_{2.1}$ slip in the sheet to flange fasteners
$\Delta_{2.2}$ slip in the seam fasteners
$\Delta_{2.3}$ slip in the sheet to gable member fasteners.

As with similar design expressions for diaphragms, the success of this approach has been justified by numerous finite element analyses as well as by a comprehensive test programme. The design expressions are given in section 9.10. As their derivation closely follows the derivation given for diaphragms in chapter 10, only the main points and points of difference will be given here.

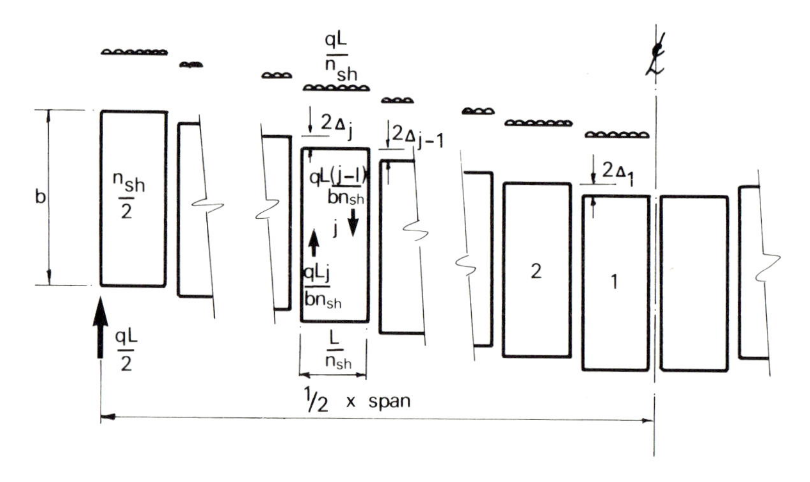

Fig. 15.7 Division of folded plate element into n_{sh} sub-panels.

The complete folded plate element is considered to be an assembly of sub-panels, each sub-panel containing a single sheet width as shown in fig. 15.7. The assumed force and displacement patterns for a typical sub-panel are shown in fig. 15.8. Two cases need to be considered, as shown in fig. 15.8. Case 1, where the seam laps are in the troughs of the corrugations, will be considered first and in detail. This is the case where the sheeting is treated as decking with insulation and weather proofing fixed on top of the sheeting. Case 2, where the seam laps are at the crests of the corrugations, will then be considered much more briefly as the derivation of the governing expressions is very similar.

Figure 15.8 shows an assumed linear distribution of relative displacement between the sheeting and the flange members with a slight discontinuity at the centre. This assumption follows from previous experience with shear panels and its validity is discussed later. In fig. 15.8, horizontal equilibrium is automatically satisfied but a relatively insignificant violation of vertical equilibrium is implied so that alternative approaches to the derivation of design expressions can result in slightly different results. The approach described leads to the simplest expressions and as these are found to be adequate for all practical purposes, nothing else is warranted. However, as with diaphragms, if the assumed linear displacement

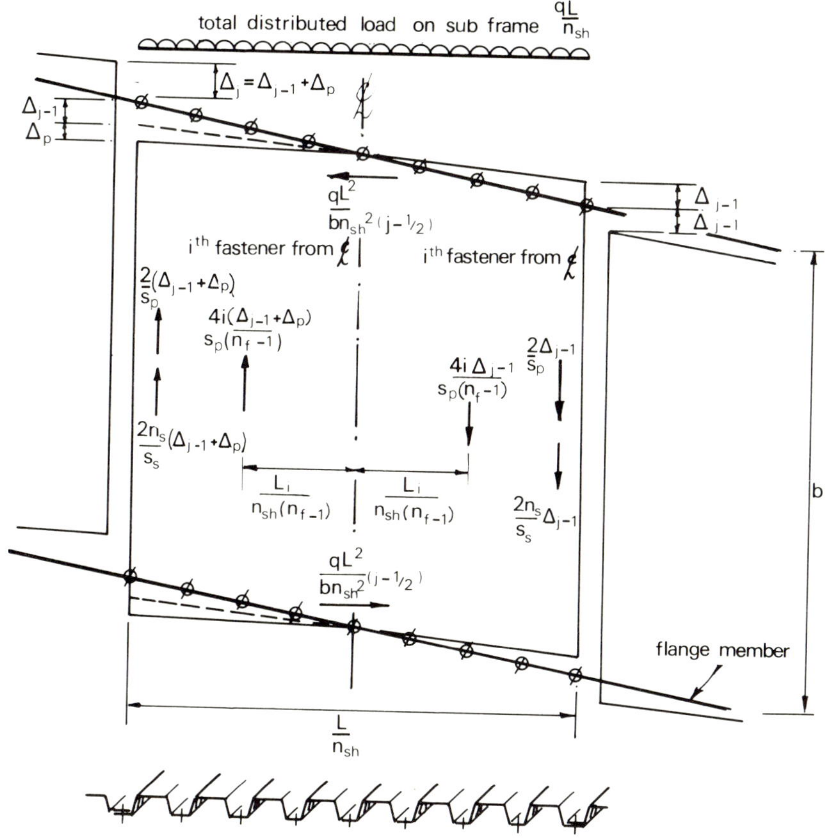

Case 1 sheeting fixing with seams in troughs (decking)

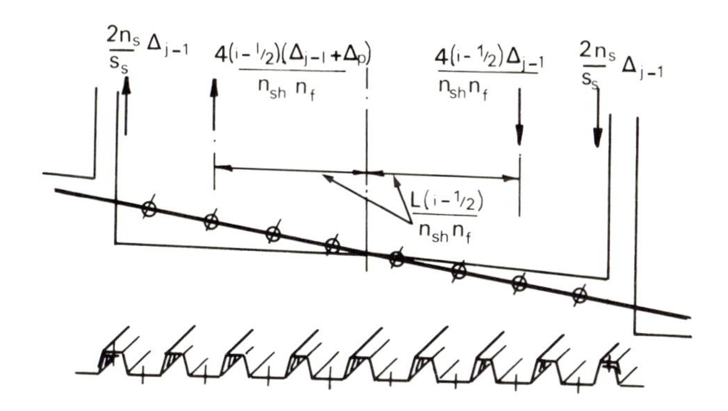

Case 2 sheeting fixed with seams at crests

Fig. 15.8 Equilibrium of typical internal sub-panel (jth panel from centre).

patterns are found to give rise to unconservative seam forces and displacements, they can be readily modified without complicating the design process.

15.2.1 Sheet to edge member fastener forces and consequent deflection

The total horizontal shear force shown in fig. 15.8 as $[qL^2/(bn_{sh}{}^2)]\ (j-\frac{1}{2})$ arises as a consequence of a shear force varying in intensity between $[qL/(bn_{sh})]\ (j-1)$ per unit length at the right hand side of the sheet width and $[qL/(bn_{sh})]\ j$ at the left hand side and reaches a maximum of $qL/(2b)$ per unit length at the gables. If the pitch of the sheet to purlin fastners is p, it follows that the maximum force in an individual fastener is $qLp/(2b)$.

Bearing in mind that the requirement for failure modes of diaphragms, whereby a diaphragm shall always be designed to fail in a seam or other line of fasteners running parallel to the corrugations, also represents good practice with folded plate elements, the strength calculated for failure of the sheet to edge member fasteners in 'horizontal' shear should be at least 25% greater than the design strength for failure in the seam or gable fasteners. It is convenient to work in terms of the maximum shear force at the gable, $V = qL/2$, which has a design value V^*. Then, if the design strength of the individual sheet to edge member fasteners is F_p, we have the general requirement that

$$0.8\, bF_p/p \geqslant V^* \qquad (15.2)$$

The horizontal forces carried by these fasteners arise as a result of the transmission of the horizontal shear forces from the sheeting to the flanges. At a distance x from the centre line of the plate element, the intensity of this horizontal shear force is qx/b per unit length. If the pitch of the fasteners is p and the slip per unit load is s_p the slip at an individual fastener at this point is

$$\delta_s \triangleq s_p\, pqx/b \qquad (15.3)$$

It then follows that the deflection $d\Delta$ in a small element of width dx at this point is

$$d\Delta = 2s_p\, pqxdx/b^2 \qquad (15.4)$$

and integrating gives the central deflection due to horizontal slip in the sheet to flange fasteners as

$$\Delta_{2.1} = s_p pqL^2/(4b^2) \qquad (15.5)$$

15.2.2 Seam forces and consequent deflection

In the assumed displacement pattern shown on fig. 15.8, the constant component of the horizontal shear force $[qL/(bn_{sh})]\ (j-1)$ per unit length is associated with the displacement Δ_{j-1}, of the left hand seam and the increment of horizontal shear force varying from zero to $qL/(bn_{sh})$ per unit length is associated with the additional increment of displacement Δ_p at the right hand seam. Considering the equilibrium between the constant component of shear force totalling $[qL^2/(bn_{sh}{}^2)]\ (j-1)$

and the vertical fastener forces associated with displacements Δ_{j-1}, vertical equilibrium is automatically ensured and moment equilibrium requires that

$$\frac{qL^2}{n_{sh}^2}(j-1) = \frac{2n_s}{s_s}\Delta_{j-1}\frac{L}{n_{sh}} + \sum_{i=1}^{\frac{n_f-1}{2}} \frac{4i\,\Delta_{j-1}}{s_p\,(n_f-1)}\,\frac{2Li}{n_{sh}\,(n_f-1)} \tag{15.6}$$

where n_s = number of seam fasteners per seam, s_s = flexibility of an individual seam fastener and s_p = flexibility of an individual sheet to edge member fastener. It then follows that

$$\Delta_{j-1} = \frac{s_s\,s_p\,qL\,(j-1)}{2(n_s\,s_p + \beta_1\,s_s)n_{sh}} \tag{15.7}$$

where here

$$\beta_1 = \sum_{i=1}^{\frac{n_f-1}{2}} \left(\frac{2_i}{n_{f-1}}\right)^2 \quad (n_f \text{ odd}) \tag{15.8}$$

Equation 15.8 is identical to the expression derived in section 10.3 for the corresponding situation in a typical sub-panel of a diaphragm. When other arrangements of fasteners or assumptions of force distributions in the sheet to purlin fasteners are considered, equation 15.7 remains unchanged and β_1 can take alternative values such as those given for a parabolic distribution in tables 9.5 and 10.2.

If equation 15.7 is to be valid for all individual sheet widths within the plate element, Δ_p must be given by:

$$\Delta_p = \Delta_j - \Delta_{j-1} = \frac{s_s\,s_p\,qL}{2(n_s\,s_p + \beta_1\,s_s)n_{sh}} \tag{15.9}$$

and it is easy to show that this same value of the incremental displacement is given by considering moment equilibrium of the vertical fastener forces associated with Δ_p and the two incremental horizontal shear forces each of which totals $qL^2/(2bn_{sh}^2)$. The displacement pattern Δ_p then implies a resultant upward force on the sub-panel centre line which can be shown to be very close to the total applied load of qL/n_{sh}. The small difference may be attributed to bending and shear forces in the flange members as well as deficiencies in the assumptions and it is here that the previously mentioned violation of equilibrium is to be found. This is not considered to be a serious objection to the basic approach which must be judged by the results it gives, particularly in comparison with finite element analyses. Having thus justified equation 15.7, an expression for the total deflection due to seam slip can be obtained by summing two times this equation over all seams in one half of the plate element. Thus:

$$\Delta_{2.2} = \frac{s_s\,s_p\,(n_{sh}-2)\,qL}{8\,(n_s\,s_p + \beta_1\,s_s)} \tag{15.10}$$

The above derivation applies strictly to cases when n_{sh} is an even number. If n_{sh} is odd, it can similarly be shown that

$$\Delta_{2.2} = \frac{s_s\, s_p\, (n_{sh} - 1)^2\, qL}{8\,(n_s\, s_p + \beta_1\, s_s) n_{sh}} \tag{15.11}$$

However, as equation 15.11 is for all practical purposes very nearly identical to 15.10 it is suggested that equation 15.10 be adopted for all n_{sh}.

As in the related work on shear diaphragms it may be recognised that actual distribution of forces in the sheet to edge member fasteners depends on the relative stiffnesses of the components and in some circumstances, the assumption of a linear distribution may be unconservative. Changing this distribution merely changes the value of the factor β_1 in the above equations and alternative values of β_1 based on a more conservative parabolic distribution of force are given in table 9.5. It has been shown[3.19] that the calculated performance of folded plate elements of conventional construction is not particularly sensitive to changes of stiffness of the components and that an adequately accurate value of β_1 can always be obtained by choosing from either table 9.5 or 10.1 according to the value of a relative stiffness parameter ρ. The procedure is detailed in section 10.5. Conservative results will always be obtained if table 9.5 is used and for this reason it is this more conservative set of values that is given in the summarised design expressions in chapter 9.

In deriving the expression for seam strength, the procedure introduced in section 10.3 is followed which results in an expression which is considered to be an improvement over that given in the European recommendations and which is described in reference 3.19. It is assumed that the seam fasteners in the critical seam have yielded with the load per fastener equal to the design strength F_s and that failure takes place when the sheet to purlin fasteners adjacent to the seam reach their design strength F_p. The situation at failure of the seam at the left hand side of a typical panel at a load factor γ is therefore as shown in fig. 15.9. Of particular note is the consideration of the panel in two halves. Only the left hand half is at failure and in order to consider the equilibrium of this half the 'horizontal' shear force of $[\gamma q L^2/(b n_{sh}^2)]\ (j - \frac{1}{2})$ at failure is split into two parts as shown.

In fig. 15.9, the considerations regarding horizontal and vertical equilibrium are similar to those already discussed in connection with fig. 15.8. It is convenient to obtain the necessary design expression by considering the moment equilibrium of the left hand half of fig. 15.9. Thus:

$$\left(\frac{\gamma q L^2}{b n_{sh}^2}\right)\left(\frac{j}{2}\right) b = (n_s\, F_s)\left(\frac{L}{2n_{sh}}\right) + \sum \Delta_j \left(\frac{\alpha L}{n_{sh}}\right)^2 \left(\frac{2n_{sh}}{L}\right)\left(\frac{2}{s_p}\right) \tag{15.12}$$

i.e.

$$\frac{(\gamma q L j/n_{sh}) - n_s\, F_s}{\Delta_j} = \left(\frac{2}{s_p}\right)(4\, \Sigma\, \alpha^2) \tag{15.13}$$

But, as $\Sigma\alpha^2$ in the above equation is only taken over half of the sub-panel,

$$4\, \Sigma\alpha^2 = \beta_1 \tag{15.14}$$

so that
$$\Delta_j = \frac{(\gamma q L_j/n_{sh}) - n_s F_s}{(2/s_p)\,\beta_1} \qquad (15.15)$$

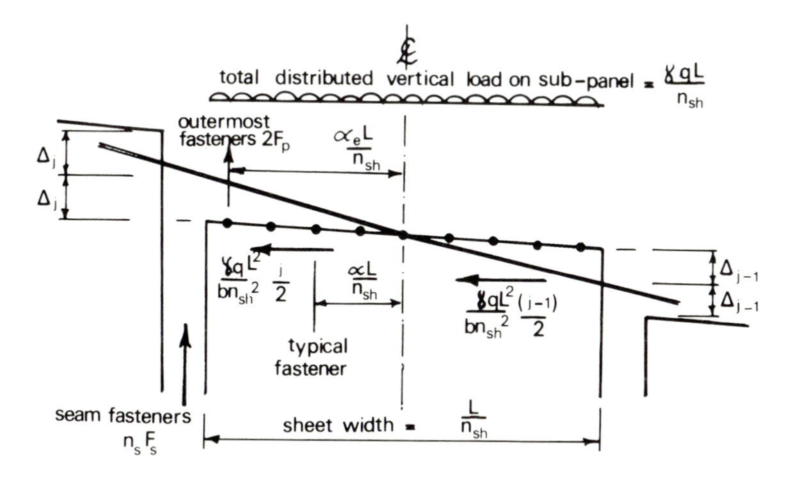

Fig. 15.9 Typical internal sub-panel at failure of left hand seam.

Finally, equating the total force in the outermost pair of sheet to edge member fasteners to their design strength gives

$$\left[\frac{\gamma q L j/n_{sh} - n_s F_s}{(2/s_p)\,\beta_1}\right](2\alpha_e)(2/s_p) = 2F_p \qquad (15.16)$$

and replacing $2\alpha_e$ by β_3, as for diaphragms,

$$\gamma q L j/n_{sh} = n_s F_s + 2\beta_1 F_p/\beta_3 \qquad (15.17)$$

In the most highly loaded seam adjacent to the gable, $j = (n_{sh} - 2)/2$ and for this critical case the maximum shear force V_{ult} is given by

$$V_{ult} = \frac{\gamma q L}{2} = \left(\frac{n_{sh}}{n_{sh}-2}\right)\left(n_s F_s + \frac{2\beta_1 F_p}{\beta_3}\right) \qquad (15.18)$$

As with the similar expression derived for diaphragms in section 10.3, and in contrast to the similar expression in the European recommendations,[3.24] this expression is good for both the sheeting and decking cases. The distinction is made solely in the values of β_1 and β_3.

15.2.3 Strength and deflection in end sub-panels

In deriving an expression for $\Delta_{2.3}$, the reasonable assumption is made that the flexibility of the connection of the flange member to the gable can be ignored in comparison with the flexibility of the fasteners connecting the sheeting to its perimeter members. This simplifying assumption will normally be valid but it is not essential and the full expression including the additional flexibility terms may be derived as in reference 3.16. The assumed distribution of forces and displacements is shown in fig. 15.10. In this figure, n_{sc} is the total number of fasteners to the gable member and s_{sc} their individual flexibility. These symbols, normally used for fasteners to shear connectors in diaphragms, are used here also in order to preserve the analogy between diaphragm behaviour and plate element behaviour.

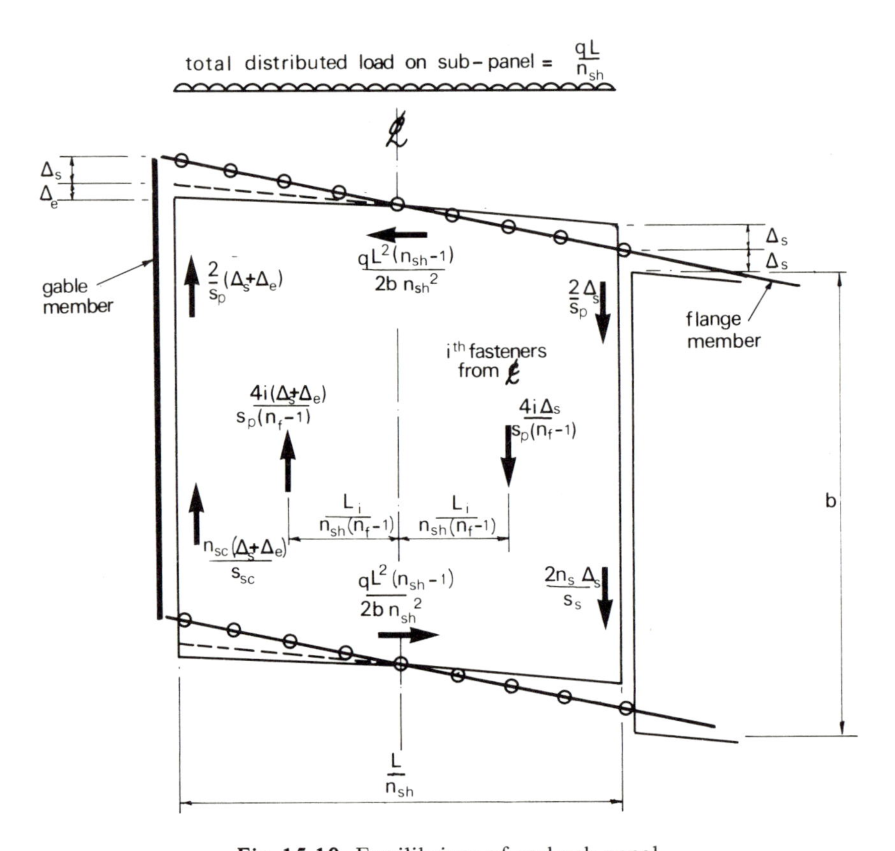

Fig. 15.10 Equilibrium of end sub-panel.

In fig. 15.10, Δ_s is in fact half of the displacement of the seam to the right of the panel numbered $n_{sh}/2$ so that from equation 15.7

$$\Delta_s = \frac{s_s\, s_p\, (n_{sh} - 2)qL}{4(n_s\, s_p + \beta_1\, s_s)n_{sh}} \tag{15.19}$$

As equilibrium of both moments and vertical forces cannot be satisified simultaneously, the design expression is again obtained by satisfying moment equilibrium and allowing a small out of balance of vertical forces. The condition for equilibrium of moments about the centre line is

$$\frac{qL}{n_{sh}} + \frac{2n_s}{s_s} \Delta_s = \frac{2\beta_1}{s_p} \Delta_e + \frac{n_{sc}}{s_{sc}} (\Delta_s + \Delta_e) \tag{15.20}$$

Substituting for Δ_s and rearranging gives the expression for flexibility at the gable as

$$\Delta_{2.3} = \Delta_s + \Delta_e = \frac{s_p\, s_{sc}\, qL}{2(2\beta_1\, s_{sc} + n_{sc}\, s_p)} \tag{15.21}$$

which is simpler than the corresponding expression based on vertical equilibrium but gives very similar results while being somewhat more conservative.

Again, fig. 15.10 and the above derivation specifically consider the sheeting fixed as decking with an odd number of flange fasteners per sub-panel but the various alternative arrangements will merely modify the value of the factor β_1. In this connection it may be noted that the gable will normally be detailed with the gable frame member at the same level as the flanges, so that the gable fasteners will pass through the troughs of the sheeting even if the seam fasteners lie along the crests. In deriving the expression for strength in the fasteners to the gable members it is convenient to recognise that the high shear force will necessitate the provision of a substantial direct connection between the sheeting and the gable and that the influence of the distribution of sheet to edge member fastener force will be small. The design expression then follows directly by equating the gable shear force to the strength of the fasteners at the gable, thus

$$V_{\text{ult}} = \frac{\gamma qL}{2} = n_{sc}\, F_{sc} + 2F_p \tag{15.22}$$

15.2.4 Deflection due to distortion of the corrugation profile

When an element of corrugated sheeting of length b and width a is subject to a uniform shear force V, it has been shown in sections 10.6, 10.7 and 10.8 that the shear deflection Δ is given by:

$$\Delta = \frac{a\, d^{2.5}\, \bar{K}\, V}{Et^{2.5}\, b^2} \tag{15.23}$$

where d = pitch of the corrugations, E = Young's modulus, $\bar{K}$ = a constant for a given cross section (tables 9.6, 9.7, 9.8) and t = net thickness of the sheeting. As the distribution of shear force in the web of a plate element subjected to a uniformly distributed load is linear, it follows that the shear deflection $d\Delta$ in a small element distant x from the centre of the element is given by

$$d\Delta = \frac{d^{2.5}\, \bar{K}\, qx\, dx}{Et^{2.5}\, b^2} \tag{15.24}$$

Integrating over half of the length of the element gives the central deflection due to corrugation distortion as

$$\Delta_{1.1} = \frac{\bar{d}^{2.5}\,\bar{K}\,qL^2}{8Et^{2.5}\,b^2} \qquad (15.25)$$

15.2.5 Deflection due to shear strain in the sheeting

The expression for the shear deflection of an element of sheeting in a uniform shear field for this component of flexibility is

$$\Delta = \frac{2a(1+\nu)\,[1+(2h/d)]\,V}{Etb}\ \text{mm} \qquad (15.26)$$

and integrating this over half the area of the plate element as above gives the central deflection due to shear strain in the sheeting as

$$\Delta_{1.2} = \frac{(1+\nu)\,[1+(2h/d)]\,qL^2}{4Etb}\ \text{mm} \qquad (15.27)$$

15.2.6 Design of fold-line members and deflection due to axial strain

The fold-line members are usually cold formed from steel sheet. Minimal fold-line members could have a single bend to accommodate the angle of slope of the roof though fold-line members which are too flexible in bending or twisting could lead to difficulties in erection. In the completed structure, the fold-line members serve solely to carry the axial forces due to bending moments in the roof elements. They may be assumed to be fully restained against lateral buckling by the sheeting and should be designed so that the cross-sectional area A, reduced as necessary for local buckling, is sufficient to carry 1.25 times the design axial thrust. Thus, for an isolated plate element, the maximum axial force in the fold-line members at mid-span is $\gamma qL^2/(8b)$ and for a satisfactory design on the basis of strength it is merely necessary that

$$A\,\sigma_{\text{perm}} \geqslant \gamma qL^2/(6.4b) \qquad (15.28)$$

In a complete roof, where the fold-line members carry axial forces arising from bending action in the two adjacent planes, it is necessary that the area should be sufficient to carry the total axial force on the same basis. The factor of 1.25 implied in equation 15.28 arises, as before, from the consideration that failure should take place in the seam or gable fasteners and that the element should be designed to have an additional 25% reserve of safety against any other mode of failure.

The component of deflection due to axial strain in the fold-line members is simply calculated from first principles on the assumption that the bending moment is carried entirely in the flanges. If each flange has cross-sectional area A, the second moment of area of the flanges as

$$I = Ab^2/2 \qquad (15.29)$$

and it follows directly that the central deflection due to axial strain in the flanges is

$$\Delta_{1.3} = \frac{5\,q\,L^4}{384EI} = \frac{qL^4}{38.4EAb^2} \qquad (15.30)$$

Equation 15.30 applies strictly to individual plate elements. When such elements are connected together to form a complete folded plate roof, individual flange members form part of two plate elements and attract loads from them both. The precise calculation of the deflection component $\Delta_{1.3}$ then requires consideration of strain compatability though it may often be sufficient to associate an area of $A/2$ with each plate element, merely doubling $\Delta_{1.3}$ in equation 15.30. An example of the precise calculation is given in section 7.7. Similarly, if the two fold-line members forming the flanges are of different areas A_1 and A_2, equation 15.30 requires amplification, the correct form being obtained by replacing A with the expression $2A_1 A_2/(A_1 + A_2)$.

15.2.7 Shear buckling in folded plate elements

Shear buckling in diaphragms has been considered in section 10.13. A typical buckling failure in a folded plate element is shown in fig. 15.11. The proportions of folded plate elements are such that this mode of failure is relatively much more important than in the case of conventional diaphragms and here it provides one of the main constraints on the design. The design limitation is centred on the ability of the sheeting to sustain the maximum shear force at the gable. The mathematics of this problem is identical to that given previously for diaphragms in section 10.13 with the simplication that there is never the need to consider the influence of intermediate purlins or their equivalent.

15.2.8 Modification factors for variations in fastener spacing

The necessary fastener spacing at any point along a plate element is directly related to the shear force and it will often be found economic to vary the fastener spacings along the length of the element. For long spans, close fastener spacings are usually necessary near to the gables but the spacing can be reduced as the shear force reduces towards zero at the centre of the element. Two of the fastener systems may be varied over the length of the plate element, namely: sheet to flange fasteners – any variation in the pitch of these fasteners changes the profile constant $\bar{K}$ and therefore both $\Delta_{1.1}$ and $\Delta_{2.1}$ must be modified. Furthermore, the factor β_1 also changes and this modifies the calculation of $\Delta_{2.2}$; seam fasteners – any variation in the pitch of these fasteners affects only the value of $\Delta_{2.2}$. It is assumed that there may be up to three different fastener pitches within a given plate element and expressions will be derived for this case. Related expressions for two fastener pitches may then be deduced as a special case. Thus the situation to be considered is shown in fig. 15.12.

Fig. 15.11 Shear buckling in a folded plate element.

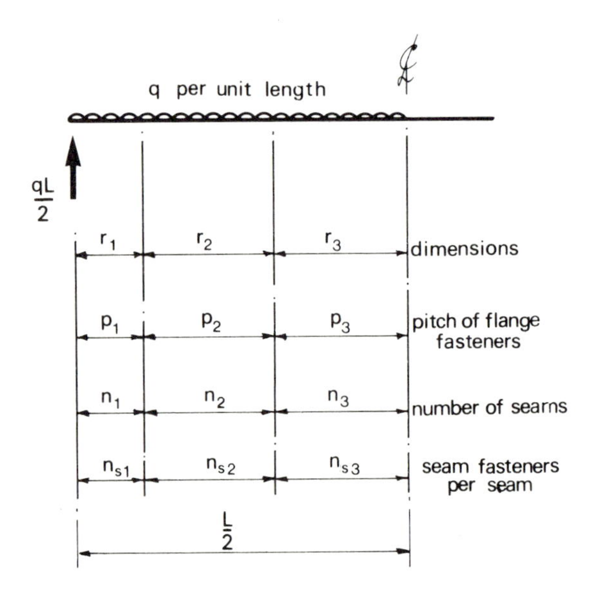

Fig. 15.12 Most general arrangement of fasteners.

(a) Modification to $\Delta_{1.1}$

It is assumed that for length r_1 of the plate element, the sheeting constant is $\bar{K}_1$ and for lengths r_2 and r_3 it is $\bar{K}_2$ and $\bar{K}_3$ respectively. Then it follows from equation 15.24 that

$$\Delta_{1.1} = \frac{d^{2.5}\, q}{Et^{2.5}\, b^2}\left[\int_0^{r_3} \bar{K}_3\, x\, dx + \int_{r_3}^{r_2+r_3} \bar{K}_2\, x\, dx + \int_{r_2+r_3}^{L/2} \bar{K}_1\, x\, dx\right] \quad (15.31)$$

If $R_1 = 2r_1/L, R_2 = 2r_2/L, R_3 = 2r_3/L$ so that $R_1 + R_2 + R_3 = 1$, it also follows that

$$\Delta_{1.1} = \frac{d^{2.5}\bar{K}'\, qL^2}{8Et^{2.5}\, b^2} \quad (15.32)$$

which is identical to equation 15.25 with $\bar{K}$ replaced by $\bar{K}'$ where

$$\bar{K}' = \bar{K}_1 R_1\,(2 - R_1) + \bar{K}_2 R_2\,(R_2 + 2R_3) + \bar{K}_3 {R_3}^2 \quad (15.33)$$

Equation 15.33 can be regarded as providing a modification factor for use in equation 15.25. If there are only two different pitch values used, equation 15.33 reduces to

$$\bar{K}' = \bar{K}_1 R_1\,(2 - R_1) + \bar{K}_2 {R_2}^2 \quad (15.34)$$

which is an alternative modification factor for this simpler case.

(b) Modification factor to $\Delta_{2.1}$

Here it follows from equation 15.5 that

$$\Delta_{2.1} = \frac{2s_p\, q}{b^2}\left(\int_0^{r_3} p_3\, x\, dx + \int_{r_3}^{r_2+r_3} p_2\, x\, dx + \int_{r_2+r_3}^{L/2} p_1\, x\, dx\right) \quad (15.35)$$

which reduces in a similar manner to:

$$\Delta_{2.1} = s_p p'\, qL^2/(4b^2) \quad (15.36)$$

where p' is a modified pitch value given by

$$p' = p_1 R_1\,(2 - R_1) + p_2 R_2\,(R_2 + 2R_3) + p_3 {R_3}^2 \quad (15.37)$$

For two different pitch values only, the reduced form of equation 15.37 giving the alternative modification factor for this simpler case is:

$$p' = p_1 R_1\,(2 - R_1) + p_2 {R_2}^2 \quad (15.38)$$

(c) Modification of $\Delta_{2.2}$ for varying numbers of seam fasteners

Unfortunately, equation 15.11 is not readily amenable to modification in the same way as equations 15.25 and 15.5 above although the correct approach is apparent. The calculation is best done on an individual basis for each particular case in the following way. If, commencing at the centre of the panel, each half plate has n_1 seams with n_{s1} fasteners, n_2 seams with n_{s2} fasteners and n_3 seams with n_{s3}

fasteners, then $\Delta_{2.2}$ can be found from equations of the form

$$\Delta_{2.2} = \frac{s_s\, s_p\, qL}{n_{sh}} \left[\sum_{j=1}^{n_1} \frac{j-1}{(n_{s1}\, s_p + \beta_1\, s_s)} + \sum_{j=n_1+1}^{n_1+n_2} \frac{j-1}{(n_{s2}\, s_p + \beta_1\, s_s)} + \sum_{j=n_1+n_2+1}^{n_{sh}/2} \frac{j-1}{(n_{s3}\, s_p + \beta_1\, s_s)} \right] \quad (15.39)$$

noting that β_1 will vary if the pitches of the sheet to flange fasteners are also varied along the length of the panel.

15.3 Comparison of theory with finite element analysis

In justifying the expressions proposed in the previous paragraphs two steps may be considered necessary. In the first place, the proposed internal force distributions and resulting deflection predictions should be compared with those given by a more comprehensive analysis which takes full account of internal compatability. Then there should follow comparison with the results of tests on full-scale diaphragms. It should be appreciated that, while testing is indispensable in ensuring that accurate predictions of failure modes have been made, it is of limited value in justifying a theory. This is because it is virtually impossible to instrument a complete plate element in order to establish the internal force distribution and the distribution of displacements between the individual components of the complete plate. The only quantities that are readily amenable to measurement in the working range are overall displacements and possibly the axial strains in the flange members; these, while useful, do not provide a complete justification of a comprehensive new theory. Consequently, an extensive series of numerical experiments was undertaken in order to compare theoretical predictions with the results of finite element analysis over a range of different plate element configurations. This investigation is reported in full in reference 3.19. Here just one typical example will be given.

The finite element representation of panel T_4 with a span of 16.8 m and a depth of 2.56 m is shown in fig. 15.13. The finite element analysis of plate elements is identical in basis to that used for shear panels and will not be described further. The analyses described here and in reference 3.19 merely required modifications to the data generator in order to allow the application of a uniformly distributed load over the length of the upper flange. It was considered unnecessary to model a large number of seam and gable fasteners precisely and so lumped values were used, the seven fasteners shown representing a larger number of more flexible fasteners. The results of this analysis are shown in fig. 15.14. These are typical of results obtained over a wide range of configurations and component flexibilities and in all cases the comparison was excellent. Clearly the theory is capable of reproducing the finite element results with a high degree of success.

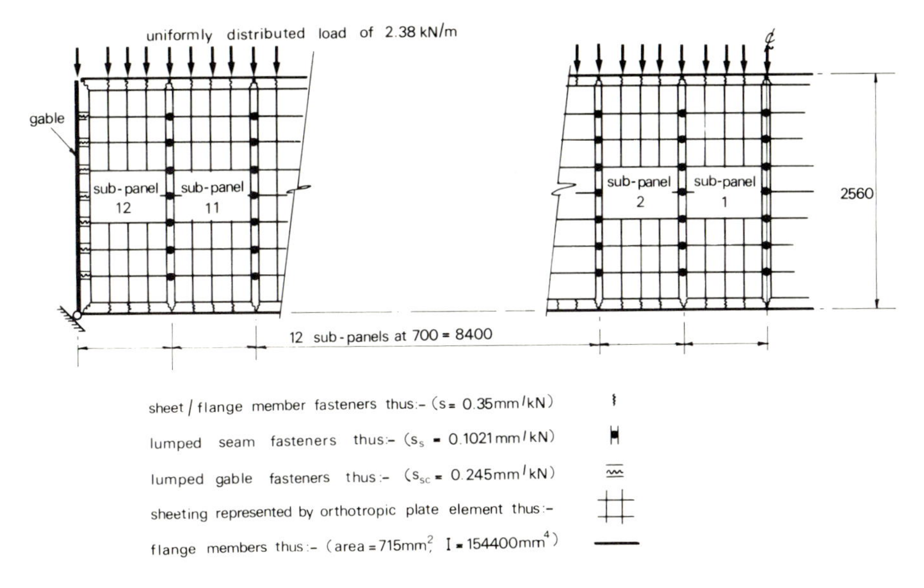

Fig. 15.13 Finite element representation of plate element T_4 span = 16.8 m.

15.4 Tests on full-scale plate elements (first series E1–E8)

Two separate test series were carried out, the first of which was reported in reference 3.19. In order to initiate this test series, a specific situation was considered and a plate element designed to be an element of a complete roof as shown in fig. 15.1. In order to suit the fixings in the laboratory floor the overall dimensions shown in

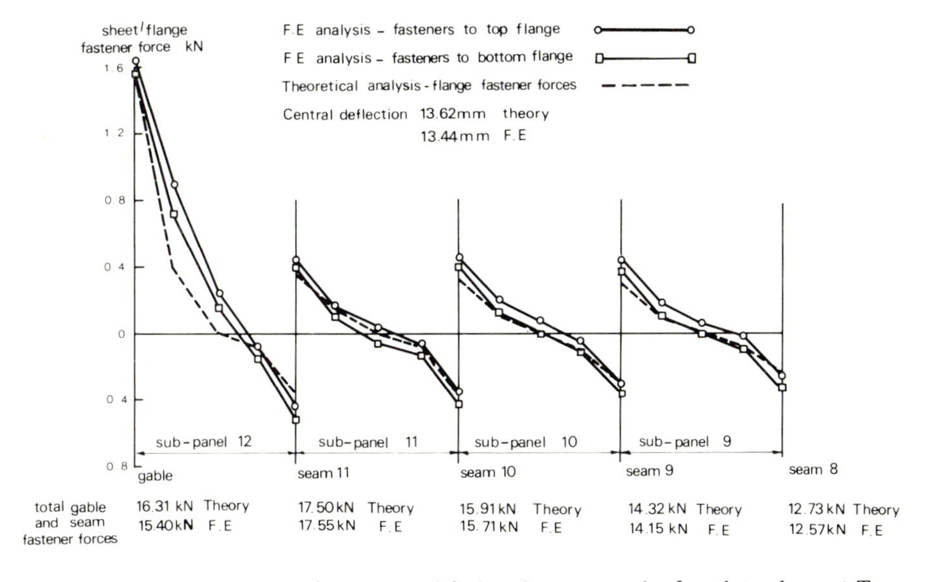

Fig. 15.14 Comparison of theory and finite element results for plate element T_4.

fig. 15.15 were adopted. It was assumed that the roof slope was 36.90° (3–4–5 triangle) and that the total vertical loading on the roof was 0.7 kN/m^2 and for this loading Everclad L5 plastic coated sheeting with a steel thickness of 0.46 mm was found adequate to span between fold lines. The equivalent uniformly distributed load on the plate element was simulated by 5 jacks as shown, the equivalent working jack load being 5.04 kN. Figure 15.16 shows a typical test in progress in the structures laboratory at the University of Salford. Eight separate tests were carried out, differing in the arrangement of fasteners adopted, as summarised in table 15.1. Tests E1, E6 and E8 were continued to collapse, the remainder being confined to the working load range. A summary of the results is also included in table 15.1 and full details will be found in references 3.15 and 3.16. However, before discussing these results, three points need to be made.

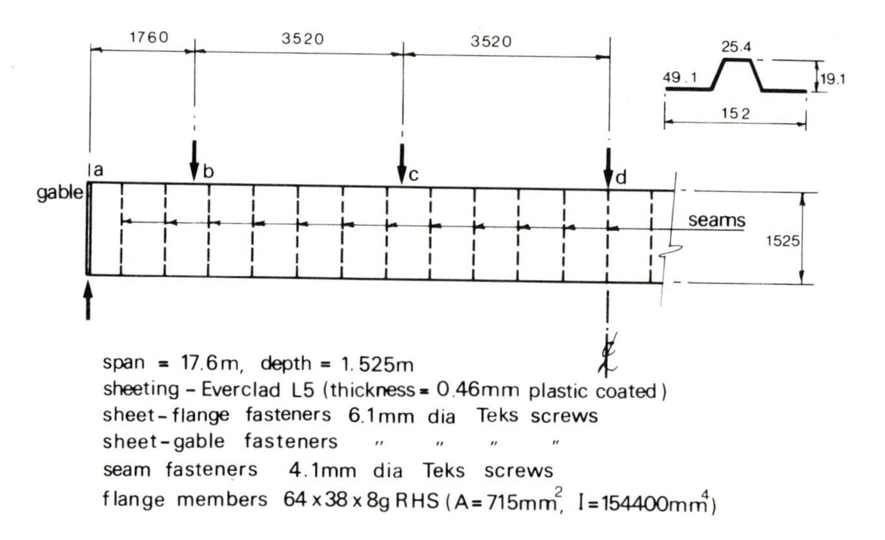

Fig. 15.15 General arrangement for tested elements designated E1 to E8.

15.4.1 The importance of buckling

These tests were carried out at an early stage in the development of folded plate theory and at the time a less successful buckling theory was being used. The full significance of buckling as far as this test series was concerned was not appreciated until the first test failed by buckling at a load much less than was expected. As a consequence, all of the plate elements in this series with the exception of number E8 were limited by buckling at a load close to the working load and comparisons of failure load are not possible.

15.4.2 Fastener slip characteristics

Typical load-deflection curves for the fasteners used are shown in fig. 15.17. As with most sheeting fasteners the initial stiffness is considerable but non-linearity

Fig. 15.16 Test in progress (first series).

is apparent at an early stage and the flexibility at the working load (taken during this investigation to be half the average ultimate load) bears no relationship to the initial stiffness. However, on unloading and reloading the initial very high stiffness is evident throughout the complete reloading range and indeed cyclic loading reveals that this behaviour is stable. Over twenty cycles of unloading and reloading cause no detectable change in the initial unloading and reloading curve. This poses some difficulty in testing as the stiffness of subsequent tests tends to be appreciably higher than that of the first test after fastening the sheeting. For this reason all of the fastener tests carried out in conjunction with these plate tests were subject to reloading and as a result the following fastener properties were obtained. Barber Colman no. 8 Teks seam fasteners in 0.46 mm thick sheeting (thin to thin): s_s = 0.20 mm/kN initial, s_s = 0.10 mm/kN reload and F_s = 0.95 kN; Barber Colman $\frac{1}{4}$/14 Teks sheet to purlin and gable fasteners in 0.46 mm thick sheeting (thin to thick): s_p = 0.15 mm/kN initial, s_p = 0.02 mm/kN reload and F_p = 2.5 kN. It is clearly necessary to be aware of the great disparity between initial and reloading stiffness and to bear this in mind in interpreting the test results. The differences can be considerable and for the tests described here both the initial and reloading deflections were calculated and are quoted in table 15.1.

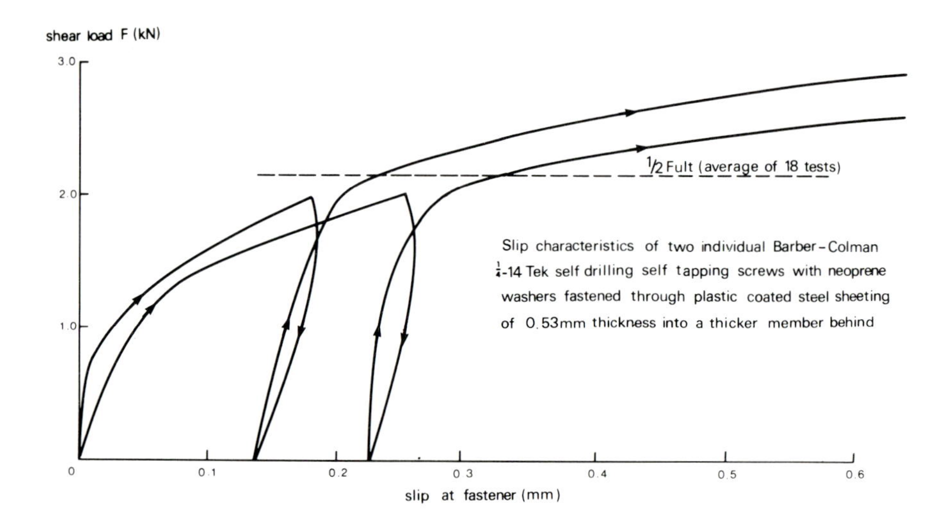

Fig. 15.17 Fastener slip characteristics for test series.

15.4.3 Theoretical calculations

As shown in fig. 15.15, the tests involved using five point loads rather than the uniformly distributed load assumed by the theory. The theoretical predictions given in table 15.1 are correct for this loading case and their derivation requires some additional mathematical manipulation. These derivations are not given here as in most cases they can be written down directly by treating the portions of the plate elements between loads as simple diaphragms under uniform shear. The only exception is the component $d_{1.3}$ which requires some elementary structural mechanics. Further guidance on this point will be found in reference 3.21.

Table 15.1 Summary of fastener arrangements and experimental results for first test series (theoretical buckling loads are the full value predicted by Easley's theory with no reductions; deflection values are per 1 kN of jack load, ultimate loads are loads per jack)

test number	pitch of flange fasteners			no. of gable fasteners	no. of seam fasteners			test results		theoretical predictions		
	a–b	b–c	c–d	n_{sc}	a–b	b–c	c–d	central deflection (mm)	ultimate load (kN)	initial deflection (mm)	reloading deflection (mm)	ultimate load (kN) and mode of failure
E1	152	152	152	17	21	21	13	4.7/3.9	5.0	4.16	3.87	7.46 (buckling)
E2	152	152	152	17	21	17	9	3.9		4.18	3.88	
E3	152	152	304	17	21	17	9	5.2		5.78	5.44	
E4	152	152	152	11	21	13	5	3.9		4.25	3.90	
E5	152	152	304	11	21	13	5	5.2		5.84	5.47	
E6	152	152	456	11	21	13	5	6.8	5.3	8.37	7.96	7.46 (buckling)
E7	152	304	304	11	21	13	5	10.4		10.6	10.2	
E8	304	304	304	6	11	9	5	10.6	3.3	14.7	14.1	4.48 (seam failure)

15.4.4 Conclusions from test results

The first conclusions from the test results must be that the proposed theory demonstrates that an adequate prediction of stiffness can be made over a wide range of fastener arrangements. The test result values were read from the slope of the load deflection curves which were obtained for jack loads of up to 3 or 4 kN in 0.5 kN increments. There was very little deviation from the linear in any of the tests, even test E8 only showing non-linearity over the last 0.5 kN or so prior to failure. The majority of results show excellent agreement between theory and experiment and all are within the range of experimental error. However, practical reasons prevented sufficient comparisons of failure load to be obtained and, where these were available they were thought to be influenced by the unusually thin sheeting. This is particularly true of the seam failure as self-drilling, self-tapping screws are known to be less reliable in sheeting less than 0.7 mm thick. For these reasons, it is difficult to draw firm conclusions from the ultimate load tests and a further test series was initiated which incorporated more realistically proportioned sheeting.

15.5 Tests on full-scale plate elements (second series E9–E17)

The second series of tests on plate elements was reported in reference 3.21 and utilised a greater plate depth and stronger sheeting than was used for the first series. The parameters of the design were unchanged, in that the basic panel was designed to have a span of 17.6 m and to sustain a load of 0.7 kN/m^2 with a roof slope of 36.9°. The general arrangement is shown in fig. 15.18. In order to facilitate the loading of the test panel by five hydraulic jacks simulating the uniformly distributed load, the flange members were chosen from the available range of rectangular hollow sections. 64 mm × 38 mm × 8 S.W.G.(2½ in × 1½ in) R.H.S. were found to be adequate to carry the flange forces and were adopted. With the benefit of hindsight it is evident that more useful information regarding failure loads would have been obtained if a section with greater resistance to local bending from the jack forces had been chosen. Even with spreader beams and flexible packing there was a tendency for extensive local distortion in the vicinity of the jacks to occur before the failure load of the panel could be attained. Thus, although a total of nine different tests were carried out, only two of these were carried through to failure, the remainder being either confined to the working load range or terminated before failure due to excessive local distortion at the loading points.

With the dimensions and details described above, the working load was 8.4 kN per jack. Tests were carried out using a variety of arrangements of fasteners giving (with the exception of test no. E16) theoretical factors of safety against fastener failure of the order of 2.0 and giving a reasonable range of panel flexibilities. The entire test series is described in table 15.2, the meaning of the symbols defining the fastener arrangements being according to fig. 15.12. Figure 15.19 shows a typical test in progress. It may be observed that the compression flange was prevented from buckling laterally by suitable restraints incorporating needle bearings to eliminate friction. The only measurements taken during loading were deflection

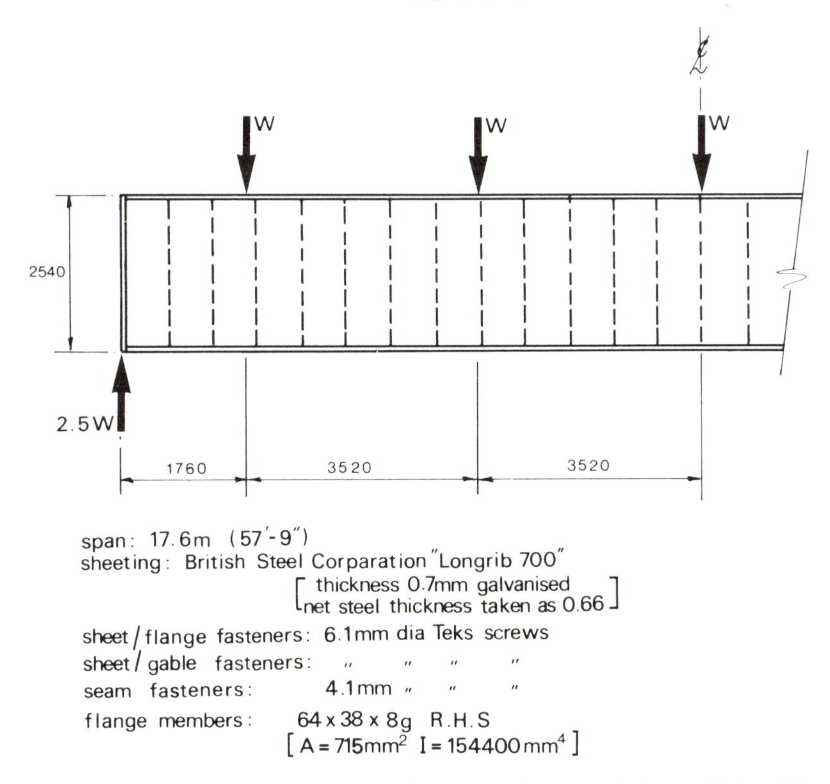

Fig. 15.18 General arrangement for tested elements designated E9–E17.

readings opposite the loading points. In each test, load was applied in increments of 1 kN at each jack and deflection readings taken. The load-deflection curves were linear up to the working load and from the slope of these curves the test results for central deflection given in table 15.2 were obtained. Two tests were continued to failure. In test E11 a seam failure was obtained adjacent to the left hand support as shown in fig. 15.20. In test E17 the tension flange fasteners tore first followed immediately by buckling of the sheeting as shown in fig. 15.21. The excessive number of seam fasteners shown in fig. 15.22 serves solely to ensure that a different mode of failure from that of test E11 was obtained.

It may be noted that in table 15.2, two values of deflection are given for tests E9, E11 and E16, each of which was repeated. As was pointed out in the previous section, the structure is always more flexible under the initial loading than under the subsequent loadings as a consequence of fasteners 'bedding in' and the pairs of values reflect this effect. The higher of the two central deflection results shown for tests E9 and E11 were both obtained for panels that had been completely refastened before the test and therefore represent the only genuine results for initially unloaded panels. The remaining results all reflect some degree of prior loading. In order to accommodate this state of affairs, theoretical predictions based on both the initial and reloading flexibility of the fasteners are included in table 15.2. It

Fig. 15.19 Test in progress (second series).

can be seen that the difference is not marked as much of the theoretical flexibility is in the distortion of the corrugation profile and in axial strain in the flange members, while fastener flexibility plays a comparatively minor role.

15.5.1 Comparison of experimental and theoretical results

The complete comparison summarising both deflection and strength is shown in table 15.2. In almost every test, the experimentally obtained flexibilities fall slightly below the theoretical values, even when the reloading value of fastener flexibility is used. The differences become proportionally greater as the panels become more flexible. As this additional flexibility is due almost entirely to the increase in sheet distortion when the ends of the sheeting are fastened in alternate or every third corrugations, it may be concluded that the theoretical flexibilities used for these cases are on the high side. A similar conclusion was also made in

Table 15.2 Summary of fastener arrangements and experimental results for second test series

test number	pitch of flange fasteners (mm)			no. of gable fasteners	no. of seam fasteners			test results		theoretical predicitions		
	p_1	p_2	p_3	n_{SC}	$n_1 = 2$ n_{S_1}	$n_2 = 5$ n_{S_2}	$n_3 = 5$ n_{S_3}	central deflection (mm)	ultimate load (kN)	initial deflection (mm)	reloading deflection (mm)	ultimate load (kN) and mode of failure
E9	175	175	175	18	24	24	12	2.13 / 1.63		1.94	1.76	
E10	175	175	175	18	24	24	6	1.64		1.97	1.77	
E11	175	175	175	18	24	16	6	1.73 / 1.84	16.1	2.01	1.78	20.3 (seam a–b)
E12	175	175	175	10	24	16	6	1.71		2.02	1.78	
E13	175	175	350	10	24	16	6	2.31		2.81	2.57	
E14	175	350	350	10	24	16	6	4.54		5.22	4.94	
E15	175	350	525	10	24	16	6	5.18		6.27	5.97	
E16	350	350	350	10	24	16	6	6.30 / 5.07		7.22	6.91	
E17	175	175	175	10	49	26	12	1.64	16.7	1.92	1.76	17.8 (tension flange fasteners)

Note Central deflections are per unit jack load, ultimate loads are load per jack.

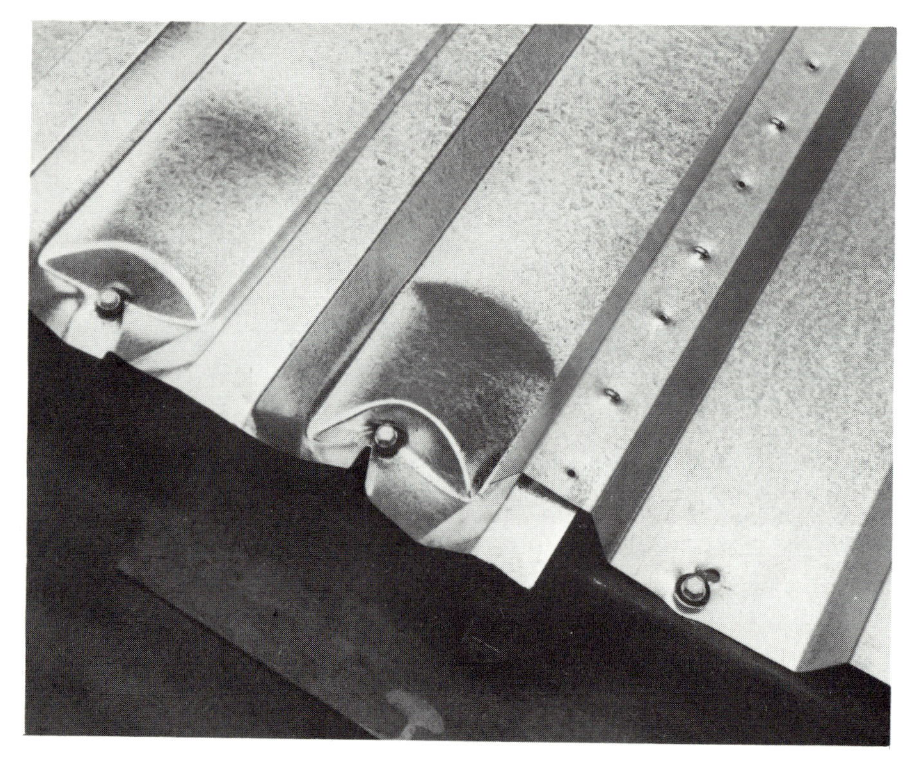

Fig. 15.20 Seam failure; test E11.

section 10.14 as a result of tests on diaphragms. As any discrepancy is on the safe side it may be concluded that it is readily possible to predict adequately the deflections of discretely fastened folded plate roofs.

Relatively limited information is available regarding failure loads. The seam failure (test E11) was about 20% low which may possibly represent a deficiency in self-drilling self-tapping screws, when used in thin-to-thin connections at the thinner end of the range of sheeting thicknesses. The sheet/flange fastener failure (test E17) lay again slightly below the full theoretical value but well above the value taking account of the 25% extra reserve of strength required for this failure mode which takes into account some lack of conservatism in the theory and this must be regarded as a satisfactory test result. The theoretical buckling load was 18.5 kN per jack and the mode of failure for test E17 may suggest that buckling was about to take place at a load not greatly in excess of the maximum achieved of 16.7 kN. There is room for more test results for failure loads but it is already clear that all failure modes can be predicted with reasonable accuracy because failure at the gable fasteners cannot have any independent significance.

15.6 Full-scale testing of a hipped roof structure

The first full-scale testing of a complete folded plate roof was carried out on the

Fig. 15.21 Tearing of flange fasteners and buckling; test E17.

hipped roof structure shown diagrammatically in fig. 15.22. This test was carried out on behalf of the Metropolitan Architectural Consortium for Education (MACE) in the South of England and is fully described in references 3.17 and 3.18. The prototype structure was designed as a low-cost nurșery school for 30 children and, as the tested building was intended for use, only an acceptance test according to *B.S. 449* was required. Figure 15.23 shows the structure carrying the full vertical and horizontal load.

The roof was square in plan and had the shape of a truncated pyramid. Light framing members shown in fig. 15.23 followed the changes in slope and formed the flanges of four trapezoidally shaped folded plates which comprised the complete roof structure. The four framing members forming the boundary of the opening at the top of the roof were designed to support a roof light which was omitted

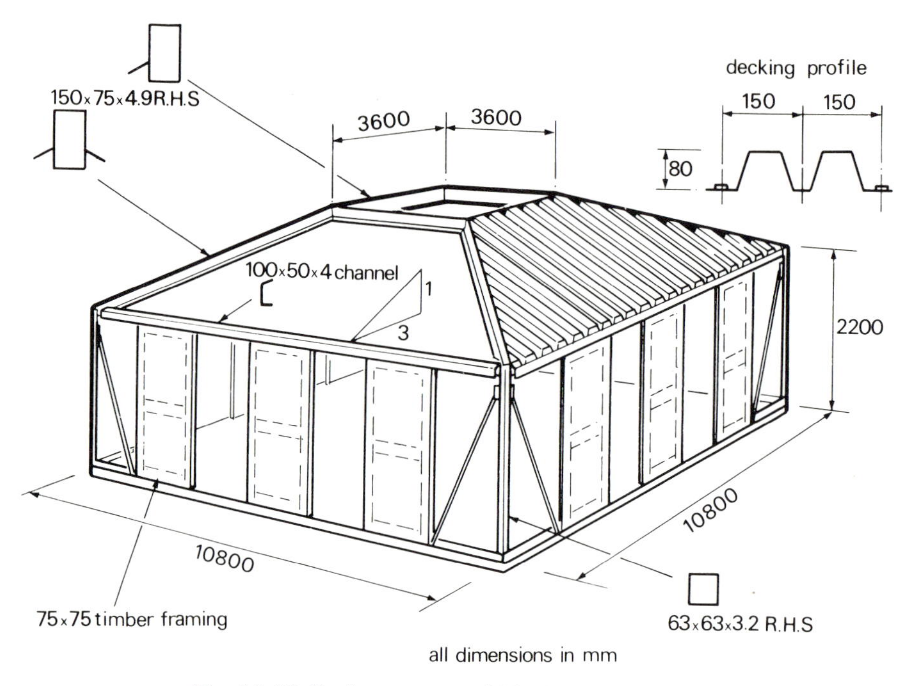

Fig. 15.22 Basic structure of MACE type 30 unit.

Fig. 15.23 Structure subjected to full vertical and side load.

for the test. Simulated loads from the roof light were applied through a temporary timber deck. It may be noted that the roof is supported on braced steel stanchions at the four corners which transmit most of the load in the roof to the foundations. However, the channel section which forms the lower chord of the roof panels has to carry the out-of-plane component of any load applied to these panels and is unable to span 10.8 m between corner columns under this loading. In the complete structure intermittent vertical support for this member is provided by cladding panels. For the purposes of the test, temporary timber supporting panels were provided as shown in figs. 15.22 and 15.23.

The test programme was in two parts and included both stiffness and strength tests. The maximum load carried was self-weight + 2X (dead + imposed load) over the entire roof. This vertical load was applied both with and without wind load. Another severe loading case was that of dead load + 1.5X (imposed load) applied over half the roof only. During the tests, deflections were measured at a total of 38 locations using dial gauges supported on internal scaffolding. For each test the load was raised to its maximum value in 4 or 5 increments so that any false deflection readings could be detected.

15.6.1 Structural behaviour and analysis under vertical load

Analysis of this structure was only attempted under vertical load and wind load. At the time of the test no analysis was available for the full three-dimensional clad structure under asymmetric load. It may be reasonably assumed that under surface loads the sheeting spans unidirectionally giving rise to readily determined line loads at the frame members. The lower horizontal frame members form a tension ring which is supported by the corner columns and the cladding panels. The upper horizontal frame members form a compression ring which is supported by the hip members and (possibly) also by stressed skin action in the sheeting. Under uniform loading the upper horizontal members carry their line loads back to the apex joints by beam action and a balanced set of forces results which can be resolved into axial components in the three members meeting at these joints. Thus the frame forces are statically determinate and no primary stressed skin action results. As a result of these determinate axial and bending forces, frame deflections can be readily calculated and these are compared later with the measured values. Under asymmetrical loading, the stability of the structure is dependent on stressed skin action which could only be evaluated by testing. It may be noted that both the upper horizontal frame member and the hip member carry their respective line loads back to their points of support by bending action. This bending action is restrained by stressed skin action in the plane of the roof which is essentially of a secondary nature. However, as a result of this effect the bending stress and deflection in the hip member in particular are reduced to a very small fraction of their calculated values.

15.6.2 Behaviour under wind load

For the test, all of the wind load was concentrated into a horizontal line load of 2.46 kN/m along one eaves member. For the purposes of analysis it is assumed that this load resolves itself into a component in the plane of the roof which is carried back to the adjacent columns by stressed skin action and a vertical component which is carried by the edge member spanning between cladding panels. The problem requiring analysis can therefore be simplified to the analysis of a trapezoidally shaped folded plate element under an in-plane load as shown in fig. 15.24. The analysis of this irregular folded plate element required the use of finite elements and has already been used in section 5.2 as an illustration of the finite element analysis of diaphragms. As a result of this analysis, some high fastener forces were predicted and additional fasteners introduced at these points.

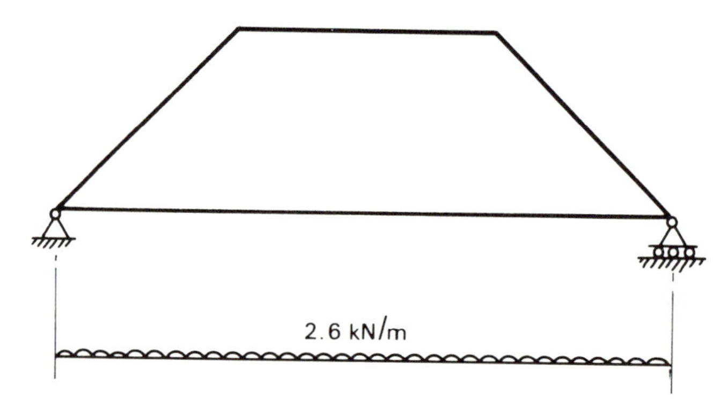

Fig. 15.24 Analytical problem for the analysis of the wind load case.

15.6.3 Experimental results and comparison with theory

Experimental and theoretical results for the uniformly loaded case are compared in table 15.3, where the deflection and recovery values given are averaged over the 4 relevant measuring points. The response showed a tendency to non-linear behaviour with the higher levels of load causing increasing deflection rates. This

Table 15.3 Measured and theoretical deflections (mm) under vertical load

position \ loading	dead load only (0.25 kN/m²)	working load only (0.81 kN/m²)	1.5 × working load only (1.22 kN/m²)	% recovery from 1.5 × working load	theoretical value at working load
apex joint (vertical)	5.3	12.6	21.5	85	9.2
mid-hip (vertical)	3.8	7.5	13.5	86	11.2
mid-apex member (vertical)	6.9	13.9	24.4	82	12.6

was probably associated with movement in the joints though no visible evidence of joint slip was observed. The movement at the apex joint is entirely due to axial strains in the members together with any movement in the joints and, not surprisingly, the experimental value is approximately 37% greater than the corresponding theoretical value. As the analysis did not take account of movement in the bolted joints between the framing members it is assumed that movement in these joints is responsible for the difference.

The theoretical vertical movement at the mid-point of the hip is obtained by adding the bending deflection of this member to the mean joint movement at its ends. The experimental value of this deflection is very much less than its theoretical counterpart which was calculated assuming simple bending of the hip member. An examination of the numerical results revealed that bending deflection of this member was virtually non-existent as a result of stressed skin restraint from the adjacent sheeting and an approximate numerical analysis verified that this must be the case. The bending deflection of the apex number is likewise restrained by stressed skin action, though not to the same extent as the hip member, and this is revealed by the comparison between experimental and theoretical deflections at the mid-point. The recovery values shown on table 15.3 and others not so shown were all within the limits permitted by the relevant British Standard, B.S. 449.

When wind load was applied, apart from a small sway of the entire structure, deformation was confined to the loaded panel as assumed in the analysis. The experimental response again showed marked non-linearity at higher levels of load and comparison between experiment and theory is most reasonably made at the working load. At this load, and when the deflection is corrected for sway of the entire structure, a measured horizontal deflection of 2.98 mm at mid-span may be compared with a theoretical value of 1.59 mm. These are very small values for a structure of this size and reflect the considerable in-plane stiffness of stressed skin panels. It is therefore not surprising that the measured value is greater than the theoretical value, the difference again being attributable to movement in the bolted joints between the framing members.

In the subsequent tests under asymmetrical vertical load and under higher levels of uniform vertical load the structure successfully carried the required load with recovery values well within those required. The tests showed the structure to be extremely stiff with respect to side load and uniform vertical load though rather less stiff with respect to asymmetric vertical load. Both strength and stiffness were within the very stringent requirements of the current British Standard for loading tests on steel structures.

15.7 Full-scale testing of a folded plate roof[3.25]

The 21.6 m span folded plate roof which is the subject of this section is shown in fig. 15.25. The design, construction and testing of this roof marked the culmination of four years of development work at the University of Salford during which time the theory was developed and verified by finite element analyses and the large-scale testing of individual plate elements as described above. In order to stimulate interest in this form of construction the final test to failure was successfully conducted before an invited audience of over 100 guests. A BBC television team was also present. The test was carried out in the open air at the University of Salford on a specially constructed reinforced concrete slab.

Fig. 15.25 Full-scale folded plate roof under test.

The basic dimensions of the tested structure are shown in fig. 15.26. The span of 21.6 m and the bay width of 3.6 m were selected to comply with preferred multiples of a 0.9 m module. The choice of a simple saw-toothed arrangement with a roof slope of 35° was considered to be important. Many other cross-sections are available but the one adopted represents a reasonable compromise between the possibly conflicting demands of structural efficiency, aesthetics and enclosed volume. Figures 15.25 and 15.26 show a downstand beam running along the two outer longitudinal edges of the roof. This stabilises the outer edges of the outermost roof slopes, which function would normally be performed by the side cladding and/ or its supporting members. The construction of this downstand beam was similar to that of the roof slopes although its bottom flange was a rectangular hollow section rather than a cold-formed member.

Although the initial development work on this form of construction used conventional trapezoidally profiled steel sheet, for this final test a novel purpose-made form of sheeting was introduced. The form of this sheeting is shown in fig. 15.27. It was pressed out of a flat sheet in the same manner as radiator panels and possesses the following advantages when compared with conventional profiled sheet.

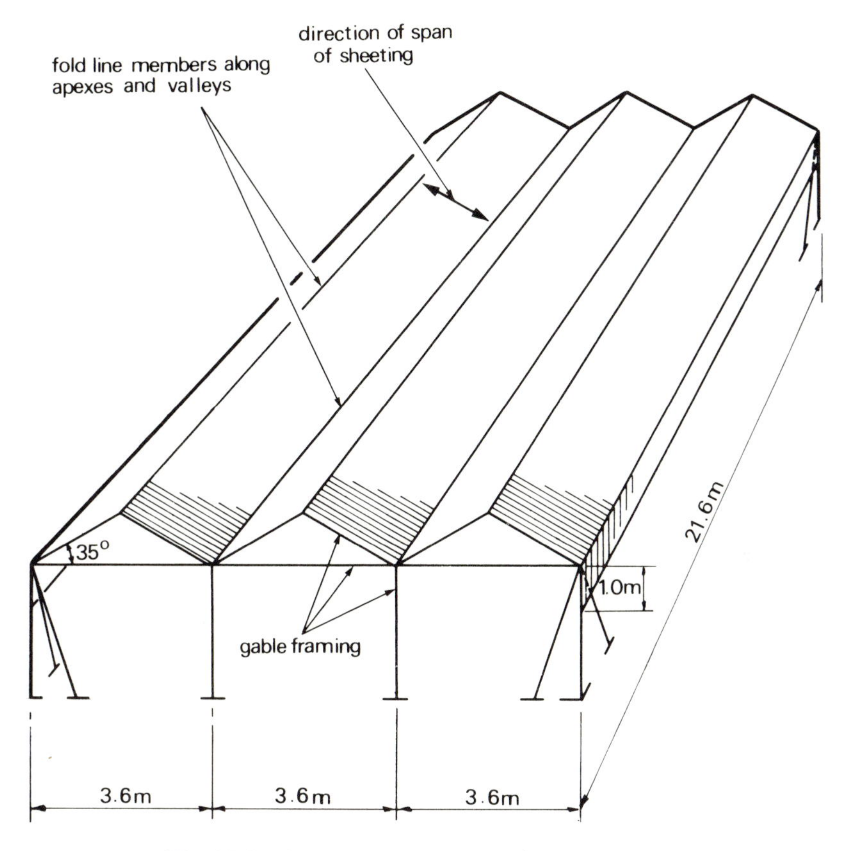

Fig. 15.26 General arrangement of test structure.

(a) A significant proportion of the shear flexibility of conventional sheeting arises as a result of distortion of the corrugations. This effect is concentrated towards the ends of the corrugations so that by closing down the ends the effect is reduced by an order of magnitude.
(b) Problems of weather-proofing the open ends of the corrugations are eliminated.
(c) Although the sheeting thickness is reduced at the corrugations due to stretching, all the fasteners pass through the full sheet thickness. As fastener strength is directly proportional to sheet thickness, and is crucial to the strength of the structure, this results in enhanced efficiency.
(d) The cover width of each individual panel of sheeting is almost the full coil width so that fewer seams are necessary.

Although an equivalent conventional sheeting would have satisfied the requirements for strength and stiffness of the test structure, it would have resulted in increased deflections due to the greater shear distortion of the sheeting.

The roof was designed to carry the loads detailed in table 15.4 with a load factor against failure of approximately 2.0. The detailed design calculations follow closely

Fig. 15.27 Purpose-made sheeting on test structure.

the approach described above and are given as a design example in section 7.7. The following considerations should be noted.

(a) The design procedure recognises that roof cladding may be fixed with the seam fasteners either in the troughs of the corrugations (as in the case of decking), or in the crests of the corrugations (as in the case of sheeting). It gives different design expressions for the two cases. The seam detail actually used is shown in fig. 15.27 and is intermediate between the two cases as far as both strength and stiffness is concerned. The true behaviour is believed to be closer to the decking case and for the purposes of the deflection calculation is treated as such. For the strength calculation with respect to seam failure, both cases are considered and load factors of 1.91 and 2.02 are obtained. The higher of these two values is thought to be nearer to the true load factor for seam failure.

Table 15.4 Loading assumed in design

imposed load	0.75 kN/m^2
dead load (insulation)	0.23 kN/m^2
self-weight	0.22 kN/m^2
total load measured on plan	1.20 kN/m^2

(b) The values of fastener strength and flexibility used in the calculations were obtained by testing samples of the actual fasteners and sheeting used in the test structure. The sheet to flange fasteners were Teks/4 screws and their characteristics were found using the standard two fastener lap joint test. The seams were fastened using blind rivets and their characteristics were found by setting up a section of the actual seam detail in the simulated diaphragm action test. Both of these tests have been described in chapter 13.

(c) Slip at the fasteners contributes a signficant part of the total flexibility of many light gauge steel structures and has been found to be greatly reduced on reloading. It was therefore considered necessary to establish accurate values for both the initial and reloading values of fastener flexibility. Consequently each fastener test was conducted by loading the fastener up to approximately half of its failure load before unloading and then finally reloading to failure. Six tests were carried out on each type of fastener. The fastener strengths quoted in the calculations are average values of ultimate load and the flexibility values are likewise mean slip values obtained at half the mean ultimate load.

(d) Safe design values of fastener strength are usually obtained by deducting from the mean test value a multiple of the standard deviation which varies according to the number of tests carried out. In order to obtain meaningful comparison between theory and experiment, no such deduction has been made here.

(e) In the present state of the art the shear flexibility of corrugated steel sheeting with pressed-out corrugations cannot be determined analytically, although the flexibility due to corrguation distortion is known to be small. For this test the distortion flexibility was estimated from the experimentally determined flexibility of a small diaphragm as described in reference 1.78.

(f) In establishing the factor of safety of the complete structure it is necessary to consider all potential modes of failure and to choose the most critical. The calculations recognise the failure modes shown in table 15.5 and predict the given load factors. Thus the most likely mode of failure was predicted to be failure of a seam at a load factor approaching 2.02. However, because there were other failure modes with load factors only marginally higher, the actual failure mode remained in slight doubt. The deflection pattern at the working load was predicted to be as shown in

Table 15.5 Summary of strength calculations for folded plate roof

modes of failure	load factor
bending failure of the sheeting	approximately 3.9
failure of the fold line members in axial tension or compression	2.59
buckling of the sheeting	2.19
failure of the sheet to flange fasteners	2.02
failure of seam fasteners	1.91–2.02 (probably nearer 2.02)
failure of sheet to gable fasteners	2.30

fig. 15.28. Two sets of values are given in fig. 15.28, the figures in brackets correspond to reloading values for fastener flexibility.

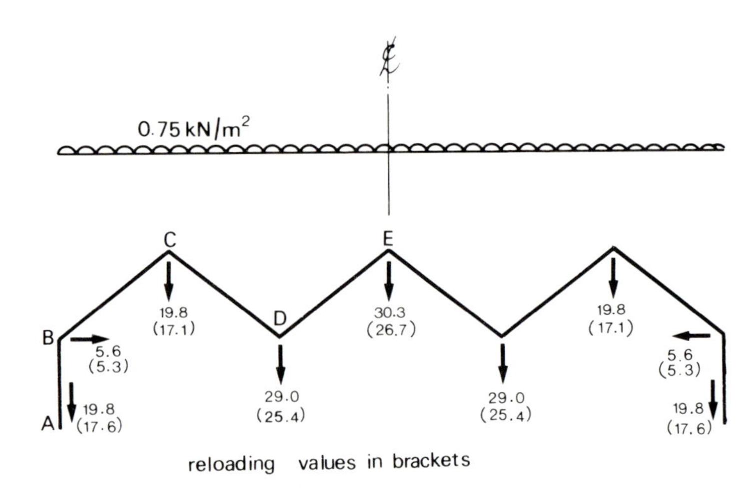

Fig. 15.28 Calculated mid-span deflections at working loads.

15.7.1 Construction of the test structure

The detailing of the test structure was strongly influenced by the decision taken at an early stage, to build the complete roof on the ground and to lift it into position using climbing jacks on the eight gable columns. This decision was fully vindicated as the lifting operation was extremely smooth and rapid and the erection cost was only a fraction of that which would have been incurred had the roof been built in situ on scaffolding.

The gable columns were first positioned and the entire roof structure built on the ground between them. At this stage the wind bracing members were temporarily positioned outside the structure to allow the roof to be lifted. The valley and apex members, which were produced on a press brake in three sections approximately 7.2 m long, were placed in position on light temporary timber trestles before being butt welded. The valley members also acted as gutters so that a total camber of 200 mm was incorporated at this stage to ensure that rain-water would run off the ends of the structure. Figure 15.29 shows the structure at this stage of construction.

The sheeting was next placed in position and fastened to the fold-line and gable members with self-drilling, self-tapping screws at 150 mm centres. The seams near the gable ends were each fastened with 22 blind rivets at nearly 100 mm centres, reducing by two rivets per seam to a minimum of four fasteners in the seams near mid-span. The upstand seam detail shown in fig. 15.27 allowed the holes for the blind rivets to be punched rather than drilled, so that fixing of the sheeting was extremely rapid. The fact that the work was at ground level and that all the components could be easily manhandled also helped greatly at this stage. The gable framing was designed to slide up the columns with provision for temporary fixing

Fig. 15.29 Structure on ground before cladding and lifting.

at 250 mm intervals. The roof was therefore lifted in stages by jacks supported on brackets which could be repositioned at 250 mm intervals. The complete lifting process took four men approximately six hours and proceeded without incident. For the last stage of lifting the wind bracing was disconnected and then reconnected in its final position inside the building. When the downstand edge beam had been completed and the temporary timber trestles removed it was found that no more than 15 mm of the initial 200 mm camber had been lost due to the self-weight of the roof (0.22 kN/m^2).

15.7.2 Design of loading system

In order to apply an approximately uniform loading over the entire roof a tree type loading system was used. Nine hydraulic jacks, each of 80 kN capacity, distributed their load through a system of rods and beams to 72 timber trestles giving 288 equal point loads on the roof. The jacks reacted against a steel grillage rigidly fastened to the reinforced concrete test slab and were jointly operated by an electric pump. Provision was also made for the application of side load to one outside eave of the building. This side load consisted of five separate dead loads connected to the eaves by wire ropes passing over rollers.

15.7.3 Test procedure

Light gauge steel structures fastened with discrete fasteners are invariably stiffer on reloading as a result of the fasteners bedding in. This means that there is only one opportunity to test a structure such as this in the completely unloaded condition. This consideration influenced the testing sequence and the interpretation of results. The sequence of tests was as shown in table 15.6. Tests 1 and 4 were performed twice, because it was considered that for these tests meaningful comparisons with the initial and reloading theoretical deflections would be obtained. Tests 2, 3 and 5 were not reloaded because it was considered that the fasteners would already exhibit preloaded characteristics as a result of previous tests. The only readings taken during testing were deflection readings. Vertical deflections at the mid-span point (and in some cases at the quarter-span point) of each fold line member, were read by observing suspended tapes through an optical level. Horizontal movements at the eaves were likewise measured by observing the movements of horizontally mounted scales through a theodolite.

Table 15.6 Test sequence for folded plate roof

test	loading applied	range of loading
1	vertical over entire roof	elastic to 1.3 kN/m^2
2	vertical on centre bay only	elastic to 1.3 kN/m^2
3	vertical on outer bay only	elastic to 1.3 kN/m^2
4	side load	elastic to 0.78 kN/m
5	vertical over entire roof	load to failure

15.7.4 Test results in comparison with theory

Test 1 The load-deflection curve for the mid-point of the roof is shown in fig. 15.30. As anticipated, the stiffness on initial loading was appreciably less than the stiffness on reloading, but both stiffnesses were adequately predicted by the theory. The distribution of deflection across the transverse centre line is shown in fig. 15.31 for both initial loading and reloading. This should be compared with the values shown in fig. 15.28; again there is reasonable agreement between theory and experiment. The general tendency is for the structure to be slightly less stiff than the theory predicts for vertical deflections within the body of the roof, although rather stiffer than the theory near the edges. The reduced stiffness is primarily associated with the higher levels of loading and is probably a consequence of movement at the gables and non-linear fastener behaviour. The reloading stiffness and the lower levels of initial stiffness are accurately predicted. Near the edges of the roof, the increase in stiffness is probably due to the influence of continuity of bending action in the sheeting together with the consideration that the bending stiffness of the edge members may be significant in the downstand edge beam.

Tests 2 and 3 As well as supplying loading cases which were important in their own right, tests 2 and 3 provided an opportunity to check that the structure and its loading system were behaving according to the principle of superposition. The

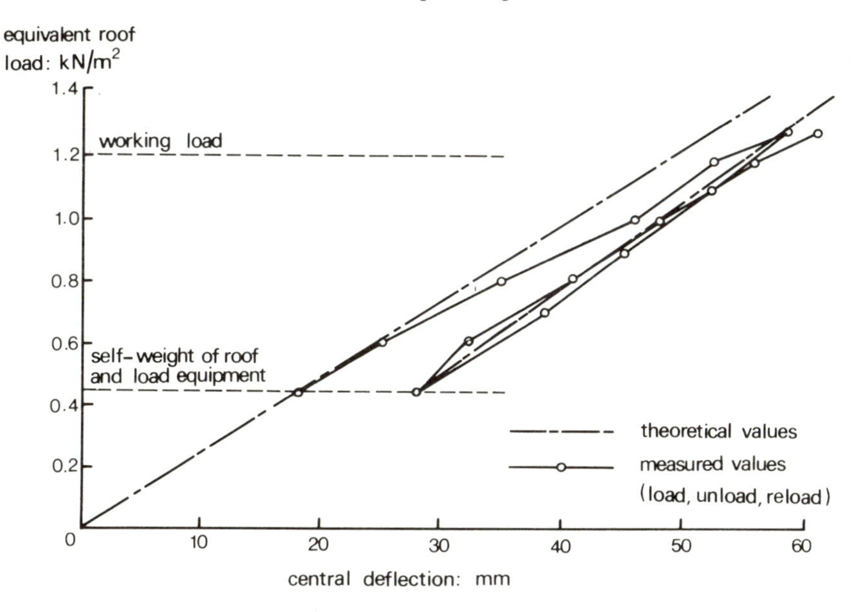

Fig. 15.30 Load–deflection curves under vertical load (test 1).

structure performed very much as expected, the considerations being similar to those described above for test 1.

Test 4 For test 4 a side load of 0.78 kN/m run was applied at eaves level along one edge only to simulate the effect of wind on one side of the structure. The theoretical and experimental deflections at the centre of the structure are shown in fig. 15.32. The structure was significantly stiffer than the theoretical calculations suggested. Obviously the edge effect noticed in tests 1 to 3 would be expected to have greater significance in test 4, where the load is applied directly to the eaves. However, the magnitude of the discrepancy suggests that something more may have been involved.

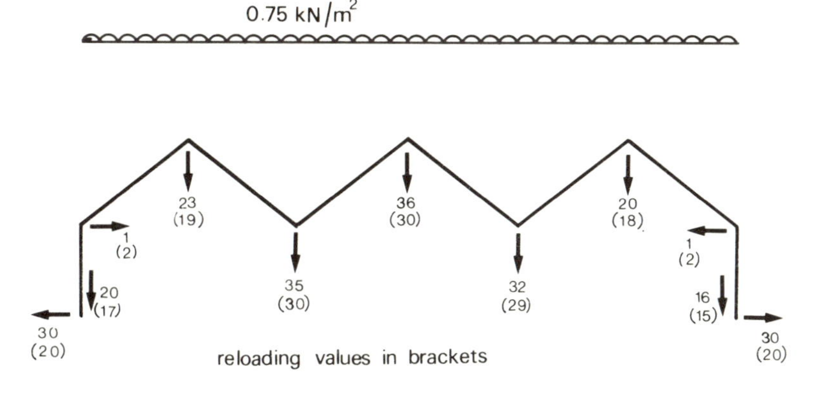

Fig. 15.31 Measured mid-span deflections for test 1 (mm).

The most likely cause was frictional losses in the loading system where the wires applying the side load passed over the rollers.

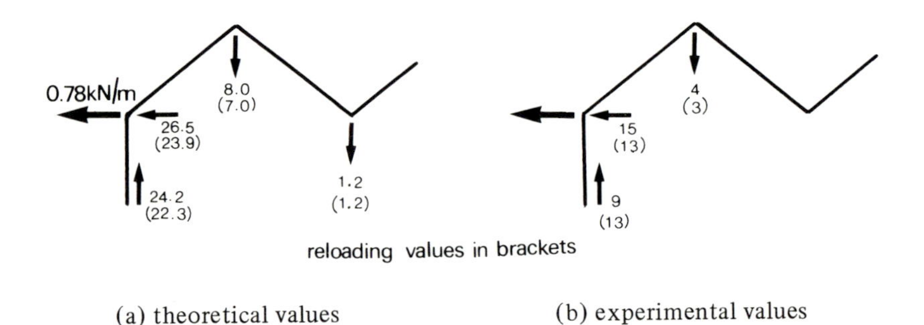

Fig. 15.32 Central deflections under side load for test 4 (mm).

Test 5 The load–deflection curve to failure under full vertical load is shown in fig. 15.33. The structure finally failed at a load equivalent to 2.3 kN/m² with a load factor of 1.92. This is fully in accordance with the theory which predicted a load factor between 1.91 and 2.02. Failure of the structure was initiated, as expected, by failure of the end seam of one of the middle pair of roof slopes. The failure was sudden and accompanied by a rapid release of energy causing additional damage.

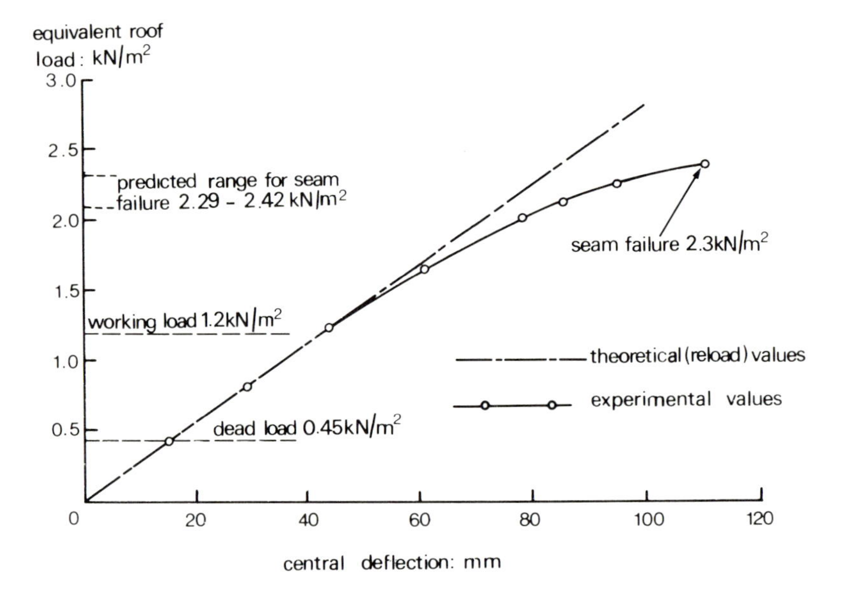

Fig. 15.33 Load–deflection curve to failure for test 5.

15.7.5 Conclusions from test results

This test has been reported fully because the authors consider it to be of great importance in the continuing development of light gauge steel, roof structures in general and folded plate roofs in particular. It has been conclusively demonstrated that such structures are practically viable and that their strength and stiffness can be accurately predicted. The authors are also confident that such structures are economically viable and look forward to their further exploitation in practice.

15.8 Design charts for folded plate roofs

In the design of a folded plate roof, there are a number of primary variables which are inter-related and it is not easy to visualise the relationship between them. If a folded plate roof is required to span L metres under a design load w then the remaining global parameters which must be chosen are the bay width B and the roof slope θ as shown in fig. 15.34. In addition the profile itself includes a number of important variables, notably the height h, the thickness t and the pitch d. Bearing in mind that it is always possible to add additional seam and gable fasteners in order to accommodate the maximum shear force in the roof plane, the major constraint on the design concerns the choice of the sheeting profile. In order to increase the buckling load it is necessary to increase the profile height h but this in turn increases the deflection and the designer faces a conflict of requirements. Lawson[3.28] has shown that with certain simplifications the design problem can be reduced to three inter-related equations which can be expressed graphically so that the designer can see at a glance where the design constraints are for a given problem. The procedure is as follows.

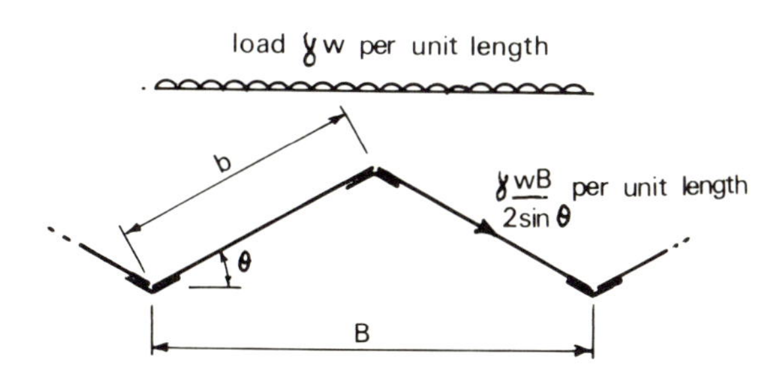

Fig. 15.34 Section through folded plate roof.

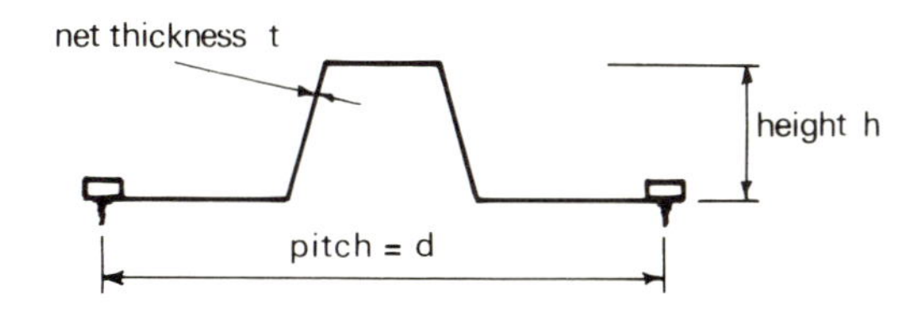

Fig. 15.35 Profile for construction of design charts.

Consider the sheeting profile shown in fig. 15.35 which is fastened to the supporting structure through every trough and the roof shape and loading shown in fig. 15.34. The design expressions are given in section 9.10. The maximum shear force at the gable is $\gamma wBL/(4\sin\theta)$ and therefore the requirement for shear buckling is

$$(28.8/b)\, D_x^{\frac{1}{4}}\, D_y^{\frac{3}{4}} \geqslant \frac{\gamma wBL}{4\sin\theta} \tag{15.40}$$

i.e.

$$L \leqslant \frac{115.2 \sin 2\theta}{\gamma wB^2} \cdot Dx^{\frac{1}{4}}\, D_y^{\frac{3}{4}} \tag{15.41}$$

Now if the second moment of area of a single corrugation is Dt,

$$D_y = DtE/d \tag{15.42}$$

and for typical profiles,

$$D_x \simeq \frac{t^3 E}{12\,(1-\nu^2)}(1-0.01h) \qquad (h \text{ measured in mm}) \tag{15.43}$$

$$\therefore L \leqslant \frac{115.2 \sin 2\,\theta}{\gamma wB^2}\left[\frac{t^3\, E\,(1-0.01\,h)}{12\,(1-\nu^2)}\right]^{\frac{1}{4}} \left(\frac{Dt\,E}{d}\right)^{\frac{3}{4}}$$
$$\simeq \frac{63.4 \sin 2\,\theta\; t^{\frac{3}{2}}\, E\, D^{\frac{3}{4}}}{\gamma wB^2\;(1+0.0025\;h)d^{\frac{3}{4}}} \tag{15.44}$$

The deflection of a folded plate roof is found as the sum of six components. In general however, two of these, namely $\Delta_{1.3}$ = deflection due to axial strain in the fold-line members and $\Delta_{1.1}$ = deflection due to sheet distortion, predominate. For the purposes of this study, therefore, the maximum deflection Δ at mid-span of a folded plate roof at unit load factor can be approximated as

$$\Delta = \frac{1}{\sin\theta}\left(\frac{d^{2.5}\,\bar{K}\,L^2}{8\,Et^{2.5}\,b^2} + \frac{10\,L^4}{384\,EA\,b^2}\right)\frac{wB}{2\sin\theta} \tag{15.45}$$

Now the area of the fold-line members must be sufficient to carry the axial load occasioned by bending action in the roof planes so that the minimum area A per roof plane at a design stress σ is given by

$$A = \frac{\gamma wL^2}{6.4\,\sigma\tan\theta} \tag{15.46}$$

and if the deflection under live load alone is limited to span/360 and this is considered to be approximately span/240 under total load, in the limit

$$\frac{L}{240} = \frac{wB}{2\sin^2\theta\, E}\left(\frac{d^{2.5}\,\bar{K}\,L^2}{8t^{2.5}\,b^2} + \frac{\tan\theta\,\sigma\,L^2}{6\,b^2\,\gamma w}\right) \tag{15.47}$$

It follows that in order to satisfy the above deflection requirements

$$L \leqslant E\,B \tan\theta \bigg/ \left(\frac{60 d^{2.5}\,\bar{K}\,w}{t^{2.5}\,\tan\theta} + \frac{80\,\sigma}{\gamma} \right) \tag{15.48}$$

If the sheet to foldline fasteners are to pass through every trough, the requirement for adequate fastener strength is

$$L \leqslant \frac{1.6\,F_p \tan\theta}{p\,\gamma\,w} \tag{15.49}$$

and finally there is the additional requirement that the sheeting must be adequate to span between the fold-line members under the action of the vertical load w.

Lawson[3.28] has shown that equations of the above form can be plotted on graphs of L versus B to indicate a region of feasible designs. For the particular design constraints used in the structure for the full-scale tests described previously the graphical construction is shown in fig. 15.36. Curves are given for various profile heights, the shape of the permissible region for each height is shown in the inset. Other arrangements give curves of similar shape to fig. 15.36. If follows that, in a given case, there may be only a narrow range of values of the column separation B for an efficient design at a given depth of profile. It can also be seen that with a conventional roof sheeting of thickness 0.9 mm and height about 30 m the tested structure would have been a near-optimum design with the first three constraints active. However, for the test, by using the specially made sheeting the deflection constraint was avoided. It should also be noted that, by providing two fasteners per trough between the sheeting and the fold line members near the gable, the deflection and fastener capacity constraints can be broadened to allow even longer spans to be achieved.

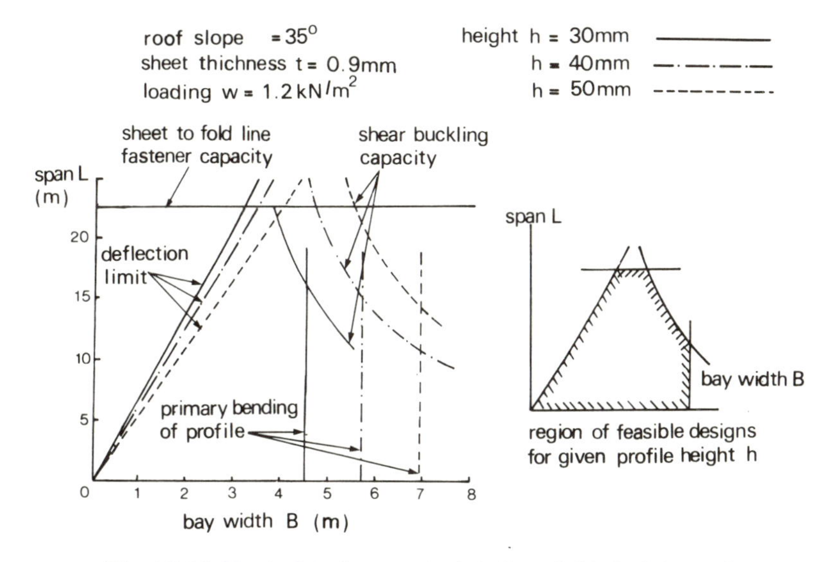

Fig. 15.36 Typical design constraints for a folded plate roof.

15.9 An alternative form for the basic folded plate structure

The basic folded plate cross-sections shown in fig. 15.4 are both aesthetically pleasing and efficient. They have one potential disadvantage, however, namely that in some countries the governing codes of practice may demand that extra load has to be applied in order to allow for a build-up of snow in the valleys. Indeed, many designers may consider it prudent to make such an allowance in any case and the extra loading may somewhat impair the economy of the design. The details of the valley gutters also have to be worked out.

There is an alternative arrangement that avoids these difficulties and this is shown in fig. 15.37. The advantages may be summarised as follows:

(a) There are no valleys to collect snow, etc.
(b) The basic triangular support units can be made stable in the temporary unsheeted condition. They can therefore be prefabricated, erected separately, and the roof sheeting can be installed in the usual way.
(c) The roof sheeting can therefore be continuous with resulting economies which help to offset the extra sheeting necessary in the webs.
(d) Roof lights are readily possible in the region between support units.
(e) The triangular voids in the support units can act as service ducts.

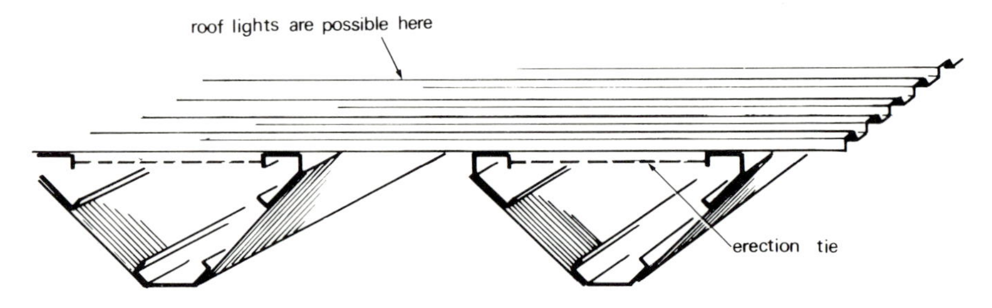

Fig. 15.37 Alternative folded plate roof structure.

An alternative cross-section which would allow prefabricated support units to nest for transport is shown in fig. 15.38. There is evidently room for research into the optimum shape for roofs based on the above cross-sections but the basic calculations are all within the scope of the foregoing sections of this chapter.

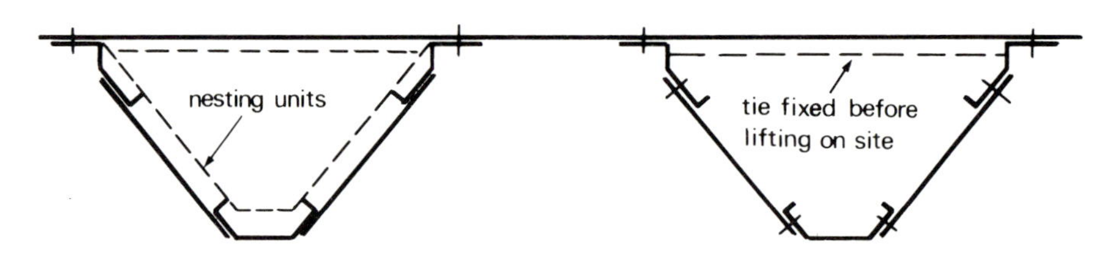

Fig. 15.38 Alternative cross-section for ease of transport.

15.10 Alternative shapes for folded plate and related structures

The majority of the folded plate structures built in practice have been of the conventional saw-tooth cross-section which has been the main subject of this chapter. A number of hipped plate structures, as described in section 15.6, have also been built in the U.K. not only by the Metropolitan Architectural Consortium for Education but also in an alternative prefabricated form. As shown previously in fig. 15.4, a number of alternative cross-sectional shapes are available although these have not been utilised to any great extent to date. A further range of shapes becomes available if the plates are tapered to form pleated domes as shown schematically in fig. 15.39. A number of such structures have been built in the U.S.A. and one was subjected to acceptance tests. Even more exciting structures become possible if the fold lines are curved as shown in figs. 15.40 and 15.41. Very long spans become possible but this may be expensive since individual cutting of the sheets is required as well as curvature of the fold line members themselves. The Dane County Coliseum[3.10] is an impressive example of the type of structure shown in fig. 15.40. Another possibility when the fold lines are curved is shown in fig. 15.41. Here the construction forms a deep and immensely stiff and strong cylindrical shell.

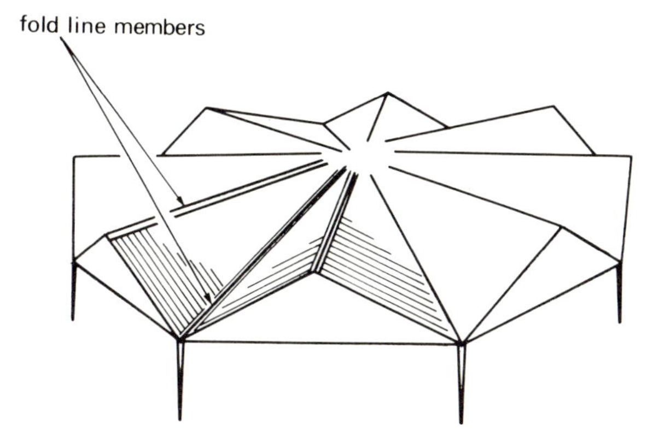

Fig. 15.39 Pleated dome.

Fig. 15.40 Pleated dome with curved fold lines.

Fig. 15.41 Folded plate structure of cylindrical section.

The above examples serve to illustrate that there are many varied and exciting possibilities with light gauge steel folded plate construction which merit practical exploitation. It is hoped that this brief section will stimulate further interest in the subject which has scarcely been considered by engineers and architects responsible for the design of large span roofs.

15.11 Practical considerations in conventional folded plate design

15.11.1 Sheeting

For the purposes of the test described in section 15.7, a purpose-made sheeting was produced and its advantages over conventional sheeting in folded plate action have already been outlined. Notwithstanding these advantages, it is appreciated that, at least for the time being, practical exploitation of the light gauge steel folded plate roof is likely to use conventional sheeting and conventional detailing. The extensive series of tests on individual roof elements reported in sections 15.4 and 15.5 all used conventional sheeting and the theory was developed with such sheeting in mind. For structures of span up to about 22 metres, conventional detailing of a soundly designed structure will give acceptable strength and stiffness.

15.11.2 Fasteners

Seam fasteners for light gauge steel roofs are typically monel metal blind rivets although self-drilling, self-tapping screws are satisfactory provided that the seam thickness is at least 0.7 mm. Sheet to fold-line member fasteners are typically self-drilling, self-tapping screws although fired pins are also satisfactory provided that the fold line members are at least 4 mm thick. Fasteners of increased diameter are becoming available (e.g. 8 mm diameter self-drilling, self-tapping screws) and their greater shear strength can be advantageously used in folded plate design. Strength and flexibility values for many suitable fasteners are given in tables 9.9, 9.10 and 9.11.

15.11.3 Fold-line members

Fold-line members are usually cold-formed from steel sheet. Minimal fold-line members could have a single bend to accommodate the angle of slope of the roof though it must be appreciated that fold line members which are too flexible in bending or twisting can cause difficulties in erection. The fold-line members for the full-scale test described in section 15.7 had the cross-sections shown in fig. 15.42. On the basis of required cross-sectional area, these members are about 70% too heavy. They certainly possessed adequate stiffness during erection and could have been reduced in size. The minimum practical size remains a matter for judgement.

15.11.4 Valley detail

In the large-scale test structure referred to above, the lower fold line members also

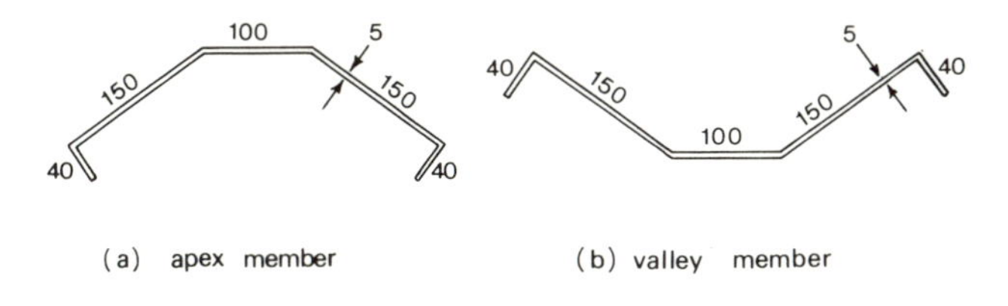

Fig. 15.42 Fold-line members used in test structure.

served as valley gutters and incorporated a significant camber in order to ensure adequate run-off rainwater. A better detail is shown in fig. 15.43 in which the gutter is non-structural and can be packed to falls and replaced without disturbance to the primary structure.

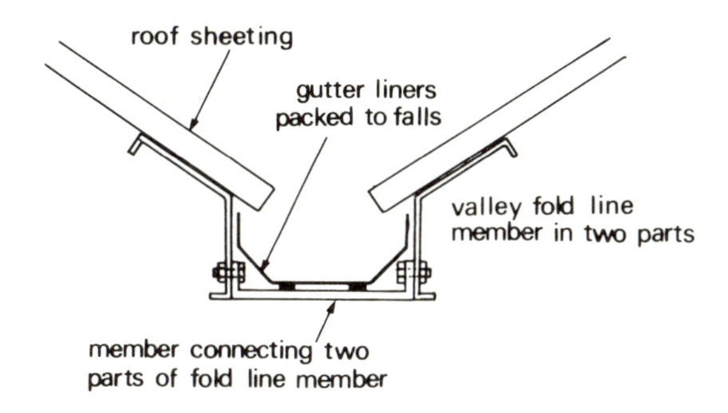

Fig. 15.43 Improved detail at valley.

15.11.5 Erection of folded plate roofs

In the U.S.A. where many folded plate structures have been built, the structure is usually constructed piece-small in situ on light scaffolding. One of the advantages claimed for this procedure is that the components are all light and easily handled. Alternatively, the structure can be built on the ground and jacked or lifted into position. One of the advantages of the gutter detail shown in fig. 15.43 is that it allows the lifting operation to be carried out one bay at a time.

15.11.6 Point loads on folded plate roofs

Local point loads such as those from lifting points or light overhead runways can be readily supported off the fold-line members. Design expressions for the increased local forces are given in section 5.6.

15.11.7 Openings

Openings within the areas of the plate elements cause discontinuities in the internal force systems and considerable practical and theoretical complications. It is therefore recommended that they be avoided if at all possible.

15.12 Conclusions

The light gauge steel folded plate roof provides an aesthetically pleasing alternative to the more familiar methods of achieving moderate spans. The use of sheeting as an integral part of the total structure and the consequent elimination of conventional framing ensures that the total weight of construction is considerably less than that of the alternatives. Folded plate structures therefore offer an attractive and economic form of construction that is now ripe for exploitation.

CHAPTER SIXTEEN

Light gauge steel shells

16.1 Introduction

In theory a wide variety of shell configurations is available in light gauge steel construction but in practice the range is severely curtailed by the practical problems of forming and cutting profiled steel sheeting. With the exception of shapes which are special cases of the light gauge steel folded plate and considered in the previous chapter, only two true shell configurations have practical importance. The first of these is the light gauge steel hyperbolic paraboloid which derives its importance from the fact that profiled metal sheeting deforms easily into such a surface. The hyperbolic paraboloid has curvature in two directions and its shape is defined by the equation:

$$z = hxy/(ab) \tag{16.1}$$

in which x, y and z are orthogonal axes and where x and y are usually horizontal as shown in fig. 16.1. In the above equation, h is the amount of corner depression or rise of the quarter surface having horizontal dimensions a and b. An important characteristic of the hypar surface is that lines on the surface in the directions of x and y (known as the generators) are straight lines. This means that profiled steel sheets readily warp into a hypar surface and, once connected to adjacent sheets and edge members in the warped position, hold this shape. Thus a doubly curved surface is created which carries its loads as a true shell primarily by in-plane membrane stresses. The second configuration of practical importance is the light gauge steel cylindrical shell which arises because profiled steel sheeting can be readily rolled to a constant radius. Such shells fall into two basic types, as shown in fig. 16.2, though many variations are possible when several shells are grouped together. Light gauge steel shells have a number of advantages in comparison with their more familiar concrete counterparts. In particular, they require only a minimum of temporary formwork, are piece-small and may be rapidly erected using discrete fasteners such as self-drilling screws, small bolts, blind rivets or spot welds. This form of construction was used for factory buildings in the U.K. from the end of the last century. Present use tends to be concentrated towards inexpensive agricultural buildings.

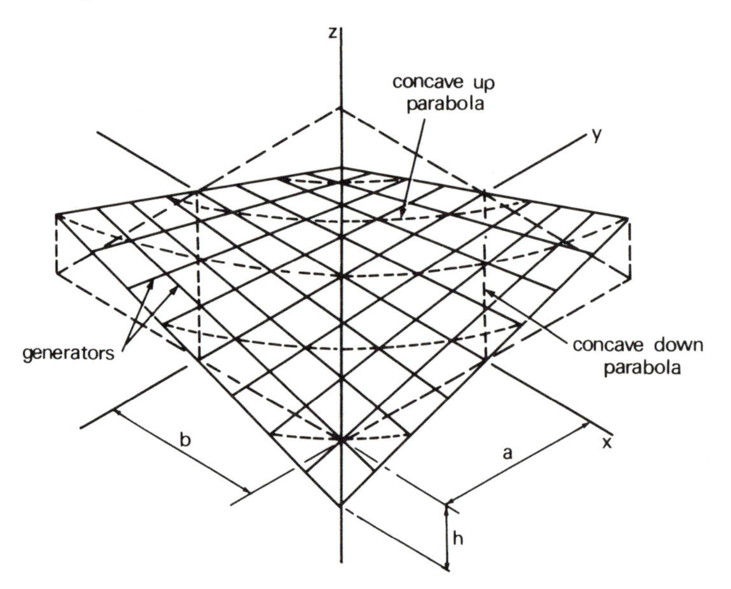

Fig. 16.1 Geometry of hyperbolic paraboloid surface

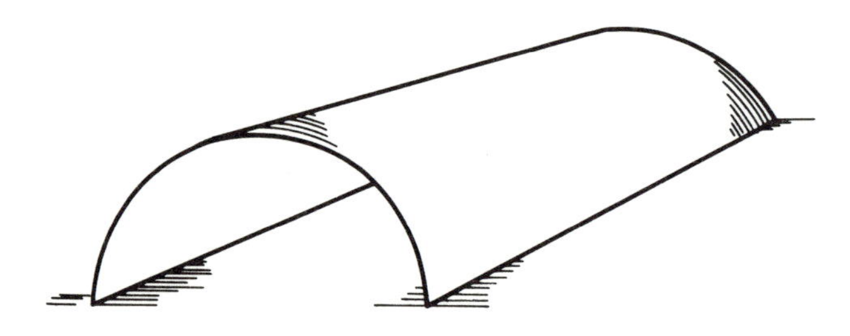

(a) simply supported barrel vault

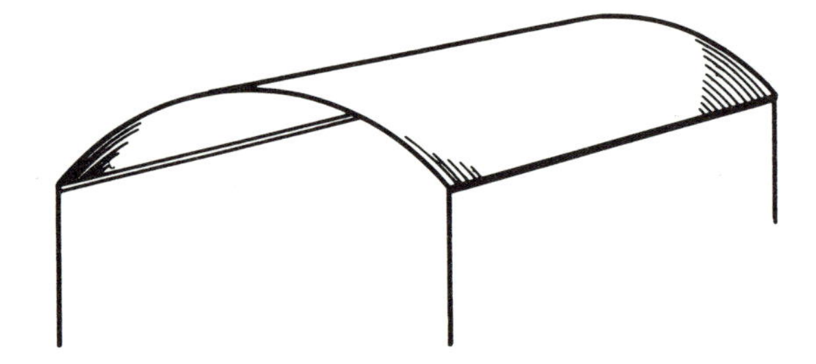

(b) suspended "beam - shell"

Fig. 16.2 Types of cylindrical shells

16.2 Basic form of the hyperbolic paraboloid roof

A number of alternative forms of the hyperbolic paraboloid roof are shown in fig. 16.3. Case (a) is the pure case of a single hypar surface which forms a most pleasing shape. However, this form of construction gives rise to large horizontal thrusts at the two supporting columns and, unless these are kept very short, a horizontal tie is required as shown by the broken line in the figure. In case (b) the roof is supported from a single column. This form is readily constructed and is probably the least expensive of the alternatives. Type (c) is supported from two columns and again usually requires a horizontal tie between them. It is a suitable form for a canopy entrance structure when an unusual effect may be obtained by making one half of the roof horizontal with the other half tilted up. Case (d) is a most useful arrangement by which a large uninterrupted clear span may be obtained. Horizontal ties are required between the columns on all four sides but these can be readily incorporated in the wall construction. Case (e) is an alternative arrangement for a large-span roof similar in some respects to (d) but requiring an additional central column.

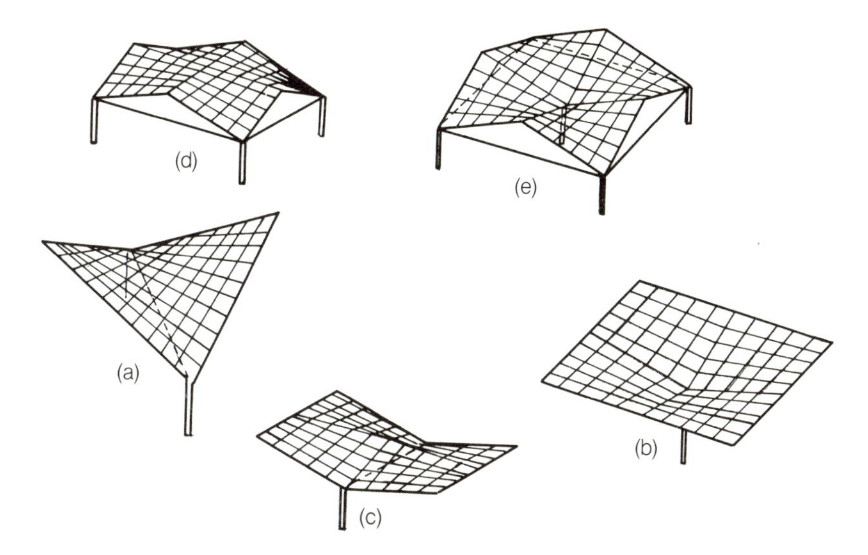

Fig. 16.3 Roof structures comprising hyperbolic paraboloid shell elements with linear edge stiffening.

16.3 Analysis and design of hyperbolic paraboloid roofs

Equation 16.1 can be conveniently rewritten

$$z = kxy \qquad (16.2)$$

where $k = h/(ab)$ and is a function of the overall dimensions of the surface as shown in fig. 16.1. If the coordinate axes are rotated by 45°, as shown in fig. 16.4, the equation of the surface can be obtained with reference to alternative axes which would run from corner to corner of a surface square in plan. The necessary transformations to the new axes x' and y' are

$$x = x'/\sqrt{2} - y'/\sqrt{2}, y = x'/\sqrt{2} + y'/\sqrt{2} \tag{16.3}$$

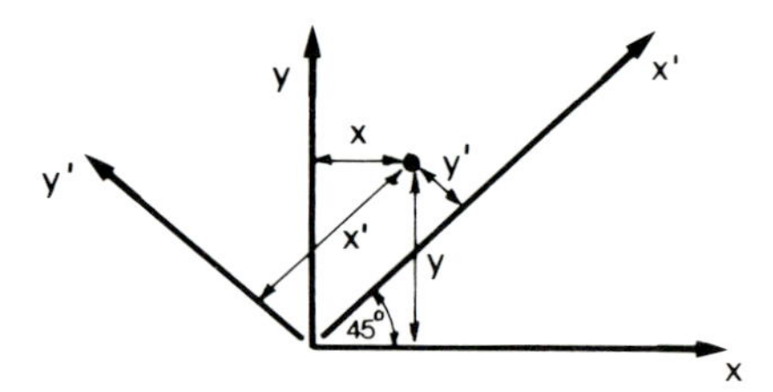

Fig. 16.4 Rotation of co-ordinate axes.

and the alternative equation of the hypar surface is

$$z = (k/2)(x'^2 - y'^2) \tag{16.4}$$

It follows from this equation that lines drawn on the surface parallel to the axis of x' form concave upward parabolas and lines parallel to the axis of y' form concave downward parabolas. It may also be readily shown that horizontal planes cut the surface on lines whose equations are those of hyperbolae, hence the description 'hyperbolic paraboloid'.

The concept of concave-down parabolas (arches) and concave-up parabolas (suspended cables) gives a useful clue to the way in which hyperbolic paraboloid shells carry vertical load. It can be readily shown by membrane shell theory that a uniformly distributed vertical load is equally shared between the two parabolic systems resulting in an in-plane stress system which incorporates equal stresses on two planes that are mutually at right angles. This is, of course, equivalent to a state of pure shear. Thus membrane theory predicts that the entire surface of a uniformly loaded shell carries a shear stress resultant of

$$V = w\,ab/(2h) \tag{16.5}$$

where w is the uniform vertical load per unit area of projected surface and V has units of shear force per unit length. This is a highly advantageous state of affairs for profiled steel sheeting is particularly well suited to carrying in-plane shear forces and very efficient structures result. The connections must be designed for this shear force and the edge members carry axial forces arising from the integration of this shear along the boundaries of the shell.

On the face of it, therefore, the design of a light gauge steel hyperbolic paraboloid would appear to be remarkably simple and small shells of appreciable curvature can be designed on the above basis. However, the above account is a simplification of a rather more complex state of affairs. In the first place, the in-plane shear stresses themselves tend to be quite small and the design is likely to be governed by considerations of deflection and buckling. For relatively small shells, buckling can be treated by a suitable approximate analysis but the estimate of deflections is more problematical, particularly at unsupported corners. Furthermore, there is the question of the validity of the simple membrane stress analysis. It is certainly only valid for shells of relatively high curvature, say span divided by corner depression less than about five, and shallow shells will always require a more sophisticated analysis. Furthermore the behaviour is also influenced by the bending stiffness of the edge members which are necessary to build up the membrane action and their eccentricity to the middle surface of the shell. Such factors can only be considered in an analysis which considers bending stresses in the shell. Finally, it should be realised that the simple analysis described above is only applicable to uniformly distributed vertical load. Hypars are sensitive to asymmetrical loading which causes significant bending stresses and which can again only be determined by a full analysis.

The definitive papers on the analysis of light-gauge steel hypars are those by Gergely (see Part III, Bibliography, section 20.4). Reference 4.17, in particular, is a very complete account of the subject. Full details of the available analyses are outside the scope of this book. It is sufficient to say that the best analysis appears to be a finite element analysis using flat elements which were found to perform better than curved shallow shell elements. Further details of suitable finite elements will be found in references 4.17 and 4.24.

16.4 Light gauge steel hyperbolic paraboloid roofs in practice

Only a few roofs of this type are known to the authors. However, these structures are almost all structures of note and it is worth mentioning some of these, albeit briefly. By far the most important light gauge steel hypars that have been built to date roof the world's largest aircraft hangars at Los Angeles and San Francisco. These two structures also form the world's largest light gauge steel primary structures and hold an important place in the evolution of light gauge structural steelwork. They have been fully reported in the technical press.[4.10, 4.11, 4.12, 4.14, 4.27] Essentially these hangars are tapering folded plates cantilevering 230 feet (70 metres) off a central spine. The folded-plate surfaces are, however, warped into the shape of hypars, one advantage of this being that the curved surfaces have a significantly higher resistance to buckling than similar flat plates. The surfaces are of two skin construction in which a flat sheet of 13 swg (2.4 mm) is stiffened by hat sections welded on.

In a review paper on steel sheel roof structures,[4.3] Nilson mentions two further structures of note, namely the Johnson and Hardin printing plant and Frisch's restaurant, both in Cincinnati. Both of these used two layers of 38 mm deep sheeting laid at right angles to each other. In the case of the Johnson and Hardin roof, this shell construction is adequate to cover an area 33 m × 40.5 m with just four columns.

Finally, such structures are not confined to the U.S.A. Egger *et al.*[4.18] give an example of a large canopy in the form of eight inter-connected hypars supported on two columns which has been built in West Germany.

16.5 Analysis and design of cylindrical shell roofs

The two basic types of cylindrical shell roofs are shown in fig. 16.2. From the point of view of design, type (a), the simply supported barrel vault, only needs to be considered as a shell for relatively small values of the length to span ratio. It has been shown[5.11, 5.12] that, when the length becomes more than about four times the span, the central region is acting effectively as a two-pinned arch and this consideration dominates the design so that the complete structure can be conveniently designed on this basis. For shorter lengths, the influence of relatively rigid gables together with the shear stiffness of the sheeting results in the primary bending stresses being significantly less than those calculated on the basis of arch behaviour and, if advantage is to be taken of this in design, a shell analysis is required. Suspended 'beam-shells' always require a full analysis. Three alternative approaches to analysis are available. Space allows only a brief discussion of these here. A fuller account will be found in reference 5.11.

16.5.1 Classical shell theory

In classical shell theory, the eighth order characteristic differential equation is solved for the particular boundary conditions and loading. As usually formulated, classical shell theory has not proved to be applicable to light gauge steel cylindrical shells[5.11] as a consequence of the highly orthotropic nature of profiled steel sheeting. However, more recent work[5.13] has shown that the addition of extra terms can overcome the difficulty so that solutions of adequate accuracy can be obtained. Classical solutions are approximate because a number of assumptions are necessary to make the mathematics tractable. Even then, a computer is usually necessary to carry out the arithmetic, and solutions are limited to certain boundary conditions and loading. For this reason, alternative methods of analysis have been sought and the two alternatives which follow may both be considered to have advantages over the classical solution.

16.5.2 Energy method for shell analysis

Energy methods offer alternative approximate solutions for shells based on minimising the total potential energy of the loaded shell when it is displaced according to assumed displacement functions. The success of the method depends critically on the accuracy with which the assumed displacement functions can produce the actual displacements of the shell and this is related to the number of terms in the displacement functions. It is essential that the displacement functions satisfy the static boundary conditions (i.e. the boundary conditions expressed in terms of displacements and their first derivatives). It is not so important that they satisfy the kinematic boundary conditions (expressed in terms of second derivatives or bending moments). It has been shown[5.11] that if the energy summation is restricted to axial strain energy, circumferential bending strain energy and in-plane shear strain energy and if quite simple displacement functions are used, remarkably accurate solutions can be obtained. Indeed, the simplest possible set of displacement functions, leads to an explicit solution which is sufficiently accurate for practical purposes. This solution is given in detail in reference 5.11 and is a notable illustration of the success of such Rayleigh-Ritz solutions and a very useful example for teaching purposes.

16.5.3 Finite element analysis of cylindrical shells

As with so many other structures, finite element methods provide the most powerful and general methods of analysis. It is, of course, necessary to take due account of the highly orthotropic nature of the shell surface and to develop the analysis accordingly. It has been shown[5.11, 5.12] that flat rectangular elements are entirely suited to the problem in question and give good results. Full details of these elements are given in reference 5.9. They can successfully accommodate such practical factors as openings for windows and doors.

16.6 Cylindrical shell roofs in practice

Cylindrical shell roof construction in its most basic form has been known since the beginning of the twentieth century. Figure 16.5 shows an early example in the

Fig. 16.5 Corrugated steel cylindrical shell roofs at Price's Chemicals Ltd.

North of England. As far as roof construction is concerned, little progress has been made since the early days as a consequence of the difficulty of curving deeper profiles. Curved profile sheets have mainly been used in more utilitarian fashion as coverings for conveyors and walls of silos, etc. More recently, however, has come evidence that the possibilities of this form of construction are being exploited more widely. Trapezoidally profiled steel sheeting of about 65 mm depth is being successfully curved in Spain and used to form roofs of quite appreciable span. In the U.S.A. and Canada, sinusoidal profiles of much greater depth are being successfully curved using a novel process and with quite exciting potentialities.

CHAPTER SEVENTEEN

The use of diaphragm action to stabilise rafters and to replace bracing at the gable and eaves

17.1 Requirements for the lateral support of beams

It is a requirement of the current British standard for structural steelwork that beams should either be provided with adequate lateral restraint to their compression flanges or, alternatively, they must be designed to a reduced permissible stress in order to safeguard against lateral buckling. In most cases of roof beams, effective lateral restraint can be provided by the roof sheeting acting as a diaphragm. B.S. 449: Part 2: 1969, clause 26e, defines effective lateral restraint in terms of capacity to resist a given force as follows:

(a) For beams which are provided with members giving effective lateral restraint of the compression flange at intervals along the span, the effective lateral restraint shall be capable of resisting a force of 2½% of the maximum force in the compression flange taken as divided equally between the number of points at which the restraint members occur.
(b) In a series of such beams, with solid webs, which are connected together by the same system of restraint members, the sum of the restraining forces required shall be taken as 2½% of the maximum flange force in one beam only.

In the case of a series of latticed beams, girders or roof trusses which are connected together by the same system of restraint members, the sum of the restraining forces required shall be taken as 2½% of the maximum force in the compression flange plus 1¼% of this force for every member of the series other than the first up to a maximum of 7½%.

The above provisions are not strictly sufficient, since effective lateral restraint should be defined in terms of stiffness and strength rather than strength alone. Nevertheless, the rules have been found to work in practice. The requirement based on strength is particularly easy to meet in terms of stressed skin design and it is merely necessary to show that the roof acting as a diaphragm is strong enough to transmit 2½% (or up to 7½% for lattice beams) of the maximum compression flange force uniformly distributed over the length of the member back to the support positions of the member. This is a very simple calculation as the following example demonstrates.

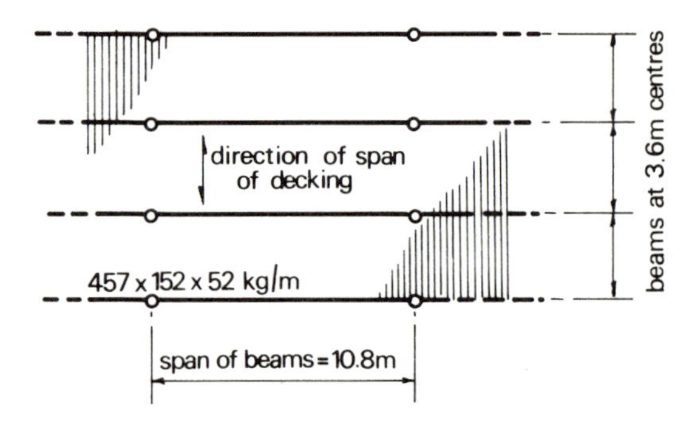

Fig. 17.1 Plan showing roof construction

Consider the roof construction shown in fig. 17.1 in which profiled steel decking spans directly over the main beams. The total live and dead load on the roof will be assumed to be 2 kN/m^2. The maximum bending moment in the simply supported beam $= 2 \times 3.6 \times 10.8^2/8 = 105.0$ kNm. Therefore, maximum bending stress in beam (Z_{xx} = 949.0 cm^3) = $(105.0 \times 10^6)/(949.0 \times 10^3) = 110.6$ N/mm^2. Assuming that this stress acts over the whole area of the compression flange (152.4×10.9) mm^2 the compressive force $= 110.6 \times 152.4 \times 10.9 \times 10^{-3} = 183.8$ kN. For a series of solid-web beams, the lateral force required to be resisted by the decking is 2½% × 183.8 kN = 4.60 kN over a 10.8 m span (0.426 kN/m). Bearing in mind the general rule that a diaphragm should not be considered to be deeper than its span, the diaphragm to resist this force is shown in fig. 17.2.

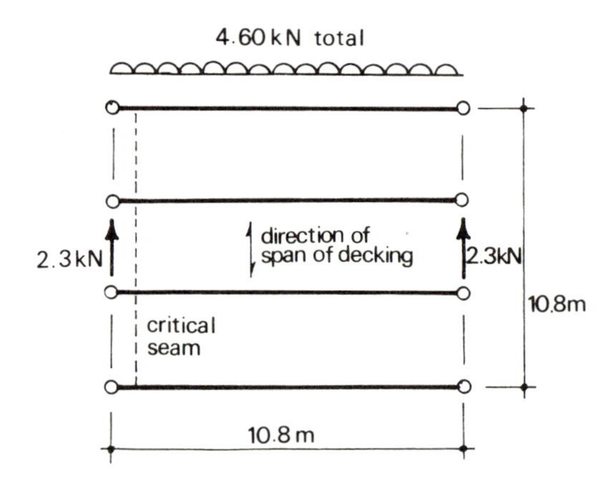

Fig. 17.2 Diaphragm for lateral support calculation.

Suppose the sheeting is 0.7 mm thick (0.65 mm net) and that the fastener specification is that of a typical roof deck, as considered in chapter 6, i.e. sheet to beam fasteners, design strength F_p = 3.56 kN at 304 mm centres; seam fasteners, design strength F_s = 1.51 kN, at 450 mm centres. Then, considering for brevity only the two most common modes of failure, seam strength $V_{ult} = n_s F_s + (\beta_1/\beta_3)$ $n_p F_p$ = [(10800/450) X 1.51] + (1.04/1.0) X 4 X 3.56] = 51.0 kN; sheet to purlin strength $V_{ult} = \beta_2 n_p F_p$ = 1.11 X 4 X 3.56 = 15.8 kN. Therefore, the design shear capacity V^* is 15.8 kN and the load factor is 15.8/2.30= 6.9, which is more than ample. Alternatively, the strength of the diaphragm can be checked approximately using table 9.21 (deep profile fastened on two sides with the decking spanning perpendicular to the span of the diaphragm) for a diaphragm of span 10.8 m and depth 10.8 m. By interpolation, the permissible load q_{perm2} = 1.65 kN/m. This gives a load factor of 1.65/0.426 = 3.9. The diaphragm is therefore amply strong. If the beams had been latticed, while still having the same flange forces, the lateral restraint would have been [2½% + (3 X 1¼%)] X 183.8 = 11.5 kN (1.06 kN/m) and the diaphragm would have had a load factor of 15.8/(½ X 11.5) = 2.7.

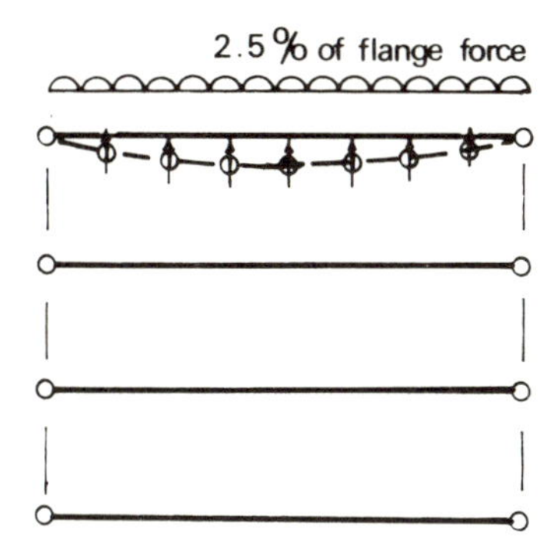

Fig. 17.3 Fastener forces set up in a lateral bracing situation.

It should be noted that in order for the sheeting to act as a diaphragm, the sheet to purlin fasteners must accommodate compressive or tensile sheet to purlin fasteners as shown in fig. 17.3. However, it is easy to show that these forces are small and they may usually be neglected. For the example given previously, 2½% of the flange force has been shown to be 0.426 kN/m. The available capacity when the fastener forces are compressive depends on the sheeting profile as discussed in section 5.6 but it is unlikely to be significantly less than the corresponding capacity when the forces are tensile. In any case, compressive forces in one long bay will normally be accompanied by tensile forces in the adjacent bay. The capacity is therefore of the order of (3.56 X 1000)/304 = 11.7 kN/m and the load factor of the order of 11.7/0.426 = 27.5. It follows that this effect may usually be disregarded.

17.2 Bracing requirements based on stiffness

The consideration mentioned above, namely that the definition of adequate lateral restraint should be based on stiffness and strength rather than strength alone has been taken up by a number of researchers in the context of diaphragm action. Practicable design procedures for diaphragm-braced I beams have been presented by Nethercot and Trahair[1.75] and Errera and Apparao[1.84]. These represent a good start to the problem of defining a general approach and have a sounder theoretical basis than the entirely intuitive approach described in section 17.1. They are of practical use in many instances of roof decking. However, the vast majority of purlins supporting roof sheeting are of Z or channel section and, as such, require a different treatment. These theoretical methods will not be reproduced here; the interested reader is therefore referred in particular to the work of Nethercot and Trahair[1.75].

It is the authors' experience that cladding is very effective in resisting the tendency to side-sway movement and twisting that is characteristic of Z purlins. Furthermore, they have found that the behaviour of a practical purlin system is also strongly influenced by the connection details to the rafters, e.g. cleats, and may involve sleeves or overlap of the purlins themselves. Such details are not amenable to calculation. For these reasons it is suggested that purlin systems are best designed using data obtained from tests and that the test arrangement must include suitable sheeting with appropriate practical connections so that full benefit may be taken of the stressed skin action. Figure 17.4 shows such a test in progress at the University of Salford. It should be noted here that wind uplift is often a more critical loading condition than downward load.

17.3 Diaphragm bracing to end gables

A typical situation at the gable of a pitched roof building is shown in fig. 17.5. Gable wind loads are resisted by a lattice truss of depth equal to one bay of the building. This form of construction usually places purlins in axial compression with the requirement that they should be checked under combined bending and wind load (using a slenderness ratio l/r_x appropriate for purlins fixed to metal sheeting). It is necessary to make provision within the side walls to transmit the gable wind forces to the foundations. In many instances, gable wind bracing may be omitted and the gable wind forces transmitted to the sides of the building by diaphragm action. In this connection it should be observed that wind bracing is often used to square up the building and the provision of some nominal bracing members (which may be temporary or alternatively designed to act in conjunction with stressed skin action) should be considered. As most buildings are longer than they are wide, it is necessary to make a decision regarding the depth of diaphragm to be considered. It is usual to consider the diaphragm to have a depth equal to one or two frame spacings but the only restriction is the general one that the depth of a diaphragm should always be less than its span.

A typical situation in which gable wind bracing is replaced by diaphragm action is shown in fig. 17.6. The depth of the diaphragm is reasonably taken as two frame spacings. Suppose the sheeting is 0.7 mm thick (0.65 mm net) and that the fastener specification is as for the previous example, namely: sheet to purlin fasteners,

Fig. 17.4 Test on a Z purlin system.

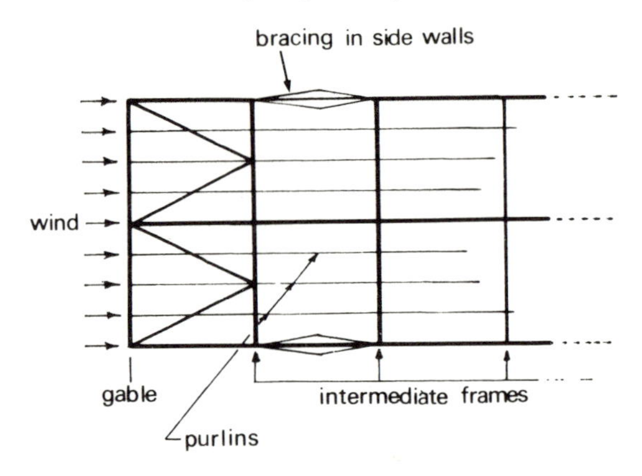

Fig. 17.5 Plan of pitched roof building.

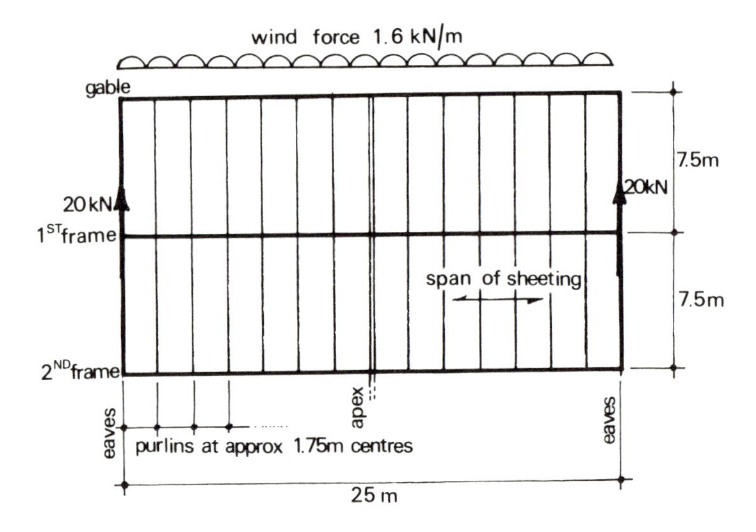

Fig. 17.6 Gable diaphragm.

design strength $F_p = 3.56$ kN at 304 mm centres and seam fasteners, design strength $F_s = 1.51$ kN at 450 mm centres. Again, for brevity, only the more common modes of failure are considered. The analysis demands detailed consideration of a corner sheet width as shown in fig. 17.7. This diagram assumes that the cover width is 912 mm so that the eaves force is $(20 \times 912)/15000 = 1.216$ kN. The direct connection to the gable, shown in fig. 17.7 as a shear connector, may or may not be present. If there is no such connection at either the gable or the rafter forming the boundary of the diaphragm, the sheet to purlin fastener forces are critical and the shear capacity is $\beta_2 n_p F_p = 1.11 \times 2 \times 3.56 = 7.90$ kN compared with the applied force of 2.333 kN giving a load factor of $7.90/2.333 = 3.4$. If the shear connectors or their equivalent are provided, the seam becomes critical where the capacity is (assuming the seam fasteners are at the crests of the profile) $n_s F_s + (\beta_1/\beta_3) n_p F_p =$ $(4 \times 1.51) + [(0.44/0.75) \times 2 \times 3.56] = 10.2$ kN which is even more favourable. The diaphragm is therefore amply strong.

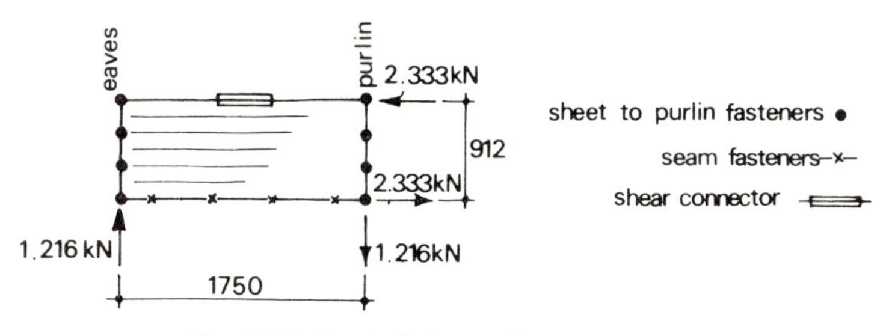

Fig. 17.7 Typical sheet adjacent to eaves.

It should be noted that if there are no shear connectors, it should also be checked that the purlin to rafter cleats are adequate and roof lights should not be permitted in gable diaphragms unless detailed calculations are carried out in order to verify that the strength is adequate.

17.4 Gable bracing when sheeting spans parallel to the length of the building

A typical example in which decking spans directly over frames at 5 m centres, is shown in fig. 17.8. In this case, in addition to its function as gable bracing, the diaphragm has to provide lateral support to the beams. In such a case it is conservative to design the diaphragm for the sum of the two load cases. The case is directly analogous to the situation shown in fig. 17.2 and can be analysed in the same way either from first principles or using the design tables in chapter 9.

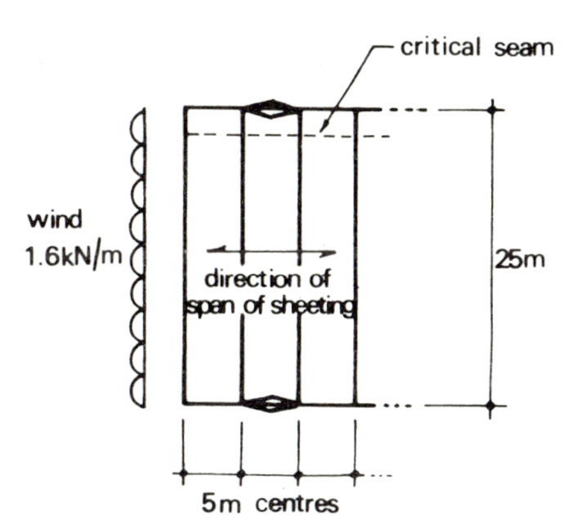

Fig. 17.8 Gable bracing case with sheeting parallel to length of building

17.5 Use of diaphragm action as eaves bracing

This situation is shown in fig. 17.9. When the sheeting is supported on purlins and spans perpendicular to the length of the building the eaves truss can be replaced by a series of eaves diaphragms. The span of each diaphragm is equal to the frame spacing and the depth can be 1, 2 or more purlin spacings subject to the requirement that the depth should not be greater than the span. Again, the eaves diaphragm is directly analogous to fig. 17.2 and the analysis can proceed in the same way either from first principles or using the design tables. It should be noted that in this system the purlins bounding the diaphragms carry axial load and must be designed for combined axial force and bending. For purlins in compression supporting steel sheeting, the relevant radius of gyration r_x is the major value taken about the x–x axis and the factor α in Addendum No. 1 to B.S.449 clause 117 may be taken as unity.

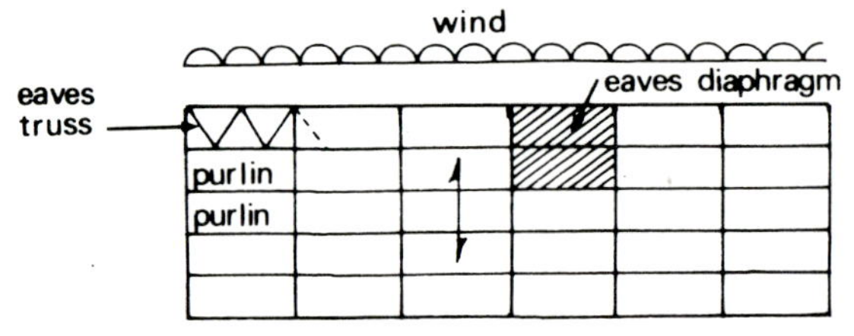

Fig. 17.9 Roof plan showing alternative eaves bracings.

It should be noted that the case shown in fig. 17.9 requires care in the treatment of the forces in the sheet to purlin fasteners at the sides of the diaphragm as these are transmitting the forces from two diaphragms into the supporting structure. They should always be checked from first principles using the equation:

$$V_{ult} = \beta_2 n_p F_p \tag{17.1}$$

CHAPTER EIGHTEEN

Diaphragms in multi-storey buildings

18.1 Introduction

Previous chapters of this book have been almost entirely concerned with stressed skin action in low-rise lightweight structures. It is, however, common knowledge that the interior and exterior walls, floors and roof have a significant influence on the stresses and deflections in multi-storey framed structures. In general, these effects are difficult to quantify. In recent years the non-structural components of typical tall buildings have become lighter and more flexible so that the complete structure has become more flexible and this has led designers to take an increasing interest in the methods to control the sidesway of tall buildings. Clearly, the overall problem is outside the scope of this book but it is in many respects closely related to the subject under consideration. It is therefore useful to review briefly two aspects of the problem that are relatively easily defined and to consider one of them in more detail.

18.2 Diaphragm action of floors

A somewhat simplified diagram of a multi-storey steel-framed building is shown in fig. 18.1. The behaviour under side load is three-dimensional although it is usually convenient to consider the structure to be a series of independent plane sway frames. Although designers are aware that these frames are not free to sway independently as a consequence of the relatively rigid floors and roof, it is not at all easy to take account of this in design as the calculations for the complete three-dimensional problem are cumbersome. Indeed, the only practical alternative to the individual sway frame approach is to assume that the floors and roof are completely rigid in their own planes and to design sufficient vertically braced frames to transfer all of the side load to the foundations. The unbraced frames can then be designed on a no-sway basis. This is an approximation to the real situation that is only valid if the floors are sufficiently stiff and strong. Floors of multi-storey buildings can take many forms and it is not easy to make general statements regarding the requisite stiffness and strength. However, the forces are readily calculable on a no-sway basis, and it is therefore possible to make approximate calculations. Most methods of floor construction include in situ concrete and it is not difficult to satisfy the requirements within the floor itself.

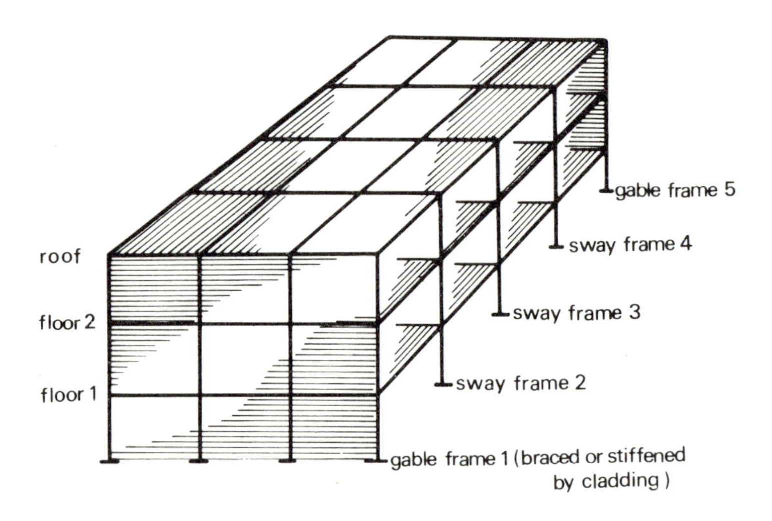

Fig. 18.1 Schematic diagram of multi-storey building.

The main point where difficulties arise is in the connection between the steel frame and the floors (or roof) because the connections must be adequate to transfer the sway forces from the frames to the floors. Little is known regarding this problem and, in general, the designer must make his own calculations for the particular details adopted. However, the most critical form of construction in this respect is the steel concrete composite floor without the use of shear connectors connecting the concrete to the top flange of the beam and for this particular form of construction information is available. Ideally, in such circumstances, the beams supporting the floors should act compositely with the concrete topping and be provided with shear connectors to transfer the shear forces associated with the composite action. The shear connectors can then be designed to carry the additional shear forces associated with the diaphragm action of the floors. When such shear connectors are not provided, diaphragm action is only possible if fasteners connecting the steel deck to the beams are adequate to carry the diaphragm forces. These fasteners are usually fired pins or self-drilling, self-tapping screws and the problem is closely related to the calculation of the strength of a light gauge steel roof diaphragm as considered elsewhere in this book. Design expressions for this case and also for the calculation of diaphragm stiffness have been given by Davies and Fisher[7.6]. It should also be noted that composite diaphragms admit other modes of failure at load levels which may arise in practice and it should not be automatically assumed that the strength is adequate, particularly if the topping is thin or constructed of lightweight concrete. The other relevant references in this field are numbered 7.1 and 7.2.

18.3 Diaphragm action of walls and partitions

As stated above, in the design of multi-storey buildings, it is frequently convenient to design a limited number of frames to carry the side load and to transfer load from other frames to these braced frames through the floors and roof. The braced frames are frequently the gable frames or the walls of lift shafts and stair wells and are often constructed in in situ concrete or diagonally braced steelwork. Alternatively, these braced frames can be constructed as plane frames infilled by diaphragms. One form of construction that has received considerable attention recently is the plane steel frame infilled by brickwork. The behaviour of this type of infilled frame is quite complicated and the current state of the art is described in reference 2.43.

An alternative form of construction is to form a braced frame by infilling a steel frame by a panel or partition of profiled steel sheeting, as shown in fig. 18.2. The profiling of the sheeting in fig. 18.2 serves three important purposes. In the first place it stiffens the panel in the lateral direction and provides the necessary bending strength. Secondly, profiling the sheeting creates a degree of shear flexibility which may be necessary to ensure that the panel is not excessively stiff in comparison with the surrounding frame. Finally, the profiles serve to strengthen the panel against failure by buckling. A frame infilled by profiled steel sheeting in this way thus becomes a special case of a light gauge steel diaphragm and can be designed on a similar basis to the horizontal diaphragms described previously. Because of the magnitudes of the loads involved, structural diaphragms in tall buildings are likely to be heavily fastened and in practice welded details will be required in most cases.

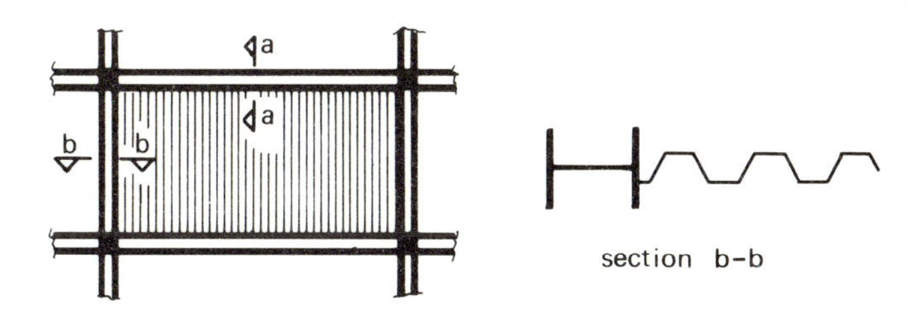

Fig. 18.2 Typical light gauge steel infill panel

A fundamental problem of this application of the light gauge steel diaphragm concerns the method of fixing the diaphragm to the primary structure. It is assumed that the diaphragm will have a greater width than height so that the corrugations will run vertically in the direction of the shorter span. This being the case, the ends of the sheeting require to be connected to the primary beam by a connection which provides resistance in both horizontal directions. However, a completely rigid fixing is not possible as considerable relative vertical displacement is likely between the primary beams above and below the panel and a rigid fixing could result in vertical forces on the diaphragm of sufficient magnitude to cause failure of either the diaphragm or its fixings. A suitable detail (section *a–a* in fig. 18.2) to avoid this is shown in fig. 18.3 and many alternatives are possible.

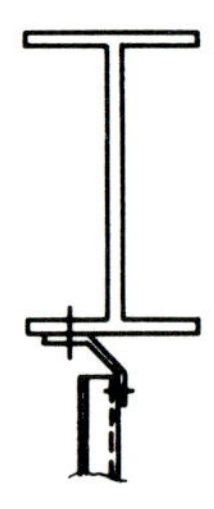

Fig. 18.3 Possible detail at the top of a steel infill panel.

18.4 Analysis and design of infilled frames

The analysis and design of the infill panel itself falls directly within the scope of the previous chapters and requires no further explanation. The treatment of the complete infilled frame requires further consideration as it raises not only an analytical problem but also considerations of design philosophy. For the purposes of analysing the complete composite structure for both deflections and panel forces it is sufficient to consider the infill panels to be replaced by equivalent diagonal bracing members as shown in fig. 18.4. The bending stiffness of the bracing member is zero and its cross-sectional area A is given by

$$A = a/(c\,E\cos^3\theta) \tag{18.1}$$

where c is the required flexibility, E is the modulus of elasticity and the relevant dimensions are shown in fig. 18.5. The analysis of the equivalent frame such as that shown in fig. 18.4 will normally be carried out with the aid of a computer using a conventional program for plane frame analysis. There are, however, alternative manual methods of analysis available using a simplified substitute frame and these are described in reference 2.43.

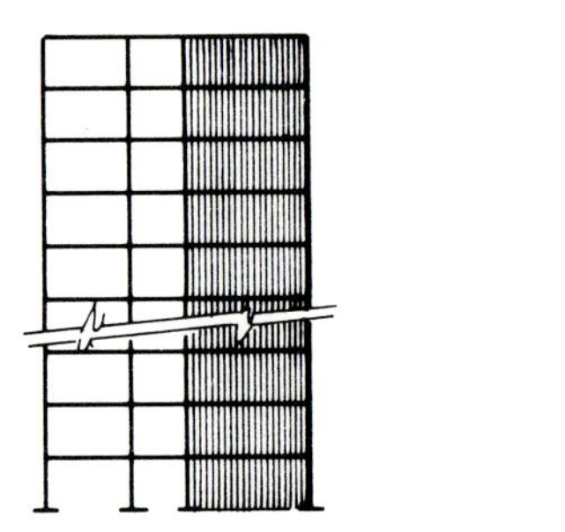

(a) frame with infill panels (b) equivalent structure for analysis

Fig. 18.4 Analysis of frame with steel infill panels.

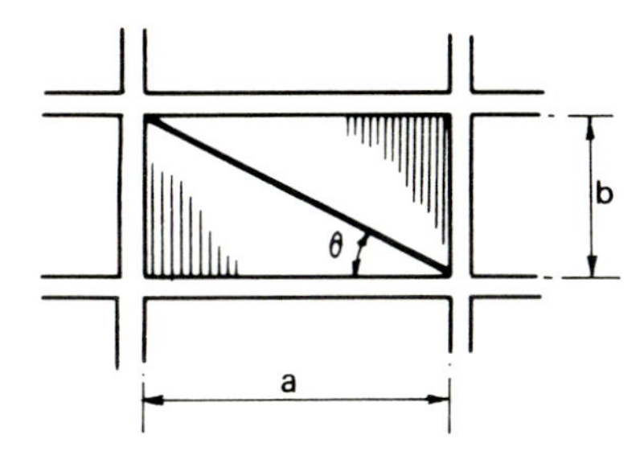

Fig. 18.5 Dimensions of infill panel.

For the design of frames infilled by steel panels, a number of alternative design philosophies are available and the most appropriate must be chosen by the designer bearing in mind such factors as the height of the structure and the relative importance of vertical and side loading. The most important of the alternative approaches are as follows:

(a) The use of infill panels solely to control sidesway deflection. This approach is appropriate to tall buildings in which side loads strongly influence the design. The frames are designed on the basis of strength requirements alone and sufficient infill panels are incorporated to ensure that the sidesway is within permissible limits. This approach is less critical than (b) and (c), in that the *strength* of the frame is adequate without any assistance from the infill panels. However, it is of little practical benefit unless the structure is very tall or slender and it fails to recognise that in many instances the infill panels will carry most of the shear load.
(b) The use of infill panels interacting with frames in a fully composite design. This approach is similar in basis to the interaction of roof panels and portal frames described in chapter 4. It is appropriate here for structures of moderate height and should normally be subject to the requirement that the frames alone are capable of carrying the design load though with an appropriately reduced reserve of safety.
(c) The use of infill panels to carry all of the side load. Here the frames can be nominally pin-jointed. This philosophy, if considered acceptable, is confined to low-rise structures and demands safe-guards to ensure that critical panels are not removed for any reason during the lifetime of the structure. In this connection, it should be noted that the danger of inadvertent removal of an infill panel is not nearly so great as the similar danger in a roof diaphragm. This is because a profiled steel partition may be detailed so that it is immediately apparent that it has structural significance.

When either of the above approaches (a) or (b) is used, load is shared between the frames and shear panels according to their relative stiffness. This gives rise to the necessity of designing an infill panel which will have the right balance between stiffness and strength when acting compositely in the completed structure. In order to investigate this problem, a number of case studies have been made[2.43] in which panels of varying stiffness have been incorporated in realistic multi-storey steel frames. These studies have shown that there is no problem in obtaining the required stiffness balance over a wide range of frame heights and have given rise to design curves which give guidance regarding the choice of a suitable infill panel. As these case studies illustrate a number of important points, one of them will be discussed in more detail.

18.5 Case study of eleven-storey frame

The frame used for this case study was designed as a sway frame. The design of the bare frames is given in considerable detail in the following reference: Bates, W. (1963) *Modern Design of Steel Frames for Multi-Storey Buildings*, B.C.S.A. publication no. 20. The design was carried out according to the British Standard current at the time (*B.S. 449*, 1959). The frame is eleven storeys high and has three bays of width 9.14 m, 3.05 m, 9.14 m respectively. For the bottom two storeys, the width is increased to five bays. For the purpose of the study, the more usual trapezoidal profile was simplified to the box profile shown in fig. 18.6. The panel dimensions are described by the symbols shown in fig. 18.5. It was assumed that the panels were connected to the bounding frame by welded details such as the one shown in fig. 18.3. The flexibility c was therefore calculated to sufficient accuracy by neglecting movement at the welds and axial strains in the substantial frame members and by assuming that all of the flexibility arose as a result of distortion of the profile and shear strain in the sheeting. The flexibility of the complete panel can then be shown to be given by the following equation where the symbols not shown in figs. 18.5 and 18.6 have their usual meanings. Values of $\bar{K}$ were obtained by interpolation from table 9.6 with $\theta = 0°$ and $l/d = 0.5$:

$$c = \left(\frac{a\, d^{2.5}\, \bar{K}}{E\, t^{2.5}\, b^2} + \frac{2.6a\,(1 + k_1)}{E\, t\, b} \right) \tag{18.2}$$

For the purpose of analysis of the infilled frame, the panel was replaced by an equivalent diagonal strut of area A given by equation 18.1. It was assumed that the panels incorporated sufficient welds to ensure that failure was by buckling. Thus the maximum panel strength attainable with a given profile was considered and the failure load could be calculated as the smaller of the following equations:

$$V_{crit} = \frac{36\, a\, D_x^{\frac{1}{4}}\, D_y^{\frac{3}{4}}}{b^2} \quad \text{(overall buckling)} \tag{18.3}$$

$$V_{crit} = \frac{19.3E\, a\, t^3}{d^2} \quad \text{(local buckling)} \tag{18.4}$$

where

$$\left.\begin{aligned} D_x &= \frac{Et^3}{10.92\,(1 + k_1)} \\ D_y &= \frac{E\, t\, d^2\, k_1{}^2\,(3 + k_1)}{48}. \end{aligned}\right\} \tag{18.5}$$

A load factor of 2.0 against buckling was included in the analysis as a conservative combination of the usual load factor for wind load and the requirement that the possibility of failure by buckling should be guarded against by an additional 25% reserve of safety when compared with the more ductile modes of failure involving fasteners.

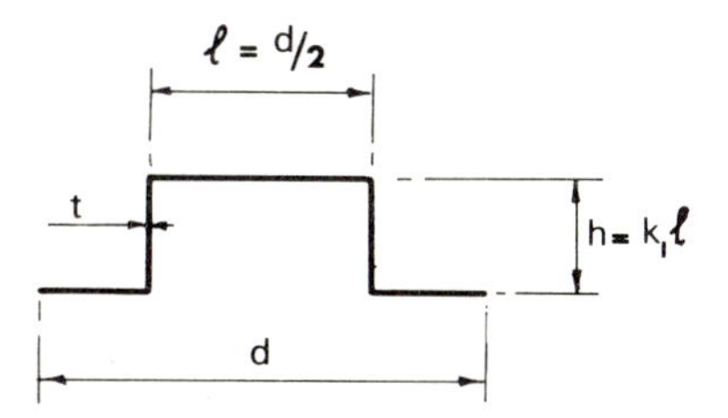

Fig. 18.6 Details of assumed box profile.

On the basis of the above assumptions, curves of strength versus stiffness were obtained for a wide range of infill panels fitting within the given frame by considering variations of the parameters h (profile height), d (profile pitch) and t (sheet thickness). These strength versus stiffness curves were plotted on the same diagram as the curve of stiffness versus induced panel force when the panel was used to infill the given frame. A typical result is shown in fig. 18.7. It is quite clear from fig. 18.7 that there is no difficulty in obtaining the requisite balance between the conflicting requirements of panel stiffness and strength and that there is a wide range of suitable panels for the eleven-storey frame in question. Similar results were obtained for other frames designed as both braced and unbraced and up to twenty-six storeys high. It is also of interest to consider the reduction of sidesway with panels of varying stiffness and this is shown in fig. 18.8. Clearly a small amount of infill stiffness is sufficient to cause a significant reduction in sidesway. However, as the stiffness increases the benefits become proportionately less and there is little point in increasing the stiffness of the infill beyond some limiting value (perhaps about 25 kN/mm for the frame under consideration) as there is little to be gained by way of improved performance. By this stage, most of the side load on the structure is being carried by cantilever beam action in which the infill panel acts as a web and the columns act as flanges. The deflection is primarily due to axial strain in the columns and this cannot be reduced by increasing the infill panel stiffness. A further consequence of this state of affairs is that it is essential to consider axial strains in the analysis of tall infilled structures. The true performance cannot be given by an approximate analysis which neglects the influence of these strains.

18.6 Economy of frames with profiled steel infills

It has been observed[2.20] that a similar effect to that of a properly designed infill panel can be obtained with a single diagonal bracing member of similar weight and requiring less fabrication. The economic success of light gauge steel infills is evidently dependent on the panel also acting as a base for partition finishing material and this can only be assessed in individual circumstances.

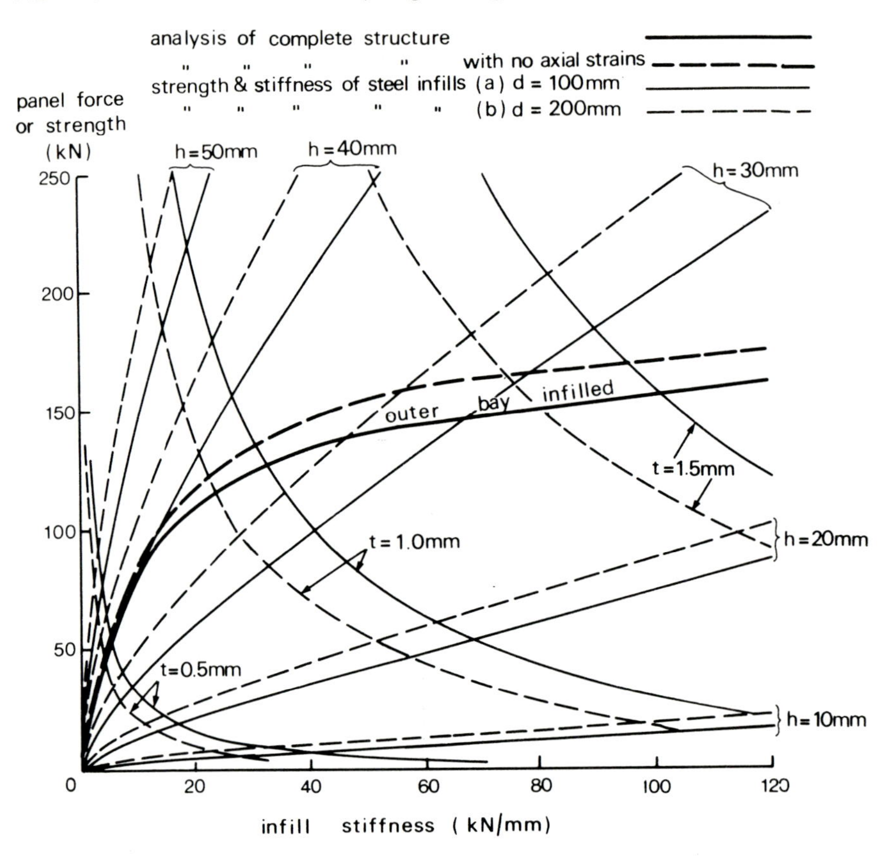

Fig. 18.7 Case study of eleven-storey frame with one outer bay infilled.

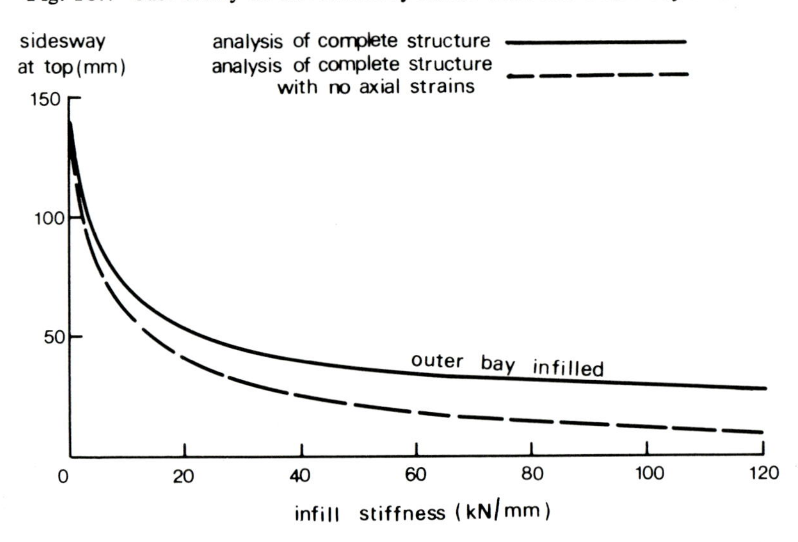

Fig. 18.8 Deflection of eleven-storey frame with one outer bay infilled.

CHAPTER NINETEEN

Other considerations

19.1 Introduction

Up to this point, the content of this book has been mainly concerned with technical aspects of stressed skin design and construction and has defined the current state of the art and the way in which the current position has been reached. Certain practical considerations have also been discussed at appropriate points, notably in section 3.5 where the questions of thermal stresses, combined normal and shear loads and repeated loading were raised. However, there are a number of other important questions which are fundamental to stressed skin design. The authors have lectured widely on the subject and are well aware of many of these problems which have been raised during the discussion periods. It is with this background that the present chapter has been conceived. It is an attempt to group together the most important of the practical considerations and questions which have arisen over the years that the authors have been concerned with stressed skin design.

19.2 Economics

Some preliminary consideration of this important topic was given in section 1.9 where it was shown that in a representative flat-roofed structure, there was a potential saving of about 10% of the cost of the steelwork. However, it must be emphasised again that it is very difficult to obtain meaningful cost comparisons between two alternative forms of construction. In developing more general principles, however, it is convenient to draw again the general distinction between the two basic types of stressed skin construction, namely: (a) diaphragm action in conjunction with rigid-jointed frames and (b) structures with nominally pin-joined frames which are entirely stabilised by diaphragm action. There is very little practical experience of the former type of stressed skin construction, perhaps because of the analytical difficulties involved, but also because the economic advantages are harder to see. Indeed, in the common case of a pitched roof frame of less than 10° pitch, stressed skin action is of little help in carrying vertical load and only comes into play when the structure is sensitive to side load. it follows that typical cases where a designer may obtain economic advantages by appealing to stressed skin action are:

(a) Tall-framed structures where sway deflection is an important design criterion. An important possibility is to design such structures on the basis of strength alone and to utilise stressed skin action to keep deflections within permissible limits.
(b) The above possibility can be particularly important in crane buildings which are particularly sensitive to deflections. In such buildings, crane surge can often be resisted mainly by stressed skin action.
(c) Tied pitched roof portals represent a type of structure in which stressed skin action is particularly useful for resisting side loads and can result in substantial savings.

By far the widest application of stressed skin action has been in flat-roofed construction where roof diaphragms have been used to carry all of the side load back to suitably stiffened points with the consequent elimination of all or most of the wind bracing. The main economic advantage of this is easy to see and assess and, as wind bracing often represents a substantial proportion of the structural steelwork cost, the savings can be considerable. It should also be appreciated that wind bracing is relatively expensive in terms of detailing, fabrication and erection so that the real saving is usually greater than that indicated by the proportion of the weight of steel saved. This advantage has been particularly appreciated in system building where simplication of the system and reduction in the number of components has been perhaps the biggest asset of all.

Another advantage that came to light as a consequence of the needs of system building during the boom in the school building programme in the 1960s and 70s, is the possibility of simplifying the stability calculations. For two systems that were, at that time, responsible for building work worth many millions of pounds per annum, simplified procedures were derived[1.46] whereby stability could be readily checked by the Architect or other personnel who were not familiar with detailed stressed skin calculations. This advantage is now more widely available as a consequence of the preparation of design tables of more universal application.[1.126]

19.3 Corrosion

There is a legitimate worry that stressed skin action in a roof may be reduced in effectiveness because of corrosion of the sheeting around the fasteners or deterioration of the fasteners themselves. However, accelerated weathering tests on fasteners in plastic coated steel sheeting subject to very corrosive conditions, as described briefly in section 13.7, have not resulted in corrosion of the sheet or the fasteners. The plastic washers of the fasteners have indented the plastic coating of the steel and formed an effective seal. Nevertheless, this factor must be carefully watched and a background of experience built up. Because the same points are even more important with regard to wind suction forces at fasteners, the problem is not unique to stressed skin design. Corrosion of the sheet itself is not a potential problem in stressed skin design because the level of membrane stress induced is very low – usually of the order of one tenth of the normal bending stress. If such corrosion were to take place, the sheeting would fail in primary bending long before there was any problem with regard to stressed skin action.

19.4 Divided responsibility

Another fear that has been expressed is that stressed skin design might cause a division of responsibility between the designer, the steelwork contractor and the sheeting contractor and that this responsibility might be reflected in increased prices. One way of avoiding this would be to place package deal contracts but even if this is not done the position may not be worse than in conventional construction for the following reasons:

(a) At present, if there is a leaky roof, it is often difficult to assign full blame to the sheeting contractor who may claim that the roof steelwork was too flexible. Some compromise has often to be worked out.
(b) Stressed skin action is present whether the designer is aware of it or not. As a consequence, the end roof panels in conventional buildings often attract a great deal of shear and any failure of fasteners due to this cause can hardly be attributed to the sheeting contractor. As the stressed skin design method acknowledges this fact and makes allowance for it, there should be less trouble from this cause than there has been in the past.

19.5 Construction and the provision of wind bracing

One of the virtues of stressed skin design is that it avoids the necessity of wind bracing and relies on the sheeting to perform this duty with a consequent saving in both material and fabrication costs. As a consequence, a stressed skin structure may not be stable until at least part of the cladding is in position. This consideration places some constraint on the methods of construction which must ensure that the building is safe at all stages. An obvious precaution is to construct the floors and roof before the side cladding in order to ensure that the diaphragms are complete before any appreciable side load can occur. Some temporary propping may also be necessary. It may, however, be considered necessary in some buildings to provide a limited amount of bracing in the plane of the roof both to ensure that the building is square and to ensure stability during construction. This bracing need not be of sufficient strength to accommodate the full wind force on the completed structure and can be considered to share load with the sheeting with a possible saving in fastenings in the latter. Details of a building incorporating limited wind bracing and the appropriate calculation procedures are given in section 12.8.3.

19.6 Extensions and changes of occupancy

The structural problems of extending or otherwise modifying a stressed skin building are, in principle, no different from any other building. There is, however, the possibility, albeit remote, that at some later date changes may be made without taking into account their effect on the stressed skin action in the original building. This problem diminishes as designers become more used to thinking in terms of stressed skin action and has so far created no difficulties although there are already considerable numbers of stressed skin buildings in existence. However, with this problem in mind, the European recommendations incorporate the requirement that two or more suitable notices identifying the structure as being of stressed skin design should be permanently fixed in conspicuous positions and that reference should be made on these notices to the safety precautions necessary before the removal of any of the cladding. While such a solution may be appropriate in an industrial building it is hardly appropriate in an office, school or other similar building and in such cases the authors would suggest that, if such notices are considered necessary, they could be positioned in such a way that they are revealed before the sheeting is removed.

It is always, of course, advantageous if possible extensions to a structure are anticipated at the design stage. This is equally so with stressed skin design where increasing the length of a building by moving the gables outwards without making other provisions to carry the diaphragm forces may result in the existing diaphragm(s) becoming inadequate and may necessitate strengthening of the gables. As all that may be necessary is an increase in the number of fasteners there are particular advantages if extensions to a stressed skin building are anticipated at an early stage. Alternatively, in a building to be extended, it may be possible to strengthen the original gable so that this acts as a stiff frame.

19.7 Maintenance

It will now be obvious that as the cladding of a stressed skin building is fundamental to its stability, it cannot be removed, even temporarily, for maintenance purposes without the proper precautions being taken. The most important consideration follows from the previous section, namely that those who are responsible for maintenance must be aware that they are dealing with a stressed skin building. Once this is the case, there are a number of possibilities depending on the nature of the maintenance required. If only a small area of cladding has to be removed, there is often no problem as the temporary reduction in the factor of safety may be within acceptable limits. In other cases, some temporary bracing may be required in order to allow the work to proceed. Another possibility is to design the diaphragms in such a way that quite large areas of cladding may be removed without reducing the factor of safety below permissible limits. This was, in fact, done in the case of the very large factory building constructed in Nottingham (see section 8.5).

19.8 Site supervision

As the cladding of a stressed skin building is an integral part of the structure, it must be subject to the same degree of site supervision as the remainder of the structure, for example the steel framework. In particular, the number and position of the fasteners must be carefully checked. This can hardly be regarded as an onerous task and will result in an improvement in the quality of sheet fixing. Moreover, its effect on the overall performance of the building will be beneficial.

PART THREE

BIBLIOGRAPHY

CHAPTER TWENTY

Complete bibliography on the stressed skin action of light gauge metal cladding

The references are grouped in chronological order within the following subject headings. The lists contain all the significant references up to the end of 1980 that are known to the authors.

1. Shear panels and their use to stabilise pin-jointed framed structures
2. Interaction of steel sheet cladding and rigid-jointed steel frames
3. Light gauge steel folded plate structures
4. Light gauge steel hyperbolic paraboloids
5. Light gauge steel cylindrical shells
6. Fasteners for light gauge steel diaphragms
7. Diaphragms of aluminium and other materials

Note

(a) Some papers appear in more than one of the above categories.

(b) This survey is concerned specifically with light gauge steel applications and does not consider the vast literature on the analysis and concrete construction of folded plates, hypars and shells.

(c) References in languages other than English are restricted to the more important of the papers known to the authors.

20.1 Shear panels and their use to stabilise pin-jointed structures

1.1 Nilson, A. H. (Nov. 1960) 'Shear diaphragms of light gauge steel'. *Proc. A.S.C.E., J. Struct. Div.*, **86** (ST11).

1.2 English, J. M. (July 1961) Discussion of above. *Proc. A.S.C.E., J. Struct. Div.*, **87** (ST7).

1.3 McKenzie, K. I. (June 1962) *The Shear Stiffness of a Corrugated Web.* R.A.E. report no. struct. 275.

1.4 El-Dakhakhni, W. M. (1963) 'The effect of membranes in stiffening pitched roof portal frame sheds'. Ph. D. thesis, Univ. of Manchester.

1.5 Bryan, E. R. and El-Dakhakhni, W. M. (Aug. 1964) 'Shear in thin plates with flexible edge members'. *Proc. A.S.C.E., J. Struct. Div.*, **90** (ST4).

1.6 Bryan, E. R. and El-Dakhakhni, W. M. (Dec. 1964) 'Behaviour of sheeted portal frame sheds: theory and experiments'. *Proc. I.C.E.*, **29**.

1.7 *Proc. I.C.E.* (June 1966) Discussion on the above. *Proc. I.C.E.*, **34**.

1.8 Luttrell, L. D. (Aug. 1965) *Structural Performance of Light Gauge Steel Diaphragms*. Rep. no. 319, Dept. of Struct. Engrg., Cornell Univ.

1.9 Luttrell, L. D. (1965) *Light Gauge Steel Shear Diaphragms*. Civ. Eng. Dept. Publ., W. Virgina Univ.

1.10 Yu, W. W. (1965) *Design of Light Gauge Cold-Formed Steel Structures*. Eng. Expt. Station, W. Virgina Univ.

1.11 Hlavacek, V. (1965) *Stability of Orthotropic Panels Subject to Shear*. Res. rep., Bldg. Res. Inst. Tech., Univ. of Prague (in Czech).

1.12 Jackson, P. (1965) 'The shear behaviour of corrugated sheeting'. M. Sc. thesis, Univ. of Manchester.

1.13 Apparao, T. V. S. R. (Dec. 1966) 'Tests on light gauge steel diaphragms'. Report no. 328, Dept. of Struct. Engrg., Cornell Univ.

1.14 Hlavacek, V. (1967) 'Critical shear stresses in markedly orthotropic webs'. *Acta Polytechnica*, **7** (1), Prague.

1.15 A.I.S.I. (1967) *Design of Light Gauge Steel Diaphragms*. A.I.S.I., New York.

1.16 Luttrell, L. D. (1967) *Strength and Behaviour of Light Gauge Steel Shear Diaphragms*. Cornell eng. res. bul. no. 67 (1), Dept. of Struct. Engrg., Cornell Univ.

1.17 Falkenberg, J. C. (April 1968) *Tests and Analysis of the Diaphragm Stiffness of Corrugated Roof Panels Used as Wind Bracing Elements*. Res. rep. to Robertson-Nordiak A/S, N.B.I. (in Norwegian).

1.18 Bryan, E. R. and Jackson, P. (1968) 'The shear behaviour of corrugated steel sheeting'. *Proc. of Symposium on Thin-Walled Steel Structs*, Univ. of Swansea (Sept. 1967), Crosby Lockwood.

1.19 Rothwell, A. (Aug. 1968) 'The shear stiffness of flat-sided corrugated webs'. *Aero. Quarterly*.

1.20 Bryan, E. R. and El-Dakhakhni, W. M. (Nov. 1968) 'Shear flexibility and strength of corrugated decks'. *Proc. A.S.C.E., J. Struct. Div.*, **14** (ST11).

1.21 Falkenberg. J. C. (June 1969) Discussion of above. *Proc. A.S.C.E., J. Struct. Div.*, **95** (ST6).

1.22 Bryan, E. R. and El-Dakhakhni, W. M. (Nov. 1968) 'Shear of corrugated decks: calculated and observed behaviour'. *Proc. I.C.E.*, **41**.

1.23 Hlavacek, V. (1968) 'Shear instability of orthotropic panels'. *Acta Technica, Csav.* **1**.

1.24 Easley, J. T. and McFarland, D. E. (July 1969) 'Buckling of light gauge metal shear diaphragms'. *Proc. A.S.C.E., J. Struct. Div.*, **95** (ST7).

1.25 Nilson, A. H. (Dec. 1969) Discussion of above. *Proc. A.S.C.E., J. Struct. Div.*, **95** (ST12).

1.26 Bryan, E. R. and El-Dakhakhni, W. M. (Oct. 1969) 'Shear tests on light gauge steel decks'. *Acier-Stahl-Steel*, **10**.

1.27 Raslan, R. A. S. (1969) 'The structural behaviour of corrugated plates'. Ph. D. thesis, Univ. of Manchester.

1.28 Lin, C. and Libove, C. (May 1970) *Theoretical Study of Corrugated Plates: Shearing of a Trapezoidally Corrugated Plate with Trough Lines Held Straight.* Rep. no. MAE 1833-T1, Dept. of Mech. and Aerospace Eng., Syracuse Univ.

1.29 M.R.D.A. (1970) *Light Gauge Metal Roof Decks*, Metal Roof Deck Association, London.

1.30 Lin, C. and Libove, C. (June 1970) *Theoretical Study of Corrugated Plates: Shearing of a Trapezoidally Corrugated Plate with Trough Lines Permitted to Curve.* Rep. no. MAE 1833-T2 (re-issued as NASA CR-1750, Dec. 1971), Dept. of Mech. and Aerospace Eng., Syracuse Univ.

1.31 Steinhardt, O. and Einsfield, U. (1970) *Trapezblechscheiben im Stahlhochbau – Wirkungsweise und Berechnung (Design of sheeting panels of trapezoidal cross-section for steel structures).* Bautechnik (in German).

1.32 Johns, D. J. (1970) *Shear Buckling of Isotropic and Orthotropic Plates: A Review.* Dept. of Transport Tech., Loughborough Univ. of Tech.

1.33 Hsiao, C. and Libove, C. (July 1971) *Theoretical Study of Corrugated Plates: Shear Stiffness of a Trapezoidally Corrugated Plate with Discrete Attachments to a Rigid Flange at the Ends of the Corrugations.* Rep. no. MAE 1833-T3 (re-issued as NASA CR-1966, Feb. 1972), Dept. of Mech. and Aerospace Eng. Syracuse Univ.

1.34 Ellifritt, D. S. and Luttrell, L. D. (Aug. 1971) 'Strength and stiffness of steel deck shear diaphragms.' *Proc. 1st Speciality Conf. on Cold-Formed Steel Structs.* Rolla, Missouri.

1.35 Horne, M. R. and Raslan, R. A. S. (1971) *An Energy Solution to the Shear Deformation of Corrugated Plates.* Publ. I.A.B.S.E. 31-I.

1.36 Horne, M. R. and Raslan, R. A. S. (1971) *A Finite Difference Approach to Corrugated Shear Panels.* Publ. I.A.B.S.E. 31-I.

1.37 Wu, L. H. and Libove, C. (Jan. 1972) *Theoretical Study of Corrugated Plates: Shearing of a Corrugated Plate with Curvilinear Corrugations.* Rep. no. MAE 1833-T4 (re-issued as NASA CR-2080, June 1972), Dept. of Mech. and Aerospace Eng., Syracuse Univ.

1.38 Bryan, E. R. (March 1972) 'Structural behaviour of cladding systems' published in *Sheet Steel in Building. Proc. symp. Iron and Steel Institute/R.I.B.A.*, London.

1.39 Libove, C. (April 1972) 'Survey of recent work on the analysis of discretely attached corrugated shear webs'. Paper no. 72-351, *Proc. A.I.A.A./A.S.M.E./S.A.E. 13th Structures, Structural Dynamics and Materials Conf.*, San Antonio, Texas.

1.40 Libove, C. (May 1972) 'Buckling of corrugated plates in shear'. *Proc. Int. Coll. Stability of Structs. under Static and Dynamic Load*, Washington.

1.41 S.D.I. (Oct. 1972) *Tentative Recommendations for the Design of Steel Deck Diaphragms.* Steel Deck Institute, Illinois.

1.42 Hlavacek, V. (1972) 'The effect of support conditions on the stiffness of corrugated sheets subjected to shear'. *Acta Technica Csav*, 2.

1.43 C.S.S.B.I. (Dec. 1972) *Diaphragm Action of Cellular Steel Floor and Roof Deck Construction*. Canadian Sheet Steel Building Institute, Ontario.

1.44 Hlavacek, V. (1972) 'Flexibility of corrugated sheets in shear'. *Stavebnicky Casopis* **SAV XIX** (3-4), Bratislava.

1.45 Ammar, A. R. and Nilson, A. H. (Aug. 1972, April 1973) *Analysis of Light Gauge Steel Shear Diaphragms Parts I and II.* Res. reps. nos. 350 and 351, Dept. of Struct. Eng., Cornell Univ.

1.46 Bryan, E. R. (March 1973) *Stressed Skin Roof Decks for SEAC and CLASP Building Systems.* CONSTRADO.

1.47 Butler, W. H. (April 1973) 'Steel in the new Covent Garden'. *Constructional Steelwork.*

1.48 U.S. Army (April 1973) *Seismic Design for Buildings.* U.S. Army technical manual, TM 5-809-10. Published by U.S. Army, Navy and Air Force. (The method of diaphragm design described in this publication is usually known as the 'Tri-Services Method'.)

1.49 Beck, V. R. (May 1973) 'Stressed skin design of steel claddings'. *Proc. A.I.S.C. Conference on Steel Developments.* University of Newcastle, N.S.W.

1.50 Libove, C. (Oct. 1973) 'On the stiffness, stresses and buckling analysis of corrugated shear webs'. *Proc. 2nd Speciality Conf. on Cold-Formed Steel Structs.*, Rolla, Missouri.

1.51 Nilson, A. H. (Oct. 1973) 'Analysis of light gauge steel shear diaphragms'. *Proc. 2nd Speciality Conf. on Cold-Formed Steel Structs.*, Rolla, Missouri.

1.52 Luttrell, L. D. (Oct. 1973) 'Screw connected shear diaphragms'. *Proc. 2nd Speciality Conf. on Cold-Formed Steel Structs.*, Rolla, Missouri.

1.53 Chern, C. and Jorgenson, J. L. (Oct. 1973) 'Shear strength of deep corrugated steel panels'. *Proc. 2nd Speciality Conf. on Cold-Formed Steel Structs.*, Rolla, Missouri.

1.54 Fisher, J. M. and Johnson, D. L. (Oct. 1973) 'Behaviour of light gauge diaphragms coupled with X bracing'. *Proc. 2nd Speciality Conf. on Cold-Formed Steel Structs.*, Rolla, Missouri.

1.55 CONSTRADO (Nov. 1973) *Stressed skin construction – principles and practice.* CONSTRADO Publ. 3/73.

1.56 CONSTRADO (Nov. 1973) *Stressed Skin Roof on Dalestorth Primary School.* CONSTRADO project study 4, publ. 7/73.

1.57 Bryan, E. R. (1973) *The Stressed Skin Design of Steel Buildings*. CONSTRADO Monographs, Crosby Lockwood Staples.

1.58 Nilson, A. H. and Ammar, A. R. (April 1974) 'Finite elements analysis of metal deck shear diaphragms'. *Proc. A.S.C.E., J. Struct. Div.*, ST4.

1.59 Wu, L. H. and Libove, C. (May 1974) *Theoretical Stress and Stiffness Data for Discretely Attached Corrugated Shear Webs with Trapezoidal Corrugations.* Rep. no. MAE 5170-T2, Dept. of Mech. and Aerospace Eng., Syracuse Univ.

1.60 *Tubular Structures* (July 1974) 'New Covent Garden market'. *Tubular Structures*, 24, British Steel Corporation Tubes Division.

1.61 Davies, J.M. (Sept. 1974) *The Design of Shear Diaphragms of Corrugated Steel Sheeting.* Rep. no. 74/50, Univ. of Salford. Dept. of Civil Eng.

1.62 Hussain, M. I. and Libove, C. (Dec. 1974) *Stress and Stiffness Data for Discretely Attached Corrugated Shear Webs with Trapezoidal Corrugations.* Rep. no. MAE 5170-T3, Dept. of Mech. and Aerospace Eng., Syracuse Univ.

1.63 Tarlton, D. L. (1974) 'Diaphragm action' in *Design in Cold Formed Steel.* Solid Mech. Div., Univ. of Waterloo Press. Waterloo, Ontario.

1.64 Baehre, R. and Nyberg, G. (1974) *Stabilisering av byggnader genom ytbärverk av profilerad plät (Stabilisation of Buildings by Structural Cladding of Corrugated Sheeting – Review of Literature).* Report R4, Svensk Byggtjanst, Stockholm (in Swedish with English summary).

1.65 Standards Association of Australia (1974) 'Appendix F – stressed skin design' in *The Use of Steel in Structures.* Standards Association of Australia, Sydney.

1.66 Lapin, D. (1974) 'Behaviour of insulated metal decking under shear load', M.Sc. thesis, University of Salford.

1.67 Baehre, R. and Konig, J. (Feb. 1975) 'Provning av skivverkan med trapetsprofilerad plät'. *Plannja*, **TRP 110**, Kungliga Tekniska Högskolan, Stockholm (in Swedish).

1.68 Bryan, E. R. (Feb. 1975) 'Metal roof deck diaphragms in buildings'. *Architects Journal*, **161** (8).

1.69 Libove, C. (March 1975) *Asymtotic Behaviour of Discretely Attached Corrugated Shear Webs.* Rep. no. MAE 5170-T4, Dept. of Mech. and Aerospace Eng., Syracuse Univ.

1.70 Strehl, C. (1975) 'Berechnung regel massig periodisch aufgebauter Faltwerksquerschnitte unter Schubbelastung am Beispiel des Trapezbleches'. Thesis (in German), Darmstadt Univ.

1.71 Easley, J. T. (July 1975) 'Buckling formulas for corrugated metal shear diaphragms'. *Proc. A.S.C.E., J. Struct. Div.*, ST7.

1.72 Sexsmith, R. G. (Sept. 1975) *Behaviour of a Light Gauge Steel Diaphragm.* Report of project 169, Dept. of Struct. Eng., Cornell Univ.

1.73 Bryan, E. R. (Sept. 1975) 'Wand-Dach-und Deckenscheiben im Stahlochbau'. *Der Bauingenieur*, **50** (in German).

1.74 Bryan, E. R. (Sept. 1975) 'Diaphragm action in metal roof decks'. *Proc. Conf. of Int. Waterproofing Assoc.*, Zurich.

1.75 Nethercot, D. A. and Trahair, N. S. (Oct. 1975) 'Design of diaphragm braced I-beams'. *Proc. A.S.C.E., J. Struct. Div.*, **101** (ST10).

1.76 Bryan, E. R. (Nov. 1975) 'Calculation of sheet steel diaphragms in the U.K.'. *Proc. 3rd Int. Speciality Conf. on Cold-Formed Steel Structs.*, Rolla, Missouri.

1.77 Bryan, E. R. and Davies, J. M. (Nov. 1975) 'Stressed skin construction in the U.K.'. *Proc. 3rd Int. Speciality Conf. on Cold-Formed Steel Structs.*, Rolla, Missouri.

1.78 Davies, J. M. and Lawson, R. M. (Nov. 1975) 'The shear flexibility of corrugated steel sheeting'. *Proc. 3rd Int. Speciality Conf. on Cold-Formed Steel Structs.*, Rolla, Missouri.

1.79 Seden, M. R. (1975) 'The stiffening effect of light cladding on steel structures', Ph. D. thesis, Univ. of Salford.

1.80 Baehre, R. and Konig, J. (1975) *Skivverkan av trapetsprofilerad plät (Membrane action of corrugated steel sheets).* Svensk Byggtjanst, Stockholm (Swedish specification for stressed skin design – in Swedish).

1.81 Crisinel, M. (1975) *Effet de contreventment des tôles minces de planchers, toitures, façades.* Schweizerische Zentralstelle für Stahlbau, Zurich (in French and German).

1.82 Swedish Institute of Steel Construction (1975) 'Diaphragm action', chapter 5 in *Tunnplåtskonstruktioner.* Swedish Institute of Steel Construction. Stockholm (in Swedish).

1.83 Schardt, R. and Strehl, C. (April 1976) 'Theoretisch Grundlagen für die Bestimmung der Schubsteifigkeit von Trapezblech Scheiben – Vergleich mit anderen Berechnungsansätzen und Versuchsergebnissen'. *Der Stahlbau* (in German).

1.84 Errera, S. J. and Apparao, T. V. S. R. (April 1976) 'Design of I-shaped beams with diaphragm bracing. *Proc. A.S.C.E., J. Struct. Div.*, **102** (ST4).

1.85 Lawson, R. M. (May 1976) Discussion of reference 1.71 (J. T. Easley, July 1975). *Proc. A.S.C.E., J. Struct. Div.*, ST5.

1.86 Davies, J. M. (July 1976) 'Calculation of steel diaphragm behaviour'. *Proc. A.S.C.E., J. Struct. Div.*, **102**, (ST7).

1.87 Lawson, R. M. (July 1976) 'A look at North American practice in the use of corrugated sheeting'. Struct. Eng. **54** (7).

1.88 Bryan, E. R. (Sept. 1976) 'Stressed skin design and construction: a state of the art report'. Struct. Eng., **54** (9).

1.89 Atrek, E. (Sept. 1976) *Non-Linear Finite Element Analysis of Light Gauge Steel Shear Diaphragms.* Rep. no. 363, Dept. of Struct. Engrg., Cornell Univ., Ithaca.

1.90 Lawson, R. M. (1976) 'The flexibility and strength of corrugated diaphragms and folded plates'. Ph. D. thesis, Univ. of Salford.

1.91 Baker, K. N. and Kavanagh, K. T. (1976) 'Behavour of light steel buildings in high wind environments'. *Proc. Metal Structures Conf., Inst. of Engrs.*, Australia.

1.92 Schardt, R. (1976) *Scheibenwirkung von Dächern und Decken aus Stahl oder Aluminium Trapezblechen.* Teil 4, Forschungsvorhaben des Instituts fur Bautechnik, Berlin (in German).

1.93 Schutze (1976) *Ein Satz von Ekotal – Trapezprofilblechen als Dach und Wendelemente.* Bauinformation 12/1976, Serie *Bauaufsight*, **101**, D.D.R. (in German).

1.94 *Installation of Sheet Metal Diaphragms.* TI Sheet 080-07, Hilti, Liechtenstein.

1.95 E.C.C.S./CONSTRADO (1976) *Stressed Skin Design.* No. 21, E.C.C.S.-XVII-2E, CONSTRADO, Croydon. (German version (1977) *Schubfeld Konstruktion* I.F.B.S., Düsseldorf. Spanish version (July 1977) *Recommendaciones sobre cerramientos métalicos* S.C.G., Madrid.)

1.96 Fischer, M. (1976) 'Zum Tragverhalten und Einsatz von Trapezprofilblechen-scheiben' ('On the behaviour under load and use of trapezoidally profiled thin sheet metal diaphragms'). Vortrage aus der Fachsitzung III des Deutschen Stahlbautages, (Paper to Deutscher Stahlbautag), Stuttgart (in German).

1.97 Nyberg, G. (1976) *Diaphragm Action of Assembled C-Shaped Panels.* Doc. D9, Swedish Council for Building Research (in English).

1.98 Easley, J. T. (Jan. 1977) 'Strength and stiffness of corrugated metal shear diaphragms'. *Proc. A.S.C.E., J. Struct. Div.*, **103** (ST1).

1.99 E.C.C.S. (March 1977) *European Recommendations for the Stressed Skin Design of Steel Structures.* Pub. no. XVII-77-1E, European Convention for Constructional Steelwork. English version published by CONSTRADO. (French version in Construction Métallique (1977), **3**.

1.100 Libove, C. (May 1977) 'Buckling of corrugated plates in shear'. *Proc. Int. Coll. Stability of Structs. under Static and Dynamic Loads*, Washington.

1.101 Bartak, A. J. J. *et al.* (July 1977) 'The new grandstand at the Crystal Palace National Sports Centre'. *Struct. Engr.*, **55** (7).

1.102 Fazio, P., Ha, H. K. and Chockalingham, S. (Nov. 1977) *Strength of light gauge steel corrugated diaphragms.* Report no. CBS 30, Centre for Building Studies, Concordia Univ., Montreal.

1.103 Davies, J. M. (Nov. 1977) 'Simplified diaphragm analysis'. *Proc. A.S.C.E., J. Struct. Div.*, **103** (ST11).

1.104 Chockalingham, S., Ha, K. H. and Fazio, P. (Jan. 1978) Discussion of 'Strength and stiffness of corrugated metal shear diaphragms' (J. T. Easley, Jan. 1977). *Proc. A.S.C.E., J. Struct. Div.*, **104** (ST1).

1.105 Bryan, E. R. (April 1978) 'Stressed skin design'. Institution of Structural Engineers, symposium on new draft standard for 'The structural use of steelwork in building', London.

1.106 McCreless, C. S. and Tarpy, T. S. (June 1978) 'Experimental investigation of steel stud shear wall diaphragms'. *Proc. 4th Int. Speciality Conf. on Cold-Formed Steel Structs.* Univ. of Missouri – Rolla.

1.107 Chockalingham, S., Fazio, P. and Ha, K. (June 1978) 'Strength of cold-formed shear diaphragms'. *Proc. 4th Int. Speciality Conf. on Cold-Formed Steel Structs.* Univ. of Missouri – Rolla.

1.108 Davies, J. M. and Lawson, R. M. (Aug. 1978) 'Light gauge steel diaphragms with openings'. *Proc. I.A.B.S.E. P-16/78.*

1.109 Davies, J. M. (1978) 'Concentrated loads on light gauge steel diaphragms'. *J. Struct. Mech.*, **6** (2).

1.110 Davies, J. M. and Lawson, R. M. (1978) 'The shear deformation of profiled metal sheeting'. *Int. J. Numr. Methods in Engrg.* **12** (10).

1.111 C.T.I.C.M. (1978) 'Exemple de calcul d'une structure compte tenu de la collaboration des parois'. *Construction Métallique*, **2** (in French).

1.112 Bryan, E. R. and Davies, J. M. (Nov. 1978) 'Design code and tables for diaphragm action in light gauge steel roof decks'. Draft, Metal Roof Deck Association.

1.113 B.S.I. (1978) 'The structural use of steelwork in building, part I, chapter 13 – stressed skin construction'. Draft, British Standards Institution.

1.114 A.I.S.I. (Feb. 1979) 'Design of cold-formed steel diaphragms'. Draft for comment, American Iron and Steel Institute, Washington.

1.115 Ha, H. K. (March 1979) 'Corrugated shear diaphragms'. *Proc. A.S.C.E., J. Struct. Div.*, **105**(ST3).

1.116 Fazio, P., Ha, K. and Chockalingham, S. (March 1979) 'Strength of cold-formed steel shear diaphragms'. *Canadian Jour. of Civil Eng.*, **6** (1).

1.117 Davies, J. M. and Bryan, E. R. (April 1979) 'Design tables for light gauge steel diaphragms'. *Proc. Int. Conf. on Thin-Walled Structures*, Univ. of Strathclyde, Glasgow.

1.118 Ha, K. H., El-Hakim, N. and Fazio, P. (July 1979) 'Simplified design of corrugated shear diaphragms'. *Proc. A.S.C.E., J. Struct. Div.*, **105** (ST7).

1.119 (July 1979) *Richtlijen voor de toepassing van geprofileerde stalen platten als schijfkonstruktie – R.S.P.S. 1979.* (Dutch standard for stressed skin design). T.N.O.

1.120 Eggert, H. and Kanning, W. (1979) 'Feinbleche aus Stahl für ebene Dächer'. *Bauingenieur*, **54** (in German).

1.121 Huang, H. T. (1979) 'Theoretical and physical approach to light gauge steel shear diaphragms'. Ph. D. thesis, W. Virginia Univ.

1.122 Atrek, E. and Nilson, A. H. (March 1980) 'Non-linear analysis of cold-formed steel shear diaphragms.' *Proc. A.S.C.E., J. Struct. Div.*, **106** (ST3).

1.123 Huang, H. T. and Luttrell, L. D. (Nov. 1980) 'Theoretical and physical evaluations of steel shear diaphragms'. *Proc. 5th Int. Speciality Conf. on Cold-Formed Steel Structs.* Univ. of Missouri – Rolla.

1.124 Balazs, P. (1980) *Stressed Skin Action in Composite Panels Comprising Steel Sheeting and Boards.* Doc. D40, Swedish Council for Building Research.

1.125 Luttrell, L. D. (Jan. 1981) *Steel Deck Institute Diaphragm Design Manual.* Steel Deck Institute, St. Louis.

1.126 Bryan, E. R. and Davies, J. M. (1981) *Steel Diaphragm Roof Decks*. Granada.

20.2 Interaction of steel sheet cladding and rigid-joined steel frames

2.1 El-Dakhakhni, W. M. (1963) 'The effect of membranes in stiffening pitched roof portal frame sheds'. Ph. D. thesis, Univ. of Manchester.

2.2 Bryan, E. R. and El-Dakhakhni, W. M. (Dec. 1964) 'Behaviour of sheeted portal frame sheds: theory and experiments'. *Proc. I.C.E.*, **29**.

2.3 (June 1966) Discussion of above. *Proc. I.C.E.* **34**.

2.4 Bryan, E. R. (Aug. 1964) *The Stiffening Effect of Sheeting in Buildings*. Prelim. Publn., I.A.B.S.E. 7th Congr., Rio de Janeiro.

2.5 Bates, W., Bryan, E. R. and El-Dakhakhni, W. M. (June 1965) 'Full scale tests on a portal frame shed'. *Struct. Engr.*, **43**.

2.6 El-Dakhakhni, W. M. (1965) *Stiffening Effect of Roof Slabs on Pitched Roof and Polygonal Sheds.* J. Egypt. Soc. Civ. Engrs. annual vol.

2.7 Bryan, E. R. and El-Dakhakhni, W. M. (1968) *The Design and Analysis of Buildings with Light Cladding.* Publ. I.A.B.S.E. **28** (II), Zurich.
2.8 Bolton, M. D. (Oct. 1969) 'An assessment of the effect of cladding on the overall stability of framed structures'. M. Sc. thesis, Univ. of Manchester.
2.9 Bryan, E. R. (Aug. 1970) 'Cladding stiffens buildings'. *Building with Steel*, **4**.
2.10 Bryan, E. R. (Jan. 1971) 'Research into the structural behaviour of a sheeted building'. *Proc. I.C.E.*, **48**.
2.11 Sexsmith, R. G. and Miller, C. J. (March 1971) *Interaction of diaphragms and Multi-Storey Building Frames*. 1st progress rep., Cornell Univ.
2.12 *Constructional Steelwork* (June 1971) 'Research on the stiffening effect of sheeting on steel-framed buildings'. *Constructional Steelwork*.
2.13 Koerner, R. J. (June 1971) 'The interaction between rigidly jointed frames and light cladding'. M.E. thesis, Univ. of Melbourne.
2.14 Miller, C. J. (Sept. 1971) *Interaction of Diaphragms and Multi-Storey Building Frames.* 2nd progress rep., Cornell Univ.
2.15 Bryan, E. R. (Oct. 1971) 'The design of stressed skin steel buildings'. *Civ. Eng. and Publ. Wks. Rev.*
2.16 *Building with Steel* (Nov. 1971) 'Tests at Salford'. *Building with Steel*, **8**.
2.17 Lawrence, S. J. (Jan. 1972) 'Stiffening effect of cladding on light-weight structures'. M.E. thesis, Univ. of Melbourne.
2.18 El-Dakhakhni, W. M. and Daniels, J. H. (April 1972) *Integrated Structural Behaviour of Buildings.* Preprint no. 1669, A.S.C.E. Nat. Struct. Engrg. mtg. Cleveland.
2.19 Bryan, E. R. and Mohsin, M. E. (May 1972) *The Design and Testing of a Steel Building Taking Account of the Sheeting.* Prelim. rep. I.A.B.S.E. 9th Congr., Amsterdam.
2.20 Miller, C. J. (Aug. 1972) *Analysis of Multi-Storey Frames with Light Gauge Steel Panel Infills.* Res. rep. no. 349, Dept. of Struct. Engrg., Cornell Univ.
2.21 Bryan, E. R. and Davies, J. M. (Aug. 1972) *Stiffening Effect of Light Cladding.* Preprints vol. II-17, state of art rep. 3A, Tech. Committee 17, A.S.C.E.-I.A.B.S.E. Int. Conf. on Tall Buildings.
2.22 Davies, J. M. (Nov. 1972) 'Computer analysis of stressed skin buildings'. *Civ. Eng. and Publ. Wks. Rev.*
2.23 Lawrence, S. J. and Sved, G. (1972) 'A finite element analysis of clad structures'. Conf. on Metal Structures Research and its Applications, Inst. Engrs. Australia, Sydney.
2.24 Oppenheim, I. J. (1972) 'The effect of cladding on tall buildings'. Ph. D. thesis, Cambridge Univ.
2.25 Davies, J. M. (March 1973) 'The plastic collapse of framed structures clad with corrugated steel sheeting'. *Proc. I.C.E.*, **55**.
2.26 Bryan, E. R. (1973) *The Stressed Skin Design of Steel Buildings*. CONSTRADO monograph, Crosby Lockwood Staples.
2.27 El-Dakhakhni, W. M. (April 1973) *Effect of Light Gauge Partitions on Multi-Storey Buildings*. Egypt. Soc. Civil Engrs., Cairo.

2.28 El-Dakhakhni, W. M. and Daniels, J. H. (April 1973) *Frame–Floor–Wall System Interaction in Buildings.* Fritz. Engrg. Lab. rep. no. 376.2, Lehigh Univ.

2.29 Oppenheim, I. J. (June 1973) 'Control of lateral deflections in planar frames using structural partitions'. *Proc. I.C.E. Part 2*, **55**.

2.30 Miller, C. J. (Oct. 1973) 'Drift control with light gauge steel infill panels'. *Proc. 2nd Speciality Conf. on Cold-Formed Steel Structs.* Rolla, Missouri.

2.31 CONSTRADO (Nov. 1973) *Stressed Skin Construction – Principles and Practice.* CONSTRADO Publn. 3/73.

2.32 Bryan, E. R. (1973) 'Structural behaviour of cladding systems'. *Sheet Steel in Building.* Iron and Steel Inst.

2.33 Oppenheim, I. J. (1973) 'Dynamic behaviour of tall buildings with cladding'. *Proc. 5th World Conf. on Earthquake Engrg.*, Rome.

2.34 Freeman, D. J. (June 1974) 'The structural action of light cladding'. M.E. thesis, Univ. of Melbourne.

2.35 Bryan, E. R. and Davies, J. M. (Nov. 1975) 'Stressed skin construction in the U.K.'. *Proc. 3rd Speciality Conf. on Cold-Formed Steel Structs.* Rolla, Missouri.

2.36 Seden, M. R. (1975) 'The stiffening effect of light cladding on steel structures'. Ph. D. thesis, Univ. of Salford.

2.37 Rubin, H. (1972) 'The design of composite building structures as discontinuous systems'. Thesis (in German), Karlsruhe University.

2.38 Strnad, M. (1975) *Spolôpusobeni plášťu u lehkých ocelovýchhal* (*Interaction of the Sheeting and Portal Frames in Light Steel Halls*) Praha, Stavebni informačni stręddisko.

2.39 Bryan, E. R. (Sept. 1976) 'Stressed skin design and construction: a state of the art report'. *Struct. Eng.*, **54** (9).

2.40 E.C.C.S. (March 1977) *European Recommendations for the Stressed Skin Design of Steel Structures.* Publ. no. XVII-77-1E, European Convention for Constructional Steelwork. English version published by CONSTRADO. (French version in *Construction Métallique* (1977), **3**.

2.41 Davies, J. M. (April 1978) 'Diaphragm action in multi-storey buildings'. *Proc. 2nd Int. E.C.C.S. Symposium*, London.

2.42 Miller, C. J. and Serag, A. E. (June 1978) 'Dynamic response of infilled multistorey steel frames'. *Proc. 4th Int. Speciality Conf. on Cold-Formed Steel Structs.* Univ. of Missouri, Rolla.

2.43 Davies, J. M. (Aug. 1978) *The Design of Multi-Storey Buildings Stiffened by Diaphragm Action.* Rep. no. 77/95 (2), a state of the art report prepared for E.C.C.S. Committee 11, Dep. of Civil Engrg., Univ. of Salford.

2.44 Strnad, M. and Pirner, M. (Sept. 1978) 'Static and dynamic full scale tests on a portal frame structure'. *Struct. Engr.*, **56B** (3).

2.45 Strnad, M. (1978) 'Zasady pro navrhovani lehkych ocelovych hal se spolupůsobicimi plášti' ('Basic rules for light steel hall design with interaction between the frame and the cladding'). *Technicky Zpravodaj ocelove konstukie*, **1** (78).

2.46 *Construction Métallique* (1978) 'Example de calcul d'une structure compte tenu de la collaboration des parois' ('an example of stressed skin design'). French version of a document prepared by E.C.C.S. Committee 17, *Construction Métallique* **2**.

20.3 Light gauge steel folded plate structures

3.1 Baer, O. A. (June 1961) 'Steel frame folded plate roof'. *Proc. A.S.C.E., J. Struct. Div.*, **87** (ST5).

3.2 Shapiro, D. (27 July 1961) 'Loads test steel folded plate roof'. *Engrg. News Record.*

3.3 Nilson, A. H. (Oct. 1961) 'Folded plate structures of light gauge steel'. *Proc. A.S.C.E., J. Struct. Div.*, **87** (ST7).

3.4 *Building Construction* (April 1965) 'Folded plate metal roof tops new school'. *Building Construction.*

3.5 Martinez, M. E. (3rd quarter 1965) 'Library on a shoe-string budget'. *Modern Steel Construction.*

3.6 Hanson, R. D. (Aug. 1965) *Static and Dynamic Tests of a Full-Scale Steel Frame Structure.* California Inst. of Technology, Pasadena.

3.7 Nilson, A. H. (Jan. 1966) 'Steel shell roof structures'. *A.I.S.C. Engrg. Jnl.*, **3** (1).

3.8 *Building Construction* (Sept. 1966) 'Cost control for educational facilities'. *Building Construction.*

3.9 Campbell, C. H. (1967) 'Simplified analysis of tapered light gauge steel folded plates', Masters thesis, Arizona State Univ., Tempe, Arizona.

3.10 H. H. Robertson & Co. (1967) *Folded Plate Design.* H. H. Robertson & Co., Pittsburgh, Pa.

3.11 Scalzi, J. B. (Sept. 1968) *Light Gauge Cold Formed Structures*. Prelim. Publ. I.A.B.S.E. 8th Congr., New York.

3.12 Fruitet, L. (1970) 'Thin self-supporting metallic roofs, folded or vaulted'. *Proc. I.A.S.S. Symposium*, Vienna (in French).

3.13 Schoeller, W. C., Lundgren, H. R. and Pian, R. H. J. (Aug. 1971) 'Cold-formed folded plate structures'. *Proc. 1st Speciality Conf. on Cold-Formed Steel Structs.*, Rolla, Missouri.

3.14 Falkenberg, J. C. (1972) *Shell and Folded Plate Roofs of Corrugated Sheet Steel Panels.* rapport 73, Norwegian Bldg. Res. Inst., Oslo. (Also published (1970) in *Proc. I.A.S.S. Symposium*, Vienna.)

3.15 Thompson, F. (1974) 'The design development of light gauge steel folded plate structures. M. Sc. thesis, Univ. of Salford.

3.16 Davies, J. M. (Jan. 1975) *Light Gauge Steel Folded Plate Roofs.* Rep. no. 75/78, Dept. of Civil Eng., Univ. of Salford

3.17 Lamb, A. R. (1975) 'The design and testing of a stressed skin structure for a range of nursery school buildings (United Kingdom)'. *Acier-Stahl-Steel*, **11**.

3.18 Davies, J. M., Lawson, R. M. and Young, J. G. (March 1976) 'Calculated and observed behaviour of the folded plate roof of a nursery school'. *Proc. Conf. on the Performance of Building Structs.*, Glasgow.

3.19 Davies, J. M. (May 1976) 'Light gauge steel folded-plate roofs'. *Struct. Engr.*

3.20 *New Civil Engr.* (22 July 1976) 'Roof failure proves theory'. *New Civil Engr.*

3.21 Davies, J. M. and Thompson, F. (1976) 'Light gauge steel folded plate construction'. *I.A.B.S.E. Memoires*, **36** (II).

3.22 *Acier-Stahl-Steel* (1976) 'Full scale test to failure on a light gauge steel folded plate roof'. *Acier-Stahl-Steel*, **11–12.**

3.23 Lawson, R. M. (1976) 'The flexibility and strength of corrugated diaphragms and folded plates'. Ph. D. thesis, Univ. of Salford.

3.24 E.C.C.S. (March 1977) *European Recommendations for the Stressed Skin Design of Steel Structures*. Publ. no. XVII-77-1E, European Convention for Constructional Steelwork. English version published by CONSTRADO. (French version in *Construction Métallique* (1977), **3**.

3.25 Davies, J. M., Bryan, E. R. and Lawson, R. M. (June 1977) 'Design and testing of a light gauge steel folded plate roof'. *Proc. I.C.E., Part II.*

3.26 Davies, J. M. (June 1978) 'Developments in inexpensive lightweight structures'. *Proc. 4th Int. Speciality Conf. on Cold-Formed Steel Structs.*, Univ. of Missouri – Rolla.

3.27 Davies, J. M. (June 1978) *Light Gauge Steel Folded Plate Roofs.* CONSTRADO.

3.28 Lawson, R. M. (Oct. 1978) 'Design formulas for steel folded plate roofs'. *Proc. A.S.C.E., J. Struct. Div.*, **104** (ST10).

3.29 Iffland, J. S. B. (Jan. 1979) 'Folded plate structures', *Proc. A.S.C.E., J. Struct. Div.*, **105** (ST1).

3.30 Hangelbroek, P. B. and van Ouwerkerk, E. N. J. (1979) 'Building with self-supporting surface elements'. *Acier-Stahl-Steel*, **3**.

3.31 Zucka, J. (1979) 'Modern Buildings with self-supporting roof elements'. *Acier-Stahl-Steel*, **4**.

20.4 Light gauge steel hyperbolic paraboloids

4.1 Graham, H. T. (March 1962) 'New way to build a shell: roof is welded steel deck'. *Architectural Record.*

4.2 Nilson, A. H. (Oct. 1962) 'Testing a light gauge steel hyperbolic paraboloid shell'. *Proc. A.S.C.E., J. Struct. Div.*, **88** (ST5).

4.3 Nilson, A. H. (Jan. 1966) 'Steel shell roof structures'. *A.I.S.C. Eng. Jnl.*, **3** (1).

4.4 McDermott, J. F. (June 1968) 'Single layer corrugated steel sheet hypars'. *Proc. A.S.C.E., J. Struct. Div.*

4.5 Engrg. News Record (1 Aug. 1968) 'Hyperbolic paraboloid hangar fits jet to a Tee'. *Engrg. News Record.*

4.6 Scalzi, J. B. (Sept. 1968) *Light Gauge Cold-Formed Structures.* Prelim. Publ. I.A.B.S.E. 8th Congr., New York.

4.7 Muskat, R. (1968) 'Buckling of light gauge steel hyperbolic paraboloid roofs', Ph. D. thesis, Cornell Univ.

4.8 Gergely, P. and Parker, J. E. (1968) *Thin Walled Steel Hyperbolic Paraboloid Structures*. Final rep., I.A.B.S.E. 8th Congr., New York.

4.9 Parker, J. E. (1969) 'Behaviour of light gauge steel hyperbolic paraboloid shells'. Ph. D. thesis, Cornell Univ.

4.10 Thornton, C. H., and Tomasetti, R. L. (Nov. 1970) 'Hangar features stressed-skin hypars'. *Civil Engrg. – A.S.C.E.*

4.11 Zetlin, L. and Thornton, C. H. (1970) 'Worlds largest light gauge steel folded hyperbolic paraboloidal shell roof structure'. *Proc. I.A.S.S. Symposium*, Vienna.

4.12 *Engrg. News Record* (7 Jan. 1971) 'Hyperbolic paraboloids roof world's largest jet hangars'. *Engrg. News Record.*

4.13 Banavalkar, P. V. (Jan. 1971) 'Analysis and behaviour of light gauge hyperbolic paraboloid shells'. Ph. D. thesis, Cornell Univ.

4.14 Zetlin, L., Thornton, C. H. and Tomasetti, R. L. (Aug. 1971) 'World's largest light gauge steel primary structure'. *Proc. 1st Speciality Conf. on Cold-Formed Steel Structs.*, Rolla, Missouri.

4.15 Gergely, P. (Aug. 1971) 'Design of cold-formed hyperbolic paraboloid shells'. *Proc. 1st Speciality Conf. on Cold-Formed Steel Structs.*, Rolla, Missouri.

4.16 Trofimov, V. I. (July/August 1971) 'How to build hangars for jumbo jets'. *Build International.*

4.17 Gergely, P., Banavalkar, P. V. and Parker, J. E. (Sept. 1971) *The Analysis and Behaviour of Thin Steel Hyperbolic Paraboloid Shells.* Rep. no. 338, Dept. of Struct. Engrg., Cornell Univ., Ithaca.

4.18 Egger, H., Fischer, M. and Reslinger, F. (1971) 'Hyparschalen aus Profilblechen'. *Der Stahlbau*, **12** (in German).

4.19 Gergely, P. (Jan. 1972) 'Buckling of orthotropic hyperbolic paraboloid shells'. *Proc. A.S.C.E., J. Struct. Div.*, **98** (ST1).

4.20 Gergely, P. (May 1972) *Stability of Thin-Steel Hyperbolic Paraboloid Roofs.* Prelim. rep., I.A.B.S.E. 9th Congr., Amsterdam.

4.21 Egger, H. (May 1972) *Shells of Stiffened Profile Sheets of Hyperbolic Paraboloid Form.* Final rep. (in German), I.A.B.S.E. 9th Congr., Amsterdam.

4.22 Fischer, M. (1972) 'Versuche zur Ermittlung des Tragverhaltens einer hyperbolischen Paraboloidischale aus ein lagigen Trapezprofilblechen'. *Der Stahlbau*, **4** and **5** (in German).

4.23 Gergely, P. and Winter, G. (Oct. 1972) 'Experimental investigation of thin-steel hyperbolic paraboloid structures'. *Proc. A.S.C.E., J. Struct. Div.*, **98** (ST10).

4.24 Banavalkar, P. V. and Gergely, P. (Nov. 1972) 'Analysis of thin-steel hyperbolic paraboloid shells'. *Proc. A.S.C.E., J. Struct. Div.*, **98** (ST11).

4.25 Tomasetti, R. L. (Oct. 1973) 'Innovative designs with cold-formed members and sheets'. *Proc. 2nd Speciality Conf. on Cold-Formed Steel Structs.*, Rolla, Missouri.

4.26 Biswas, M. and Iffland, J. S. B. (Oct. 1973) 'Metal decks used to form hyparshell panels'. *Proc. 2nd Speciality Conf. on Cold-Formed Steel Structs.*, Rolla, Missouri.

4.27 Thelen, J. F., Thornton, C. H. and Tomasetti, R. L. (1973) 'Computerised structural analysis of the world's largest light-gauge steel primary structural system'. *Computers and Structures*, **3** Pergamon Press.

4.28 Fischer, M. (1974) 'Das Beulproblem der flachen, orthotropen, hyperbolischen Paraboloidschale'. *Der Stahlbau*, **2** (in German).

20.5 Light gauge steel cylindrical shells

5.1 El-Atrouzy, M. N. (1969) 'Structural properties of corrugated sheets used in cylindrical shells'. M. Sc. thesis, Univ. of Windsor, Ontario.

5.2 Abdel-Sayed, G. (Dec. 1970) 'Critical shear loading of curved panels of corrugated sheets'. *Proc. A.S.C.E., J. Eng. Mech. Div.*, **96** (EM6).

5.3 Fruitet, L. (1970) 'Thin self-supporting metallic roofs, folded or vaulted'. *Proc. I.A.S.S. Symposium*, Vienna.

5.4 Abdel-Sayed, G. (Aug. 1971) 'Critical shear loading of curved panels of corrugated sheets with restrained edges'. *Proc. 1st Speciality Conf. on Cold-Formed Steel Structs.*, Rolla, Missouri.

5.5 El-Atrouzy, M. N. (1972) 'Cylindrical shell roofs made of corrugated sheets'. Ph. D. thesis, Univ. of Windsor, Ontario.

5.6 Abdel-Sayed, G. and El-Atrouzy, M. N. (1972) *Cylindrical Shells Made of Corrugated Sheets.* Prelim. rep., I.A.B.S.E. 9th Congr., Amsterdam.

5.7 El-Atrouzy, M. N. and Abdel-Sayed, G. (Oct. 1973) 'Shell roofs and grain bins made of corrugated steel sheets'. *Proc. 2nd Speciality Conf. on Cold-Formed Steel Structs*., Rolla, Missouri.

5.8 Marzouk, O. A. and Abdel-Sayed, G. (Nov. 1973) 'Linear theory of orthotropic cylindrical shells'. *Proc. A.S.C.E., J. Struct. Div.*, (ST11).

5.9 Young, J. G. (1976) 'Analysis of corrugated cylindrical shell roofs'. Ph. D. thesis, Univ. of Salford.

5.10 Ghobrial, M. M. and Abdel-Sayed, G. (April 1978) 'Analysis of orthotropic cylindrical cantilever shells'. *Proc. A.S.C.E., J. Eng. Mech. Div.*, **104** (EM2).

5.11 Davies, J. M. and Young, J. G. (June 1978) 'Light gauge steel cylindrical shells'. *Proc. 4th Int. Specialty Conf. on Cold-Formed Steel Structs.*, Univ. of Missouri – Rolla.

5.12 Davies, J. M. and Young, J. G. (1979) 'Test on light gauge steel cylindrical shells'. *Proc. I.C.E. Part 2.*

5.13 El-Atrouzy, M. N. and Abdel-Sayed, G. (Nov. 1978) 'Pre-buckling analysis of orthotropic barrel-shells'. *Proc. A.S.C.E., J. Struct. Div.*, **104** (ST11).

20.6 Fasteners for light gauge steel diaphragms

6.1 Baehre, R. (1969, 1971) *Hopfogning av tunnväggiga stalkonstruktioner* [1 and (with L. Berggren) 2] (*Jointing of Thin-Walled Steel Structures*). Reps. 4/69 and R30:1971, Statens Institut for byggnadsforskning, Stockholm.

6.2 Klee, S. and Seeger, T. (Oct. 1973) 'Schwingfestigkeitsuntersuchungen an Profilblech – bestigungen mit Setzbolzen'. *Der Stahlbau*, **42** (10) (in German).

6.3 Baehre, R. and Berggren, L. (1973) *Joints in Sheet Metal Panels*. Doc. D8, National Swedish Building Research, Stockholm.

6.4 Bakker, C. and Stark, J. W. (1974) 'Requirements specified for joints'. *Acier-Stahl-Steel*, **10**.

6.5 Hill, H. V. (1974) 'Connections and fasteners for light gauge steel structures'. *Acier-Stahl-Steel*, **10**.

6.6 *Building with Steel* (1974) 'Fabrication of steel sheet: joining'. *Building with Steel*, **17**.

6.7 Beck, V. R. and Morgan, J. W. (Feb. 1975) *Appraisal of Metal Roofing under Repeated Wind Loading – Cyclone Tracy, Darwin, 1974.* Techn. rep. no. 1, Australian Dept. of Housing and Construction, Melbourne.

6.8 Morgan, J. W. and Beck, V. R. (July 1975) *Sheet Metal Roof Failures by Repeated Loading.* Techn. rep. no. 2, housing research branch, Australian Dept. of Housing and Construction, Melbourne.

6.9 Fraczek, F. (Sept. 1975) *Mechanical Connections in Cold-Formed Steel: Comprehensive Test Procedures and Evaluation Methods.* Rep. no. 359, Dept. of Struct. Engrg., Cornell Univ.

6.10 Grossberndt, H. and Kniese, A. (Oct. 1975, Nov. 1975) 'Untersuchung über Querkraft und Zugkraftbeanspruchungen sowie Folgerungen über kombinierte Beanspruchungen von Schraubenverbindungen bei Stahlprofilblech Konstructionen'. *Der Stahlbau*, **44** (10 and 11) (in German).

6.11 Baehre, R. (Nov. 1975) 'Sheet metal panels for use in building construction: current research projects in Sweden'. *Proc. 3rd Int. Speciality Conf. on Cold-Formed Steel Structs*., Univ. of Missouri – Rolla.

6.12 *B.S.T. 1099* (1975) 'Draft Swedish Standard for the testing of shear connections in thin-walled structural members'. *B.S.T. 1099*, Stockholm.

6.13 Stark, J.W.B. and Toma, A. W. (Feb. 1976) *Connections in Cold-Rolled Sections*. Rep. no. BI-76-78, I.B.B.C.-T.N.O., Delft. (Note this is the final report of a research programme of the E.C.S.C. Reference should also be made to earlier documents in the same series.)

6.14 Berry, J. E. (July 1976) *Sheeting Connections.* Rep. no. 76/77, Dept. of Civil Engrg., University of Salford.

6.15 Berry, J. E. (1977) 'European Recommendations for the testing of connections in profiled sheeting'. *Acier-Stahl-Steel*, **2**.

6.16 Nissfolk, B. (1977) *Fatigue Strength of Joints in Sheet Metal Panels, 1, Riveted Connections.* Doc. D5, Swedish Council for Building Research.

6.17 Stol, H. G. A. and Toma, A. W. (April 1978) *Fastening of Steel Sheets for Walls and Roofs on Steel Structures – IV. Comparison of the Test Set-Up for Connections Prescribed in the European Recommendations with the Real Behaviour of the Connections.* Rep. no. BI-78-33/63.5.5461, T.N.O., Delft.

6.18 E.C.C.S. (May 1978) *European Recommendations for the Testing of Connections in Profiled Sheeting and Other Light Gauge Steel Components.* E.C.C.S.-XVII-77-3E, no. 21, English version published by CONSTRADO.

6.19 Blodgett, O. W. (June 1978) 'Report on proposed standards for sheet steel structural welding'. *Proc. 4th Int. Speciality Conf. on Cold-Formed Steel*

Structs., Univ. of Missouri-Rolla.

6.20 Toma, A. W. (June 1978) *Fastening of Steel Sheets for Walls and Roofs on Steel Structures – Final Report.* Rep. no. BI-78-43/63.5.5461, T.N.O., Delft.

6.21 Stark, J. W. B. and Toma, A. W. (June 1978) 'Connections in cold-formed sections and steel sheets'. *Proc. 4th Int. Speciality Conf. on Cold-Formed Steel Structs.*, Univ. of Missouri-Rolla.

6.22 Davies, J. M. (1978) 'Concentrated loads on light gauge steel diaphragms'. *J. Struct. Mech.*, **6** (2).

6.23 American Welding Society (1978) *Welding Sheet Steel in Structures.* AWS D1, 3-78 1978 edn., American Welding Society, Miami, Florida.

6.24 Pekoz, T. and McGuire, W. (Jan. 1979) *Welding of Sheet Steel.* Rep. to A.I.S.I. (Note this report refers to 5 separate test reports on a total of 342 tests carried out at Cornell University. The summarised results and conclusions are incorporated in this reference.)

6.25 Strnad, M. (May 1979) 'Screwed connections in profiled sheeting'. Int. Scientific and Technical Conf. on Metal Construction, Katowice.

6.26 Grimshaw, J. A. (July 1979) *Shear Tests on Mechanical Connections in Light Gauge Steel Components.* Rep. no. 79/121, Dept. of Civil Engrg., Univ. of Salford.

6.27 E.C.C.S. (Feb. 1981) 'Preliminary European recommendations for the design of connections in thin-walled structural elements, part 1: design of connections'. Draft for comment, E.C.C.S.-T7-1981, TWG 7.2., European Convention for Constructional Steelwork.

20.7 Diaphragms of aluminium and other materials

7.1 Barnes, S. B. and Associates (1963) *Report on the Use of H. H. Robertson Steel Roof and Floor Decks as Horizontal Diaphragms.* Barnes and Associates, California.

7.2 Luttrell, L. D. (1971) 'Shear diaphragms with lightweight concrete fill'. *Proc. 1st Int. Speciality Conf. on Cold-Formed Steel Structs.* Univ. of Missouri-Rolla.

7.3 Cranston, W. B., Sturrock, R. D. and Clements, S. W. (May 1973) *Structural Effects of Asbestos Cement Sheeting.* Tech. report 42.481, Cement and Concrete Association. (An abbreviated version of this report was published (March 1976) in *Proc. Int. Conf. on Performance of Building Structs.*, Glasgow.)

7.4 Bryan, E. R. (Feb. 1974) 'Aluminium diaphragms'. *Civil Engrg.*

7.5 E.C.C.S. (June 1977) 'European recommendations for the stressed skin design of aluminium structures'. Draft European Convention for Constructional Steelwork, Committee 16. (To be published as Part 2 of reference 1.99.)

7.6 Davies, J. M. and Fisher, J. (Dec. 1979) 'The diaphragm action of composite slabs'. *Proc. I.C.E., Part 2*, **67**.

7.7 Balazs, P. (1980) *Stressed Skin Action in Composite Panels Comprising Steel Sheeting and Boards.* Doc. D40, Swedish Council for Building Research.

Index